Introduction to Control System Design

First Edition

Harry Kwatny and Bor-Chin Chang
Drexel University

cognella®
SAN DIEGO

ii

Bassim Hamadeh, CEO and Publisher
John Remington, Executive Editor
Gem Rabanera, Senior Project Editor
Christian Berk, Production Editor
Emely Villavicencio, Senior Graphic Designer
Trey Soto, Licensing Coordinator
Natalie Piccotti, Director of Marketing
Kassie Graves, Vice President of Editorial
Jamie Giganti, Director of Academic Publishing

3970 Sorrento Valley Blvd., Ste. 500, San Diego, CA 92121

Preface

As an introduction to the design of automatic control systems, the book's primary objective is to provide students with the basic concepts and tools that are used in present-day practice. We not only want our students to know *how* to design a control system, but also to understand *why* we do things the way we do. In this way, the students will be prepared to innovate and expand current methods to address new automation technology challenges in the coming years. Part of this process is to give students a sense of the evolution of control theory and practice.

Control system engineering in today's technology environment requires a much broader set of concepts and tools than even a decade ago—and the field continues to evolve. Class time is fixed, the scope of the material is extensive, and rigor is essential. Consequently, subjects having lesser importance today have less emphasis herein. Of course, such judgments are personal and not always easy to make. In making these choices, we have been guided by two central objectives. First, the content must be aligned with the needs of present-day applications and make use of modern computational tools. Second, the narrative must reflect a respect and acknowledgement of the historical evolution of control analysis and design theory.

This book is intended for a two quarter/semester course. Correspondingly, the book is structured with two main parts. The level of complexity of Part I is somewhat mitigated by the fact that a typical student will have had some prior exposure to some of the information, albeit in a different context. Part I also contains preliminary hints of material to come in Part II, with the idea of smoothing the exposure to complex new ideas. Part I introduces basic linear system analysis and model-assembly concepts. It begins, in Chapter 1, with a short history of control system design, highlighting the applications driving its evolution, along with the contributions of control theory pioneers from late 19th century to the current era.

Although practical systems can be complex and of high order, their building blocks are first-order and second-order dynamic systems. Understanding the fundamental concepts of the first-order and second-order systems is essential to the analysis and design of high-order systems. Chapter 2 is focused on systems with typical first-order dynamics such as mass–friction systems, RC circuits, and DC motor speed dynamics. These systems, although physically different, are mathematically equivalent sharing the same form of differential equation characterized by just two parameters: the time constant and the steady-state step response value. This enables us to systematically integrate the essentials of complex variables and Laplace transforms with the learning of the fundamental system concepts in both time and frequency domains including *transfer functions*, *characteristic equations*, *poles*, *time constants*, step responses, sinusoidal steady-state responses, frequency responses, frequency filtering, *Bode plot*, and so on, while maintaining a connection with applications and mathematical modeling.

Chapter 3 expands the applications to the typical second-order dynamics such as mass–spring–damper systems, RLC circuits, and position control of a DC motor. Similar to the group of first-order systems mentioned in the previous paragraph, these second-order systems are mathematically equivalent sharing the same form of differential equation characterized by just three parameters: the *damping ratio*, the *natural frequency*, and the steady-state step response value. The fundamental system concepts we learn in Chapter 2 are largely applicable to the second-order systems. One of the main differences is that second-order systems enable the appearance of complex poles in a physical context. Their dynamics are interpreted in the time domain and the frequency domain. Transfer functions concepts are expanded and partial fraction expansion introduced. The ability to change pole location by using feedback is illustrated. Both time response and *frequency response* perspectives and interpretations are developed in the context of easily understood physical systems.

An essential requirement of control system design is that the engineer has a full grasp of the system's physical behavior in order to be successful. Control design in today's world begins with a mathematical model of the system to be controlled. It is essential that the control design team understands its formulation and the assumptions on which it is based even if they do not assemble the model. With this in mind, the next two chapters deal, respectively, with the modeling of mechanical and electrical systems. Mechanical systems modeling, Chapter 4, addresses and compares Newtonian and Lagrange techniques. Both approaches eventually will lead to exactly the same dynamic model equations. However, they have completely different road maps to reach the same destination. The *Newtonian approach* involves the geometry and vector relationship of each component in the mechanical system. On the other hand, the *Lagrange approach* only needs the information of the kinetic energy, the potential energy, the power dissipation, and the external forces, but it requires differential calculus computations.

Both have advantages and disadvantages, but they complement each other perfectly—the disadvantage of one is the advantage of the other, and vice versa. The Newtonian approach is more intuitive, providing clear picture of the interactions among components inside the system, but the modeling process can be tedious, especially for large multi-body systems. Conversely, the Lagrange approach is more elegant without the need to worry about the directions of vectors and detailed interconnection of components, but it allows virtually no insight of the interactions among components within the system. Students are urged to employ both approaches, especially for complicated systems, to minimize modeling errors. Since it is rare to commit same modeling errors using the two fundamentally different approaches, the modeling result is more trustworthy if it is confirmed by both approaches.

Shortly after obtaining the *nonlinear dynamics model* of the inverted pendulum system in Chapter 4, we felt obligated to digress a little bit to explain how the unstable nonlinear system is relevant to the linear control theory. The discussion articulates the process of determining a *local linear design model* from the nonlinear model as well as the integration of the linear controller with the actual nonlinear system. Working with this relatively simple nonlinear system provides the opportunity to introduce an intuitive state-space analysis and design approach that stabilizes the originally unstable system using a basic *pole placement concept* the students have just learned in Chapter 3. Computer tools also are introduced as the examples progress, for instance, Simulink is used to provide a computer simulation of the stabilized inverted pendulum. Formal definition of stability, controllability, and more advanced state space analysis and design approaches will be given in later chapters.

For the electrical system model building in Chapter 5, we first review Kirchhoff's voltage and current laws (KVL and KCL), and the characteristics of fundamental two-terminal electrical elements, which includes resistor, capacitor, inductor, voltage source, and current source. Then we demonstrate how to employ the *NTD* (node-to-datum) *voltages approach*, the *mesh currents approach*, and the *direct state-space approach* to assemble electric system models. The NTD voltages and the mesh currents approaches have two versions: one in time domain, and the other is in frequency domain. The frequency-domain version, also called the impedance version, is basically a Laplace transform of the time-domain version; thus, all KVL and KCL equations have become algebraic and the characteristics of capacitors and inductors are now governed by the generalized Ohm's law: $V(s) = Z(s)I(s)$, where Z(s) is the impedance. In the direct state-space approach, the voltages across the capacitors and the currents through the inductors are selected as state variables, and then the KCL and the KVL, respectively, are employed to obtain a KCL equation at a node connecting to the capacitor, and a KVL equation around a mesh containing the inductor. These KCL and KVL equations can be easily rewritten in the form of state equations.

The Lagrange approach can also be applied to electrical systems modeling, in which the electric charge q and its derivative $\dot{q}$ (the electric current) are considered as configuration variables. The constructions of the Lagrangian function and the Lagrange equation are similar to those for the mechanical systems except that for electrical systems the kinetic energy and the potential energy are stored in the inductors and the capacitors, respectively, while the generalized external force vector can be obtained using the virtual work, which is contributed by the voltage source and the dissipation in the resistors.

In Section 5.6, we introduce the operational amplifier, usually called op amp, which is an almost ideal electronic amplifier due to its three special properties: extremely large voltage gain, extremely high input impedance, and almost zero output impedance. These three properties not only make the op amp circuit a perfect building block in interconnected systems due to its extremely low loading effect, but also lead to the development of the *virtual-short concept approach* for the op amp circuit analysis and design. The virtual-short concept approach has made it possible to greatly simplify the analysis and design of *op amp circuits*, which otherwise would be extremely complicated. Op amp circuits can be easily built to perform a variety of functions like signal addition, substraction, integration, detection, amplification, filtering, PID controller implementation, binary–to–decimal conversion, decimal–to–binary conversion, common-mode disturbance cancelation, and so on.

In the beginning of Chapter 2, the DC motor system, together with the simple RC low-pass filter circuit and the mass–friction system, was considered a typical first-order dynamic system. It seems to be impossible for its dynamics model to be so simple since the DC motor physically is a complicated system, consisting of an electric circuit, a gear train, and a rotational mechanical system. In Section 5.7, we first briefly review *Ampere's force law* and *Faraday's law of induction*. The former provides the torque equation, which describes how the mechanical torque is dictated by the armature electric current, and the latter gives the back EMF (electromagnetic force) equation, which explains how the back EMF voltage is related to the motor rotor speed. Applying Kirchhoff's voltage law to the armature electric circuit will give a first-order KVL differential equation that relates the armature current to the applied control input voltage. Meanwhile, the Newtonian or the Lagrange approach can be applied to the rotational mechanical system with gear train to obtain the mechanical rotational motion equation, which is another first-order differential equation that describes how the armature current will affect the motor rotor speed.

The four equations—the torque equation, the back EMF equation, the KVL equation, and the mechanical motion equation—can be combined and simplified to a second-order differential equation that describes how the applied input voltage will control the motor rotor speed. Since the inductor impedance of the armature coil is negligible compared to the resistor resistance, the order of the differential equation is reduced to one. Hence, the *DC motor system dynamics* can be represented by a typical first-order differential equation characterized by two parameters: the time constant and the steady-state step response value. These two parameters are functions of the *torque constant* K_m, the *back EMF constant* K_b, and the resistor resistance R_a of the armature coil, which can be found from the manufacturer's data sheet. These two parameters also can be obtained from a simple step response experiment in the lab.

At the end of Chapter 5, we conduct an open-loop simulation to observe the open-loop step response of a DC motor. Then we design a simple *integral feedback controller* K_i/s to achieve perfect *steady-state speed tracking*, and a desired transient response with small maximum overshoot by select-ing the integration constant K_i so that the desired closed-loop system damping ratio is $\varsigma = 0.9$. Since there is only one design parameter K_i in the controller, we can only choose a desired value for either the damping ratio or the natural frequency. Later in Chapter 6, we will revisit this speed tracking con-trol problem using a dual-loop controller structure with two design parameters, which can be chosen to achieve the desired damping ratio as well as the desired natural frequency for the closed-loop system. For instance, if the natural frequency is double while keeping the damping ratio unchanged at $\varsigma = 0.9$, then the step response will rise up approximately two times faster while keeping the maximum overshoot unchanged.

The final chapter of Part I discusses the *assembly of models for interconnected systems*. Block di-agrams and signal flow graphs as well as Mason's gain formula are introduced. Thus, the ability to assemble more complex models composed of interconnected elements is achieved. This construction re-sults in either a state-space model or a transfer function model. This provides the opportunity to discuss the solution of the state equation and to introduce the concept of the state transition matrix. In addition, the construction of the transfer function from a state-space model and its reverse, the construction of a state-space model from the transfer function, are both discussed.

Part II is focused on linear control system design. Both frequency-domain and time-domain meth-ods are included, and both single-input/single-output (SISO) systems and multiple-input/multiple-output (MIMO) systems are discussed. The first chapter in Part II, Chapter 7, is focused on the fundamentals of feedback systems. It begins with a discussion of how feedback affects the system dynamics and de-scribes the *benefits and limitations of feedback*. System representations in time and frequency domain are again discussed, but at a somewhat deeper level than in Part I. Stability of linear systems is formally discussed, both bounded-input/bounded-output *(BIBO) stability* and *internal stability* are defined and the differences articulated. Again, this is to set the stage for deeper consideration later in the book. *Similarity transformation* of state-space models are addressed, and both diagonal and companion forms are highlighted. Naturally, this leads to another discussion of pole placement via state feedback. A sec-tion is again devoted to the cart-inverted pendulum system as a means to summarize the control design methods introduced at this point.

Chapter 8 provides a complete discussion of compensator design via the *root locus method* to achieve stability, regulation, and a best possible transient response implied by pole locations. It be-gins with a study of steady-state error and introduces the concept of system *type* and its role in achieving zero steady-state error. The *internal model principle* is also briefly introduced. A cruise control exam-ple is used to provide an overview of the design process, including performance objectives, the role of feedback and feed-forward in achieving those goals, as well as the notion of performance robustness with respect to model uncertainty. The root locus method is presented in some detail, including the ba-sic construction rules, why they are useful in design, and how to do the computations using MATLAB. Simple examples illustrate key points throughout this discussion. More expansive examples are given in the last three sections. First, a DC motor *sinusoidal position tracking* controller is used to illustrate the application of the internal model principle along with root locus design. The next section examines the *longitudinal flight path control* of the F/A–18 aircraft. In this example, manual control is simulated to illustrate the difficulty level of controlling the extremely low-damping, long-period (phugoid-mode) os-cillations. A sophisticated root locus design with integral regulation and *state-feedback pole placement* is employed to achieve stability and flight path tracking. The last section illustrates how altitude regula-tion can be accomplished using the flight path angle tracking controller.

One of the most important requirements in the design of feedback control systems is robust sta-bility, since an unstable system is not only useless but can be harmful or potentially cause a disas-ter. The *robust stability issue caused by time delay and plant uncertainties* is considered in Chapter 9.

Chapter 9 focuses on robust stability beginning with a discussion of plant uncertainty, including time delay, and how it can degrade closed-loop stability. A discussion of complex contour mapping and *Cauchy's principle* precedes a discussion of the *Nyquist plot* and the *Nyquist stability criterion*. The emphasis on Nyquist's theorem is not as a tool for determining closed-loop systems stability—in today's world that is more easily accomplished by direct computation—but to establish the concepts of gain and phase margins. The relationship between Nyquist and Bode plots as a means to obtain these margins is also discussed.

Gain and phase margins do not extend to multiple-input/multiple-output systems because there is no meaningful definition for the phase of a matrix loop transfer function. The final section of this chapter considers the *generalized stability margin*, an approach conceived to address this deficiency. This new approach of defining a generalized stability margin for MIMO systems was discovered in the 1980s based on the magnitude (or the maximum singular value for MIMO case) of the complementary sensitivity function. The frequency-dependent generalized stability margin function gives the maximum allowable variation of the magnitude (or the maximum singular value for MIMO systems) of the plant for every frequency so that the closed-loop system can still remain stable.

State-feedback design, introduced briefly in previous chapters, is the focus of Chapters 10 and 11. The *state-space approach* became popular in the early 1960s beginning with the publications of Rudolf Kalman. Instead of frequency-domain methods (i.e., Laplace transform approaches) attention returned to earlier methods of analysis and design using differential equations initiated by James Clerk Maxwell. The *main reasons for this paradigm shift* are listed in the following:

- the state-space approach resolved basic theoretical problems that had impeded the extension of frequency-domain tools to MIMO systems;
- the nonlinear system state-space representation is elegant and versatile, allowing systematic ways to identify the equilibria of the system, and to find a local (linear or nonlinear) model at each equilibrium of interest that can be employed in analysis and controller design;
- the state-space framework makes it easier to formulate the control problems as constrained optimization problems like the LQR (linear quadratic regulation), the LQG (linear quadratic Gaussian), the H_2 optimization, and the H_∞ optimization control problems;
- the computing capability and the miniaturization of the digital computer have facilitated the applications of the state-space control approaches in almost every product used to achieve automation, precision, reliability, and performance enhancement.

The emergence of the state-space approach did not mean the end of the frequency-domain approach. Instead, the state-space model framework has made it possible to incorporate frequency-domain performance requirements into design of large-scale MIMO control systems. The frequency-domain properties and the time-domain properties both remain important aspects of any system. They are inseparable. In fact, the time-domain responses, stability, and robustness are dictated by the pole locations and the frequency response of the system, as will be witnessed throughout the book.

Our treatment of state-space control system design consists of two parts: the state-feedback control part in Chapter 10, which assumes that all state variables are available for feedback, and the observer part in Chapter 11 that is capable of providing an estimate of all state variables based on the information of the physical system model, the input, and the measured output. These two parts complement each other in a perfect fashion. The state-feedback control theory and the observer theory are related by an amazingly flawless duality relationship.

Chapter 10 focuses on the state-feedback control theory and implementation either via the pole placement or the linear quadratic regulator (LQR) design approaches. After a short overview in Section 10.1 of the previous state-feedback content in earlier chapters, Section 10.2 considers a lightly damped pendulum position control example, illustrating the entire process, from linearizing the nonlinear dynamics to state-feedback stabilization via pole placement and tracking. The concept of *controllability* is introduced in Section 10.3. MIMO system poles and zeros are defined and the classification of zeros into input-decoupling, output-decoupling and transmission zeros is discussed in Section 10.4. *Linear quadratic regulator* design is the subject of Section 10.5. It is an optimal control problem to design a state-feedback controller that stabilizes the closed-loop system and minimizes a weighted quadratic performance index. Stabilization properties that result from this approach and the structure and role of the performance weighting matrices are discussed.

State-space design fundamentals are completed in Chapter 11 where the concept of *observability* and observer design are introduced. It provides a thorough investigation of observer theory and implementation by either pole placement or the linear quadratic Gaussian estimation (LQG) approaches. The duality of controllability and observability is noted, and the notion of a minimal realization is discussed highlighting the significance of controllability and observability. Section 11.5 is devoted to observer-based output feedback design (i.e., the LQG problem). As a result of the *separation principle*, the state feedback controller and the observer can be designed separately and then combined to form an output feedback control solution for the standard H_2 control design problem. Section 11.6 reformulates LQG as an H_2 problem, thereby generalizing its control design capabilities.

The final section of the book contains five appendices intended primarily to review prerequisite mathematical concepts necessary to the main topics of the book. Appendix A contains a review of complex numbers, including alternative representations, Euler's formula, and algebraic operations. Appendix B includes a discussion of Laplace transforms and examples of their application. A summary of the dynamic system model linearization process is provided in Appendix C. An understanding of how linear models and linear controllers fit in real (e.g., nonlinear) applications is a theme of the book. Appendix D provides a discussion of Mason's gain formula and its application to the reduction of multi-loop feedback block diagrams and/or signal flow graphs. Finally, Appendix E provides a review of matrices and vectors including a discussion of the geometry of vector spaces.

We want to emphasize the importance of modern computational devices and methods. As noted throughout the book computation is an essential part of the control system design and analysis process. Not only do modern tools allow us to easily execute required control design computations, but they also provide essential mechanisms for learning and validation of controller design concepts. The ability to assemble computer simulations of physical systems along with their controllers provides an important virtual laboratory. Here students can gain insight into the physical processes and complete a preliminary evaluation of the effectiveness of the control design. Throughout the book we use MATLAB/Simulink for performing the required computations and simulations.

Preliminary versions of the book were used and updated through all four quarters of the calendar years 2018 and 2019 as well as the first two quarters of 2020. Multiple colleagues and friends, including Professor Ajmal Yousuff, Dr. Mark Ilg, Dr. Mishah Salman, Dr. Christine Belcastro, Professor Sorin Siegler, Professor Baki Farouk, and Dr. Hossein Rastgoftar taught multiple classes and provided important feedback. We gratefully acknowledge their contributions. We also acknowledge the valuable contributions of our teaching assistants and graduate students, including Nilan Jayasuriya, Po-Chun Chan, Mevlut Bayram, Fatih Catpinar, Brian Amin, Joseph Masgai, and David Hartman. Student response, both solicited and unsolicited, was critically important to us. Special thanks go to Ms. Gem Rabanera and Ms. Abbey Hastings, the editors of Cognella Inc., for their editorial guidance and assistance. Finally, we are profoundly appreciative of the support and patience of our wives Miriam Kwatny and Janet Chang.

Contents

Part I

Basic Concepts of Linear Systems

1

Introduction

FEEDBACK control is a centuries-old tool applied to quite primitive machinery in its earliest days. The last century saw an explosion of applications as mankind conceived of new machines and devices for manufacturing, communication, land and air travel, space exploration, and more. These applications provoked new functionalities of control that required a deeper understanding of how control systems worked. Hence, control systems emerged as a true engineering science. In this chapter, the basic structure of control systems will be discussed, along with a brief history of the evolution of the control discipline to where it is today.

1.1 Control Engineering

Control engineering is a discipline dealing with the design of devices, called controllers, that manage the performance of a system through manipulation of control inputs. The control-input commands can be based solely on the anticipated response of the system or they can adjust in accordance with observations of system behavior. The former is called *open-loop control* and the latter is *feedback control*. Feedback control is important when there is imprecise knowledge of how the system will respond or there are environmental uncertainties that can affect behavior. Mechanisms of this sort have been employed for centuries, but today they are truly ubiquitous. Control systems are an essential part of chemical and manufacturing processes, communication systems, electric power plants and systems, ground vehicles, ships, aircraft and spacecraft, robots and manipulators, computers, and so on.

In the last century engineering was transformed from a craft into a science. Those interested in profiting from society's thirst for new technology have found it impossible to rely on time-consuming trial and error to develop new products or resolve problems in existing ones. Modern technologies like automobiles, aircraft, telecommunications, and computers are too complex to thrive solely on vast compilations of empirical data and decades of experience. Some intellectual constructs that organize and explain essential facts and principles are required. So, engineering in general and control engineering in particular have come to adopt the style and methods of the natural sciences.

At the core of this point of view is the distinction between two thought processes: the physical, and the mathematical. While engineers conceive of problems in the physical world and construct solutions intended for application in the physical world, the solution is almost always developed in the mathematical world. Today's engineers must be comfortable with translating between them. In the mathematical domain we work with abstractions of the physical. Abstraction is essential because most systems or devices involve so many irrelevant attributes that their complete characterization would only obscure practical solutions. On the other hand, abstraction can be dangerous because it is often easy to overlook important features and, consequently, to develop designs that fail to perform adequately in the physical world. Herein lies the challenge and the art of engineering.

Because of its interdisciplinary nature and the breadth of its applications, control engineering is especially reliant on a scientific perspective. Unifying principles that bring together seemingly diverse subjects within a single inclusive concept are of great significance. Mathematics, which may be regarded as the ultimate unifying principle in science and technology, is very much at the heart of control engineering. In some circles control theory is considered a branch of applied mathematics. But while mathematics is a necessary part of control engineering there is much more to it. A control system design project begins with a problem definition and ends with a solution implemented in the physical world.

1.2 A Little History

It is almost certain that feedback controllers in primitive form existed many centuries ago. But the earliest to receive prominence in the written history is James Watt's fly-ball governor, a device that was incorporated in Boulton-Watt steam engine of 1788. Governors, or speed regulators, were important in many systems of the late 18th and 19th centuries during which time several alternatives were developed to meet increasingly stringent performance requirements. An article by the noted physicist James Clerk Maxwell, "On Governors," published in [Maxwell, 1868], is considered the first paper dealing directly with the theory of automatic control. In that paper Maxwell considers Watt's governor and contemporary governing mechanisms developed by J. Thompson, L. Foucault, H. C. Jenkin, and C. W. Siemens [Siemens, 1866]. He emphasizes the distinction between moderators and regulators—what we now refer to as *proportional control* and *proportional plus integral control*. In addition, Maxwell posed the problem of stabilization of a linear feedback system and solved it for a third-order system. A solution method for higher order systems was developed independently by [Routh, 1877] and [Hurwitz, 1895]. At that time period, the Russian engineer Vyshnegradskiy worked on similar control problems, publishing his results in Russian [Vyshnegradskiy, 1877]. A discussion in English can be found in [Pontryagin, 1962].

Subsequent advances through the mid-1930s dealt with turbine speed control and other applications such as ship steering and stabilization published in [Minorsky, 1922], electric power systems static stability in [Clarke, 1926, Clarke and Lorraine, 1933], navigation and aircraft autopilots in [McRuer and Graham, 2003]. These technology contributions also stimulated a formal definition of the basic feedback control problem called the servomechanism design problem as described in [Hazen, 1934]. The 1930s also saw the development of frequency response methods for dealing with stability issues in feedback systems. While these techniques were developed in the context of feedback amplifier design and not control systems per se, the methods of [Nyquist, 1932] and [Bode, 1940] have become basic tools of control systems analysis. The WWII years produced many new results. Radar, artillery fire control, navigation, and communications problems pushed control system technology to its limits and beyond. For the first time *optimal* control design problems were posed and solved (using frequency-domain methods). The most prominent example is the formulation and solution of the single-input/single-output optimal control problem, now known as the Weiner–Hopf–Kolmogorov problem [Wiener, 1949].

The 1950s saw dissemination of the war years' efforts and also new results, including Evan's root locus method [Evans, 1948]. For the first time multiple-input/multiple-output control problems were formulated. Frequency (transform) domain methods were by now well entrenched. The 1960s saw this state of affairs turned upside down when R. E. Kalman argued that time-domain or state-space methods were more appropriate for multivariable and nonlinear control. Kalman and Bucy solved the multivariable version of the Weiner–Hopf–Kolmogorov optimal control problem in the time domain [Kalman, 1960a,b, Kalman and Bucy, 1961]. New, important concepts of *controllability* and *observability* were introduced [Kalman, 1960a, Kalman et al., 1963]. Indeed, state-space and optimal control methods seemed tailor-made for the "race to the moon" in this decade.

Through the 1970s and 1980s the theory attempted to reconcile the frequency-domain and time-domain perspectives. State-space methods merged and enriched the classical frequency-domain point of view. The notions of controllability and observability contributed to resolving the definition of multiple-input/multiple-output (MIMO) system zeros [Rosenbrock, 1973, 1974, MacFarlane and Karcanias, 1976]. Concerns about robustness to model uncertainty came, once again, into focus. While Kalman's optimal control design provided many advantages in terms of stabilization, it was recognized that some applications required improved output tracking and robustness with respect to model uncertainty. The *tracking* or *regulator* problem was formulated in early 1970s [Johnson, 1968, 1970, Kwatny, 1972, Davison, 1972, Wonham and Pearson, 1974]. A feedback regulator is a controller that both stabilizes the system and ensures that the error of selected performance variables go to zero when the system is subjected to a specified class of disturbances. The robust regulator problem adds the requirement that stability and error zeroing is preserved even if selected plant parameters vary [Francis and Wonham, 1976].

A new control design method for linear multivariable systems became a focus in the 1980s. Known as *robust control* or H_∞ *control*, this approach was intended to reduce performance sensitivity to disturbances as well as plant uncertainty [Zames, 1981, Doyle et al., 1989]. Nonlinearity has been a concern for many decades, but a renewed focus emerged, spurred by developments in control theory [Hermann and Krener, 1977, Brockett, 1978] and new technology requirements, including aerospace, robotics, and electric power systems. Another important aspect of control systems was mode switching based on logical decision making. While it was a long-standing element of control implementation there had been very little theory until the late 1980s. Modern technologies require increasingly more complex decisions, sometimes based on large amounts of incoming data and often involving dynamics as well as logic. Early theoretical work involved discrete event decision making (e.g., without considering system dynamics) [Ramadge and Wonham, 1989]. More recently, a hybrid system theory has emerged that integrates logic and dynamics [Branicky et al., 1998, Bemporad and Morari, 1999].

The articles cited are noted because of their foundational significance. They may represent a challenging starting point because they are forward-looking research papers. A more expansive and accessible account of the history of control system design can be found in numerous more recent publications that look backward from a broader context. Notable articles include the paper [Kang, 2016], which elucidates the foundational contributions of Maxwell. The papers [Bernstein, 2002] and [Bissel, 2009] articulate the emerging technologies that drove the evolution of control theory. And, finally, the papers of [Sussman and Willems, 1997] and [Pesch and Plail, 2009] deal with the development of optimal control.

1.3 Impact of the Digital Computer

Not only has the theory of control engineering evolved quite substantially over the last several decades—driven largely by a dramatically expanding domain of applications—but the tools of the discipline have also changed radically. In fact, one could argue that it is the availability of new tools for analysis, design, and, particularly, implementation that underlies the pervasive inclusion of feedback control in all manner of present-day systems and devices. Digital computers only became widely available in the 1960s and workstations and personal computers really came of age in the 1980s. During the past decade microprocessors have become so powerful and inexpensive that they have opened the door for applications of control not conceived of in earlier years.

Many systems and products require feedback control in order to function. Examples include computer disk drives, robots, spacecraft, aircraft, and electric power systems, to name a few. It would be impractical and often impossible to operate modern manufacturing systems or power plants efficiently and safely without automatic control. But even consumer products, from washing machines to CD players to automobiles, require or benefit in terms of cost and performance when actuation, sensing, and control are integrated in their design. In automobiles, for example, control systems are increasingly used in engines for improved efficiency and emission control, in airbags, anti-lock brakes, and skid and traction control and in suspension systems for improving both ridability and handling quality, not to mention cruise control and climate control. So pervasive is the design of mechanical systems integrated with sensing, actuation, and control that the name *mechatronics* has been coined to identify this branch of engineering.

What makes this possible is the advent of compact and powerful microprocessors. The early feedback controllers were large mechanical devices. These, over the years, were superseded by more compact hydraulic, pneumatic, and electronic devices. But, the improved controllers were still physically large and could perform only limited computations. The advancement of computer and semiconductor technology has dramatically reduced the cost and miniaturized the hardware required in control system implementations. The ability to rapidly execute complex algorithms in small, low power devices was truly a game changer.

1.4 A First Example: Cruise Control

Automotive cruise control systems present a convincing example of introducing modern control concepts for several reasons. To begin with, most automobile drivers are familiar with them. More importantly, cruise control systems have evolved from extremely simple devices with a single goal of manipulating the throttle to maintain a specified speed to highly complex systems with multiple inputs (manipulators) and outputs (sensors) and several distinct objectives. In addition, vehicles are becoming increasingly equipped with additional driver assist controllers such as dynamic stability control, active lane keeping, distance control, active braking, and controlled collision avoidance. All of these controllers need to be coordinated to avoid interference with each other.

In classical cruise control, speed is measured and the throttle is adjusted in response to speed error. Design of the controller requires an understanding of how the vehicle speed responds to a change in engine torque as well as disturbances, the key disturbance being road slope. We generally organize the design process by first constructing a block diagram consisting of the major elements to be considered, as illustrated in Figure 1.1.

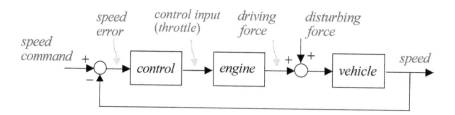

Fig. 1.1: Feedback configuration of a simple cruise control system.

To design the controller, we need to know how the engine torque responds to throttle change. Thus, we begin by assembling models of the plant (i.e., the vehicle and its engine). The models are built with a combination of physical principles and empirical data. Finally, the model consists of a set of differential and algebraic equations. The process of model building also involves a set of assumptions concerning the vehicle and its environment. Some are simple, and we just need to know the vehicle mass, so we need to make assumptions about how it is loaded. Others may be more complex, such as how we model the vehicle aerodynamic resistance. In designing the controller, we are concerned with, of course, how well speed is regulated. Is the closed-loop system, composed of the plant with controller, stable? How does the system respond to a change in speed command (i.e., does the speed error go to zero)? How long does that take? Is there too much overshoot? We also need to test our assumptions. Is closed-loop performance acceptable if the mass is different from what was assumed for controller design? Or if aerodynamic coefficients or engine parameters differ from assumptions? The cruise control or the speed tracking control design will be discussed in Example 5.26 of Section 5.7.4, Example 6.1 of Section 6.1, and a mid-size SUV cruise control example in Section 8.2.

In contemporary versions of cruise control there are additional complexities. For example, some automobiles have as many as nine gears. Gear shifting becomes an important factor in the change of torque at the wheels. How should we coordinate gears and throttle? Note that each time a gear is changed, the vehicle model from throttle to speed changes significantly. Ordinarily, gear change is based on logical decisions based on vehicle speed, engine speed, and possibly other factors. Now it is necessary to integrate dynamics with logic. Another factor of significance is that performance criteria has become more complex. Today, we are not only concerned about speed regulation, but fuel economy has become an equally important factor, especially in long-haul trucks.

Another new element in cruise control is the ability to switch from speed control to distance following control. Here, again, there are logical decisions based on data from multiple sensors that trigger switching from one mode of operation to another. How does this affect performance? The integration of dynamics and logic is a key component of control design in our current world.

Linear Systems Analysis I

THE goal of the following two chapters is to make it easier for beginning students of control to associate mathematical terms and abstract concepts with real practical systems. We begin with a few rather simple mechanical, electrical, and electromechanical systems that can be described by typical first-order and second-order differential equations in this chapter and the following chapter, respectively. The first-order systems will be characterized by a time constant τ, and the second-order systems will be specified in terms of damping ratio ς and natural frequency ω_n. Although these characterization parameters are related to physical component values, they have the advantage of directly revealing essential properties of the system dynamics. Moreover, they underscore the notion that different physical domains can be understood and examined within a common framework of abstraction.

Throughout this chapter, the simple yet typical first-order system will be employed to demonstrate fundamental terminology, concepts, and analysis tools including the transfer functions, characteristic equations, system poles, and the time-domain analysis that consists of the step responses and the steady-state sinusoidal responses. The frequency-domain analysis, including the frequency responses and Bode plot, will also be introduced. Readers will find these fundamental concepts and basic approaches quite tangible since they are all applied to simple but real practical systems. Fully understanding these fundamentals will be very helpful in the study of more complicated high-order systems in later chapters.

2.1 Typical First-Order Dynamic Systems

Although not all physical systems fall into the categories of the typical first-order systems or second-order systems, **the fundamental concepts and problem-solving skills we learn from these two typical systems provide a necessary knowledge base that can be easily extended to more complicated high-order systems.** In this chapter we will begin with the three simple physical systems shown in Figure 2.1: The mass-friction system in (a) is a mechanical system, the RC low-pass filter system in (b) is an electrical circuit, and the DC motor system in (c) is an electromechanical system.

2.1.1 Mathematical Equivalency Among First-Order Dynamic Systems

The governing dynamic differential equation for the **mass-friction system** in Figure 2.1(a) can be easily derived from Newton's law of motion—the effective force $f_{eff}(t)$ applying to the mass M will cause the mass to move with acceleration $\dot{v}(t) = f_{eff}(t)/M$, where $v(t)$ is the velocity variable of the system. The friction force $f_{fri}(t) = -Bv(t)$ is proportional to the magnitude of the velocity while it is always against the motion of the mass. Hence, we have $f_{eff}(t) = f_a(t) - Bv(t)$, which leads to the following:

$$M\dot{v}(t) + Bv(t) = f_a(t) \tag{2.1}$$

Note that $v(t)$, the velocity of the mass M, is the output or the variable of interest in the system, and $f_a(t)$, the applied force, is the control input by which the motion of the system can be changed or controlled.

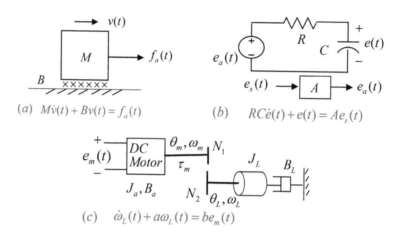

(a) $M\dot{v}(t) + Bv(t) = f_a(t)$ (b) $RC\dot{e}(t) + e(t) = Ae_s(t)$

(c) $\dot{\omega}_L(t) + a\omega_L(t) = be_m(t)$

Fig. 2.1: Mathematically equivalent systems: (a) Mass-friction system, (b) RC low-pass filter circuit, and (c) DC motor system.

The **RC low-pass filter system** in Figure 2.1(b) consists of a voltage amplifier with gain A, a voltage source $e_a(t) = Ae_s(t)$, a resistor R, and a capacitor C. According to the characteristics of the capacitor, the current flowing (downward) through the capacitor is $i_C(t) = C\dot{e}(t)$, where $e(t)$ is the voltage variable across the capacitor with the polarity specified on the diagram. Similarly, according to Ohm's law, the current flowing (rightward) through the resistor is $i_R(t) = (1/R)(e_a(t) - e(t))$. Based on Kirchhoff's current law (KCL), the current $i_R(t)$ flowing from the resistor into the junction of R and C should be equal to the current $i_C(t)$ flowing from the junction into the capacitor. The current equivalence leads to $C\dot{e}(t) = (1/R)(e_a(t) - e(t))$, and with $e_a(t) = Ae_s(t)$ we have the following:

$$RC\dot{e}(t) + e(t) = Ae_s(t) \tag{2.2}$$

Note that $e(t)$, the voltage across the capacitor, C, is the output or the variable of interest in the system, and $e_s(t)$, the voltage signal at the input of the amplifier, is the control input by which the behavior of the electrical system can be changed or controlled.

A schematic diagram of a **DC motor system** is given in Figure 2.1(c). The system consists of a DC motor driven by an electric voltage source $e_m(t)$, a gear reduction box with gear ratio N_1/N_2, and the load with moment of inertia J_L and rotational friction coefficient B_L. The mathematical modeling of the electromechanical system will be given later in Chapter 5. Although the modeling process will not be trivial, under some fair practical assumptions the behavior of the system can be described by a rather simple first-order linear ordinary differential equation as follows:

$$\dot{\omega}_L(t) + a\omega_L(t) = be_m(t) \tag{2.3}$$

where $\omega_L(t)$ and $e_m(t)$ are the output angular velocity of J_L and the control-input voltage, respectively. The coefficients a and b are constants determined by the given motor system component values. Note that $\omega_L(t)$, the angular velocity of the load J_L, is the output or the variable of interest in the system, and $e_m(t)$, the voltage signal at the input of the DC motor, is the control input by which the behavior of the electromechanical system can be changed or controlled.

2.1.2 Characterization of Typical First-Order Dynamic Systems

These three systems obviously are different in appearance—the first one is a mechanical system, the second one is electrical, and the third is electromechanical. However, these three systems intrinsically share some common properties. In fact, all of the governing equations of the three systems, Equations 2.1, 2.2, and 2.3, can be rewritten into the same form as the following **typical first-order differential equation:**

$$\tau \dot{x}(t) + x(t) = x_{ss} u(t) \tag{2.4}$$

where $x(t)$ represents the output or the variable of interest in the system, $u(t)$ is the control input by which the behavior of the system can be changed or controlled. The parameters τ and x_{ss} stand for the time constant and the steady-state step response of the system, respectively. Their physical meaning will be clearly described later in this section.

After rewriting the mass-friction system governing equation, Equation 2.1, in the form of the typical first-order differential equation, Equation 2.4, we obtain

$$(M/B)\dot{v}(t) + v(t) = (1/B)f_a(t) \tag{2.5}$$

where the output variable is $x(t) = v(t)$, the control input is $u(t) = f_a(t)$, the **time constant is** $\tau = M/B$, and the **steady-state step response is** $x_{ss} = 1/B$.

The RC low-pass filter system equation in Equation 2.2 is already in the form of Equation 2.4,

$$RC\dot{e}(t) + e(t) = Ae_s(t) \tag{2.6}$$

where the output variable is $x(t) = e(t)$, the control input is $u(t) = e_s(t)$, the time constant is $\tau = RC$, and the steady-state step response is $x_{ss} = A$.

Rewriting the DC motor system governing equation, Equation 2.3, into the form of Equation 2.4 will give

$$(1/a)\dot{\omega}_L(t) + \omega_L(t) = (b/a)e_m(t) \tag{2.7}$$

where the output variable is $x(t) = \omega_L(t)$, the control input is $u(t) = e_m(t)$, the time constant is $\tau = 1/a$, and the steady-state step response is $x_{ss} = b/a$.

From these discussions, it is clear to see the mathematical equivalency among these three systems. **The mathematical equivalency and the characterization of the typical first-order systems have boiled down the dynamic behavior study of a group of typical first-order systems to the investigation of the two parameters** τ **and** x_{ss} **in the first-order differential equation, Equation 2.4.**

2.2 A Brief Review of Complex Numbers

2.2.1 Significance of the Imaginary Number $\sqrt{-1}$

It is well known that a complex number $X = a + ib$ consists of two parts: the real part a and the imaginary part ib, where a and b are real numbers and i is the imaginary number $i = \sqrt{-1}$. Although the imaginary number $\sqrt{-1}$ has eventually become one of the most important inventions in human history, originally it was created by mathematicians merely for a simple mathematical completeness purpose so that an n-th order algebraic equation would always have n solutions. The term *imaginary number* seemed to reflect the reality that it was created out of imagination, but this derogatory term might have misled students to wrongly believe that the complex numbers are not real and thus not practical or useful.

It is quite the opposite: **The complex number is extremely important in the study of mathematics, physical science, computer science, and engineering.** It is fair to say that the modern technical world we enjoy today would probably not be possible if the imaginary number had never been invented or discovered; the world most likely would have no radio communication, no TV, no satellite, and no reliable control system for aircraft flight, space exploration, or industrial automation.

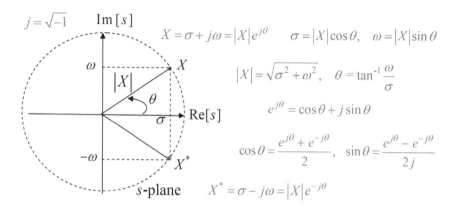

Fig. 2.2: Geometry of complex numbers and Euler's formula.

Another obstacle that might prevent students from learning the complex number subject well is the discouraging word *complex*, which seems to imply the subject is complex and complicated. **As a matter of fact, the fundamental concept of the complex number is rather simple and straightforward if the geometrical aspect of the complex number shown in Figure 2.2 is well understood.**

In addition to the $i = \sqrt{-1}$ notation, the alternative notation $j = \sqrt{-1}$ is also well adopted, especially in the engineering community. The reason for choosing i seemed to be related to the term imaginary number, yet the rationale of the engineering community's choice for j probably was to avoid using the same notation as the electrical current i. In the rest of the book, j will represent the imaginary number $\sqrt{-1}$ unless otherwise specified.

In Figure 2.2, the complex number $X = \sigma + j\omega$ is represented by a point X on the complex plane (s-plane) in which the horizontal axis Re[s] is the real axis and the vertical axis Im[s] is the imaginary axis. Note that the complex number $X = \sigma + j\omega$ geometrically is a point or a vector (σ, ω) on the Cartesian coordinate plane. It can be seen from the geometry that the magnitude $|X|$ and the phase angle θ of the vector can be computed in terms of σ and ω as follows:

$$|X| = \sqrt{\sigma^2 + \omega^2}, \quad \theta = \tan^{-1}\frac{\omega}{\sigma} \tag{2.8}$$

On the other hand, the projections of the vector X on the real axis and the imaginary axis are σ and ω, respectively. Hence, σ and ω can be written as functions of $|X|$ and θ,

$$\sigma = |X|\cos\theta, \quad \omega = |X|\sin\theta \tag{2.9}$$

Therefore, a complex number can be either represented in rectangular form,

$$X = \sigma + j\omega \tag{2.10}$$

or in polar form,

$$X = |X| \angle\theta = |X| e^{j\theta} \tag{2.11}$$

Although both $\angle\theta$ and $e^{j\theta}$ in Equation 2.11 reveal that the phase angle of the complex number is θ, the latter is required in algebraic manipulations especially when differentiation and integration are involved.

The polar form of a complex number is at least as important as its rectangular form counterpart, although the latter is better known to the general public. The rectangular form is suitable for addition and subtraction, yet the polar form is more efficient in multiplication and division computations. The conversion from rectangular form to polar form and vice versa can be carried out easily using Equation 2.8 and Equation 2.9, respectively.

2.2.2 Polar Form, Rectangular Form, and Euler's Formula

Theorem 2.1 (Euler's Formula)

Show that the following Euler's formula is valid for all θ:

$$e^{j\theta} = \cos\theta + j\sin\theta \tag{2.12}$$

Proof:

The complex number X can be represented in both polar form and rectangular form:

$$X = |X| e^{j\theta} = \sigma + j\omega \tag{2.13}$$

Since σ and ω can be expressed in terms of $|X|$ and θ, as given in Equation 2.9: $\sigma = |X|\cos\theta$ and $\omega = |X|\sin\theta$, Equation 2.13 becomes

$$X = |X| e^{j\theta} = \sigma + j\omega = |X|\cos\theta + j|X|\sin\theta \tag{2.14}$$

which leads to Equation 2.12.   ∎

Corollary 2.2 (Euler's Formula and Sinusoidal Functions)

Show that $\cos\theta$ and $\sin\theta$ can be expressed in terms of the complex variables $e^{j\theta}$ and $e^{-j\theta}$ as the following:

$$\cos\theta = \frac{e^{j\theta} + e^{-j\theta}}{2}, \quad \sin\theta = \frac{e^{j\theta} - e^{-j\theta}}{2j} \tag{2.15}$$

Proof: *Left as an exercise.*   ∎

Remark 2.3 (Complex Number and Geometry)

Euler summarized the relationship between the complex numbers and the trigonometric functions into an elegant simple Euler's formula: $e^{j\theta} = \cos\theta + j\sin\theta$. The complex number geometry approach, together with Euler's formula, has made it much easier to study trigonometry and vector analysis on two-dimensional space.   ∎

Remark 2.4 (Computation Rules of Complex Numbers)

Addition and subtraction

$$(a_1 + jb_1) \pm (a_2 + jb_2) = (a_1 \pm a_2) + j(b_1 \pm b_2) \tag{2.16a}$$

$$M_1 e^{j\theta_1} \pm M_2 e^{j\theta_2} = M_1(\cos\theta_1 + j\sin\theta_1) \pm M_2(\cos\theta_2 + j\sin\theta_2)$$
$$= (M_1\cos\theta_1 \pm M_2\cos\theta_2) + j(M_1\sin\theta_1 \pm M_2\sin\theta_2) \tag{2.16b}$$

Multiplication

$$M_1 e^{j\theta_1} \cdot M_2 e^{j\theta_2} = M_1 M_2 e^{j(\theta_1 + \theta_2)} \tag{2.17a}$$

$$(a_1 + jb_1) \cdot (a_2 + jb_2) = \sqrt{a_1^2 + b_1^2}\, e^{j\tan^{-1}(b_1/a_1)} \cdot \sqrt{a_2^2 + b_2^2}\, e^{j\tan^{-1}(b_2/a_2)}$$
$$= \sqrt{a_1^2 + b_1^2}\sqrt{a_2^2 + b_2^2}\, e^{j\left(\tan^{-1}(b_1/a_1) + \tan^{-1}(b_2/a_2)\right)} \tag{2.17b}$$

$$(a_1 + jb_1) \cdot (a_2 + jb_2) = (a_1 a_2 - b_1 b_2) + j(a_1 b_2 \pm a_2 b_1) \tag{2.17c}$$

Division

$$\frac{M_1 e^{j\theta_1}}{M_2 e^{j\theta_2}} = \frac{M_1}{M_2} e^{j(\theta_1 - \theta_2)} \tag{2.18a}$$

$$\frac{a_1 + jb_1}{a_2 + jb_2} = \frac{\sqrt{a_1^2 + b_1^2}\, e^{j\tan^{-1}(b_1/a_1)}}{\sqrt{a_2^2 + b_2^2}\, e^{j\tan^{-1}(b_2/a_2)}} = \sqrt{\frac{a_1^2 + b_1^2}{a_2^2 + b_2^2}}\, e^{j\left(\tan^{-1}(b_1/a_1) - \tan^{-1}(b_2/a_2)\right)} \tag{2.18b}$$

$$\frac{a_1 + jb_1}{a_2 + jb_2} = \frac{(a_1 + jb_1)(a_2 - jb_2)}{(a_2 + jb_2)(a_2 - jb_2)} = \frac{(a_1 a_2 + b_1 b_2) + j(a_2 b_1 - a_1 b_2)}{a_2^2 + b_2^2} \tag{2.18c}$$

∎

Example 2.5 (Practicing Computation of Complex Numbers)

- Compute $X_1 = 2e^{j\pi/6} + 2e^{j3\pi/4}$

$$X_1 = 2\cos(\pi/6) + j2\sin(\pi/6) + 2\cos(3\pi/4) + j2\sin(3\pi/4)$$
$$= \sqrt{3} + j - \sqrt{2} + j\sqrt{2} = (\sqrt{3} - \sqrt{2}) + j(1 + \sqrt{2}) = 0.3178 + j2.4142 \tag{2.19}$$

- Compute $X_2 = (\sqrt{3} + j)(-1 + j)$

$$X_2 = \sqrt{3+1}\, e^{j\tan^{-1}(1/\sqrt{3})} \cdot \sqrt{1+1}\, e^{j\tan^{-1}(1/-1)}$$
$$= 2e^{j30°} \cdot \sqrt{2} e^{j135°} = 2\sqrt{2}\, e^{j165°} = -2.732 + j0.732 \tag{2.20}$$

- Compute $X_3 = (\sqrt{3} + j)/(-1 + j)$

$$X_3 = \sqrt{3+1}\, e^{j\tan^{-1}(1/\sqrt{3})} \Big/ \sqrt{1+1}\, e^{j\tan^{-1}(1/-1)}$$
$$= 2e^{j30°} \Big/ \sqrt{2} e^{j135°} = \sqrt{2}\, e^{-j105°} = -0.366 - j1.366 \tag{2.21}$$

∎

2.2.3 Geometrical Aspects of Complex Numbers

Since a complex number can be represented by a point on the complex plane, which has the horizontal axis as its real axis and the vertical axis as its imaginary axis, a complex number on the complex plane is an equivalent vector on the two-dimensional real space. The position change of a complex number on the complex plane can be easily accomplished using complex number addition or multiplication. The complex number addition is similar to vector addition, but the complex number multiplication is unique in a way that a vector rotation and translation motion can be carried out by simply multiplying the complex number vector by another complex number. The multiplication capability has made the complex number a powerful tool in geometry, trigonometry, and broad applications in engineering and science.

Example 2.6 (Using Euler's Formula to Derive Trigonometrical Equations)

Show that (a) $\cos 2\theta = \cos^2\theta - \sin^2\theta$, and (b) $\sin 2\theta = 2\sin\theta\cos\theta$ using Euler's formula.

Proof:

$$
\begin{aligned}
e^{j2\theta} &= \cos 2\theta + j\sin 2\theta \\
&= e^{j\theta}e^{j\theta} = (\cos\theta + j\sin\theta)(\cos\theta + j\sin\theta) \\
&= (\cos^2\theta - \sin^2\theta) + j(2\sin\theta\cos\theta)
\end{aligned}
\tag{2.22}
$$

∎

Exercise 2.7 (Make Trigonometry Easy)

Use Euler's formula to prove the following two fundamental trigonometric identity equations:

$$
\begin{aligned}
(a) \quad & \sin(\alpha \pm \beta) = \sin\alpha\cos\beta \pm \sin\beta\cos\alpha \\
(b) \quad & \cos(\alpha \pm \beta) = \cos\alpha\cos\beta \mp \sin\alpha\sin\beta
\end{aligned}
\tag{2.23}
$$

Note that these two essential trigonometric identities were employed in the high school trigonometry course to derive many other trigonometric identity equations like the one in Equation 2.22.   ∎

Remark 2.8 (Using Complex Number Multiplication to Perform a Vector Rotation)

It is rather a simple task to rotate a vector in a two-dimensional space using complex number multiplication. The rotation of a vector $X_1 = M_1 e^{j\theta_1}$ by an angle α can be accomplished by multiplying a complex number $e^{j\alpha}$ to X_1 so that the resultant vector will be $M_1 e^{j\theta_1} \cdot e^{j\alpha} = M_1 e^{j(\theta_1 + \alpha)}$. As shown in Figure 2.3, the multiplication of $e^{j45°}$ to $X_1 = 2e^{j30°}$ will rotate the vector CCW (counter clockwise) by $45°$ to

$$
X_3 = 2e^{j30°}e^{j45°} = 2e^{j75°}
\tag{2.24}
$$

The complex number employed to accomplish the rotation can be further modified to a more general form as $Ae^{j\alpha}$. In addition to rotation, this more general linear operator can also change the magnitude of resultant vector. In other words, by complex number multiplication the vector position can be moved from X_1 to anywhere in the two-dimensional space.

The same rotation process can also be achieved using the conventional rotation matrix multiplication, but the computation is more complicated:

$$
X_3 = \begin{bmatrix} \cos 45° & -\sin 45° \\ \sin 45° & \cos 45° \end{bmatrix} \begin{bmatrix} \sqrt{3} \\ 1 \end{bmatrix} = \frac{1}{\sqrt{2}} \begin{bmatrix} 1 & -1 \\ 1 & 1 \end{bmatrix} \begin{bmatrix} \sqrt{3} \\ 1 \end{bmatrix} = \begin{bmatrix} 0.5176 \\ 1.9318 \end{bmatrix}
\tag{2.25}
$$

The complex number representation of the vector X_3 is $0.5176 + j1.9318$, which is equal to $2e^{j75°}$.   ∎

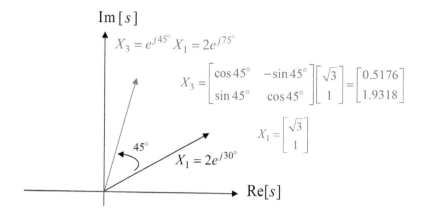

Fig. 2.3: Using complex number multiplication to rotate the vector X_1 CCW by $45°$ to X_3.

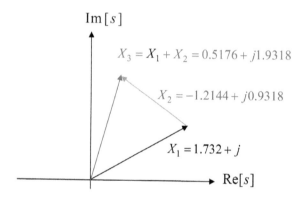

Fig. 2.4: Using complex number addition to change the vector position from X_1 to X_3.

Remark 2.9 (Using Complex Number Addition to Change Vector Position)

The rotation or position change of vectors also can be accomplished using complex number addition. If the initial vector position X_1 and the end vector position X_3 are all given, the difference can be computed as $X_2 = X_3 - X_1$, and then obviously we have $X_3 = X_1 + X_2$. As demonstrated in Figure 2.4, by adding $X_2 = -1.2144 + j0.9318$ to $X_1 = 1.732 + j$, the resultant vector will be $0.5176 + j1.9318$, which is the same as the result obtained by rotating X_1 CCW by $45°$. ∎

Remark 2.10 (Quaternions—a Generalization of Complex Numbers)

Inspired by the success of the complex numbers in two-dimensional space geometry applications, William Rowan Hamilton determined to find a generalization of complex numbers that can be applied to mechanics in three-dimensional space. Since a complex number consists of only two numbers, one real and one imaginary, it is quite natural to believe that one more number is needed to add one more dimension. Initially, Hamilton spent most of his effort in looking for a triple-number solution. Some progress was made, but he never found a meaningful way to multiply triples like the complex number multiplication. As one of the greatest mathematicians of all time, Hamilton still needed about 16 years to find out that four numbers, instead of three, are required to solve this important problem. **The quaternion,** a generalization of complex numbers to 3D space, was discovered by William Rowan Hamilton on October 16, 1843. The quaternions have been widely applied to 3D mechanics, 3D graphics, aerospace engineering, robotics, 3D animation video, and so on. ∎

In addition to their impact on geometry, trigonometry, and mechanics, the complex numbers and variables have fundamentally enriched the mathematical tools and methodologies used in almost all engineering disciplines. The concepts, tools, and methodologies sprouted from the theory of complex numbers and variables include the Laplace transform, the transfer function, the poles and zeros of systems, the stability theory, the frequency response, and anything related to the frequency-domain analysis and design, which are almost the entire contents of a typical systems and control book.

In the following subsection, we will briefly review the fundamentals of Laplace transform, including a short list of Laplace transform pairs that are frequently used, basic Laplace transform theorems, partial fractional expansion, and inverse Laplace transforms, which are essential in solving differential equations and understanding the frequency-domain properties of systems.

2.3 A Brief Review of the Laplace Transform

Once a renowned mathematician said, "Mathematics is a transformation that transforms a difficult problem into an easy one." Although some students may not agree on the remark in general, most of the engineering students do realize that the Laplace transform indeed transforms a differential equation problem into an algebraic equation problem, which is much easier to solve. In fact, the Laplace transform performs two transformations in the same act: one is from differential to algebraic and the other is the transformation from the time domain to the frequency domain. The transformation to the frequency domain is a big step forward in the development of systems and control theory. James C. Maxwell's 1868 historical paper, "On Governors," was believed the first to address the stability issue from the time-domain perspective. However, the frequency-domain analysis and design approach was not fully developed until the Laplace transform became widely known in engineering community after 1940.

2.3.1 Laplace Transform Pairs

The Laplace transform is an indispensable tool in the design and analysis of almost every engineering problem. In addition to the capability of transforming a differential equation into an algebraic one, the Laplace transform serves as a bridge connecting the two worlds: the time-domain and the frequency-domain worlds. In the time domain, the signals and systems are represented as functions and differential equations in terms of time t, which is an understandable real variable. On the other hand, the signals and systems in the frequency domain are described in terms of s, which is a complex variable that seems to be a mystery. Although this complex variable s appears intangible, we soon will witness the tremendous benefits brought forth by the frequency-domain functions and equations.

Although the time-domain and frequency-domain attributes of signals and systems are closely related, they provide quite different aspects that are both essential in system analysis and design. To achieve both time-domain and frequency-domain performance, it is necessary to be able to cross the Laplace transform bridge back and forth between the time and frequency domains. In the following, we will derive the Laplace transform pairs of the unit step function, the unit impulse function, the ramp function, and the exponential function based on the defined Laplace transform integral. Then the Laplace transform pair of the exponential function, together with Euler's formula, can be employed to derive more Laplace transform pairs for damped and undamped sinusoidal functions. These Laplace transform pairs will be employed in the study of time-domain and frequency-domain responses later in this and the next chapters.

Definition 2.11 (Laplace Transform)

The Laplace transform of $f(t)$ is defined as

$$F(s) = \mathcal{L}[f(t)] = \int_{0_-}^{\infty} e^{-st} f(t) dt \tag{2.26}$$

where $s = \sigma + j\omega$ is a complex variable, $0_- = \lim_{\varepsilon \to 0}(0 - \varepsilon)$ is the instant right before $t = 0$, and $f(t)$ is piecewise continuous when $t \geq 0$. The lower integration limit is set at $t = 0_-$ to resolve the issue caused by some $f(t)$ with discontinuity at $t = 0$. Thus, the initial condition of $f(t)$ and its derivatives are meant to be their values at $t = 0_-$. ∎

Example 2.12 (Laplace Transform of the Unit Step Function $u_s(t)$)

Recall that the unit step function is defined as

$$f(t) = u_s(t) = \begin{cases} 0 & t < 0 \\ 1 & t > 0 \end{cases} \tag{2.27}$$

The Laplace transform of $u_s(t)$ is

$$\mathcal{L}[1] = \int_{0_-}^{\infty} e^{-st} dt = \int_{0_-}^{\infty} e^{-st} dt = \left[\frac{-1}{s} e^{-st}\right]_{0_-}^{\infty} = \frac{-1}{s}\left(e^{-\infty} - e^{-0_-}\right) = \frac{1}{s} \tag{2.28}$$

∎

Example 2.13 (Laplace Transform of the Impulse Function $\delta(t)$)

Recall that the unit impulse function is defined as

$$f(t) = \delta(t) = \begin{cases} 0 & t < 0 \\ 0 & t > 0 \end{cases} \quad \text{and} \quad \int_{-\infty}^{\infty} \delta(t) dt = 1 \tag{2.29}$$

The Laplace transform of $\delta(t)$ is

$$\mathcal{L}[\delta(t)] = \int_{0_-}^{\infty} e^{-st} \delta(t) dt = \int_{0_-}^{\infty} \delta(t) dt = 1 \tag{2.30}$$

∎

Example 2.14 (Laplace Transform of the Ramp Function t)

Recall that the unit ramp function is defined as

$$f(t) = t, \quad t > 0 \tag{2.31}$$

The Laplace transform of t is

$$\mathcal{L}[t] = \int_{0_-}^{\infty} t e^{-st} dt := \int_{0_-}^{\infty} u\, dv = [uv]_{0_-}^{\infty} - \int_{0_-}^{\infty} v\, du \tag{2.32}$$

where the formula of integration by parts is employed with u and dv, chosen as $u = t$, $dv = e^{-st} dt$; hence, $v = -e^{-st}/s$, $du = dt$. Therefore,

$$\mathcal{L}[t] = \left[t\frac{-e^{-st}}{s}\right]_{0_-}^{\infty} - \int_{0_-}^{\infty} \frac{-e^{-st}}{s} dt = \left[\frac{-e^{-st}}{s^2}\right]_{0_-}^{\infty} = \frac{1}{s^2} \tag{2.33}$$

∎

Example 2.15 (Laplace Transform of the Exponential Function e^{-at})

The Laplace transform of e^{-at} is

$$\mathcal{L}\left[e^{-at}\right] = \int_{0_-}^{\infty} e^{-st} e^{-at} dt = \int_{0_-}^{\infty} e^{-(s+a)t} dt = \left[\frac{e^{-(s+a)t}}{-(s+a)}\right]_{0_-}^{\infty} = \frac{1}{s+a} \qquad (2.34)$$

∎

Remark 2.16 (Laplace Transform of the Complex Exponential Function $e^{-(\alpha-j\omega)t}$)

Note that Laplace transform pair $e^{-at} \rightleftharpoons \frac{1}{s+a}$ is also valid when a is a complex number, and therefore we have the following Laplace transform pair:

$$e^{-(\alpha-j\omega)t} \rightleftharpoons \frac{1}{s+\alpha-j\omega} \qquad (2.35)$$

∎

Remark 2.17 (Laplace Transform of Damped Sinusoidal Functions $e^{-\alpha t}(\cos\omega t + j\sin\omega t)$)

The complex Laplace transform pair in Equation 2.35 can be rewritten as follows:

$$e^{-\alpha t} e^{j\omega t} = e^{-(\alpha-j\omega)t} \rightleftharpoons \frac{1}{s+\alpha-j\omega} = \frac{s+\alpha+j\omega}{(s+\alpha-j\omega)(s+\alpha+j\omega)} \qquad (2.36)$$

With Euler's formula $e^{j\omega t} = \cos\omega t + j\sin\omega t$, this Laplace transform pair becomes

$$e^{-\alpha t}(\cos\omega t + j\sin\omega t) \rightleftharpoons \frac{(s+\alpha)+j\omega}{(s+\alpha)^2+\omega^2} \qquad (2.37)$$

Separating the real and the imaginary parts to obtain two Laplace transform pairs,

$$e^{-\alpha t}\cos\omega t \rightleftharpoons \frac{(s+\alpha)}{(s+\alpha)^2+\omega^2}, \qquad e^{-\alpha t}\sin\omega t \rightleftharpoons \frac{\omega}{(s+\alpha)^2+\omega^2} \qquad (2.38)$$

∎

Remark 2.18 (Laplace Transform of Undamped Sinusoidal Functions $\cos\omega t$ and $\sin\omega t$)

In case that $\alpha = 0$, we have the following Laplace transform pairs for undamped sinusoidal functions:

$$\cos\omega t \rightleftharpoons \frac{s}{s^2+\omega^2}, \qquad \sin\omega t \rightleftharpoons \frac{\omega}{s^2+\omega^2} \qquad (2.39)$$

∎

Exercise 2.19 (Laplace Transform of Undamped Sinusoidal Functions with Phase Angle θ)

Prove the complex Laplace transform pair: $e^{j(\omega t+\theta)} \rightleftharpoons \frac{e^{j\theta}}{s-j\omega}$ and use it to derive the following sinusoidal Laplace transform pairs:

$$\cos(\omega t+\theta) \rightleftharpoons \frac{\cos\theta s - \omega\sin\theta}{s^2+\omega^2}, \qquad \sin(\omega t+\theta) \rightleftharpoons \frac{\sin\theta s + \omega\cos\theta}{s^2+\omega^2} \qquad (2.40)$$

∎

2.3.2 Laplace Transform Properties

So far in this section we have learned how to compute the Laplace transform of basic time-domain functions and have built a list of common Laplace transform pairs, by which we can transform a time-domain function $f(t)$ on the list to its counterpart $F(s)$ in frequency domain, and vice versa. This list of Laplace transform pairs together with the partial fractional expansion method will be employed in the next section to solve linear time-invariant differential equations. In the rest of the section, we will review the Laplace transform properties that are essential and relevant to our study in systems, controls, and general engineering. The proofs of the theorems are also given except the trivial ones, which are left as exercises.

Theorem 2.20 (Linearity)

$$\mathscr{L}\left[a_1 f_1(t) + a_2 f_2(t)\right] = a_1 \mathscr{L}\left[f_1(t)\right] + a_2 \mathscr{L}\left[f_2(t)\right] \tag{2.41}$$

Proof: *Left as an exercise.*

∎

Theorem 2.21 (Frequency Shift Theorem)

$$\text{If} \quad f(t) \rightleftarrows F(s), \quad \text{then} \quad e^{-at} f(t) \rightleftarrows F(s+a) \tag{2.42}$$

Proof: *Since $f(t) \rightleftarrows F(s) = \int_{0_-}^{\infty} e^{-st} f(t)dt$, the Laplace transform pair for $e^{-at} f(t)$ should be*

$$e^{-at} f(t) \quad \rightleftarrows \quad \int_{0_-}^{\infty} e^{-st} e^{-at} f(t)dt = \int_{0_-}^{\infty} e^{-(s+a)t} f(t)dt = F(s+a) \tag{2.43}$$

∎

Theorem 2.22 (Time Delay Theorem)

$$\text{If } f(t) \rightleftarrows F(s), \text{ then } f(t-T)\, u_s(t-T) \rightleftarrows e^{-sT} F(s) \tag{2.44}$$

Proof:

Since $f(t) \rightleftarrows F(s) = \int_{0_-}^{\infty} e^{-st} f(t)dt$, the Laplace transform pair for $f(t-T)\, u_s(t-T)$ should be

$$f(t-T)\, u_s(t-T) \quad \rightleftarrows \quad \int_{0_-}^{\infty} e^{-st} f(t-T)\, u_s(t-T)dt = \int_{T}^{\infty} e^{-st} f(t-T)\, dt \tag{2.45}$$

Let $t - T = \tau$ and change the integration variable from dt to $d\tau$, then we have

$$f(t-T)\, u_s(t-T) \quad \rightleftarrows \quad \int_{0}^{\infty} e^{-s(T+\tau)} f(\tau)\, d\tau = e^{-sT} \int_{0}^{\infty} e^{-s\tau} f(\tau)\, d\tau = e^{-sT} F(s) \tag{2.46}$$

∎

Theorem 2.23 (Scaling Theorem)

$$\text{If } f(t) \rightleftarrows F(s), \text{ then } f\left(t/a\right) \rightleftarrows aF(as) \tag{2.47}$$

Proof: *Left as an exercise.*

∎

Theorem 2.24 (Convolution Theorem)

$$If \ f_1(t) \rightleftarrows F_1(s) \ and \ f_2(t) \rightleftarrows F_2(s), \ then$$

$$f_1(t) * f_2(t) \ = \ \int_{0_-}^{t} f_1(\tau) f_2(t-\tau) d\tau \ \rightleftarrows \ F_1(s) F_2(s) \tag{2.48}$$

Proof:

Since both $f_1(t)$ and $f_2(t)$ are zero for $t < 0$, $f_2(t-\tau) = 0$ when $\tau > t$, and thus their convolution is $\int_{0_-}^{t} f_1(\tau) f_2(t-\tau) d\tau = \int_{0_-}^{\infty} f_1(\tau) f_2(t-\tau) d\tau$. According to the definition of the Laplace transform,

$$\mathscr{L}[f_1(t) * f_2(t)] = \int_{0_-}^{\infty} \left[\int_{0_-}^{\infty} f_1(\tau) f_2(t-\tau) d\tau \right] e^{-st} dt \tag{2.49}$$

Let $t - \tau = \eta$ and change the integration variable from dt to $d\eta$, then we have

$$\mathscr{L}[f_1(t) * f_2(t)] = \int_{0_-}^{\infty} \left[\int_{0_-}^{\infty} f_1(\tau) f_2(\eta) d\tau \right] e^{-s\tau} e^{-s\eta} d\eta$$

$$= \int_{0_-}^{\infty} \left[\int_{0_-}^{\infty} f_1(\tau) e^{-s\tau} d\tau \right] f_2(\eta) e^{-s\eta} d\eta = F_1(s) F_2(s) \tag{2.50}$$

∎

Theorem 2.25 (Differentiation Formula)

$$df(t)/dt \rightleftarrows sF(s) - f(0_-)$$

$$d^2 f(t)/dt^2 \rightleftarrows s^2 F(s) - sf(0_-) - \dot{f}(0_-)$$

If $f(t) \rightleftarrows F(s)$, then $\quad d^3 f(t)/dt^3 \rightleftarrows s^3 F(s) - s^2 f(0_-) - s\dot{f}(0_-) - \ddot{f}(0_-) \tag{2.51}$

$$\vdots$$

Proof:

$$\mathscr{L}[\dot{f}(t)] = \int_{0_-}^{\infty} \frac{df(t)}{dt} e^{-st} dt := \int_{0_-}^{\infty} u \, dv = [uv]_{0_-}^{\infty} - \int_{0_-}^{\infty} v \, du \tag{2.52}$$

where the formula of integration by parts is employed with u and dv, chosen as $dv = df(t)$, $u = e^{-st}$; hence, $v = f(t)$, $du = -se^{-st} dt$. Therefore, we have

$$\mathscr{L}[\dot{f}(t)] = [e^{-st} f(t)]_{0_-}^{\infty} + s \int_{0_-}^{\infty} f(t) e^{-st} dt = -f(0_-) + sF(s)$$

$$\mathscr{L}[\ddot{f}(t)] = \mathscr{L}\left[\frac{d}{dt} \dot{f}(t)\right] = s\mathscr{L}[\dot{f}(t)] - \dot{f}(0_-)$$

$$= s[sF(s) - f(0_-)] - \dot{f}(0_-) = s^2 F(s) - sf(0_-) - \dot{f}(0_-) \tag{2.53}$$

$$\mathscr{L}[\dddot{f}(t)] = \mathscr{L}\left[\frac{d}{dt} \ddot{f}(t)\right] = s\mathscr{L}[\ddot{f}(t)] - \ddot{f}(0_-) = s[s^2 F(s) - sf(0_-) - \dot{f}(0_-)] - \ddot{f}(0_-)$$

$$= s^3 F(s) - s^2 f(0_-) - s\dot{f}(0_-) - \ddot{f}(0_-)$$

∎

Theorem 2.26 (Integration Formula)

$$If \ f(t) \rightleftarrows F(s), \ then \ \int_{0_-}^{t} f(\tau) d\tau \rightleftarrows \frac{F(s)}{s} \tag{2.54}$$

Proof:

$$\mathscr{L}\left[\int_{0_-}^{t} f(\tau)d\tau\right] = \int_{0_-}^{\infty}\int_{0_-}^{t} f(\tau)d\tau \, e^{-st}dt := \int_{0_-}^{\infty} u \, dv = [uv]_{0_-}^{\infty} - \int_{0_-}^{\infty} v \, du \qquad (2.55)$$

where the formula of integration by parts is employed with u and dv, chosen as $u = \int_{0_-}^{t} f(\tau)d\tau$, $dv = e^{-st}dt$; hence, $v = -e^{-st}/s$, $du = f(t)dt$. Therefore, we have

$$\mathscr{L}\left[\int_{0_-}^{t} f(\tau)d\tau\right] = \left[\frac{-e^{-st}}{s}\int_{0_-}^{t} f(\tau)d\tau\right]_{0_-}^{\infty} - \int_{0_-}^{\infty}\frac{-e^{-st}}{s}f(t) \, dt = \frac{F(s)}{s} \qquad (2.56)$$

∎

Theorem 2.27 (Final-Value Theorem)

If $f(t) \rightleftarrows F(s)$ and the real part of all poles of $sF(s)$ are strictly negative, then the final value of $f(t)$ can be computed in the frequency domain as follows:

$$\lim_{t\to\infty} f(t) = \lim_{s\to 0} sF(s) \qquad (2.57)$$

This theorem is important since most of control system designs are carried out in the frequency domain where $f(t)$ is not available before the design is completed.

Proof:

Recall that $\mathscr{L}\left[\frac{df(t)}{dt}\right] = \int_{0_-}^{\infty}\frac{df(t)}{dt} \, e^{-st}dt = sF(s) - f(0_-)$ from Theorem 2.25. As s approaches to zero, the equation becomes

$$\lim_{s\to 0} sF(s) - f(0_-) = \int_{0_-}^{\infty}\frac{df(t)}{dt} \, dt = [f(t)]_{0_-}^{\infty} = f(\infty) - f(0_-) \qquad (2.58)$$

Therefore, we have

$$f(\infty) = \lim_{t\to\infty} f(t) = \lim_{s\to 0} sF(s) \qquad (2.59)$$

∎

Theorem 2.28 (Initial-Value Theorem)

If $f(t) \rightleftarrows F(s)$ and $\lim_{s\to\infty} sF(s)$ exists, then the initial value of $f(t)$ at $t = 0$ can be computed in frequency-domain as follows:

$$f(0_+) = \lim_{s\to\infty} sF(s) \qquad (2.60)$$

Proof:

From Theorem 2.25, $\mathscr{L}\left[\frac{df(t)}{dt}\right] = \int_{0_-}^{\infty}\frac{df(t)}{dt} \, e^{-st}dt = sF(s) - f(0_-)$. As s approaches to infinity, the term e^{-st} become zero; hence, $\lim_{s\to\infty} sF(s) = f(0_-) = f(0_+)$ if $f(t)$ has no discontinuity at $t = 0$. In the case that $f(t)$ has a discontinuity jump at $t = 0$ from $f(0_-)$ to $f(0_+)$, $df(t)/dt$ contains an impulse $[f(0_+) - f(0_-)]\delta(t)$. Now we have

$$\lim_{s\to\infty} sF(s) - f(0_-) = \lim_{s\to\infty}\int_{0_-}^{\infty}\frac{df(t)}{dt} \, e^{-st}dt = \int_{0_-}^{0_+}\frac{df(t)}{dt} \, dt$$

$$= \int_{0_-}^{0_+} [f(0_+) - f(0_-)]\delta(t) \, dt = f(0_+) - f(0_-) \qquad (2.61)$$

∎

2.4 Time-Domain Response of Typical First-Order Dynamic Systems

As discussed in Section 2.1, a large group of first-order systems share mathematical equivalency and can be characterized by the typical first-order differential equation described by Equation 2.4. The equation, for ease of reference, is repeated as follows:

$$\tau \dot{x}(t) + x(t) = x_{ss} u(t) \tag{2.62}$$

In the equation, $x(t)$ is the system output or the variable of interest, which may be the velocity $v(t)$ of the mechanical system in Figure 2.1(a), the voltage $e(t)$ on the capacitor of the electric circuit in Figure 2.1(b), or the angular velocity $\omega_L(t)$ of the electromechanical system in Figure 2.1(c). The variable $u(t)$ is the control input by which the behavior of the system can be altered or controlled. The time constant τ and the step response steady-state value x_{ss} are determined by system component values.

Given the initial state $x(0) = x_0$ and the input $u(t)$ for $t \geq 0$, we can solve the differential equation to find $x(t)$ for $t \geq 0$. After taking the Laplace transform, Equation 2.62 becomes the following algebraic equation,

$$\tau[sX(s) - x_0] + X(s) = x_{ss}U(s) \tag{2.63}$$

where $X(s) = \mathscr{L}[x(t)]$, $U(s) = \mathscr{L}[u(t)]$, and $sX(s) - x_0 = \mathscr{L}[\dot{x}(t)]$. The algebraic equation can be rearranged to give a solution for $X(s)$ as follows:

$$X(s) = \frac{\tau}{\tau s + 1} x_0 + \frac{x_{ss}}{\tau s + 1} U(s) := X_i(s) + X_u(s) \tag{2.64}$$

Note that $X(s)$ consists of two parts: $X_i(s)$, the response due to the initial state x_0, and $X_u(s)$, the response due to the control input $U(s)$. Therefore, the complete response of the typical first-order system is

$$x(t) = x_i(t) + x_u(t) = \mathscr{L}^{-1}[X_i(s)] + \mathscr{L}^{-1}[X_u(s)] \tag{2.65}$$

2.4.1 The Response of the Typical First-Order System Due to Initial Condition

The initial state response $x_i(t)$, which is the response of the first-order dynamic system due to x_0, can be computed using the exponential Laplace transform pair of Equation 2.34 and the Laplace transform linearity property of Theorem 2.20.

$$x_i(t) = \mathscr{L}^{-1}\left[\frac{\tau}{\tau s + 1} x_0\right] = \mathscr{L}^{-1}\left[\frac{1}{s + 1/\tau} x_0\right] = x_0 e^{-t/\tau} \tag{2.66}$$

The initial state responses of the first-order system with initial state $x_0 = 1$ and the time constant $\tau = 0.5\,s, 1\,s, 2\,s$ are shown in Figure 2.5(a).

Note that the initial and final values of $x_i(t)$ are $x_i(0) = x_0 e^0 = x_0$ and $x_i(\infty) = x_0 e^{-\infty} = 0$, respectively, and $x_i(\tau) = x_0 e^{-1} = 0.368 x_0$, which means the time constant τ is the time when the exponential term $e^{-t/\tau}$ equals to e^{-1}. In other words, the initial state response graph is an exponential curve line connecting the following three points : $x(0) = x_0$, $x(\tau) = 0.368 x_0$, and $\lim_{t \to \infty} x_i(t) = 0$.

Example 2.29 (The Response of the Mass-Friction System Due to Initial Velocity $v_0 = 1\,m/s$)

For the mass-friction system in Figure 2.1(a), if there is no external force other than the friction force and the initial velocity of the mass M is assumed $v(0) = v_0 = 1$ m/s, then the governing differential equation of the system will be

$$\tau \dot{v}(t) + v(t) = 0, \quad v(0) = v_0 = 1 \text{ m/s}, \quad \tau = M/B$$

and the solution $v(t)$ can be found using the Laplace transform as follows:

$$\tau(sV(s) - 1) + V(s) = 0 \quad \rightarrow \quad V(s) = \frac{1}{s + (1/\tau)} \quad \rightarrow \quad v(t) = e^{-t/\tau}, \quad t \geq 0$$

Then we have

$$B = 1 \text{ Ns/m}, \quad M = 1 \text{ kg} \quad \rightarrow \quad \tau = 1 \text{ s} \quad \rightarrow \quad v(t) = e^{-t}, \quad t \geq 0$$

$$B = 1 \text{ Ns/m}, \quad M = 0.5 \text{ kg} \quad \rightarrow \quad \tau = 0.5 \text{ s} \quad \rightarrow \quad v(t) = e^{-2t}, \quad t \geq 0$$

$$B = 1 \text{ Ns/m}, \quad M = 2 \text{ kg} \quad \rightarrow \quad \tau = 2 \text{ s} \quad \rightarrow \quad v(t) = e^{-0.5t}, \quad t \geq 0$$

The mass velocity $v(t)$ will go down exponentially from v_0 to zero as $t \rightarrow \infty$ with time constant $\tau = M/B$. Assuming the friction coefficient is constant, the velocity will go down faster if the mass M is smaller. **Note that the response curve due to the initial velocity $v(0) = v_0 = 1$ m/s is the exponential curve passing through the following three points: $v(0) = v_0 = 1$ m/s, $v(\tau) = e^{-1} = 0.368$ m/s, and $v(\infty) =$ 0.** ∎

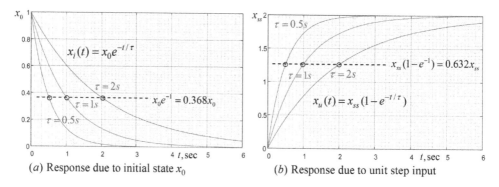

(a) Response due to initial state x_0 (b) Response due to unit step input

Fig. 2.5: The responses of the first-order system due to initial condition or unit step input.

The time response plots in Figure 2.5 are generated using the following MATLAB code:

```
% CSD Fig2.5a first-order initial state response plots
clear, t=linspace(0,6,61); figure(11),
x0=1, tau1=0.5, tau2=1, tau3=2,
x1=x0*exp(-(1/tau1)*t); x2=x0*exp(-(1/tau2)*t); x3=x0*exp(-(1/tau3)*t);
plot(t,x1,'b-',t,x2,'m-.',t,x3,'r--'), grid on, grid minor,
% CSD Fig2.5b first-order step response plots
clear t=linspace(0,6,61); figure(12)
x_ss=2, tau1=0.5, tau2=1, tau3=2,
x1=x_ss*(1-exp(-(1/tau1)*t)); x2=x_ss*(1-exp(-(1/tau2)*t));
x3=x_ss*(1-exp(-(1/tau3)*t));
plot(t,x1,'b-',t,x2,'m-.',t,x3,'r--'), grid on, grid minor
```

2.4.2 The Response of the Typical First-Order Systems Due to Unit Step Input

The step response $x_u(t)$ is the response of the first-order dynamic system due to the input $u(t) = u_s(t)$, where $u_s(t)$ is the unit step function defined by Equation 2.27. According to Equation 2.64 and the Laplace transform of the unit step function, $\mathscr{L}[u_s(t)] = 1/s$, we have

$$X_u(s) = \frac{x_{ss}}{\tau s + 1} \frac{1}{s} = \frac{x_{ss}/\tau}{s(s + 1/\tau)} \tag{2.67}$$

To find $x_u(t)$, which is the inverse Laplace transform of $X_u(s)$, a common practice is to employ the *partial fraction expansion* method to break down the right-hand side of Equation 2.67 into two parts as follows:

$$X_u(s) = \frac{x_{ss}/\tau}{s(s + 1/\tau)} = \frac{A_1}{s} + \frac{A_2}{s + 1/\tau} \tag{2.68}$$

There are three common ways to compute the residue constants A_1 and A_2. The first is the *residue approach* by which the constant A_i is evaluated as the residue at its corresponding pole as follows:

$$sX_u(s)|_{s=0} \quad \rightarrow \quad \frac{x_{ss}/\tau}{(0+1/\tau)} = A_1 + \frac{0 \cdot A_2}{0+1/\tau} \quad \rightarrow \quad A_1 = x_{ss}$$

$$(s+1/\tau)X_u(s)|_{s=-1/\tau} \quad \rightarrow \quad \frac{x_{ss}/\tau}{-1/\tau} = \frac{0 \cdot A_1}{s} + A_2 \quad \rightarrow \quad A_2 = -x_{ss} \tag{2.69}$$

The second is the *polynomial substitution approach*, which also uses pole value substitution like the residue approach but it is carried out on a polynomial equation. The first step is to multiply both sides of Equation 2.68 by the least common denominator to obtain the corresponding polynomial equation as follows:

$$x_{ss}/\tau = A_1(s + 1/\tau) + A_2 s \tag{2.70}$$

Then, by the substitution of pole values, we have the following:

$$s = 0 \quad \rightarrow \quad x_{ss}/\tau = A_1(0 + 1/\tau) \quad \rightarrow \quad A_1 = x_{ss}$$

$$s = -1/\tau \quad \rightarrow \quad x_{ss}/\tau = A_2(-1/\tau) \quad \rightarrow \quad A_2 = -x_{ss} \tag{2.71}$$

The third approach is the *coefficient comparison approach* that sets up equations to match the coefficients of each term of the polynomial. Equation 2.70 can be rearranged as the following:

$$x_{ss}/\tau = (A_1 + A_2)s + (1/\tau)A_1 \tag{2.72}$$

By comparing the coefficients of the s terms and the constant terms, we have the following:

$$A_1 + A_2 = 0 \quad \text{and} \quad (1/\tau)A_1 = x_{ss}/\tau \quad \rightarrow \quad A_1 = x_{ss} = -A_2 \tag{2.73}$$

Now, with A_1 and A_2 obtained, Equation 2.68 becomes,

$$X_u(s) = \frac{x_{ss}/\tau}{s(s + 1/\tau)} = \frac{x_{ss}}{s} + \frac{-x_{ss}}{s + 1/\tau} \tag{2.74}$$

Using two basic Laplace transform pairs, $\mathscr{L}[1] = 1/s$ and $\mathscr{L}[e^{-at}] = 1/(s+a)$, the step response of the first-order system $x_u(t)$ is found as follows:

$$x_u(t) = \mathscr{L}^{-1}[X_u(s)] = x_{ss}(1 - e^{-t/\tau}), \quad \text{when} \quad t \geq 0 \tag{2.75}$$

The step responses of the first-order system with the final steady-state value $x_{ss} = 2$ and the time constant $\tau = 0.5\,s, 1\,s, 2\,s$ are shown in Figure 2.5(b). Note that the initial and final values of $x_u(t)$ are $x_u(0) = x_{ss}(1 - e^0) = 0$ and $x_u(\infty) = x_{ss}(1 - e^{-\infty}) = x_{ss}$, respectively, and $x_u(\tau) = x_{ss}(1 - e^{-1}) = 0.632x_{ss}$, which means the time constant τ is the time when the exponential term $e^{-t/\tau}$ equals e^{-1}. In other words, **the step response graph is an exponential curve line connecting the following three points** : $x(0) = 0$, $x(\tau) = 0.632x_{ss}$, and $\lim_{t \to \infty} x_u(t) = x_{ss}$.

For the mass-friction system in Figure 2.1(a), if the initial velocity of the mass M is assumed 0 and a unit step force is applied to the system at $t = 0$, then the mass velocity would go up exponentially from 0 to $0.632x_{ss}$ when $t = \tau = M/B$ and continue to rise to the steady state x_{ss} as $t \to \infty$, where B and M are the friction coefficient and the mass of the system, respectively. Note that when the time constant is smaller, the velocity of the system rises faster.

In case that the system is subjected to both of nonzero initial condition and unit step input, the complete response of the system will be the sum of the initial state response and the step response, as shown in the following equation:

$$x(t) = x_i(t) + x_u(t) = x_0 e^{-t/\tau} + x_{ss}(1 - e^{-t/\tau})$$
$$= x_0 + (x_{ss} - x_0)(1 - e^{-t/\tau}) \tag{2.76}$$

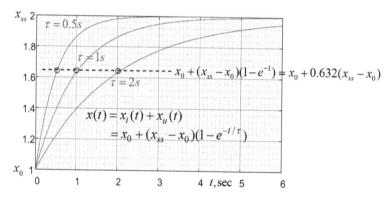

Fig. 2.6: The responses of the first-order system due to both of initial condition and unit step input.

The complete responses of the first-order system with initial state $x_0 = 1$ and the unit step input, with the final state value $x_{ss} = 2$ and the time constant $\tau = 0.5\,s, 1\,s, 2\,s$, are shown in Figure 2.6. It is clear that the complete response graph is the superposition of the two graphs in Figure 2.5(a) and Figure 2.5(b) since $x(t) = x_i(t) + x_u(t)$. It also can be seen that the complete response can be rewritten as $x(t) = x_0 + (x_{ss} - x_0)(1 - e^{-t/\tau})$ from Equation 2.76. Hence, the initial and final values of $x(t)$ are $x(0) = x_0$ and $x(\infty) = x_{ss}$, respectively, and $x(\tau) = x_0 + (x_{ss} - x_0)(1 - e^{-1}) = x_0 + 0.632(x_{ss} - x_0)$, which means the time constant τ is the time when the exponential term $e^{-t/\tau}$ equals e^{-1}. In other words, the step response graph is an exponential curve line connecting the following three points : $x(0) = x_0$, $x(\tau) = x_0 + 0.632(x_{ss} - x_0)$, and $\lim_{t \to \infty} x(t) = x_{ss}$.

Example 2.30 (The Response of the Mass-Friction System Due to Unit Step Input)

For the mass-friction system in Figure 2.1(a), if the applied force input is $f_a(t) = u_s(t)\text{N}$ and the initial velocity is assumed $v(0) = 0$, then the governing differential equation of the system will be

$$\tau\dot{v}(t)+v(t)=x_{ss}u_s(t), \quad v(0)=0, \quad \tau=M/B, \quad x_{ss}=1/B$$

and the solution $v(t)$ can be found using the Laplace transform as follows.

$$\tau sV(s)+V(s)=\frac{x_{ss}}{s} \quad \rightarrow \quad V(s)=\frac{x_{ss}/\tau}{s(s+1/\tau)}=\frac{x_{ss}}{s}+\frac{-x_{ss}}{s+1/\tau}$$

$$\rightarrow \quad v(t)=x_{ss}(1-e^{-t/\tau}), \quad t \geq 0$$

Then we have

$$B=1\,\text{Ns/m}, \quad M=1\,\text{kg} \quad \rightarrow \quad \tau=1\,\text{s} \quad \rightarrow \quad v(t)=1-e^{-t}, \quad t \geq 0$$

$$B=1\,\text{Ns/m}, \quad M=0.5\,\text{kg} \quad \rightarrow \quad \tau=0.5\,\text{s} \quad \rightarrow \quad v(t)=1-e^{-2t}, \quad t \geq 0$$

$$B=1\,\text{Ns/m}, \quad M=2\,\text{kg} \quad \rightarrow \quad \tau=2\,\text{s} \quad \rightarrow \quad v(t)=1-e^{-0.5t}, \quad t \geq 0$$

The mass velocity $v(t)$ will go up exponentially from $v(0)=0$ m/s to $v(t)=1$ m/s as $t \rightarrow \infty$ with time constant $\tau=M/B$. Assuming the friction coefficient is constant, the velocity will go up faster if the mass M is smaller. **Note that the step response curve is the exponential curve passing through the following three points: $v(0)=0$ m/s, $v(\tau)=1-e^{-1}=0.632$ m/s, and $v(\infty)=1$ m/s.** ∎

2.5 Frequency-Domain Properties of Typical First-Order Systems

In the study of the typical first-order dynamic systems, up to now our focus has been in time-domain properties and analysis. In this section, we will study the frequency-domain properties of the system including the transfer functions, the poles and zeros, the characteristic equations, the frequency responses, and the Bode plot.

2.5.1 Transfer Functions and Differential Equations

As described in Section 2.4, the Laplace transform of the system output, $X(s)=\mathscr{L}[x(t)]$ is related to the initial state $x(0)=x_0$ and the control input $U(s)=\mathscr{L}[u(t)]$ according to Equation 2.64, which is rewritten in terms of $G_0(s)$ and $G(s)$ as follows:

$$X(s)=\frac{\tau}{\tau s+1}x_0+\frac{x_{ss}}{\tau s+1}U(s):=G_0(s)x_0+G(s)U(s) \tag{2.77}$$

It is noted that the initial state x_0 and the control input $U(s)$ affect the output $X(s)$ via the two channels $G_0(s)$ and $G(s)$, respectively. The function $G(s)=x_{ss}/(\tau s+1)$, which specifies the input-output relationship between $U(s)$ and $X(s)$ in frequency domain, is called the *transfer function* of the system described by the differential equation Equation 2.62. In addition to being another convenient way of representing systems, the transfer function allows the investigation of the frequency-domain properties and facilitates the early development of the classical control theory.

Since the transfer function $G(s)$ only specifies the relationship between the control input $U(s)$ and the output $X(s)$, it has nothing to do with the initial condition x_0. But the assumption of the initial condition being zero in the definition of the transfer function

$$G(s)=\frac{X(s)}{U(s)}\bigg|_{x_0=0}=\frac{x_{ss}}{\tau s+1} \tag{2.78}$$

may cause some confusion. In fact, this zero initial condition assumption is made only for the computation of the transfer function. **As for the computation of $X(s)$ or in the process of solving a differential**

equation, the effect of the initial condition should not be discounted.

From this discussion, we know how to obtain the transfer function from a given differential equation by using the Laplace transform. Conversely, the same procedure can be implemented reversely to find the corresponding differential equation. Consider the system described by the following transfer function representation:

$$X(s) = \frac{b_1 s + b_0}{s^2 + a_1 s + a_0} U(s) \tag{2.79}$$

This equation can be rewritten as the following algebraic equation:

$$s^2 X(s) + a_1 s X(s) + a_0 X(s) = b_1 s U(s) + b_0 U(s) \tag{2.80}$$

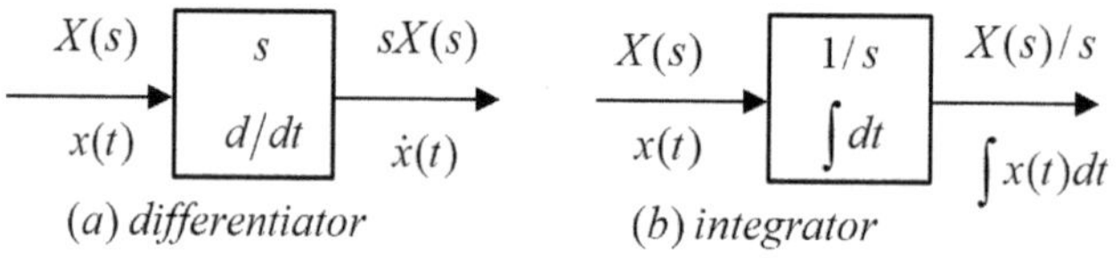

(a) differentiator   (b) integrator

Fig. 2.7: The frequency-domain and time-domain representations of differentiators and integrators.

According the Laplace transform theory regarding the frequency-domain and time-domain representations of the differentiation and integration operators as shown in Figure 2.7, **the complex variable s here actually represents a differentiation operator, with which $sX(s)$ and $s^2X(s)$ mean $\dot{x}(t)$ and $\ddot{x}(t)$ in time domain, respectively.** Therefore, the differential equation corresponding to Equation 2.80 can be easily obtained as

$$\ddot{x}(t) + a_1 \dot{x}(t) + a_0 x(t) = b_1 \dot{u}(t) + b_0 u(t) \tag{2.81}$$

2.5.2 Characteristic Equation and System Poles

Observing the initial state response in Equation 2.66 or the step response in Equation 2.75, we can see that the transient response is mainly determined by the exponential term $e^{-t/\tau}$. This exponential term clearly is associated with the denominator polynomial $\tau s + 1$ of the transfer function in Equation 2.77. This polynomial is named the *characteristic polynomial* of the system, and its associated polynomial equation, $\tau s + 1 = 0$, is called the *characteristic equation* of the system. In general, if the transfer function of a system is represented by

$$G(s) = \frac{N(s)}{D(s)} \tag{2.82}$$

then the characteristic equation of the system will be

$$D(s) = 0 \tag{2.83}$$

and **the roots of the characteristic equation are defined as the *poles* of the system. Similarly the roots of the equation, $N(s) = 0$, are defined as the *zeros* of the system.** For the system with transfer function shown in Equation 2.77, there is no zero, but there is one pole at $s = -1/\tau$, where τ is the time constant and the pole is located on the left-hand side of the complex plane. **If this pole were located at $s = 1/\tau$, which is on the right-hand side of the complex plane, the corresponding exponential term would be $e^{t/\tau}$ and would increase without bound as time increases.** In this case, the system is said to be *unstable*. The formal definition and more detailed discussion of system stability will be given in later chapters.

For the system with transfer function defined in Equation 2.79, there is one zero at $s = -b_0/b_1$, which is the root of the equation $b_1 s + b_0 = 0$. The characteristic equation is $s^2 + a_1 s + a_0 = 0$, and the system poles are the two roots of the quadratic equation. The two roots can be a pair of conjugate complex numbers or both real numbers. We will see that the behavior of the system is mainly determined by the location of the system poles on the complex plane. Detailed discussion will be given in the next chapter regarding the typical second-order systems.

2.5.3 The Responses of the Typical First-Order Systems Due to Sinusoidal Inputs

In Section 2.4, we investigated the time-domain response of the typical first-order system using the step function as the input testing signal and observed that the transient responses due to the initial state x_0 and the unit step input are related to the time constant τ. Later, the discussions of the transfer functions, the characteristic equations, and the system poles in Section 2.5.1 and 2.5.2 confirmed that the transient response of the system is mainly determined by the location of the system poles. In this section, we will investigate how the typical first-order system will respond to sinusoidal input signals with different frequencies.

Before considering the more general problem posted on Figure 2.8 at which the sinusoidal frequency ω is a variable, we will consider a special case of the problem $\omega = 1$ rad/s in the following example.

Example 2.31 (Response of a First-Order System Due to Sinusoidal Input)

Consider the system described in Figure 2.8. Assume the initial condition of the system is zero, the parameters in the transfer function $G(s)$ are $x_{ss} = 2$ and $\tau = 2s$, and the control input is $u(t) = \cos t$, which means the frequency of the signal is $\omega = 1$ rad/s. Find the output response $y(t)$ that includes both transient response $y_{tr}(t)$ and steady-state response $y_{ss}(t)$. The transient response will die out as the time increases, and the steady-state response is the output response after the system reaches the steady state.

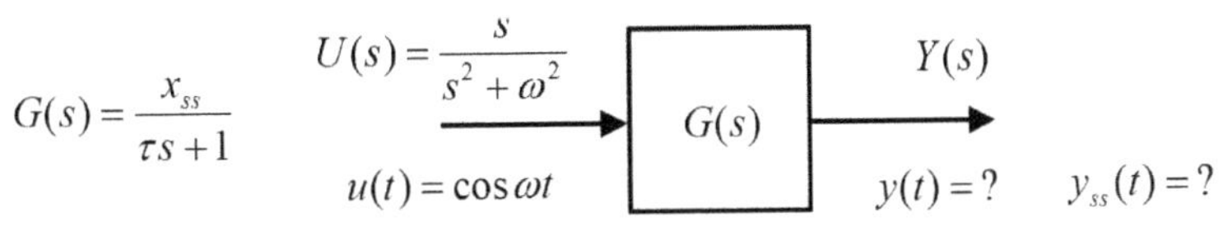

$$G(s) = \frac{x_{ss}}{\tau s + 1} \qquad U(s) = \frac{s}{s^2 + \omega^2} \qquad \boxed{G(s)} \qquad Y(s)$$

$$u(t) = \cos \omega t \qquad y(t) = ? \quad y_{ss}(t) = ?$$

Fig. 2.8: Output response due to sinusoidal input.

The output $Y(s)$ is obtained as follows:

$$Y(s) = G(s)U(s) = \frac{2}{2s+1} \cdot \frac{s}{s^2+1} = \frac{s}{(s+0.5)(s-j)(s+j)} \tag{2.84}$$

The output response $y(t)$ is the inverse Laplace transform of $Y(s)$. To find the inverse Laplace transform, first we should decompose the rational function into the sum of several simpler parts using the partial fractional decomposition in

$$Y(s) = \frac{s}{(s+0.5)(s-j)(s+j)} = \frac{A_1}{s+0.5} + \frac{c}{s-j} + \frac{c^*}{s+j} \tag{2.85}$$

where A_1 is a real number and c is a complex number to be determined. There is no need to compute c^* since it is the complex conjugate of c. These partial fraction expansion residue constants can be evaluated using the residue approach as follows:

$$A_1 = \lim_{s \to -0.5}(s+0.5)Y(s) = \frac{-0.5}{(-0.5)^2+1} = \frac{-0.5}{1.25} = -0.4$$

$$c = \lim_{s \to j}(s-j)Y(s) = \frac{j}{(j+0.5)(2j)} = \frac{1}{1+j2} = \frac{1}{\sqrt{1+2^2}e^{j\arctan 2}} = \frac{1}{\sqrt{5}e^{j63.4°}} = \frac{1}{\sqrt{5}}e^{-j63.4°} \tag{2.86}$$

Since c^* is the complex conjugate of c, we have $c^* = \left(1/\sqrt{5}\right)e^{j63.4°}$. Now, plug the values of A_1, c, and c^* into Equation 2.85, and use the Laplace transform pair $1/(s+a) \rightleftarrows e^{-at}$; we have the output response in

$$\begin{aligned}
y(t) &= -0.4e^{-0.5t} + \left(1/\sqrt{5}\right)e^{-j63.4°}e^{jt} + \left(1/\sqrt{5}\right)e^{j63.4°}e^{-jt} \\
&= -0.4e^{-0.5t} + \left(1/\sqrt{5}\right)\left(e^{j(t-63.4°)} + e^{-j(t-63.4°)}\right) \\
&= -0.4e^{-0.5t} + \left(2/\sqrt{5}\right)\cos(t - 63.4°) \\
&= -0.4e^{-0.5t} + 0.8944\cos(t - 63.4°) = y_{tr}(t) + y_{ss}(t)
\end{aligned} \tag{2.87}$$

where the first term of the solution, $y_{tr}(t) = -0.4e^{-0.5t}$, is the transient response part that will decay quickly. After a few seconds, the output response will reach the following steady state, which is a sustained sinusoidal function with the same oscillation frequency, $\omega = 1$ rad/s, but the amplitude has changed from 1 to 0.8944 and the phase dropped from 0° to -63.4°. That means the steady-state response part of the response is

$$y_{ss}(t) = 0.8944\cos(t - 63.4°) \tag{2.88}$$

∎

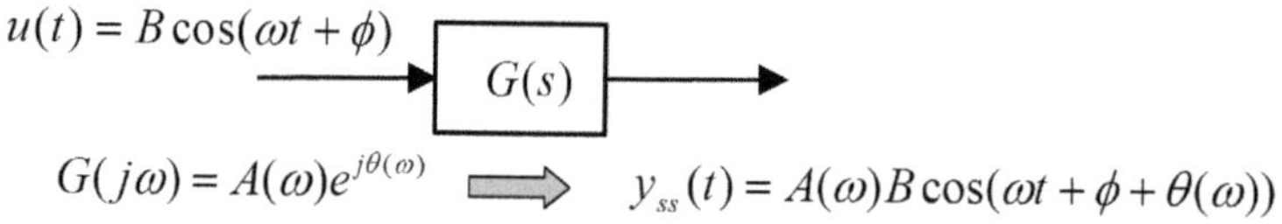

$$u(t) = B\cos(\omega t + \phi) \quad \boxed{G(s)} \longrightarrow$$

$$G(j\omega) = A(\omega)e^{j\theta(\omega)} \implies y_{ss}(t) = A(\omega)B\cos(\omega t + \phi + \theta(\omega))$$

Fig. 2.9: Efficient way of computing the sinusoidal steady-state response $y_{ss}(t)$.

Since only the steady-state response term, $y_{ss}(t)$, is of interest in almost all the applications of the sinusoidal analysis and design and there exists a much easier way to compute $y_{ss}(t)$, usually it is not required to go through the inverse Laplace transform procedure to compute the complete response. A much more efficient way of computing $y_{ss}(t)$ is given in the following theorem.

Theorem 2.32 (Steady-State $e^{j(\omega t + \phi)}$ Complex Response)

Assume the system $G(s)$ shown in Figure 2.9 is stable, which means it has no poles on the imaginary axis or in the right half of the complex plane. If the input is $u(t) = Be^{j(\omega t+\phi)}$, then the steady-state response of the system will be

$$y_{ss}(t) = A(\omega)Be^{j(\omega t+\phi+\theta(\omega))} \tag{2.89}$$

where A(ω) and θ(ω) are the magnitude and the phase of G(jω), respectively.

Proof:

Since $U(s) = \mathscr{L}[u(t)] = Be^{j\phi}/(s - j\omega)$, the output $Y(s) = \mathscr{L}[y(t)]$ consists of the transient response part $Y_{tr}(s)$ and the steady-state response part, $Y_{ss}(s)$, we have

$$Y(s) = G(s)U(s) = G(s)\frac{Be^{j\phi}}{s - j\omega} = Y_{tr}(s) + Y_{ss}(s) \tag{2.90}$$

Based on the assumption that G(s) has no poles on the imaginary axis or in the right half of the complex plane, the only pole that would contribute to the steady-state response is $s = j\omega$, and, hence,

$$Y_{ss}(s) = G(j\omega)\frac{Be^{j\phi}}{s - j\omega} = \frac{A(\omega)e^{j\theta(\omega)}Be^{j\phi}}{s - j\omega} = \frac{A(\omega)Be^{j(\phi + \theta(\omega))}}{s - j\omega} \tag{2.91}$$

Then use the Laplace transform pair $e^{j\omega t} \rightleftarrows 1/(s - j\omega)$ to obtain the inverse Laplace transform of $Y_{ss}(s)$ as follows:

$$y_{ss}(t) = \mathscr{L}^{-1}[Y_{ss}(s)] = A(\omega)Be^{j(\phi + \theta(\omega))}e^{j\omega t} = A(\omega)Be^{j(\omega t + \phi + \theta(\omega))} \tag{2.92}$$

∎

Corollary 2.33 (Steady-State Sinusoidal Response)

Assume the system G(s) shown in Figure 2.9 is stable, which means it has no poles on the imaginary axis or in the right half of the complex plane (RHP). If the input is $B\cos(\omega t + \phi)$ or $B\sin(\omega t + \phi)$, then the steady-state response of the system will be

$$y_{ss}(t) = A(\omega)B\cos(\omega t + \phi + \theta(\omega)) \quad \text{or} \quad y_{ss}(t) = A(\omega)B\sin(\omega t + \phi + \theta(\omega)) \tag{2.93}$$

where A(ω) and θ(ω) are the magnitude and the phase of G(jω), respectively.

Proof:

Use Euler's formula $e^{j(\omega t + \phi)} = \cos(\omega t + \phi) + j\sin(\omega t + \phi)$ ∎

Now the efficient approach will be employed to solve the steady-state sinusoidal response problem considered in Example 2.31.

Example 2.34 (Use Corollary 2.33 to Compute the Steady-State Sinusoidal Response)

Given the transfer function,

$$G(s) = \frac{x_{ss}}{\tau s + 1} = \frac{2}{2s + 1} \tag{2.94}$$

Find the steady-state sinusoidal response of the system driven by the control-input signal $u(t) = \cos t$.

Solution:

Since the frequency of the input signal is $\omega = 1$ rad/s, the magnitude and phase of $G(j\omega) = G(j1)$ are computed as follows:

$$G(j\omega) = G(j1) = \frac{2}{1 + j2} = \frac{2}{\sqrt{5}}e^{-j\tan^{-1}2} = 0.8944e^{-j63.4°} = Ae^{j\theta} \tag{2.95}$$

Hence,

$$y_{ss}(t) = A\cos(\omega t + \theta) = 0.8944\cos(t - 63.4°) \tag{2.96}$$

which is exactly the same as Equation 2.88, the result of Example 2.31. ∎

2.5.4 Frequency Responses and the Bode Plot

For the same system $G(s)$ in Figure 2.9, if the frequency ω of the control-input signal $u(t) = \cos \omega t$ is a variable, then the magnitude $A(\omega)$ and the phase $\theta(\omega)$ of $G(j\omega)$ will also be functions of ω. Therefore, the amplitude and phase of $y_{ss}(t)$ will change with ω accordingly. The response of $y_{ss}(t, \omega)$, due to the change of the frequency ω, is called the *frequency response* of the system. **The frequency response of a system includes the magnitude frequency response $A(\omega)$ and the phase frequency response $\theta(\omega)$.**

The frequency response of the system $G(s) = \frac{x_{ss}}{\tau s + 1} = \frac{2}{2s+1} = \frac{1}{s+0.5}$ is computed as follows:

$$G(j\omega) = \frac{1}{j\omega + 0.5} = |G(j\omega)| \angle G(j\omega) = A(\omega)e^{j\theta(\omega)} \tag{2.97}$$

where

$$|G(j\omega)|_{dB} = 20\log_{10}\frac{1}{\sqrt{\omega^2 + 0.5^2}} = \begin{cases} 20\log_{10}2 = 6.02 \text{ dB} \quad \text{when} \quad \omega \ll 0.5 \\ 20\log_{10}\sqrt{2} = 3.01 \text{ dB} \quad \text{when} \quad \omega = 0.5 \\ -20\log_{10}\omega \text{ dB} \quad \text{when} \quad \omega \gg 0.5 \end{cases} \tag{2.98}$$

$$\theta = \angle G(j\omega) = -\tan^{-1}\left(\frac{\omega}{0.5}\right)$$

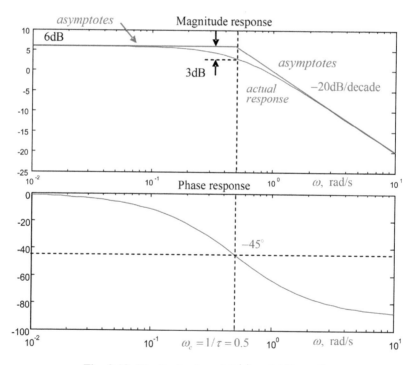

Fig. 2.10: The Bode plot of $G(s) = 2/(2s+1)$.

The following MATLAB program is employed to obtain the Bode plot shown in Figure 2.10:

```
% CSD Fig2.10 Bode plot of the system G(s)=1/(s+0.5)
num=1; den=[1 0.5]; w=logspace(-2,1); [mag,phase]=bode(num,den,w);
magb=20*log10(mag); figure(1),
```

```
semilogx(w,magb),title('Magnitude response in dB'), grid,
figure(2), semilogx(w,phase),title('Phase response in deg'), grid
```

The frequency response plots shown in Figure 2.10 are called the *Bode plot*, which consist of the magnitude response plot and the phase response plot. **The magnitude response plot is a $|G(j\omega)|_{dB}$ versus ω plot, where $|G(j\omega)|_{dB}$ is in dB scale as defined in Equation 2.98 and the frequency ω (rad/s) is in log scale.** The actual magnitude response is plotted in blue, which can be approximated by its two asymptote lines (in red) when ω is either very small or very large compared to the corner frequency ω_c. The **corner frequency ω_c, also called the 3 dB frequency,** is the ω_c that satisfies $|G(j\omega_c)| = 20\log_{10}|G(j0)| - 3$ dB. The asymptote for the frequency $\omega < \omega_c$ is a horizontal line with $|G(j\omega)|_{dB} = 20\log_{10}|G(j0)|$. The other asymptote for $\omega > \omega_c$ is the straight line with slope -20 dB/decade that intersects the horizontal asymptote at the corner frequency ω_c. Note that the asymptote approximation deviates the actual response by 3 dB at the corner frequency.

Example 2.35 (Use the Bode Plot to Compute the Steady-State Sinusoidal Responses)

From the Bode plot in Figure 2.10, at the corner frequency $\omega_c = 0.5$ rad/s we observe that

$$20\log_{10}|G(j0.5)| = |G(j0.5)|_{dB} = 6\text{ dB} - 3\text{ dB} = 3\text{ dB}$$

so that

$$|G(j0.5)| = 10^{3/20} = 1.414$$

and

$$\theta = \angle G(j0.5) = -45°$$

Hence the steady-state response due to $u(t) = \cos 0.5t$ is

$$y_{ss}(t) = |G(j0.5)|\cos(0.5t + \theta) = 1.414\cos(0.5t - 45°) \tag{2.99}$$

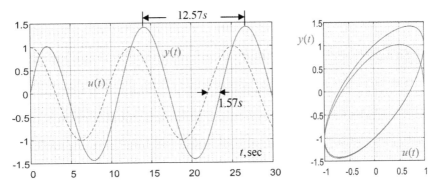

Fig. 2.11: Output response $y(t)$ of $G(s) = 1/(s+0.5)$ due to $u(t) = \cos 0.5t$.

The sinusoidal response in Figure 2.11 is obtained using the following MATLAB code:

```
% CSD Fig2.11 Sinusoidal response u=cos(0.5*t)
clear, t=linspace(0,30,301); u=cos(0.5*t);
y=-exp(-0.5*t)+1.414*cos(0.5*t-45*pi/180); figure(11),
plot(t,u,'b--',t,y,'r-'), xlabel('t,sec'), ylabel('u(t) and y(t)'),
grid on, grid minor, figure(12), plot(u,y,'b-'), xlabel('u'),
ylabel('y'), grid on, grid minor,
```

The graphs of the input $u(t) = \cos 0.5t$ and its corresponding output response are shown in Figure 2.11. Note that the transient response part of $y(t)$, $y_{tr}(t) = -e^{-0.5t}$, has decayed to 0.0027 by $t = 10$ s and thereafter $y(t) = y_{ss}(t) = 1.414\cos(0.5t - 45°)$. The steady-state response $y_{ss}(t)$ has exactly the same frequency $\omega = 0.5$ rad/s or period $T = 2\pi/0.5 = 12.57$ s as the input $u(t) = \cos 0.5t$, but with different amplitude and different phase. The amplitude is 1.414 instead of 1, and the phase is $-45°$ instead of $0°$. It also can be seen that the lag time of the output with respect to the input is 1.57 s. The lag time 1.57 s is equivalent to the phase shift $\theta = -360°(1.57/12.57) = -45°$, which is exactly the same as that shown in Equation 2.99.

When $\omega \gg \omega_c$, say $\omega = 10$ rad/s, we observe $|G(j10)|_{dB} = -20$ dB so that

$$|G(j10)| = 10^{-20/20} = 0.1 \quad \text{and} \quad \theta = \angle G(j10) = -87°$$

Therefore, the steady-state response due to $u(t) = \cos 10t$ is

$$y_{ss}(t) = A\cos(10t + \theta) = 0.1\cos(10t - 87°) \tag{2.100}$$

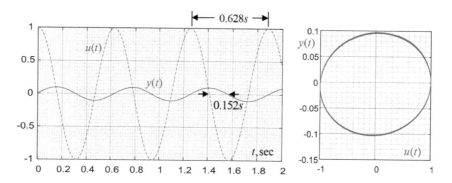

Fig. 2.12: Output response $y(t)$ of $G(s) = 1/(s+0.5)$ due to $u(t) = \cos 10t$.

The graphs of the input $u(t) = \cos 10t$ and its corresponding output response $y(t)$ are shown in Figure 2.12. The transient response part of $y(t)$, $y_{tr}(t) = -0.0052e^{-0.5t}$, has decayed to less than 0.002 by $t = 2$ s and thereafter the output response is almost at the steady state as $y_{ss}(t) = A\cos(10t + \theta) = 0.1\cos(10t - 87°)$. The steady-state response $y_{ss}(t)$ has exactly the same frequency $\omega = 10$ rad/s or period $T = 2\pi/10 = 0.628$ s, but with different amplitude and different phase. The amplitude is 0.1 instead of 1, and the phase is $-87°$ instead of $0°$. It also can be seen that the lag time of the output with respect to the input is 0.152 s. The lag time 0.152 s is equivalent to the phase shift $\theta = -360°(0.152/0.628) = -87°$, which is exactly the same as that shown in Equation 2.100. ∎

Remark 2.36 (Low-Pass Filter)

From the Bode plot in Figure 2.10, and the sinusoidal time responses to the input signals with low and high frequencies shown in Figure 2.11 and Figure 2.12, we observe that the system $G(s) = 1/(s+0.5)$, or the typical first-order system $G(s) = x_{ss}/(\tau s + 1)$ in general, allows the low-frequency signals to pass while rejecting the high-frequency signals. The ability of selectively rejecting signals in certain frequency ranges is called **frequency filtering**. Those that are particularly designed to reject the high-frequency noises, like some RC circuits, are called low-pass filters. **The low-pass filtering is widely used in practice to filter out unwanted high frequency noises;** however, not all low-pass filtering properties are desirable. Since $\omega_c = 1/\tau$, as shown in the Bode plot of Figure 2.10, **if the corner frequency ω_c decreases, the bandwidth of the system will shrink and the time constant will increase to slow down the step response, as demonstrated in Figure 2.5 and Figure 2.6 .** ∎

2.6 Exercise Problems

P2.1: Convert $X = a + jb$ to polar form $X = \rho e^{j\theta}$.

P2.2: Convert $X = \rho e^{j\theta}$ to rectangular form $X = a + jb$.

P2.3: Convert $X = \sqrt{3} + j$ to polar form.

P2.4: Convert $X = 2e^{j3\pi/4}$ to rectangular form.

P2.5: Compute $X_1 = 2e^{j\pi/6} + 2e^{j3\pi/4}$.

P2.6: Compute $X_2 = 2e^{j\pi/6} - 2e^{j3\pi/4}$.

P2.7: Compute $X_3 = (\sqrt{3} + j)(-1 + j)$.

P2.8: Compute $X_4 = \dfrac{\sqrt{3}+j}{-1+j}$.

P2.9: Show that $\sin(\alpha + \beta) = \sin\alpha\cos\beta + \sin\beta\cos\alpha$ using Euler's formula.

P2.10: Show that $\cos(\alpha + \beta) = \cos\alpha\cos\beta - \sin\alpha\sin\beta$ using Euler's formula.

P2.11: Express $\cos 2\theta$ and $\sin 2\theta$ in terms of $\cos\theta$ and $\sin\theta$ using Euler's formula.

P2.12: Express $\cos 3\theta$ and $\sin 3\theta$ in terms of $\cos\theta$ and $\sin\theta$ using Euler's formula.

P2.13: Compute $\cos 18°$ based on the fact of $e^{j90°} = \cos 90° + j\sin 90° = j$ and the formulas in P2.11 and P2.12. (Hint: Use $e^{j5\theta} = e^{j3\theta}e^{j2\theta} = (\cos 3\theta + j\sin 3\theta)(\cos 2\theta + j\sin 2\theta) = \cdots = j$)

P2.14: Consider a vector in a two-dimensional space $X_1 = \begin{bmatrix} 1 & \sqrt{3} \end{bmatrix}^T$. After a rotation of the vector clockwise by $90°$ we will obtain a new vector $X_2 = \begin{bmatrix} \sqrt{3} & -1 \end{bmatrix}^T$. Find a 2×2 rotation matrix R so that $X_2 = RX_1$.

P2.15: As described in Section (2.2.3), a vector in a two-dimensional space can be represented by a complex number, and vector rotation can be accomplished by complex number multiplication. The vector X_1 in P2.14 can be represented as $X_1 = 1 + j\sqrt{3} = 2e^{j60°}$ on a complex plane. We can rotate the vector clockwise by $90°$ to obtain the vector $X_2 = \sqrt{3} - j = 2e^{-j30°}$. Find the complex number X_3 so that the new vector X_2 is the product of X_3 and X_1 (i.e., $X_2 = X_3X_1$). Comment on the relationship between the complex number multiplication approach and the rotation matrix approach in P2.14.

P2.16a: Solve the following differential equation using Laplace transforms. Assume zero initial conditions.

$$\dot{x}(t) + 2x(t) = 4u_s(t)$$

P2.16b: Plot the solution $x(t)$ as a function of t. Specify the time constant τ and the steady-state step response value x_{ss} on the graph.

P2.16c: Repeat Problem P2.16a with initial condition $x(0) = -1$.

P2.16d: Repeat Problem P2.16b with initial condition $x(0) = -1$.

P2.17: Solve the differential equation

$$\dot{x}(t) + 2x(t) = 4\cos 2t \cdot u_s(t)$$

using the *Laplace transform/complex number approach* (see Example 2.31). Assume zero initial conditions. Specify the steady-state response part and the transient response part in your solution $x(t)$.

P2.18a: Find the transfer function $G(s) = X(s)/U(s)$ of the system described by the differential equation,

$$\ddot{x}(t) + 2x(t) = u(t)$$

where $X(s)$ and $U(s)$ are the Laplace transforms of the output $x(t)$ and the input $u(t)$, respectively.

P2.18b: Let $u(t) = 4\cos 2t \cdot u_s(t)$. Find the steady-state response of the system $x_{ss}(t)$ using the *steady-state sinusoidal response approach* (as shown in Corollary 2.33 and Example 2.34).

P2.18c: Now you have the sinusoidal steady-state response of this form $x_{ss}(t) = A\cos(\omega t + \theta)$. The transient response of the system should be $x_{tr}(t) = Be^{-t/\tau}$, where τ is the time constant of the system and B is a constant to be determined. Assume the initial condition is zero, then we have $x(0) = 0 = B + A\cos\theta$ by which the constant B can be computed.

P2.18d: Compare the solution $x(t) = x_{tr}(t) + x_{ss}(t)$ from P2.18b and P2.18c with the solution $x(t)$ obtained from Problem P2.17.

P2.18e: Plot the transient response $x_{tr}(t)$ in a red, dash line and the steady-state response $x_{ss}(t)$ in a blue solid line on the same graph.

P2.18f: Plot the complete solution $x(t) = x_{tr}(t) + x_{ss}(t)$ on a separate graph.

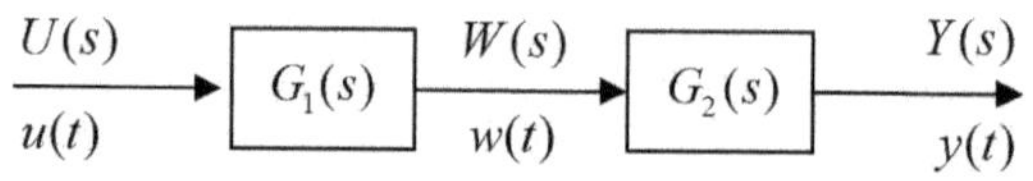

Fig. 2.13: Cascade connection of two subsystems $G_1(s)$ and $G_2(s)$.

P2.19: The differential equations of the subsystems $G_1(s)$ and $G_2(s)$ shown in Figure 2.13 are given as $2\dot{w}(t) + 3w(t) = 4u(t)$ and $5\dot{y}(t) + y(t) = w(t)$, respectively. Find the differential equation of the overall system that relates the output $y(t)$ and the input $u(t)$.

P2.20a: Consider a first-order linear time-invariant system with the differential equation

$$\dot{x}(t) + 2x(t) = u(t)$$

where $x(t)$ and $u(t)$ are the output and the input of the system. Find the transfer function $G(s)$ and the pole of the system, and explain the physical meaning of the pole.

P2.20b: Consider the same system. Draw the Bode plot of the system with asymptotes on the magnitude response graph and the corner frequency ω_c on both of the magnitude response and the phase response graphs.

P2.20c: Find the magnitude and phase of the system at the following frequencies: $\omega = 0.1\omega_c$, $\omega = \omega_c$, and $\omega = 10\omega_c$, respectively.

P2.20d: Find and plot the steady-state response $x_{ss}(t)$ of the system due to each of the following inputs: (i) $u(t) = \sin(0.1\omega_c t)$, (ii) $u(t) = \sin(\omega_c t)$, and (iii) $u(t) = \sin(10\omega_c t)$, respectively.

P2.20e: Comment on the frequency-domain behavior of the simple first-order system based on the results obtained in P2.20a, P2.20b, P2.20c, and P2.20d.

3

Linear Systems Analysis II

M ANY practical systems are stand-alone second-order systems, whose behavior is governed by second-order differential equations. Furthermore, complicated higher-order systems are fundamentally composed of several second-order and first-order systems as building blocks. For example, in the study of the aircraft flight dynamics and control, the aircraft usually is considered a rigid body with six degrees of freedom including three rotational motions and three translational motions. The mathematical modeling of the motion of each degree of freedom requires a second-order differential equation; hence the flight dynamics model would include six coupled second-order differential equations. Therefore, the study of the second-order system is essential in the analysis and design of dynamic systems and control.

Many of the fundamental concepts we learned from Chapter 2 like the mathematical equivalency, typical equation characterization, time-domain analysis and frequency-domain properties, will be extended to the study of the typical second-order dynamic systems in this chapter. Most of the extensions are quite straightforward, although the computations involved may be slightly more complicated. The basic difference between these two typical systems is that the behavior of the first-order system is mainly determined by the time constant while that of the second-order system is characterized by both the damping ratio and the natural frequency.

From the study in Chapter 2, we have a pretty clear idea on how the time constant would affect the time-domain and frequency-domain responses of the typical first-order systems. Similarly, we will learn how to select the damping ratio and the natural frequency to achieve desired performances for the typical second-order systems. For the cases that involve sinusoidal manipulations, Euler's formula will be employed to simplify the computations just as we did for the sinusoidal response computations in Chapter 2.

3.1 Typical Second-Order Dynamic Systems

As discussed in Chapter 2 regarding the typical first-order systems, we will continue to take advantage of the mathematical equivalency among systems and the typical equation characterization to enhance our learning experience. The three typical second-order physical systems to be considered in this section are shown in Figure 3.1: the mass–damper–spring system in (a) is a mechanical system, the RLC circuit system in (b) is an electrical system, and the DC motor position control system in (c) is an electromechanical feedback control system.

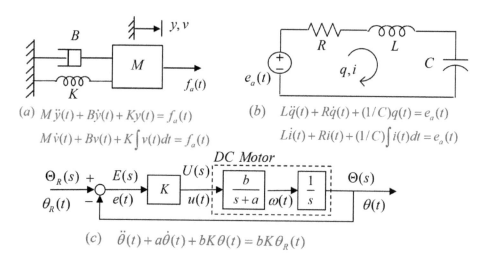

(a) $M\ddot{y}(t) + B\dot{y}(t) + Ky(t) = f_a(t)$

$M\dot{v}(t) + Bv(t) + K\int v(t)dt = f_a(t)$

(b) $L\ddot{q}(t) + R\dot{q}(t) + (1/C)q(t) = e_a(t)$

$Li(t) + Ri(t) + (1/C)\int i(t)dt = e_a(t)$

(c) $\ddot{\theta}(t) + a\dot{\theta}(t) + bK\theta(t) = bK\theta_R(t)$

Fig. 3.1: Mathematically equivalent systems: (a) mass–damper–spring (MBK) system, (b) RLC circuit, and (c) DC motor position control system.

3.1.1 Mathematical Equivalency Among Typical Second-Order Dynamic Systems

The governing dynamic differential equation for **the mass–damper–spring (MBK) system** in Figure 3.1(a) can be derived from Newton's law of motion. The effective force $f_{eff}(t)$ applying to the mass will cause the mass M to move with acceleration $\ddot{y}(t) = f_{eff}(t)/M$, where $y(t)$ is the displacement variable of the system. The friction force $f_{fri}(t) = -B\dot{y}(t)$ is proportional to the magnitude of the velocity, but its direction is always against the motion of the mass. The spring force $f_{spr}(t) = -Ky(t)$ is proportional to the magnitude of the displacement, but its direction is in the opposite direction of the displacement. Hence, we have $f_{eff}(t) = f_a(t) - B\dot{y}(t) - Ky(t)$, which leads to the following equation:

$$M\ddot{y}(t) + B\dot{y}(t) + Ky(t) = f_a(t) \tag{3.1}$$

Note that $y(t)$, the displacement of the mass M, is the output or the variable of interest in the system, and $f_a(t)$, the applied force, is the control input by which the motion of the system can be altered or controlled.

The RLC circuit in Figure 3.1(b) consists of a voltage source $e_a(t)$, a resistor R, an inductor L and a capacitor C. Let $i(t)$ be the current flowing clockwise around the loop from the positive terminal of the voltage source, $e_a(t)$, through R, L, C, and back to the negative terminal of $e_a(t)$. According to the characteristics of the resistor, $e_R(t) = Ri_R(t)$, the inductor, $e_L(t) = Ldi_L(t)/dt$, and the capacitor, $i_C(t) = C\dot{e}_C(t)$, and based on Kirchhoff's voltage law (KVL), the algebraic sum of the voltage drops around the loop should be zero:

$$-e_a(t) + Ri(t) + L\frac{di(t)}{dt} + (1/C)\int i(t)dt = 0 \tag{3.2}$$

Since $i(t) = \dot{q}(t)$, or $q(t) = \int i(t)dt$, this equation can be rewritten as follows,

$$L\ddot{q}(t) + R\dot{q}(t) + (1/C)q(t) = e_a(t) \tag{3.3}$$

The DC motor position control system in Figure 3.1(c) consists of a DC motor with transfer function $G(s) = b/(s^2 + as)$ that relates the control input $U(s)$ and the angular displacement output $\Theta(s)$, a proportional controller K with $E(s)$ and $U(s)$ as its input and output, respectively. The error signal $E(s)$ is $E(s) = \Theta_R(s) - \Theta(s)$, where $\Theta_R(s)$ is the reference or command input. The objective of the control system is to design the controller K so that the output $\theta(t)$ can follow $\theta_R(t)$ as closely as possible. We will see that the choice of K will affect the performance of the control system. To find the differential equation that relates the reference input $\theta_R(t)$ and the output $\theta(t)$, it would be easier to firstly determine the transfer function between $\Theta_R(s)$ and $\Theta(s)$ and then covert it into the corresponding differential equation. Since $\Theta(s) = KG(s)E(s)$ and $E(s) = \Theta_R(s) - \Theta(s)$, we have

$$\Theta(s) = KG(s)\left[\Theta_R(s) - \Theta(s)\right] = KG(s)\Theta_R(s) - KG(s)\Theta(s) \tag{3.4}$$

which yields the following transfer function:

$$\frac{\Theta(s)}{\Theta_R(s)} = \frac{KG(s)}{1 + KG(s)} = \frac{bK}{s^2 + as + bK} \tag{3.5}$$

Hence, we have the differential equation for the DC motor position control system:

$$s^2\Theta(s) + as\Theta(s) + bK\Theta(s) = bK\Theta_R(s) \quad \rightarrow \quad \ddot{\theta}(t) + a\dot{\theta}(t) + bK\theta(t) = bK\theta_R(t) \tag{3.6}$$

3.1.2 Characterization of Typical Second-Order Dynamic Systems

Now we have derived the mathematical models for the three systems in Figure 3.1, which are the three differential equations given in Equation 3.1, Equation 3.3, and Equation 3.6, respectively. These three systems are very different physically: one mechanical, one electrical, and the last an electromechanical position control system. However, these three systems are mathematically equivalent, and indeed they all can be represented in the same form of the **typical second-order system** differential equation:

$$\ddot{x}(t) + 2\varsigma\omega_n\dot{x}(t) + \omega_n^2 x(t) = x_{ss}\omega_n^2 r(t) \tag{3.7}$$

where $x(t)$ represents the output or the variable of interest in the system and $r(t)$ is the input, which can be the control input for an open-loop system or a reference input for a feedback control system. **The typical second-order system is characterized by three parameters: the damping ratio ς, the natural frequency ω_n, and the steady-state step response x_{ss}.** The physical meaning of these three parameters will be clearly described later in this section.

After rewriting the mass–damper–spring (MBK) system governing equation Equation 3.1 in terms of the typical second-order differential equation in Equation 3.7, we obtain the new MBK equation

$$\ddot{y}(t) + (B/M)\dot{y}(t) + (K/M)y(t) = (1/K)(K/M)f_a(t) \tag{3.8}$$

where the output variable is $x(t) = y(t)$, the input is $r(t) = f_a(t)$, the natural frequency is $\omega_n = \sqrt{K/M}$, the damping ratio is $\varsigma = 0.5B/\sqrt{MK}$, and the steady-state step response is $x_{ss} = 1/K$.

The RLC circuit system equation in Equation 3.3 can be rewritten in the form of Equation 3.7,

$$\ddot{q}(t) + (R/L)\dot{q}(t) + (1/LC)q(t) = C(1/LC)e_a(t) \tag{3.9}$$

where the output variable is $x(t) = q(t)$, the input is $r(t) = e_a(t)$, the natural frequency is $\omega_n = 1/\sqrt{LC}$, the damping ratio is $\varsigma = 0.5R\sqrt{C/L}$, and the steady-state step response is $x_{ss} = C$.

The DC motor position feedback control system governing equation, Equation 3.6, is already in the form of Equation 3.7.

$$\ddot{\theta}(t) + a\dot{\theta}(t) + bK\theta(t) = bK\theta_R(t) \tag{3.10}$$

where the output variable is $x(t) = \theta(t)$, the input is $r(t) = \theta_R(t)$, the natural frequency is $\omega_n = \sqrt{bK}$, the damping ratio is $\varsigma = 0.5a/\sqrt{bK}$, and the steady-state step response is $x_{ss} = 1$.

These discussions have clearly revealed the mathematical equivalency among the above three systems. **For this reason, the study of the large group of all typical second-order systems is boiled down to simply investigating the three parameters ς, ω_n, and x_{ss} in Equation (3.7).**

3.2 Transfer Function, Characteristic Equation, and System Poles

As discussed in Section 2.5.1, the transfer function of a given system can be derived from the corresponding differential equation using the Laplace transform. The frequency-domain algebraic equation associated with the differential equation, Equation 3.7, of the typical second-order system can be found as

$$s^2 X(s) + 2\varsigma\omega_n sX(s) + \omega_n^2 X(s) = x_{ss}\omega_n^2 R(s) \tag{3.11}$$

which yields the following transfer function between the input $R(s)$ and the output $X(s)$:

$$\frac{X(s)}{R(s)} = \frac{x_{ss}\omega_n^2}{s^2 + 2\varsigma\omega_n s + \omega_n^2} = G(s) \tag{3.12}$$

The behavior of the first-order system is mainly determined by the root of its characteristic equation, as described in Section 2.5.2. It is also true for the typical second-order system, with the exception that the second-order system has two roots instead of one. The characteristic polynomial of the system in Equation 3.12 is $s^2 + 2\varsigma\omega_n s + \omega_n^2$, which is the denominator polynomial of the transfer function. Therefore, the *characteristic equation* is

$$s^2 + 2\varsigma\omega_n s + \omega_n^2 = 0 \tag{3.13}$$

and its roots are the systems *poles*. Since **the natural frequency ω_n and the damping ratio ς are** nonnegative real numbers, the roots of the second-order algebraic equation will either be two real numbers or one pair of conjugate complex numbers, and no roots would be on the right half of the complex plane.

We will learn more about the physical meaning of the damping ratio and the natural frequency later in this chapter. By comparing Equation 3.8, the governing equation of the mass–damper–spring (MBK) system, to the typical second-order equation, Equation 3.7, we can easily see that **the damping ratio ς is proportional to the friction coefficient B.** That means more friction will cause a higher damping ratio. Similarly for the RLC electric circuit, **the damping ratio will go up if the resistance R of the resistor increases.** According to the values of the damping ratio ς, the system behaviors are classified into four cases:

Case A: $\varsigma > 1$. The system is *overdamped*, and Equation 3.13 has two distinct negative real roots.

$$\begin{matrix} s_1 \\ s_2 \end{matrix} = -\varsigma\omega_n \pm \omega_n\sqrt{\varsigma^2 - 1} = \begin{matrix} -\alpha_1 \\ -\alpha_2 \end{matrix} \tag{3.14}$$

Example A: $s^2 + 2\varsigma\omega_n s + \omega_n^2 = s^2 + 5s + 4 = (s+1)(s+4) = 0$. This characteristic equation has two distinct roots at -1 and -4, and the damping ratio and natural frequency are $\varsigma = 1.25$ and $\omega_n = 2$ rad/s, respectively.

Case B: $\varsigma = 1$. **The system is** *critically damped*, and Equation 3.13 has double real roots at

$$\begin{matrix} s_1 \\ s_2 \end{matrix} = \begin{matrix} -\omega_n \\ -\omega_n \end{matrix} \tag{3.15}$$

Example B: $s^2 + 2\varsigma\omega_n s + \omega_n^2 = s^2 + 4s + 4 = (s+2)^2 = 0$. This characteristic equation has two identical roots at -2, and the damping ratio and the natural frequency are $\varsigma = 1$ and $\omega_n = 2\,\text{rad}/\text{s}$, respectively.

Case C: $0 < \varsigma < 1$. **The system is** *underdamped*, and Equation 3.13 has a pair of complex conjugate roots at

$$\begin{matrix} s_1 \\ s_2 \end{matrix} = -\varsigma\omega_n \pm j\omega_n\sqrt{1-\varsigma^2} := -\alpha \pm j\omega \tag{3.16}$$

Example C: $s^2 + 2\varsigma\omega_n s + \omega_n^2 = s^2 + 2s + 4 = (s+1-j\sqrt{3})(s+1+j\sqrt{3}) = 0$. This characteristic equation has a pair of complex conjugate roots at $-1 \pm j\sqrt{3}$, and the damping ratio and the natural frequency are $\varsigma = 0.5$ and $\omega_n = 2\,\text{rad}/\text{s}$, respectively.

Case D: $\varsigma = 0$. **The system is** *undamped*, and Equation 3.13 has a pair of complex conjugate roots on the imaginary axis at

$$\begin{matrix} s_1 \\ s_2 \end{matrix} = \pm j\omega_n \tag{3.17}$$

Example D: $s^2 + 2\varsigma\omega_n s + \omega_n^2 = s^2 + 4 = (s - j2)(s + j2) = 0$. This characteristic equation has a pair of complex conjugate roots at $\pm j2$, and the damping ratio and the natural frequency are $\varsigma = 0$ and $\omega_n = 2\,\text{rad}/\text{s}$, respectively. ∎

3.3 Time-Domain Response of Typical Second-Order Dynamic Systems

As discussed in Section 3.1, a large group of second-order systems share mathematical equivalency and can be characterized by the typical second-order differential equation described by Equation 3.7, which is repeated in the following for ease of reference:

$$\ddot{x}(t) + 2\varsigma\omega_n\dot{x}(t) + \omega_n^2 x(t) = x_{ss}\omega_n^2 r(t) \tag{3.18}$$

In the equation, $x(t)$ is the system output or the variable of interest, which may be the displacement $y(t)$ of the mechanical system in Figure 3.1(a), the electric charge $q(t)$ on the capacitor of the electric circuit in Figure 3.1(b), or the angular displacement $\theta(t)$ of the electromechanical system in Figure 3.1(c). The variable $r(t)$ is the control input or the command by which the behavior of the system can be altered or controlled. The damping ratio ς, the natural frequency ω_n, and the steady-state step response x_{ss} are determined by system component values.

Given initial conditions $x(0)$ and $\dot{x}(0)$ and input $r(t)$ for $t \geq 0$, we can solve the differential equation to find $x(t)$ for $t \geq 0$. After taking the Laplace transform of Equation 3.18 and some straightforward algebraic manipulations, we have the solution $X(s) = \mathscr{L}[x(t)]$ as follows:

$$X(s) = [G_0(s)x(0) + G_1(s)\dot{x}(0)] + G(s)R(s) := X_I(s) + X_R(s) \tag{3.19}$$

where

$$G_0(s) = \frac{s + 2\varsigma\omega_n}{D(s)}, \quad G_1(s) = \frac{1}{D(s)}, \quad G(s) = \frac{x_{ss}\omega_n^2}{D(s)}, \quad D(s) = s^2 + 2\varsigma\omega_n s + \omega_n^2$$

In the Laplace transform manipulations, the Laplace transform pairs $\dot{x}(t) \rightleftarrows sX(s) - x(0)$ and $\ddot{x}(t) \rightleftarrows s^2X(s) - sx(0) - \dot{x}(0)$ from Theorem 2.25 were employed. Note that $X(s)$ consists of two parts: $X_I(s)$, the response due to the initial conditions $x(0)$ and $\dot{x}(0)$, and $X_R(s)$, the response due to the control or command input $R(s)$. Therefore, the complete response $x(t)$ of the typical second-order system, described by Equation 3.18, is the inverse Laplace transform of $X(s)$:

$$x(t) = \mathscr{L}^{-1}[X(s)] = \mathscr{L}^{-1}[X_I(s)] + \mathscr{L}^{-1}[X_R(s)] = x_I(t) + x_R(t) \tag{3.20}$$

3.3.1 The Response of the Typical Second-Order Systems Due to Initial Conditions

The initial state response $x_I(t)$ is the response of the second-order dynamic system due to the initial conditions $x(0)$ and $\dot{x}(0)$. It can be computed using the inverse Laplace transform in the following:

$$x_I(t) = \mathscr{L}^{-1}[X_I(s)] = \mathscr{L}^{-1}\left[\frac{x(0)s + 2\varsigma\omega_n x(0) + \dot{x}(0)}{s^2 + 2\varsigma\omega_n s + \omega_n^2}\right] \tag{3.21}$$

Note that the two poles of the function $X(s)$ are the roots of the characteristic equation $s^2 + 2\varsigma\omega_n s + \omega_n^2 = 0$. As discussed in Section 3.2, the behaviors of the typical second-order system can be classified into the following four cases according to the values of the damping ratio ς.

Case A: $\varsigma > 1$. The system is *overdamped*, and the characteristic equation has two distinct negative real roots: $-\varsigma\omega_n \pm \omega_n\sqrt{\varsigma^2 - 1}$ or $-\alpha_1$ and $-\alpha_2$. Hence, $X_I(s)$ can be decomposed into two terms as follows using the partial fraction expansion:

$$X_I(s) = \frac{x(0)s + 2\varsigma\omega_n x(0) + \dot{x}(0)}{(s + \alpha_1)(s + \alpha_2)} = \frac{A_1}{(s + \alpha_1)} + \frac{A_2}{(s + \alpha_2)} \tag{3.22}$$

Then the initial state response $x_I(t)$ for *Case A* is

$$x_I(t) = \mathscr{L}^{-1}[X_I(s)] = A_1 e^{-\alpha_1 t} + A_2 e^{-\alpha_2 t} \tag{3.23}$$

Case B: $\varsigma = 1$. The system is *critically damped*, and the characteristic equation has two identical negative real roots at $-\omega_n$. Hence, $X_I(s)$ can be decomposed into two terms as follows using the partial fraction expansion:

$$X_I(s) = \frac{x(0)s + 2\omega_n x(0) + \dot{x}(0)}{(s + \omega_n)^2} = \frac{A_3}{(s + \omega_n)} + \frac{A_4}{(s + \omega_n)^2} \tag{3.24}$$

Then the initial state response $x_I(t)$ for *Case B* is

$$x_I(t) = \mathscr{L}^{-1}[X_I(s)] = A_3 e^{-\omega_n t} + A_4 t e^{-\omega_n t} \tag{3.25}$$

Case C: $0 < \varsigma < 1$. The system is *underdamped*, and the characteristic equation has two complex conjugate roots at $-\varsigma\omega_n \pm j\omega_n\sqrt{1 - \varsigma^2}$ or $-\alpha \pm j\omega$. Hence, $X_I(s)$ can be decomposed into two terms as follows using the partial fraction expansion:

$$X_I(s) = \frac{x(0)s + 2\varsigma\omega_n x(0) + \dot{x}(0)}{(s + \alpha - j\omega)(s + \alpha + j\omega)} = \frac{Ae^{j\theta}}{(s + \alpha - j\omega)} + \frac{Ae^{-j\theta}}{(s + \alpha + j\omega)} \tag{3.26}$$

Then the initial state response $x_I(t)$ for *Case C* is

$$x_I(t) = \mathcal{L}^{-1}[X_I(s)] = Ae^{j\theta}e^{-(\alpha-j\omega)t} + Ae^{-j\theta}e^{-(\alpha+j\omega)t}$$

$$= Ae^{-\alpha t}\left(e^{j(\omega t+\theta)} + e^{-j(\omega t+\theta)}\right) = 2Ae^{-\alpha t}\cos(\omega t + \theta) \tag{3.27}$$

Case D: $\varsigma = 0$. The system is *undamped*, and the characteristic equation has two complex conjugate roots at $\pm j\omega_n$. Hence, $X_I(s)$ can be decomposed into two terms as follows using the partial fraction expansion:

$$X_I(s) = \frac{x(0)s + \dot{x}(0)}{(s-j\omega_n)(s+j\omega_n)} = \frac{A_5 e^{j\phi}}{(s-j\omega_n)} + \frac{A_5 e^{-j\phi}}{(s+j\omega_n)} \tag{3.28}$$

Then the initial state response $x_I(t)$ for *Case D* is

$$x_I(t) = \mathcal{L}^{-1}[X_I(s)] = A_5 e^{j\phi}e^{j\omega_n t} + A_5 e^{-j\phi}e^{-j\omega_n t}$$

$$= A_5\left(e^{j(\omega_n t+\phi)} + e^{-j(\omega_n t+\phi)}\right) = 2A_5\cos(\omega_n t + \phi) \tag{3.29}$$

∎

In the following example, the mass–damper–spring (MBK) system as shown in Figure 3.1(a) will be employed to demonstrate the behavior of the system in four cases.

Example 3.1 (The Responses of an MBK System Due to Initial Conditions)

Consider a mass–damper–spring (MBK) system as shown in Figure 3.1(a), where the mass and the spring constant are chosen to be $M = 1$ kg and $K = 4$ N/m, respectively. The friction coefficient B of the damper is kept as a free design parameter at this moment. Assume there is neither applied force nor initial velocity (both $f_a(t)$ and $\dot{y}(0)$ are zero), but the initial mass displacement is a little bit away from the equilibrium, say, $y(0) = y_0 = 0.1$m. The objective is to find the trajectory of the mass displacement, $y(t)$, after it is released at $t = 0$.

With these assumptions, the governing differential equation now is

$$\ddot{y}(t) + B\dot{y}(t) + 4y(t) = 0, \quad y(0) = y_0, \quad \dot{y}(0) = 0$$

Take the Laplace transform to obtain

$$s^2 Y(s) - sy_0 + B[sY(s) - y_0] + 4Y(s) = 0 \quad \rightarrow \quad Y(s) = \frac{y_0(s+B)}{s^2 + Bs + 4}$$

and then the solution $y(t)$ can be found by computing the inverse Laplace transform of $Y(s)$. Before doing that, we will see how to classify the behavior of the system into four classes according to the value of the friction coefficient B of the damper. Comparing the characteristic polynomial of the MBK system with that of the typical second-order system,

$$s^2 + Bs + 4 \quad \rightleftarrows \quad s^2 + 2\varsigma\omega_n s + \omega_n^2$$

we have $\omega_n = 2$ rad/s and $\varsigma = B/4$. Therefore, if $M = 1$ kg and $K = 4$ N/m are chosen for the MBK system, the behavior of the MBK system can be classified into the following four cases according to the values of the friction coefficient B:

Case A : $B > 4$ Ns/m, $\varsigma > 1$, $\omega_n = 2$ rad/s, $s_1, s_2 = -\alpha_1, -\alpha_2$,   *overdamped*

Case B : $B = 4$ Ns/m, $\varsigma = 1$, $\omega_n = 2$ rad/s, $s_1, s_2 = -2, -2$,   *critically damped*

Case C : $0 < B < 4$ Ns/m, $0 < \varsigma < 1$, $\omega_n = 2$ rad/s, $s_1, s_2 = -\alpha \pm j\omega$,   *underdamped*

Case D : $B = 0$ Ns/m, $\varsigma = 0$, $\omega_n = 2$ rad/s, $s_1, s_2 = \pm j2$,   *undamped*

Based on this investigation and analysis, we should be able to envision the trajectory of the motion even before solving for $y(t)$. ∎

Example 3.2 (Case A Overdamped Response of the MBK System Due to Initial Conditions)

For the MBK system considered in Example 3.1, with the assumptions $M = 1$ kg, $K = 4$ N/m, $f_a(t) = 0$, $\dot{y}(0) = 0$, and $y(0) = y_0 = 0.1$ m, we have the solution in s-domain as a function of the friction coefficient B as follows:

$$\mathscr{L}[y(t)] = Y(s) = \frac{0.1(s+B)}{s^2 + Bs + 4}$$

To investigate Case A overdamped initial state response, let $B = 5$ Ns/m so that the damping ratio and natural frequency are $\varsigma = 1.25$ and $\omega_n = 2$ rad/s, respectively, and the two real poles are $s_1 = -1$ and $s_2 = -4$. Now, to find the inverse Laplace transform of $Y(s)$, we decompose $Y(s)$ into two parts using the partial fraction expansion:

$$\frac{0.1(s+5)}{s^2 + 5s + 4} = \frac{A_1}{s+1} + \frac{A_2}{s+4} \quad \rightarrow \quad 0.1s + 0.5 = A_1(s+4) + A_2(s+1)$$

This polynomial equation is valid for any real or complex value of s; thus, the substitutions of s by -1 and -4 are the best choices, leading to easy solutions for A_1 and A_2.

$$s = -1 \quad \rightarrow \quad -0.1 + 0.5 = A_1(-1+4) \quad \rightarrow \quad A_1 = 0.4/3 = 0.1333$$
$$s = -4 \quad \rightarrow \quad -0.4 + 0.5 = A_2(-4+1) \quad \rightarrow \quad A_2 = 0.1/-3 = -0.0333$$

Taking the inverse Laplace transform, we have the following initial state response of the MBK system:

$$y(t) = 0.1333e^{-t} - 0.0333e^{-4t}, \quad t \geq 0$$

Note that the initial state response $y(t)$ has two exponential terms, $y_1(t) = 0.1333e^{-t}$ and $y_2(t) = -0.0333e^{-4t}$, which are associated with the system poles $s = -1$ and $s = -4$, respectively. **As shown from Figure 3.2,** $y_2(t)$ **decays much more quickly than** $y_1(t)$**, and therefore the pole closer to the imaginary axis plays a more dominant role than the other pole.** ∎

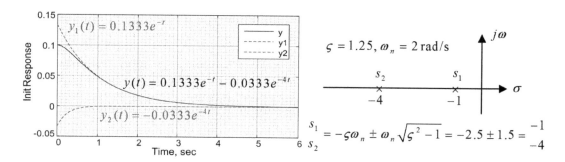

Fig. 3.2: Case A initial state response of the overdamped MBK system.

Example 3.3 (Case B Critically Damped Initial State Response of the MBK System)

The MBK system considered in the following is identical to the one in Example 3.2, except the value of the friction coefficient B in the following s-domain trajectory solution:

$$\mathscr{L}[y(t)] = Y(s) = \frac{0.1(s+B)}{s^2+Bs+4}$$

To investigate Case B critically damped initial state response, let $B = 4$ Ns/m so that the damping ratio and natural frequency are $\varsigma = 1.0$ and $\omega_n = 2$ rad/s, respectively, and the two real poles are identical $s_1 = s_2 = -2$. Now, to find the inverse Laplace transform of $Y(s)$, we decompose $Y(s)$ into two parts using the partial fraction expansion:

$$\frac{0.1(s+4)}{s^2+4s+4} = \frac{B_1}{s+2} + \frac{B_2}{(s+2)^2} \quad \rightarrow \quad 0.1s+0.4 = B_1(s+2)+B_2$$

As mentioned previously, this polynomial equation is valid for any real or complex value of s; thus, we can substitute s by any two values to obtain two linearly independent algebraic equations from which the two unknowns B_1 and B_2 can be solved. As alternative, the *coefficient comparison approach* can be employed to set up two linearly independent equations to solve for B_1 and B_2 as follows:

$$s^1 \text{ term}: \quad 0.1 = B_1 \quad \rightarrow \quad B_1 = 0.1$$
$$s^0 \text{ term}: \quad 0.4 = 2B_1 + B_2 \quad \rightarrow \quad B_2 = 0.4 - 0.2 = 0.2$$

Taking the inverse Laplace transform of $Y(s)$, we have the following initial state response of the MBK system:

$$y(t) = 0.1e^{-2t} + 0.2te^{-2t}, \quad t \geq 0$$

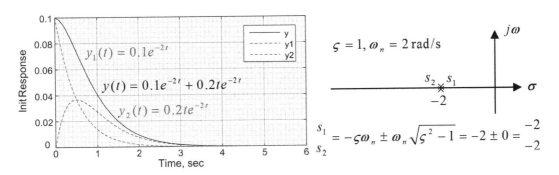

Fig. 3.3: Case B critically damped initial state response of the MBK system.

The Case B critically damped initial state response in Figure 3.3 is obtained using the following MATLAB code:

```
% CSD Fig3.3 Case B critically damped initial state response
clear, t=linspace(0,6,61); y1=0.1*exp(-2*t); y2=0.2*t.*exp(-2*t);
y=y1+y2; figure(31), plot(t,y,'k-',t,y1,'b--',t,y2,'r--'), grid,
grid minor, xlabel('Time, sec'), ylabel('Init Response'),
legend('y','y1','y2')
```

Note that the initial state response $y(t)$ has two terms, $y_1(t) = 0.1e^{-2t}$ and $y_2(t) = 0.2te^{-2t}$, which are the results of the double system poles at $s = -2$. The system considered in Example 3.2 and the one in this example are basically the same except the value of the damping ratio—the former with $\varsigma = 1.25$, overdamped, and the latter with $\varsigma = 1$, critically damped. By comparing the initial state responses in Figure 3.2 and Figure 3.3, we can observe that the critically damped step response moves towards the equilibrium faster and reaches the steady state at the equilibrium earlier than the overdamped initial state response. **The critically damped step response is the least damped one that still can avoid an overshoot and oscillations.** ∎

Example 3.4 (Case C Underdamped Response of the MBK System Due to Initial Conditions)

The MBK system considered in the following is almost identical to the previous two examples in Example 3.2 and Example 3.3. The only difference is in the value of the friction coefficient B, which is smaller in the following s-domain trajectory solution:

$$\mathscr{L}[y(t)] = Y(s) = \frac{0.1(s+B)}{s^2 + Bs + 4}$$

To investigate Case C underdamped initial state response, let $B = 2$ Ns/m so that the damping ratio and natural frequency are $\varsigma = 0.5$ and $\omega_n = 2$ rad/s, respectively, and the two complex conjugate poles are $s_1, s_2 = -1 \pm j\sqrt{3}$. Now, to find the inverse Laplace transform of $Y(s)$, we decompose $Y(s)$ into two parts using the partial fraction expansion:

$$\frac{0.1(s+2)}{s^2 + 2s + 4} = \frac{c}{s+1-j\sqrt{3}} + \frac{c^*}{s+1+j\sqrt{3}} \rightarrow 0.1(s+2) = c(s+1+j\sqrt{3}) + c^*(s+1-j\sqrt{3})$$

Note that the two complex numbers c and c^* are conjugate, which means if either one is known we will have the other one immediately. Thus, only one needs to be computed. By substituting s by $-1 + j\sqrt{3}$, the polynomial equation becomes

$$0.1(-1 + j\sqrt{3} + 2) = c(-1 + j\sqrt{3} + 1 + j\sqrt{3}) \rightarrow c = \frac{0.1(1 + j\sqrt{3})}{j2\sqrt{3}} = \frac{0.1}{\sqrt{3}}e^{-j30°}$$

hence, $c^* = \frac{0.1}{\sqrt{3}}e^{j30°}$. Taking the inverse Laplace transform of $Y(s)$, we have the initial state response of the MBK system:

$$y(t) = \frac{0.1}{\sqrt{3}}e^{-j30°}e^{(-1+j\sqrt{3})t} + \frac{0.1}{\sqrt{3}}e^{j30°}e^{(-1-j\sqrt{3})t} = \frac{0.1}{\sqrt{3}}e^{-t}\left(e^{j(\sqrt{3}t-30°)} + e^{-j(\sqrt{3}t-30°)}\right)$$

which can be rewritten in terms of cosine or sine functions:

$$y(t) = \frac{0.2}{\sqrt{3}}e^{-t}\cos(\sqrt{3}t - 30°) = \frac{0.2}{\sqrt{3}}e^{-t}\sin(\sqrt{3}t + 60°)$$

It can be seen that the initial state response $y(t)$ is a sinusoidal function with frequency $\omega = \sqrt{3}$ rad/s and exponentially decaying amplitude. **Note that oscillation frequency $\omega = \sqrt{3}$ rad/s is the imaginary part of the system pole, and the decaying rate in e^{-t} is determined by the real part of the pole. Furthermore, the phase of the sine function is $60°$, which reveals that the damping ratio is $\varsigma = \cos 60° = 0.5$.** As shown in Figure 3.4, the underdamped initial state response has much faster rise time than the overdamped or critically damped cases. But the 18% overshoot due to the choice of $\varsigma = 0.5$ is not a good design. A new selection of B to increase the damping ratio to about $\varsigma = 0.9$ will greatly improve the performance. ∎

The Case C underdamped initial state response in Figure 3.4 is obtained using the following MAT-LAB code:

```
% CSD Fig3.4 Case C underdamped initial state response
clear; t=linspace(0,6,61); y=0.1155*exp(-t).*sin(sqrt(3)*t+pi/3);
figure(32), plot(t,y,'k-'), grid, grid minor,
xlabel('Time, sec'), ylabel('Init Response')
```

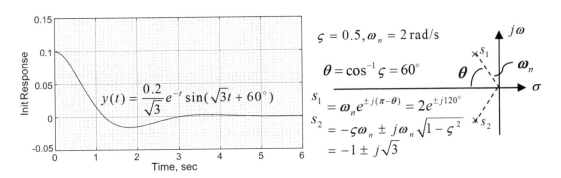

Fig. 3.4: Case C underdamped initial state response of the MBK system.

Exercise 3.5 (Redo Example 3.4 by Selecting $B = 3.6$ Ns/m)

Redesign the MBK system by selecting $B = 3.6$ Ns/m and repeat Example 3.4 to compare the performance of this particular underdamped design with the critically damped design in Example 3.3 and give your comments.   ■

Example 3.6 (Case D Undamped Response of the MBK System Due to Initial Conditions)

The MBK system considered in the following is almost identical to the previous three examples in Example 3.2, Example 3.3, and Example 3.4. The difference is in the value of the friction coefficient B, which is now zero, in the following s-domain solution:

$$\mathcal{L}[y(t)] = Y(s) = \frac{0.1(s+B)}{s^2 + Bs + 4}$$

With $B = 0$ Ns/m, the damping ratio and natural frequency are $\varsigma = 0$ and $\omega_n = 2$ rad/s, respectively, and the two complex conjugate poles are $s_1, s_2 = \pm j2$. Now, $Y(s)$ has become

$$Y(s) = \frac{0.1s}{s^2 + 2^2}$$

The initial state response $y(t)$ is the inverse Laplace transform of $Y(s)$,

$$y(t) = 0.1\cos 2t$$

which is a sinusoidal function with frequency $\omega = 2$ rad/s and undamped amplitude as shown in Figure 3.5. Note that the imaginary part of the system pole, $\omega = 2$ rad/s, is the oscillation frequency, and the zero real part of the pole means that the decaying rate in e^{0t} is zero.   ■

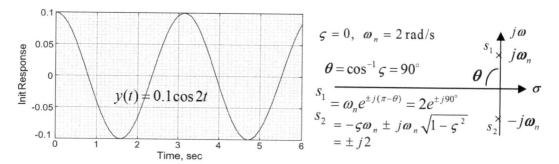

Fig. 3.5: Case D undamped initial state response of the MBK system.

3.3.2 The Response of the Typical Second-Order Systems Due to Unit Step Input

As shown in Equations 3.19 and 3.20, the output response $x(t)$ of the typical second-order system consists of two parts: $x_I(t)$, the response due to the initial conditions, and $x_R(t)$, the response due to the reference input or control input $r_R(t)$. The response due to the initial conditions has been discussed in the previous subsection, Section 3.3.1. **The initial state responses are basically transient responses— all responses due to initial conditions will decay exponentially and eventually die out unless the system has poles on the imaginary axis or in the right half of the complex plane.** On the other hand, the responses due to the input $r(t)$ will include both transient and steady-state responses. The type of input signals can be an impulse function, a step function, a sinusoidal function of a wide range of frequencies, or an irregular piecewise continuous function. However, the most common testing signals used in practice are the unit step function $u_s(t)$ and the sinusoidal function $\cos \omega t$ or $\sin \omega t$ with a wide range of frequencies.

The sinusoidal response of the second-order system will be discussed in the next subsection. In this subsection, we will investigate the effect of the damping ratio ς and the natural frequency ω_n on the transient behavior of the typical second-order system.

Recall that in Section 2.4.2 we learned how to find the step response of the typical first-order system. As shown in Figure 2.6, the procedure of finding the step response of the system $\tau \dot{x}(t) + x(t) = x_{ss}u(t)$ is fairly straightforward since the system has only one pole, $s = -1/\tau$, in which τ is the time constant of the system. The step response graph can be easily sketched without the need of solving the differential equation since the equation has revealed the information of the time constant τ and the steady-state step response x_{ss}, which provide enough information to construct the step response.

Although the step response of the typical second-order system is not as simple as that of the typical first-order system, it still can be effectively characterized by only three parameters: the damping ratio ς, the natural frequency ω_n, and the steady-state step response x_{ss}. The step response $x_R(t)$ is the response of the second-order dynamic system due to the unit step input $u_s(t)$, and can be computed as the inverse Laplace transform of $X_R(s)$:

$$x_R(t) = \mathscr{L}^{-1}[X_R(s)] = \mathscr{L}^{-1}\left[\frac{x_{ss}\omega_n^2}{s^2 + 2\varsigma\omega_n s + \omega_n^2}\frac{1}{s}\right] = \mathscr{L}^{-1}\left[\frac{x_{ss}\omega_n^2}{s(s^2 + 2\varsigma\omega_n s + \omega_n^2)}\right] \qquad (3.30)$$

where $X_R(s)$ was given in Equation 3.19. In the following, we will investigate the step response of the typical second-order system for each case of Cases A to D as we did in Section 3.3.1 for the initial state response study.

Case A: $\varsigma > 1$. The system is *overdamped*, and the characteristic equation has two distinct negative real roots: $-\varsigma \omega_n \pm \omega_n \sqrt{\varsigma^2 - 1}$ or $-\alpha_1$ and $-\alpha_2$. Hence, $X_R(s)$ can be decomposed into three terms as follows using the partial fraction expansion:

$$X_R(s) = \frac{x_{ss}\omega_n^2}{s(s+\alpha_1)(s+\alpha_2)} = \frac{x_{ss}}{s} + \frac{A_1}{(s+\alpha_1)} + \frac{A_2}{(s+\alpha_2)} \tag{3.31}$$

Then the step response $x_R(t)$ for *Case A* is

$$x_R(t) = \mathcal{L}^{-1}[X_R(s)] = x_{ss} + A_1 e^{-\alpha_1 t} + A_2 e^{-\alpha_2 t} \tag{3.32}$$

Example 3.7 (Case A Step Response Example with $\varsigma = 1.25$, $\omega_n = 2$ rad/s and $x_{ss} = 1$)

Consider the following system with $\varsigma = 1.25$, $\omega_n = 2$ rad/s, $x_{ss} = 1$, and the roots of the characteristic equation are at -1 and -4:

$$\frac{X_R(s)}{R(s)} = G(s) = \frac{x_{ss}\omega_n^2}{s^2 + 2\varsigma\omega_n s + \omega_n^2} = \frac{4}{s^2 + 5s + 4} = \frac{4}{(s+1)(s+4)} \tag{3.33}$$

With the unit step input $R(s) = 1/s$, we have the step response $X_R(s)$ with its partial fraction expansion,

$$X_R(s) = \frac{4}{s(s+1)(s+4)} = \frac{A_0}{s} + \frac{A_1}{s+1} + \frac{A_2}{s+4} \tag{3.34}$$

where A_0, A_1, and A_2 are the real partial fraction expansion residue constants to be determined. These constants can be evaluated using the residue approach as follows:

$$A_0 = \lim_{s\to 0} sX_R(s) = \frac{4}{(1)(4)} = 1, \quad A_1 = \lim_{s\to -1}(s+1)X_R(s) = \frac{4}{(-1)(3)} = \frac{-4}{3},$$

$$A_2 = \lim_{s\to -4}(s+4)X_R(s) = \frac{4}{(-4)(-3)} = \frac{1}{3} \tag{3.35}$$

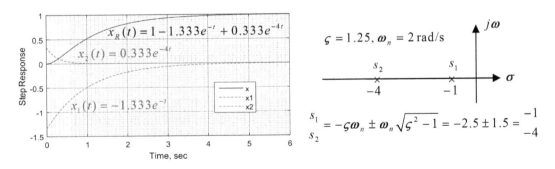

Fig. 3.6: Case A: Overdamped step response.

Now, plug the values of A_0, A_1, and A_2 into Equation 3.34, and use the Laplace transform pair $1/(s+a) \rightleftharpoons e^{-at}$, and we have the step response in the following:

$$x_R(t) = \mathcal{L}^{-1}[X_R(s)] = 1 - (4/3)e^{-t} + (1/3)e^{-4t} := 1 + x_1(t) + x_2(t) \tag{3.36}$$

Note that the step response $x_R(t)$ has two exponential terms, $x_1(t) = -1.33e^{-t}$ and $x_2(t) = 0.33e^{-4t}$, which are associated with the system poles $s = -1$ and $s = -4$, respectively. As shown from Figure 3.6, $x_2(t)$ decays much more quickly than $x_1(t)$, and therefore the pole closer to the imaginary axis plays more dominant role than the other pole. ∎

Case B: $\varsigma = 1$. The system is *critically damped*, and the characteristic equation has two identical negative real roots at $-\omega_n$. Hence, $X_R(s)$ can be decomposed into three terms as follows using the partial fraction expansion:

$$X_R(s) = \frac{x_{ss}\omega_n^2}{s(s+\omega_n)^2} = \frac{x_{ss}}{s} + \frac{A_3}{(s+\omega_n)} + \frac{A_4}{(s+\omega_n)^2} \tag{3.37}$$

Then the step response $x_R(t)$ for *Case B* is

$$x_R(t) = \mathcal{L}^{-1}[X_R(s)] = x_{ss} + A_3 e^{-\omega_n t} + A_4 t e^{-\omega_n t} \tag{3.38}$$

Example 3.8 (Case B Step Response Example with $\varsigma = 1$, $\omega_n = 2$ rad/s and $x_{ss} = 1$)

Consider the following system with $\varsigma = 1$, $\omega_n = 2$ rad/s, $x_{ss} = 1$, and the two roots of the characteristic equation are both -2:

$$\frac{X_R(s)}{R(s)} = G(s) = \frac{x_{ss}\omega_n^2}{s^2 + 2\varsigma\omega_n s + \omega_n^2} = \frac{4}{s^2 + 4s + 4} = \frac{4}{(s+2)^2} \tag{3.39}$$

With the unit step input $R(s) = 1/s$, we have the output $X_R(s)$ and its partial fraction expansion,

$$X_R(s) = \frac{4}{s(s+2)^2} = \frac{A_0}{s} + \frac{A_3}{s+2} + \frac{A_4}{(s+2)^2} \tag{3.40}$$

where A_0, A_3, and A_4 are the real partial fraction expansion residue constants to be determined. These constants can be evaluated using the *residue approach* as follows:

$$A_0 = \lim_{s\to 0} sX_R(s) = \frac{4}{2^2} = 1, \quad A_4 = \lim_{s\to -2}(s+2)^2 X_R(s) = \frac{4}{-2} = -2,$$

$$A_3 = \lim_{s\to -2}\frac{d}{ds}\left[(s+2)^2 X_R(s)\right] = \lim_{s\to -2}\frac{d}{ds}\left[\frac{4}{s}\right] = \lim_{s\to -2}\frac{-4}{s^2} = \frac{-4}{(-2)^2} = -1 \tag{3.41}$$

The partial fraction expansion residue constants can also be found using the *polynomial substitution approach* and the *coefficient comparison approach* as described in Remark 3.9. Now, plug the values of A_0, A_3, and A_4 into Equation 3.40, and use the Laplace transform pairs $1/(s+a) \rightleftarrows e^{-at}$ and $1/(s+a)^2 \rightleftarrows te^{-at}$, and we have the step response in the following:

$$x_R(t) = \mathcal{L}^{-1}[X_R(s)] = 1 - e^{-2t} - 2te^{-2t} := 1 + x_1(t) + x_2(t) \tag{3.42}$$

The Case B critically damped step response in Figure 3.7 is obtained using the following MAT-LAB code:

```
% CSD Fig3.7 Case B critically damped step response
clear, t=linspace(0,6,61); x1=-exp(-2*t); x2=-2*t.*exp(-2*t);
xR=1+x1+x2; figure(33), plot(t,xR,'k-',t,x1,'b--',t,x2,'r--'),
grid, grid minor, xlabel('Time, sec'),
ylabel('Step Response'), legend('xR','x1','x2')
```

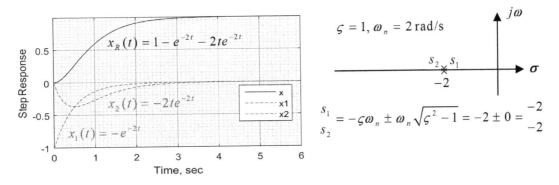

Fig. 3.7: Case B: Critically damped step response.

Note that in addition to the steady-state response $x_{ss} = 1$, the step response $x_R(t)$ has two transient response terms, $x_1(t) = -e^{-2t}$ and $x_2(t) = -2te^{-2t}$, which are the results of the double poles at $s = -2$. As shown from Figure 3.7, if there were no $x_2(t) = -2te^{-2t}$ term, the step response would be the same as that of the typical first-order system, with time constant equal to 0.5 second, or equivalently with the single pole at $s = -2$. **The additional pole at the same location $s = -2$ leads to the creation of the term $x_2(t) = -2te^{-2t}$ that apparently slows down the step response.**

∎

The systems considered in Figure 3.6 and Figure 3.7 are both typical second-order systems with identical ω_n and x_{ss}. The only difference is in the value of the damping ratio—one with $\varsigma = 1.25$, overdamped, and the other with $\varsigma = 1$, critically damped. By comparing the step responses in Figure 3.6 and Figure 3.7, we can observe that the critically damped step response rises faster and reaches the steady state earlier than the overdamped step response. **The critically damped step response is the least damped one that can still avoid an overshoot and oscillations.**

Remark 3.9 (Alternative Ways to Evaluate the Partial Fraction Expansion Residue Constants.)

As discussed in Section 2.4.2, the partial fraction expansion residue constants A_0, A_3, and A_4 in Equation 3.40 can also be evaluated using the polynomial substitution approach and the coefficient comparison approach. Multiply both sides of Equation 3.40 by $s(s+2)^2$ to obtain the following polynomial equation:

$$4 = A_0(s+2)^2 + A_3 s(s+2) + A_4 s \tag{3.43}$$

Since this polynomial equation is valid for any value of s, any set of three distinct numbers can be selected to substitute s to obtain three linearly independent equations so that the three constants can be uniquely determined. However, some particular numbers may be chosen to make the equations easier to solve. **For this example, if s is selected as 0 then Equation 3.43 will become $4 = A_0(2)^2$, which leads to $A_0 = 1$. Similarly, substituting s by -2 in Equation 3.43 will give the solution $A_4 = -2$.** After plugging these two known residue constants into Equation 3.43, there is only one unknown residue constant A_3 left in the equation:

$$4 = (s+2)^2 + A_3 s(s+2) - 2s \tag{3.44}$$

Then there are several ways to determine the value of A_3 in Equation 3.44: (1) By comparing the s^2 term, we have $0 = s^2 + A_3 s^2$, which gives $A_3 = -1$; (2) By substituting s by 1, Equation 3.44 becomes $4 = 3^2 + 3A_3 - 2$ and then $A_3 = -1$; or (3) By moving $-2s$ from the right-hand side

to the left-hand side, Equation 3.44 becomes $2(s+2) = (s+2)^2 + A_3 s(s+2)$, which is simplified to $0 = s + A_3 s$; hence, $A_3 = -1$. ∎

Case C: $0 < \varsigma < 1$. The system is *underdamped*, and the characteristic equation has two complex conjugate roots at $-\varsigma\omega_n \pm j\omega_n\sqrt{1-\varsigma^2}$ or $-\alpha \pm j\omega$. Hence, $X_R(s)$ can be decomposed into three terms as follows using the partial fraction expansion:

$$X_R(s) = \frac{x_{ss}\omega_n^2}{s(s+\alpha-j\omega)(s+\alpha+j\omega)} = \frac{x_{ss}}{s} + \frac{Ae^{j\phi}}{s+\alpha-j\omega} + \frac{Ae^{-j\phi}}{s+\alpha+j\omega} \tag{3.45}$$

Using the Laplace transform pair $1/(s+a) \rightleftarrows e^{-at}$, we have the step response $x_R(t)$ for Case C as follows:

$$x_R(t) = \mathscr{L}^{-1}\left[X_R(s)\right] = x_{ss} + Ae^{j\phi}e^{-(\alpha-j\omega)t} + Ae^{j\phi}e^{-(\alpha+j\omega)t}$$

$$= x_{ss} + Ae^{-\alpha t}\left(e^{j(\omega t+\phi)} + e^{-j(\omega t+\phi)}\right) = x_{ss} + 2Ae^{-\alpha t}\cos(\omega t + \phi) \tag{3.46}$$

The residue constant $Ae^{j\phi}$ in Equation 3.45 can be found (See Equation 3.64) in terms of the damping ratio ς and the steady-state step response x_{ss} as

$$Ae^{j\phi} = \left(0.5x_{ss}\Big/\sqrt{1-\varsigma^2}\right)e^{j(\theta+\pi/2)}, \quad \text{where} \quad \theta = \cos^{-1}\varsigma \tag{3.47}$$

Hence, Equation 3.46 can be rewritten as

$$x_R(t) = x_{ss} + 2Ae^{-\alpha t}\cos(\omega t + \phi) = x_{ss} + \left(x_{ss}\Big/\sqrt{1-\varsigma^2}\right)e^{-\alpha t}\cos(\omega t + \theta + \pi/2)$$

$$= x_{ss}\left[1 - \left(1\Big/\sqrt{1-\varsigma^2}\right)e^{-\alpha t}\sin(\omega t + \theta)\right] \tag{3.48}$$

Example 3.10 (Case C Step Response Example with $\varsigma = 0.5$, $\omega_n = 2\,\text{rad/s}$ and $x_{ss} = 1$)

Consider the following system with $\varsigma = 0.5$, $\omega_n = 2\,\text{rad/s}$, $x_{ss} = 1$, and the roots of the characteristic equation are $-1 \pm j\sqrt{3}$:

$$\frac{X_R(s)}{R(s)} = G(s) = \frac{x_{ss}\omega_n^2}{s^2 + 2\varsigma\omega_n s + \omega_n^2} = \frac{4}{s^2 + 2s + 4} = \frac{4}{(s+1-j\sqrt{3})(s+1+j\sqrt{3})} \tag{3.49}$$

With the unit step input $R(s) = 1/s$, we have the step response $X_R(s)$ and its partial fraction expansion,

$$X_R(s) = \frac{4}{s(s^2+2s+4)} = \frac{A_0}{s} + \frac{c}{s+1-j\sqrt{3}} + \frac{c^*}{s+1+j\sqrt{3}} \tag{3.50}$$

where A_0 is a real constant and c is a complex constant to be determined. There is no need to compute c^* since it is the conjugate of c. These constants can be evaluated using the residue approach as follows:

$$c = \lim_{s \to -1+j\sqrt{3}}(s+1-j\sqrt{3})X_R(s) = \frac{4}{(-1+j\sqrt{3})(j2\sqrt{3})} = \frac{-2}{3+j\sqrt{3}} = \frac{1}{\sqrt{3}}e^{j150°}$$

$$c^* = \left(1/\sqrt{3}\right)e^{-j150°}, \quad A_0 = \lim_{s\to 0}sX_R(s) = 4/4 = 1 \tag{3.51}$$

Now, plug the values of A_0, c, and c^* into Equation 3.50, and use the Laplace transform pair $1/(s+a) \rightleftarrows e^{-at}$, then we have the step response in the following:

$$x_R(t) = \mathscr{L}^{-1}[X_R(s)] = 1 + (1/\sqrt{3})\, e^{j150^\circ}\, e^{-(1-j\sqrt{3})t} + (1/\sqrt{3})\, e^{-j150^\circ}\, e^{-(1+j\sqrt{3})t}$$

$$= 1 + (1/\sqrt{3})\, e^{-t} \left(e^{j(\sqrt{3}t + 150^\circ)} + e^{-j(\sqrt{3}t + 150^\circ)} \right) \tag{3.52}$$

$$= 1 + (2/\sqrt{3})\, e^{-t} \cos(\sqrt{3}t + 150^\circ) = 1 - (2/\sqrt{3})\, e^{-t} \sin(\sqrt{3}t + 60^\circ)$$

The two complex poles are $-\varsigma\omega_n \pm j\omega_n\sqrt{1 - \varsigma^2} = -1 \pm j\sqrt{3}$ **in rectangular form, or** $\omega_n e^{\pm j(\pi - \theta)}$ $= 2e^{\pm j120^\circ}$ **in polar form, where** $\theta = \cos^{-1}\varsigma = 60^\circ$. Note that the underdamped step response in Figure 3.8 rises more quickly than the critically damped step response in Figure 3.7, but it has over-shoot and oscillations. **The oscillation frequency is determined by** ω, **the imaginary part of the complex pole, and the amplitude of the oscillation is decreasing exponentially with decreasing rate determined by** $-\alpha$, **the real part of the complex pole.** ∎

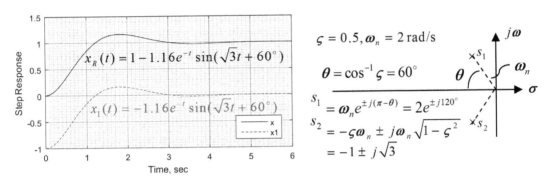

Fig. 3.8: Case C: Underdamped step response.

The Case C underdamped step response in Figure 3.8 is obtained using the following MATLAB code:

```
% CSD Fig3.8 Case C underdamped step response
clear, t=linspace(0,6,61); x1=-1.16*exp(-t).*sin(sqrt(3)*t+pi/3);
xR=1+x1; figure(34), plot(t,xR,'k-',t,x1,'b--'), grid, grid minor,
xlabel('Time, sec'), ylabel('Step Response'), legend('xR','x1')
```

Case D: $\varsigma = 0$. The system is *undamped*, and has a pair of complex conjugate roots on the imaginary axis of the complex plane at $\pm j\omega_n$. Hence, $X_R(s)$ can be decomposed into three terms as follows using the partial fraction expansion:

$$X_R(s) = \frac{x_{ss}\omega_n^2}{s(s - j\omega_n)(s + j\omega_n)} = \frac{x_{ss}}{s} + \frac{Ae^{j\phi}}{s - j\omega_n} + \frac{Ae^{-j\phi}}{s + j\omega_n} \tag{3.53}$$

Using the Laplace transform pair $1/(s + a) \rightleftarrows e^{-at}$, we have the step response $x_R(t)$ for Case D as follows:

$$x_R(t) = \mathscr{L}^{-1}[X_R(s)] = x_{ss} + Ae^{j\phi} e^{j\omega_n t} + Ae^{j\phi} e^{-j\omega_n t}$$

$$= x_{ss} + A(e^{j(\omega_n t + \phi)} + e^{-j(\omega_n t + \phi)}) = x_{ss} + 2A\cos(\omega_n t + \phi) \tag{3.54}$$

The residue $Ae^{j\phi}$ in Equation 3.53 can be found as $0.5x_{ss}e^{j\pi}$, and therefore the step response $x_R(t)$ for Case D can be rewritten as

$$x_R(t) = x_{ss} + 2A\cos(\omega_n t + \phi) = x_{ss}(1 - \cos \omega_n t) \tag{3.55}$$

Example 3.11 (Case D Example with $\varsigma = 0$, $\omega_n = 2\,\mathrm{rad/s}$ and $x_{ss} = 1$)

Consider the following system with $\varsigma = 0$, $\omega_n = 2\,\mathrm{rad/s}$, $x_{ss} = 1$, and the roots of the characteristic equation $\pm j2$:

$$\frac{X_R(s)}{R(s)} = G(s) = \frac{x_{ss}\omega_n^2}{s^2 + 2\varsigma\omega_n s + \omega_n^2} = \frac{4}{s^2 + 4} = \frac{4}{(s - j2)(s + j2)} \tag{3.56}$$

With the unit step input $R(s) = 1/s$, we have the step response $X_R(s)$ and its partial fraction expansion,

$$X_R(s) = \frac{4}{s(s^2 + 4)} = \frac{A_0}{s} + \frac{c}{s - j2} + \frac{c^*}{s + j2} \tag{3.57}$$

where A_0 is a real constant and c is a complex constant to be determined. There is no need to compute c^* since it is the conjugate of c. These constants can be evaluated using the residue approach as follows:

$$c = \lim_{s \to j2}(s - j2)X_R(s) = \frac{4}{j2(j2 + j2)} = \frac{4}{-8} = -0.5 = 0.5e^{j\pi}$$

$$c^* = -0.5 = 0.5e^{-j\pi}, \quad A_0 = \lim_{s \to 0} sX_R(s) = 4/4 = 1 \tag{3.58}$$

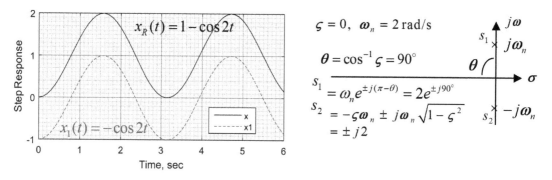

Fig. 3.9: Case D: Undamped step response.

Now, plug the values of A_0, c, and c^* into Equation 3.57. Then by taking its inverse Laplace transform, we have the step response in the following:

$$x_R(t) = \mathcal{L}^{-1}[X_R(s)] = 1 - 0.5e^{j2t} - 0.5e^{-j2t} = 1 - \cos 2t \tag{3.59}$$

The two complex poles in this example are $-\varsigma\omega_n \pm j\omega_n\sqrt{1 - \varsigma^2} = \pm j2$ in rectangular form, or $\omega_n e^{\pm j(\pi - \theta)}$ in polar form, where $\theta = \cos^{-1}\varsigma = 90°$. Note that the undamped step response $x_R(t)$ in Figure 3.9 rises more quickly than the underdamped step response in Figure 3.8, but it has 100% *overshoot* and undamped oscillations. **The oscillation frequency is $\omega = \omega_n$, which is the imaginary part of the complex pole, and the amplitude of the oscillation is sustained without damping since the real part of the complex pole is zero.** ∎

3.4 Characterization of the Underdamped Second-Order Systems

For a typical first-order system described by Equation 2.62, its step response is $x(t) = x_{ss}(1 - e^{-t/\tau})$, which can be easily characterized and plotted, as in Figure 2.5(b). The step response is basically determined by the initial value $x(0) = 0$, the steady-state value $x(\infty) = x_{ss}$, and the value of $x(t)$ at the time constant $x(\tau) = x_{ss}(1 - e^{-1}) = 0.632x_{ss}$. It has neither overshoot nor oscillations; it just simply rises exponentially with a decreasing slope $\dot{x}(t) = (x_{ss}/\tau)e^{-t/\tau}$ to approach to the steady-state final value $x(\infty) = x_{ss}$.

Although the typical second-order system can be characterized by the damping ratio ς, the natural frequency ω_n, and the step response steady-state value x_{ss}, the plotting of the second-order system step response according to the three characterization parameters is not as trivial as that of the typical first-order system. As discussed in the previous two sections, Sections 3.2 and 3.3, according to the pole locations of the system, the system can be categorized into four cases: the overdamped case with $\varsigma > 1$, the critically damped case with $\varsigma = 1$, the underdamped case with $0 < \varsigma < 1$, and the undamped case with $\varsigma = 0$. **Among these four cases, the most common and interesting case that occurs in practice is the underdamped case with $0 < \varsigma < 1$. For this reason, in this section we will focus on the study of the underdamped case to gain much more clear understanding about the geometry of the poles on the complex plane and the relationship between the geometry and the time-domain response.**

3.4.1 Geometry of Conjugate System Poles on the Complex Plane

When $0 < \varsigma < 1$, the system poles, which are the roots of the characteristic equation, Equation 3.13, are a pair of complex conjugate roots at

$$\begin{matrix} p \\ p* \end{matrix} = -\alpha \pm j\omega = \omega_n e^{\pm j(\pi-\theta)} \quad \text{where} \quad \alpha = \varsigma\omega_n, \quad \omega = \omega_n\sqrt{1-\varsigma^2}, \quad \theta = \cos^{-1}\varsigma \qquad (3.60)$$

The pair of complex numbers are either represented in rectangular form as $-\alpha \pm j\omega$ or in polar form $\omega_n e^{\pm j(\pi-\theta)}$. Both representations are important in revealing the physical meaning of the mathematical results and in serving as efficient computation tools in the analysis and design of dynamic systems.

The real part of the complex number, $-\alpha = -\varsigma\omega_n$, determines how fast the system response would converge to the steady state, and the imaginary part, $j\omega = j\omega_n\sqrt{1-\varsigma^2}$, manifests the oscillation frequency of the system response. In polar form, the complex numbers are represented in terms of their magnitude and phase angle. It can be seen that the magnitude and phase angle of the complex numbers are $\sqrt{\alpha^2 + \omega^2} = \omega_n$ and $\pm(\pi - \theta)$, respectively, where $\theta = \cos^{-1}\varsigma$. It is interesting to note that algebraically the relationship between the angle θ and the damping ratio ς can be represented in many different ways by trigonometric functions as follows:

$$\theta = \tan^{-1}\frac{\sqrt{1-\varsigma^2}}{\varsigma} = \sin^{-1}\sqrt{1-\varsigma^2} = \cos^{-1}\varsigma \quad \text{and} \quad \frac{\pi}{2} - \theta = \tan^{-1}\frac{\varsigma}{\sqrt{1-\varsigma^2}} \qquad (3.61)$$

The algebraic relationship between α, ω, θ and ς, ω_n seems complicated; however, it is rather straightforward graphically, as shown in Figure 3.10.

3.4.2 Step Response of the Underdamped Second-Order System

The step response of the system, represented by Equation 3.7, is the solution of the differential equation due to the unit step input assuming zero initial conditions: $x(0) = 0$ and $\dot{x}(0) = 0$. In Section 3.3.2, we briefly described a procedure to obtain the step response for the underdamped case in Equation 3.48.

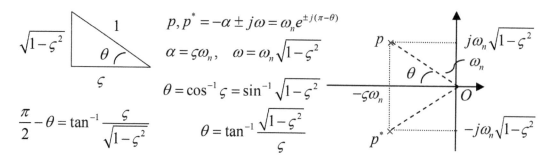

Fig. 3.10: Geometrical relationship between α, ω, θ, and ς, ω_n.

In the following, the second-order system poles geometry shown in Figure 3.10 will be employed to derive and explain the physical meaning of the step response solution in Equation 3.48. After taking the Laplace transform of Equation 3.7, the transfer function of the system can be found as follows:

$$\frac{X_R(s)}{R(s)} = G(s) = \frac{x_{ss}\omega_n^2}{s^2 + 2\varsigma\omega_n s + \omega_n^2} = \frac{x_{ss}\omega_n^2}{(s+\alpha-j\omega)(s+\alpha+j\omega)} \tag{3.62}$$

Note that $-\alpha \pm j\omega$ are the solutions of the characteristic equation, $s^2 + 2\varsigma\omega_n s + \omega_n^2 = 0$. With the unit step input $R(s) = 1/s$, we have the step response $X_R(s)$ and its partial fraction expansion,

$$X_R(s) = \frac{x_{ss}\omega_n^2}{s(s^2 + 2\varsigma\omega_n s + \omega_n^2)} = \frac{A_0}{s} + \frac{c}{s+\alpha-j\omega} + \frac{c^*}{s+\alpha+j\omega} \tag{3.63}$$

where A_0 is a real number and c is a complex number to be determined. Since c^* is the conjugate of c, only the two residue constants A_0 and c need to be evaluated:

$$c = \lim_{s \to -\alpha+j\omega} (s+\alpha-j\omega)X_R(s) = \frac{x_{ss}\omega_n^2}{(-\alpha+j\omega)(j2\omega)} = \frac{x_{ss}\omega_n^2}{\omega_n e^{j(\pi-\theta)}2\omega_n\sqrt{1-\varsigma^2}e^{j\pi/2}} = \frac{0.5x_{ss}}{\sqrt{1-\varsigma^2}}e^{j(\theta+\pi/2)}$$

$$c^* = \frac{0.5x_{ss}}{\sqrt{1-\varsigma^2}}e^{-j(\theta+\pi/2)}, \quad A_0 = \lim_{s \to 0} sX_R(s) = x_{ss}\omega_n^2/\omega_n^2 = x_{ss}$$

$$\tag{3.64}$$

In the above complex number manipulations, we used the geometrical facts that $-\alpha \pm j\omega = \omega_n e^{\pm j(\pi-\theta)}$, $\omega = \omega_n\sqrt{1-\varsigma^2}$, $j = e^{j\pi/2}$, **and** $j = e^{-j3\pi/2} = e^{j\pi/2}$. **Now, plug the values of** A_0, c, **and** c^* **into Equation 3.63, and with the Laplace transform pair** $1/(s+a) \rightleftarrows e^{-at}$, **we have the following:**

$$x(t) = \mathcal{L}^{-1}[X_R(s)] = x_{ss} + \frac{0.5x_{ss}}{\sqrt{1-\varsigma^2}}e^{j(\pi/2+\theta)}e^{(-\alpha+j\omega)t} + \frac{0.5x_{ss}}{\sqrt{1-\varsigma^2}}e^{-j(\pi/2+\theta)}e^{(-\alpha-j\omega)t}$$

$$= x_{ss}\left(1 + \frac{0.5e^{-\alpha t}}{\sqrt{1-\varsigma^2}}\left(e^{j(\pi/2+\omega t+\theta)} + e^{-j(\pi/2+\omega t+\theta)}\right)\right) = x_{ss}\left(1 + \frac{e^{-\alpha t}}{\sqrt{1-\varsigma^2}}\cos(\pi/2+\omega t+\theta)\right)$$

$$\tag{3.65}$$

Note that the Euler's formula (Theorem 2.1) and Corollary 2.2 have been employed to convert the sum of two complex functions into one real cosine function. Furthermore, with the basic trigonometric formula $\cos(\pi/2+\psi) = -\sin\psi$, Equation 3.65 can be simplified to the following:

$$x(t) = x_{ss}\left(1 - \frac{e^{-\alpha t}}{\sqrt{1-\varsigma^2}}\sin(\omega t+\theta)\right), \quad \text{where } \alpha = \varsigma\omega_n, \ \omega = \omega_n\sqrt{1-\varsigma^2}, \ \theta = \cos^{-1}\varsigma \tag{3.66}$$

3.4.3 Graphical Interpretation of the Underdamped Second-Order Step Response

In the following, we will plot the step response according to Equation 3.66, and characterize the step response in terms of the final steady-state value x_{ss}, the rise time t_r, the peak time t_p, the envelope functions $x_{ss}\left(1 \pm e^{-\alpha t} \big/ \sqrt{1-\varsigma^2}\right)$, the maximum overshoot OS, the oscillation frequency ω and period T, and the settling time t_s. All of these characterizations are determined by the damping ratio ς, the natural frequency ω_n, and the step response steady-state value x_{ss}. **The numerical example to be used for demonstration is based on $\varsigma = 0.2$, $\omega_n = 3 \, \text{rad/s}$, and $x_{ss} = 5$.**

1. **Initial and Final Steady-State Values:** With $\theta = \sin^{-1}\sqrt{1-\varsigma^2}$ and $t = 0$, we have the initial value from Equation 3.66, $x(0) = x_{ss}\left(1 - \sin(\theta)\big/\sqrt{1-\varsigma^2}\right) = 0$. It also can be seen that the final steady-state value is $\lim_{t\to\infty} x(t) = x_{ss}(1-0) = x_{ss}$ if $\alpha > 0$.

2. **A Pair of Envelope Functions:** Since the amplitude of the sinusoidal term is $e^{-\alpha t}\big/\sqrt{1-\varsigma^2}$, which is decreasing with time, the step response waveform is confined between a pair of envelope functions:

$$x_{ss}\left(1 + e^{-\alpha t}\Big/\sqrt{1-\varsigma^2}\right) \quad \text{and} \quad x_{ss}\left(1 - e^{-\alpha t}\Big/\sqrt{1-\varsigma^2}\right) \tag{3.67}$$

   As shown in Figure 3.11, these two envelopes (in blue dotted lines) are symmetrical with respect to the $x(t) = x_{ss}$ horizontal line.

3. **Sinusoidal Oscillation Frequency and Period:** The step response curve will start from $x(0) = 0$, and reaches $x(\infty) = x_{ss} = 5$ at steady state. The curve will swing up and down with decreasing oscillation amplitude at frequency $\omega = \omega_n\sqrt{1-\varsigma^2} = 2.939 \, \text{rad/s}$; hence, the oscillation period is

$$T = 2\pi/\omega = 2.138 \, \text{s} \tag{3.68}$$

4. **Valleys and Peaks of the Decaying Sinusoidal Curve:** The valleys and peaks (local minimums and maximums) of the step response will occur at $t = 0.5kT$, $k = 0, 2, 4, \cdots$ and $t = 0.5kT$, $k = 1, 3, 5, \cdots$, respectively. **The valley values are $x(0.5kT) = x_{ss}(1 - e^{-0.5k\alpha T})$ while the peak values are** $x(0.5kT) = x_{ss}(1 + e^{-0.5k\alpha T})$. Hence, the valleys at $t = 0, T, 2T, 3T, \cdots$ are $x(0) = 0$, $x(T) = x(2.138) = 3.61$, $x(2T) = x(4.276) = 4.62$, $x(3T) = x(6.414) = 4.89$, $\cdots$, respectively and the peaks at $t = 0.5T, 1.5T, 2.5T, 3.5T, \cdots$ are $x(0.5T) = x(1.069) = 7.63$, $x(1.5T) = x(3.207) = 5.73$, $x(2.5T) = x(5.345) = 5.2$, $x(3.5T) = x(7.483) = 5.06$, $\cdots$, respectively. These valleys and peaks are marked as pink dots on the graph. Note that the valleys and peaks in general are **not** on the pair of envelopes defined by Equation 3.67.

5. **Peak Time t_p:** Peak time is the time when the maximum overshoot occurs. Although the amplitude of the sinusoidal term is decreasing, the local maximums and minimums still occur according to the period $T = 2\pi/\omega$. Since the first minimum occurs at $t = 0$, the first maximum, which is also the global maximum, will occur at

$$t_p = T/2 = \pi/\omega = 1.069 \, \text{s} \tag{3.69}$$

The peak time can also be found by searching the time at which the first derivative of $x(t)$ with respect to t is zero. By setting $\dot{x}(t)$ equal to zero, we have

$$\dot{x}(t) = \left(-x_{ss}\Big/\sqrt{1-\varsigma^2}\right)\left(\frac{d}{dt}e^{-\alpha t}\sin(\omega t + \theta)\right) = 0 \tag{3.70}$$

which will lead to $\omega\cos(\omega t + \theta) - \alpha\sin(\omega t + \theta) = 0$, and therefore we have the following:

$$\tan(\omega t + \theta) = \frac{\omega}{\alpha} = \frac{\sqrt{1-\varsigma^2}}{\varsigma} = \tan\theta \qquad (3.71)$$

This equations holds only at $\omega t = k\pi$, $k = 0, 1, 2, \cdots$. The first peak occurs at $k = 1$; hence, the peak time is $t_p = \pi/\omega$, which is exactly the same as Equation 3.69.

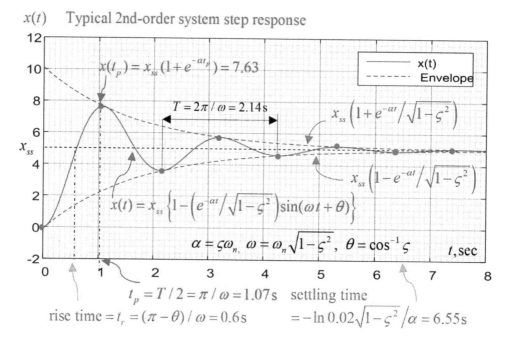

Fig. 3.11: Graphical interpretation of the typical second-order system step response.

The typical second-order system step response shown in Figure 3.11 is obtained using the following MATLAB code:

```
% CSD Fig3.11 Typical 2nd-order system step response
x_ss=5, ze=0.2, wn=3, alpha=ze*wn, w=wn*sqrt(1-ze^2), num=x_ss*wn^2,
den=[1 2*ze*wn wn^2], t=linspace(0,8,800+1); x=step(num,den,t);
x_envelope_down=5*(1-(1/sqrt(1-ze^2))*exp(-ze*wn.*t));
x_envelope_up=5*(1+(1/sqrt(1-ze^2))*exp(-ze*wn.*t)); figure(1),
plot(t,x,'r',t,x_envelope_down,'b--',t,x_envelope_up,'b--'), grid,
grid minor, xlabel('Time, sec'), ylabel('Step Response'),
legend('x(t)','Envelope')
```

6. **Maximum Overshoot OS:** Since $\sin(\pi + \theta) = -\sin\theta = -\sqrt{1-\varsigma^2}$, the value of $x(t)$ at t_p will be

$$x(t_p) = x_{ss}\left(1 - \frac{e^{-\alpha t_p}}{\sqrt{1-\varsigma^2}}\sin(\pi + \theta)\right) = x_{ss}\left(1 + e^{-\varsigma\omega_n t_p}\right) = 7.633 \qquad (3.72)$$

That means the step response overshoots over the steady-state value $x_{ss} = 5$ by 2.633. The maximum overshoot usually is measured as percentage of its steady-state value, x_{ss}; therefore, the maximum overshoot can be computed from either one of the following two formulas:

$$OS = e^{-\varsigma\pi/\sqrt{1-\varsigma^2}} = 0.5266 = 52.66\%$$
$$OS = (x_R(t_p) - x_{ss})/x_{ss} = (7.633 - 5)/5 = 0.5266 = 52.66\% \tag{3.73}$$

It can be seen from this equation that the maximum overshoot is solely determined by the damping ratio ς. In many applications like system identification or control system design, we may need to compute the damping ratio ς based on a given information of the maximum overshoot. It can be obtained as follows:

$$\ln(OS) = \frac{-\pi\varsigma}{\sqrt{1-\varsigma^2}} \quad \rightarrow \quad \tan\theta = \frac{\pi}{-\ln(OS)} \quad \rightarrow \quad \varsigma = \cos\left(\tan^{-1}\frac{\pi}{-\ln(OS)}\right) \tag{3.74}$$

Note that the geometrical relationships between θ and ς, $\tan\theta = \sqrt{1-\varsigma^2}\big/\varsigma$, and $\cos\theta = \varsigma$, were employed in the proof of Equation 3.74. For verification, the damping ratio corresponding to $OS = 0.5266$ is computed as follows:

$$\varsigma = \cos\left(\tan^{-1}\frac{\pi}{-\ln(0.5266)}\right) = \cos 78.46° = 0.2 \tag{3.75}$$

7. **Rise Time t_r:** The rise time usually is defined as the time a step response needs to rise from 10% to 90% of its desired steady-state value, x_{ss}. However, for the underdamped case, it is more meaningful to define the rise time as the time required to rise from 0 to x_{ss} (i.e., the smallest t so that $x(t) = x_{ss}$). Based on this definition, we have $\sin(\omega_n\sqrt{1-\varsigma^2}t_r + \theta) = 0$, which leads to $\omega_n\sqrt{1-\varsigma^2}t_r + \theta = \pi$. Hence, the rise time is

$$t_r = \frac{\pi - \cos^{-1}\varsigma}{\omega_n\sqrt{1-\varsigma^2}} = 0.603 \text{ s} \tag{3.76}$$

8. **Settling Time t_s:** The settling time t_s is defined as the time at which the step response is within $\pm2\%$ of the steady-state value x_{ss}. It can be computed via the amplitude of the sinusoidal term in Equation 3.66, $e^{-\varsigma\omega_n t_s}\big/\sqrt{1-\varsigma^2} = 0.02$, which leads to

$$t_s = \frac{-\ln\left(0.02\sqrt{1-\varsigma^2}\right)}{\varsigma\omega_n} = 6.55 \text{ s} \tag{3.77}$$

If approximation is allowed, this can be $t_s \approx -\ln 0.02/(\varsigma\omega_n) \approx 4/(\varsigma\omega_n) = 6.52$ s. In case that the $\pm2\%$ error is relaxed to $\pm5\%$, the settling time would be $t_s \approx -\ln 0.05/(\varsigma\omega_n) \approx 3/(\varsigma\omega_n) = 5.0$ s. ∎

3.5 Analysis and Design of a Mass–Damper–Spring System

In this section, we will analyze how the mass, damper, and spring affect the behavior of the mass–damper–spring (MBK) system in Figure 3.1(a) and then consider how to choose appropriate values of mass, friction coefficient, and spring constant, so that the system has a desired performance. For ease of reference, the schematic diagram of the mass–damper–spring system is repeated in Figure 3.12.

The transfer function corresponding to the governing differential equation of the mass–damper–spring system in Equation 3.8 is

$$\frac{Y(s)}{F_a(s)} = \frac{(1/K)(K/M)}{s^2 + (B/M)s + (K/M)} \tag{3.78}$$

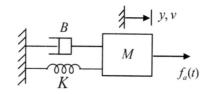

Fig. 3.12: A mass–damper–spring system.

Comparing this transfer function with the typical second-order system transfer function in Equation 3.12, we have the damping ratio ς, the natural frequency ω_n, and the steady-state step response y_{ss} as follows:

$$\varsigma = 0.5B/\sqrt{MK}, \quad \omega_n = \sqrt{K/M}, \quad y_{ss} = 1/K \tag{3.79}$$

In the following, we would like to know how the friction coefficient B, the spring constant K, and the mass M, individually affect the step response of the system. First, we would let $M = 1$ kg and $K = 1$ N/m and observe how the step response of the system varies with the change of the damper friction coefficient $B = 3, 2, 1.414, 1, 0.5$ Ns/m. As it can be seen from Equation 3.79 and Figure 3.13, the variation of the friction coefficient B does not affect the natural frequency ω_n, which is $\omega_n = \sqrt{K/M} = 1$ rad/s. However, the damping ratio ς will change with $B = 3, 2, 1.414, 1, 0.5$ Ns/m, to $\varsigma = 1.5, 1, 0.707, 0.5, 0.25$, respectively. When $B = 3$ Ns/m, the poles are on the negative real axis of the complex plane at $s = -2.618$ and $s = -0.382$, and the corresponding step response is overdamped with $\varsigma = 1.5$ and $\omega_n = 1$ rad/s. As B decreases, the two poles will move toward each other and coincide together at $s = -1$ on the complex plane when $B = 2$ Ns/m and the corresponding step response is critically damped with $\varsigma = 1$ and $\omega_n = 1$ rad/s.

The following MATLAB program is employed to plot the MBK system step responses with varying damping ratio shown in Figure 3.13:

```
% CSD Fig3.13 Effect of varying damping ratio on MBK step responses
clear, t=0:.1:20; M=1, B=0.5, K=1, num1=K/M, den1=[1 B/M K/M],
G1=tf(num1,den1), M=1, B=1, K=1, num2=K/M, den2=[1 B/M K/M],
G2=tf(num2,den2), M=1, B=1.414, K=1, num3=K/M, den3=[1 B/M K/M],
G3=tf(num3,den3), M=1, B=2, K=1,num4=K/M, den4=[1 B/M K/M],
G4=tf(num4,den4), M=1, B=3, K=1, num5=K/M, den5=[1 B/M K/M],
G5=tf(num5,den5), x1=step(G1,t); x2=step(G2,t); x3=step(G3,t);
x4=step(G4,t); x5=step(G5,t); figure(35),
plot(t,x1,'b.',t,x2,'m-',t,x3,'g-',t,x4,'k-',t,x5,'r--'),
grid, grid minor, xlabel('Time, sec'), ylabel('Step Response'),
legend ('B=0.5','B=1','B=1.414','B=2','B=3')
```

As the friction coefficient B further decreases, the two identical poles will split to become a pair of complex conjugate poles moving along the circle with radius equal to $\omega_n = 1$ centering at the origin. When $B = 1.414$ Ns/m, the poles are at $s = -0.707 \pm j0.707 = 1e^{\pm j135°}$, and the corresponding step response is underdamped with $\varsigma = 0.707$ and $\omega_n = 1$ rad/s. As the friction coefficient drops to $B = 1$ Ns/m, the poles are at $s = -0.5 \pm j0.866 = 1e^{\pm j120°}$ which is closer to the imaginary axis, and the corresponding step response is more underdamped with $\varsigma = 0.5$ and $\omega_n = 1$ rad/s. When $B = 0.5$ Ns/m, the poles are at $s = -0.25 \pm j0.968 = 1e^{\pm j104.5°}$, and the corresponding step response is even more underdamped with $\varsigma = 0.25$ and $\omega_n = 1$ rad/s, which has oscillations with high overshoot. Since the oscillation frequency is $\omega = \omega_n\sqrt{1-\varsigma^2}$ rad/s, **the step response oscillation frequency**

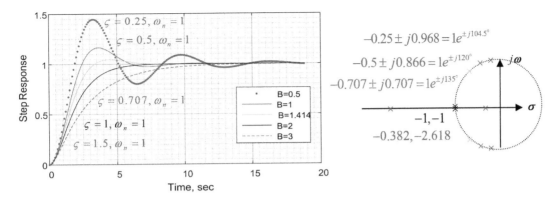

Fig. 3.13: The effect of the damping ratio ς on the step response and pole locations of the mass–damper–spring system while the natural frequency remains the same at $\omega_n = 1$ rad/s.

will increase as the damping ratio decreases and, therefore, as shown in Figure 3.13, the oscillation frequency of the step responses becomes higher as the damping ratio decreases.

Now we have observed how the step response and pole locations vary with the damping ratio ς while the natural frequency remains at $\omega_n = 1$ rad/s, as shown in Figure 3.13. Next, we would like to observe how the natural frequency ω_n affects the pole locations and the step response while keeping the damping ratio at $\varsigma = 0.707$. As discussed, for the case with $M = 1$ kg, $K = 1$ N/m and $B = 1.414$ Ns/m, the poles are at $s = -0.707 \pm j0.707 = 1e^{\pm j135°}$, and the step response is underdamped with $\varsigma = 0.707$ and $\omega_n = 1$ rad/s, as shown in both Figure 3.13 and Figure 3.14. If the mass and the friction coefficient are changed to $M = 4$ kg and $B = 2.828$ Ns/m, respectively, then the natural frequency will reduce to $\omega_n = 0.5$ rad/s and the pole location will change to $-0.354 \pm j0.354 = 0.5e^{\pm j135°}$ while keeping the damping ratio at $\varsigma = 0.707$.

Note that the step response with the smaller natural frequency is shown in Figure 3.14 in blue, which has a much slower rise time and a slower oscillation frequency than the step response in black with $\omega_n = 1$ rad/s. On the other hand, the mass and the friction coefficient can be changed to $M = 0.25$ kg and $B = 0.707$ Ns/m, respectively, to increase the natural frequency to $\omega_n = 2$ rad/s and change the pole location to $-1.414 \pm j1.414 = 2e^{\pm j135°}$ while keeping the damping ratio at $\varsigma = 0.707$. **The step response corresponding to the increased natural frequency $\omega_n = 2$ rad/s is shown in Figure 3.14 in red, which has a faster rise time and a higher oscillation frequency than the step response in black with $\omega_n = 1$ rad/s.**

The following MATLAB program is employed to plot the typical second-order system step responses with varying natural frequency shown in Figure 3.14:

```
% CSD_Fig3.14 Effect of varying natural frequency on step response
clear, t=0:.1:20; ze=0.707, wn=0.5, num1=wn^2, den1=[1 2*ze*wn wn^2],
G1=tf(num1,den1), ze=0.707, wn=1, num2=wn^2, den2=[1 2*ze*wn wn^2],
G2=tf(num2,den2), ze=0.707, wn=2, num3=wn^2, den3=[1 2*ze*wn wn^2],
G3=tf(num3,den3), x1=step(G1,t); x2=step(G2,t); x3=step(G3,t);
figure(36), plot(t,x1,'b-',t,x2,'k-',t,x3,'r-'), grid, grid minor,
xlabel('Time, sec'), ylabel('Step Response'),
legend ('\omega_n=0.5','\omega_n=1','\omega_n=2')
```

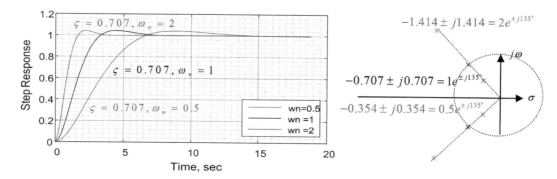

Fig. 3.14: The effect of the natural frequency on the step response and pole locations of the mass–damper–spring system while the damping ratio remains the same at $\varsigma = 0.707$.

3.6 Analysis and Design of a Simple DC Motor Position Control System

As described in the beginning of Section 3.1, there is a mathematical equivalence among the mass–damper–spring (MBK) system, the resistor–inductor–capacitor (RLC) system, and the DC motor position control system. Like the MBK mechanical system and the RLC electrical system, the DC motor electromechanical position control system is also governed by the typical second-order system differential equation. **In this section, we will design a simple proportional controller to achieve a desired position control for a DC motor system.** Consider the block diagram of the DC motor position control system shown in Figure 3.1(c), which for ease of reference is repeated here in Figure 3.15.

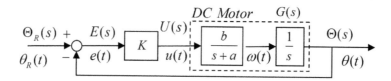

Fig. 3.15: Design of a proportional controller K for the DC motor position control system.

As given in Equation 3.5, the transfer function of the closed-loop system is

$$\frac{\Theta(s)}{\Theta_R(s)} = \frac{KG(s)}{1 + KG(s)} = \frac{bK}{s^2 + as + bK} \tag{3.80}$$

and therefore the characteristic equation is

$$s^2 + as + bK = 0 \tag{3.81}$$

The behavior of the closed-loop system is mainly determined by the closed-loop system poles, which are the roots of this characteristic equation—or, more specifically, by the corresponding damping ratio and natural frequency. By comparing this characteristic equation to the typical second-order characteristic equation, $s^2 + 2\varsigma\omega_n s + \omega_n^2 = 0$, it can be easily seen that **the damping ratio ς and natural frequency ω_n are functions of the proportional controller parameter K as follows:** $\varsigma = 0.5a \big/ \sqrt{bK}$

and $\omega_n = \sqrt{bK}$. **Increasing K will enlarge the natural frequency ω_n and reduce the damping ratio at the same time, as shown in Table 3.1.** As explained and demonstrated in Sections 3.4 and 3.5, the increase of ω_n will bump up the step response by increasing the oscillation frequency according to $\omega = \omega_n\sqrt{1-\varsigma^2}$. A smaller damping ratio ς may also lead to a faster step response, but it certainly will cause larger overshoot and oscillations.

Table 3.1: The effect of K on ς, ω_n, and the closed-loop system performance

K	ς	ω_n, rad/s	Poles	Overshoot	$\omega = \omega_n\sqrt{1-\varsigma^2}$
0.5	1.414	0.707	$-0.293, -1.707$	0	overdamped
1	1	1	$-1, -1$	0	critically damped
2	0.707	1.414	$-1 \pm j = \sqrt{2}e^{j135°}$	5%	1 rad/s
4	0.5	2	$-1 \pm j\sqrt{3} = 2e^{j120°}$	16%	1.732 rad/s
16	0.25	4	$-1 \pm j3.87 = 4e^{j104.5°}$	45%	3.75

The following MATLAB program is employed to plot the DC motor position control system step responses with varying control parameter K shown in Figure 3.16:

```
% CSD Fig3.16 Effect of varying K on DC motor position control
clear, a=2, b=1, t=0:.05:10; K=0.5, num1=b*K, den1=[1 a b*K],
G1=tf(num1,den1), x1=step(G1,t); K=1, num2=b*K, den2=[1 a b*K],
G2=tf(num2,den2), x2=step(G2,t); K=2, num3=b*K, den3=[1 a b*K],
G3=tf(num3,den3), x3=step(G3,t); K=4, num4=b*K, den4=[1 a b*K],
G4=tf(num4,den4), x4=step(G4,t); K=16, num5=b*K, den5=[1 a b*K],
G5=tf(num5,den5), x5=step(G5,t); figure(37),
plot(t,x5,'b.',t,x4,'m-',t,x3,'g-',t,x2,'k-',t,x1,'r--'), grid,
grid minor, xlabel('Time, sec'), ylabel('Step Response'),
legend('K=16','K=4','K=2','K=1','K=0.5')
```

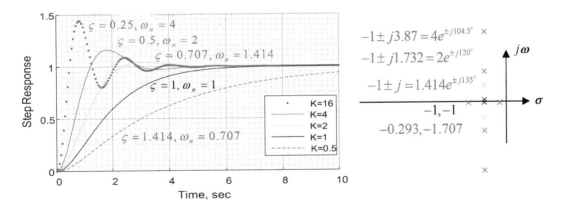

Fig. 3.16: Step responses and pole locations of the DC motor position control system with five different proportional controllers.

Without loss of generality we assume $a = 2$ and $b = 1$ in the following for ease of demonstration. Then the characteristic equation of the closed-loop system becomes $s^2 + 2s + K = 0$, and the damping ratio and natural frequency would be $\varsigma = 1/\sqrt{K}$ and $\omega_n = \sqrt{K}$. When $K = 0.5$, in Figure 3.16, we can see how the variations of the controller gain K would affect the damping ratio, the natural frequency, the pole locations, and the step response. Note that the results in Figure 3.16, associated with $K = 0.5$, are colored in red. It is clear that the two poles are at -1.707 and -0.293. The damping ratio and natural frequency are $\varsigma = 1.414$ and $\omega_n = 0.707$ rad/s, respectively, and the step response is overdamped. Similarly the results associated with $K = 1, 2, 4, 16$ are in black, green, purple, and blue, respectively. **When $K = 1$, $\varsigma = 1$, the system is critically damped. The $K = 2, 4, 16$ cases are underdamped with 0.707, 0.5, and 0.25 damping ratios, respectively.**

The performance results associated with the five simple controller designs are also tabulated in Table 3.1. It is clear that both extremes are either too overdamped or underdamped with large oscillation and overshoot. The better choice of K is between $K = 1$ and $K = 2$ where the overshoot is less than 5% and the rise time is acceptable.

3.7 Steady-State Sinusoidal Response and Bode Plot of Typical Second-Order Systems

As discussed in Section 2.5.3, particularly in Theorem 2.32 and Corollary 2.33, the steady-state sinusoidal response can be obtained simply by computing the magnitude and the phase of a complex number rather than solving for the complete solution of a differential equation. Although presented in Chapter 2 where the main emphasis was in the first-order systems, **Theorem 2.32 and Corollary 2.33 are also valid for higher-order systems as long as the system transfer function has no poles on the imaginary axis or in the right half of the complex plane.** To recap, Figure 2.9 with the essence of Corollary 2.33 is shown in Figure 3.17.

Now, let $G(s)$ be the transfer function of the typical second-order system,

$$G(s) = \frac{x_{ss}\omega_n^2}{s^2 + 2\varsigma\omega_n s + \omega_n^2} \tag{3.82}$$

and the input be $u(t) = \sin \omega t$. Then the steady-state output response will be

$$y_{ss}(t) = A(\omega)\sin(\omega t + \theta(\omega))$$

where $A(\omega) = |G(j\omega)|$ and $\theta(\omega) = \angle G(j\omega)$ are the magnitude and the phase of $G(j\omega)$, respectively. Note that $G(j\omega)$ is a just a constant complex number if the frequency ω is a constant real number. However, if the sinusoidal input frequency ω is changing, the amplitude and the phase of the steady-state output response will change accordingly.

With s replaced by $j\omega$ in Equation 3.82, we have $G(j\omega)$ as follows:

$$G(j\omega) = \frac{x_{ss}}{1 - (\omega/\omega_n)^2 + j2\varsigma(\omega/\omega_n)} = |G(j\omega)|\angle G(j\omega) = A(\omega)e^{j\theta(\omega)} \tag{3.83}$$

Let $\hat{\omega} = \omega/\omega_n$ be the normalized frequency, then Equation 3.83 becomes

$$G(j\hat{\omega}) = \frac{x_{ss}}{1 - \hat{\omega}^2 + j2\varsigma\hat{\omega}} = |G(j\hat{\omega})|\angle G(j\hat{\omega}) = A(\hat{\omega})e^{j\theta(\hat{\omega})} \tag{3.84}$$

The magnitude and the phase of $G(j\hat{\omega})$ will be

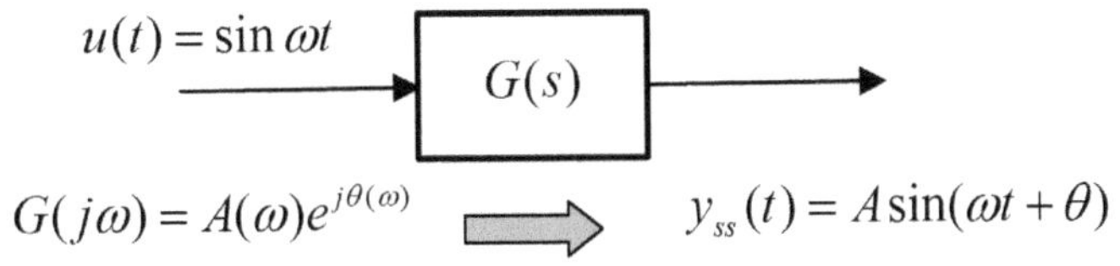

$$u(t) = \sin \omega t \longrightarrow \boxed{G(s)} \longrightarrow$$

$$G(j\omega) = A(\omega)e^{j\theta(\omega)} \implies y_{ss}(t) = A\sin(\omega t + \theta)$$

Fig. 3.17: Efficient way of computing the sinusoidal steady-state response $y_{ss}(t)$.

$$A(\hat{\omega}) = |G(j\hat{\omega})| = x_{ss}\bigg/\sqrt{(1-\hat{\omega}^2)^2 + 4\varsigma^2\hat{\omega}^2} = \begin{cases} x_{ss} & \text{when} \quad \hat{\omega} \ll 1 \\ x_{ss}/2\varsigma & \text{when} \quad \hat{\omega} = 1 \\ x_{ss}/\hat{\omega}^2 & \text{when} \quad \hat{\omega} \gg 1 \end{cases} \tag{3.85}$$

$$\theta(\hat{\omega}) = \angle G(j\hat{\omega}) = -\tan^{-1}\left(2\varsigma\hat{\omega}/(1-\hat{\omega}^2)\right)$$

The Bode plot of $G(j\hat{\omega})$ with $x_{ss} = 1$ and six damping ratio values $\varsigma = 0.05, 0.1, 0.5, 0.7, 1, 1.5$, are shown in Figure 3.18. It can be seen that these plots are very different from the Bode plot of the first-order systems. The main difference occurs when $\hat{\omega} = \omega/\omega_n = 1$ or the sinusoidal input frequency ω equals the natural frequency of the system, ω_n. The magnitude of $G(j\omega_n)$ can become very large if the damping ratio is approaching to zero. This phenomenon is called *resonance*.

Example 3.12 (Sinusoidal Response Example with $\varsigma = 0.05$, $\omega_n = 4\,\text{rad/s}$ and $x_{ss} = 1$)

Given the transfer function

$$G(s) = \frac{x_{ss}\omega_n^2}{s^2 + 2\varsigma\omega_n s + \omega_n^2} = \frac{16}{s^2 + 0.4s + 16} \tag{3.86}$$

Find the three steady-state sinusoidal responses of the system respectively driven by the following three control-input signals: $u(t) = \sin 0.4t$, $u(t) = \sin 4t$, $u(t) = \sin 40t$.

Solution:

The system shown in Equation 3.86 is a typical second-order system with the damping ratio $\varsigma = 0.05$, natural frequency $\omega_n = 4\,\text{rad/s}$, and steady-state step response gain $x_{ss} = 1$. The normalized magnitude and phase response graphs (i.e., the Bode plot) of the system, $A(\hat{\omega})$ and $\theta(\hat{\omega})$, are shown in Figure 3.18. These graphs reveal that the magnitude $A(\hat{\omega})$ and the phase $\theta(\hat{\omega})$ at the normalized frequencies $\hat{\omega} = 0.1$, $\hat{\omega} = 1$, and $\hat{\omega} = 10$ are:

$$A \simeq 0\,\text{dB} = 1, \quad \theta \simeq 0° \quad \text{when} \quad \hat{\omega} = 0.1 \quad \text{or} \quad \omega = 0.4\,\text{rad/s}$$

$$A = 20\,\text{dB} = 10, \quad \theta = -90° \quad \text{when} \quad \hat{\omega} = 1 \quad \text{or} \quad \omega = 4\,\text{rad/s} \tag{3.87}$$

$$A \simeq -40\,\text{dB} = 0.01, \quad \theta \simeq -180° \quad \text{when} \quad \hat{\omega} = 10 \quad \text{or} \quad \omega = 40\,\text{rad/s}$$

Therefore, the steady-state responses of the system given in Equation 3.86 due to the sinusoidal inputs: $u(t) = \sin 0.4t$, $u(t) = \sin 4t$, and $u(t) = \sin 40t$, are found respectively in the following:

$$y_{ss}(t) = \sin 0.4t \quad \text{when} \quad \omega = 0.4\,\text{rad/s}$$

$$y_{ss}(t) = 10\sin(4t - 90°) \quad \text{when} \quad \omega = 4\,\text{rad/s} \tag{3.88}$$

$$y_{ss}(t) = 0.01\sin(40t - 180°) \quad \text{when} \quad \omega = 40\,\text{rad/s}$$

∎

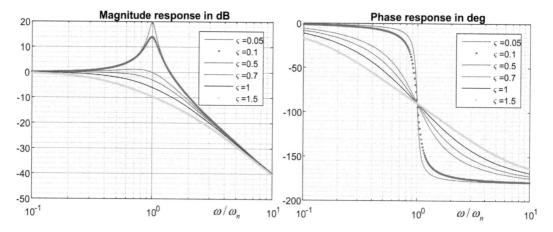

Fig. 3.18: The Bode plot of the typical second-order systems with varying ς.

The following MATLAB program is employed to plot the Bode plot of the typical second-order systems with varying ς shown in Figure 3.18:

```
% CSD_Fig3.18 Effect of varying damping ratio on Bode plot of
% typical 2nd-order systems
 w=logspace(-1,1,300); num=1; ze=0.05, den=[1 2*ze 1];
[mag,p1]=bode(num,den,w); m1=20*log10(mag); ze=0.1, den=[1 2*ze 1];
[mag,p2]=bode(num,den,w); m2=20*log10(mag); ze=0.5, den=[1 2*ze 1];
[mag,p3]=bode(num,den,w); m3=20*log10(mag); ze=0.7, den=[1 2*ze 1];
[mag,p4]=bode(num,den,w); m4=20*log10(mag); ze=1, den=[1 2*ze 1];
[mag,p5]=bode(num,den,w); m5=20*log10(mag); ze=1.5, den=[1 2*ze 1];
[mag,p6]=bode(num,den,w); m6=20*log10(mag); figure(1)
semilogx(w,m1,'b-',w,m2,'b.',w,m3,'m-',w,m4,'r-',w,m5,'k-',w,m6,'g.'),
grid, grid minor,
legend('\varsigma=0.05','\varsigma=0.1','\varsigma=0.5',...
'\varsigma=0.7','\varsigma=1','\varsigma=1.5'),
title('Magnitude response in dB'), figure(2)
semilogx(w,p1,'b-',w,p2,'b.',w,p3,'m-',w,p4,'r-',w,p5,'k-',w,p6,'g.'),
grid, grid minor,
legend('\varsigma=0.05','\varsigma=0.1','\varsigma=0.5',...
'\varsigma=0.7', '\varsigma=1','\varsigma=1.5'),
title('Phase response in deg')
```

Remark 3.13 (Resonance)

For a system with a small damping ratio like the one in the previous example, $\varsigma = 0.05$, the vibration amplitude of the system due to a disturbance input with frequency at the natural frequency ω_n will be 10 times of the input amplitude. **The vibrations near the natural frequency of a system with small damping ratio can be very damaging; the collapse of the Tacoma Narrows Bridge in 1940 is a notorious example.** ∎

3.8 Exercise Problems

P3.1a: Consider Equation 3.1, which is the governing differential equation of the mass–damper–spring system (the MBK system) shown in Figure 3.12 (or Figure 3.1(a)). Assume the mass is $M = 0.1$ kg, the spring constant is $K = 1.6$ N/m, and the damper friction coefficient $B = 0.4$ Ns/m. Then the governing equation of the system is given by

$$\ddot{y}(t) + 4\dot{y}(t) + 16y(t) = 10f_a(t) \tag{3.89}$$

where $y(t)$ and $f_a(t)$ are the displacement (m) of the mass and the external force (N) applied to the mass, respectively. Find the transfer function $Y(s)/F_a(s)$, the poles, the damping ratio ς, and the natural frequency ω_n of the system.

P3.1b: Assume zero initial conditions ($y(0) = 0$ m, $\dot{y}(0) = 0$ m/s) and let the input be $f_a(t) = 0.1u_s(t)$ N, where $u_s(t)$ is the unit step function. Solve and plot $y(t)$, the solution of Equation 3.89.

P3.1c: Use MATLAB command `step` to plot the step response of the system and verify your result in P3.1b.

P3.1d: Explain how the poles, the damping ratio ς, and the natural frequency ω_n affect the step response you obtained in P3.1b.

P3.2a: Consider the same mass–damper–spring system (MBK system) shown in Problem P3.1a. Assume the external applied force is zero, $f_a(t) = 0$. Then the differential equation becomes,

$$\ddot{y}(t) + 4\dot{y}(t) + 16y(t) = 0$$

Let the initial conditions be $y(0) = 0.01$ m, $\dot{y}(0) = 0$ m/s. Solve and plot $y(t)$ for t ≥ 0.

P3.2b: If the damper friction coefficient B is increased from 0.4 Ns/m to 1 Ns/m, then the differential equation will become

$$\ddot{y}(t) + 10\dot{y}(t) + 16y(t) = 0$$

Find the poles, the damping ratio ς, and the natural frequency ω_n of the system. Let the initial conditions be $y(0) = 0.01$ m, $\dot{y}(0) = 0$ m/s. Solve and plot $y(t)$ for t ≥ 0.

P3.2c: Consider a special case with no damping, $B = 0$. In this case, the differential equation becomes,

$$\ddot{y}(t) + 16y(t) = 0$$

Let the initial conditions be the same: $y(0) = 0.01$ m, $\dot{y}(0) = 0$ m/s. Solve and plot $y(t)$ for t ≥ 0.

P3.3a: Consider a mass–damper–spring system with the same mass M and identical spring constant K as those in P3.1a while the damper friction coefficient is changed to $B = 0.08$ Ns/m. Then the differential equation of the system is,

$$\ddot{y}(t) + 0.8\dot{y}(t) + 16y(t) = 10f_a(t)$$

Find the transfer function $Y(s)/F_a(s)$, the poles, the damping ratio ς, and the natural frequency ω_n of the system.

P3.3b: Consider the same system as the one in P3.3a. Draw the Bode plot of the system with asymptotes on the magnitude response graph and the corner frequency ω_c on both of the magnitude response and the phase response graphs.

P3.3c: Find the magnitude and phase of the system $Y(s)/F_a(s)$, at the following frequencies: $\omega = 0.1\omega_c$, $\omega = \omega_c$, and $\omega = 10\omega_c$, respectively.

P3.3d: Find and plot the steady-state response $y_{ss}(t)$ of the system due to each of the following inputs: (i) $f_a(t) = \sin(0.1\omega_c t)$, (ii) $f_a(t) = \sin(\omega_c t)$, and (iii) $f_a(t) = \sin(10\omega_c t)$, respectively.

P3.3e: Comment on the frequency-domain behavior of the typical second-order system based on the results obtained in P3.3d.

P3.4a: Consider a system with transfer function,

$$G(s) = \frac{Y(s)}{U(s)} = \frac{\omega_n^2}{s^2 + 2\varsigma\omega_n s + \omega_n^2}$$

where $Y(s)$ and $U(s)$ are the Laplace transforms of the output $y(t)$ and the input $u(t)$, respectively. Let the damping ratio and the natural frequency be $\varsigma = 0.6$ and $\omega_n = 1 \text{rad/s}$, respectively, and assume the input $u(t) = u_s(t)$, the unit step function. Then $Y(s)$ can be expressed as

$$Y(s) = \frac{1}{s(s^2 + 1.2s + 1)}$$

Find $y(t)$, the inverse Laplace transform of $Y(s)$, and plot it using the MATLAB command `plot`.

P3.4b: Repeat Problem P3.4a for (i) $\varsigma = 1$, (ii) $\varsigma = 1.4$, and (iii) $\varsigma = 0.2$, respectively, and compare the rise time, overshoot, and settling time of the four time responses including the one from P3.4a.

P3.4c: Repeat Problem P3.4a for $\omega_n = 2$ rad/s, and compare the rise time, overshoot, and settling time of the two time responses.

P3.5a: Consider a system with transfer function

$$G_1(s) = \frac{Y(s)}{U(s)} = \frac{\omega_n^2}{s^2 + 2\varsigma\omega_n s + \omega_n^2}$$

Let $\varsigma = 0.6$, $\omega_n = 1 \text{rad/s}$. Use the MATLAB command `step` to plot the step response of the system.

P3.5b: Repeat P3.5a for the system modified by adding a LHP zero at $s = -1$:

$$G_2(s) = \frac{Y(s)}{U(s)} = \frac{\omega_n^2(s+1)}{s^2 + 2\varsigma\omega_n s + \omega_n^2}$$

Comment on how the adding LHP zero affects the rise time, overshoot, and settling time.

P3.5c: Repeat P3.5a for the system modified by adding a RHP zero at $s = 1$:

$$G_3(s) = \frac{Y(s)}{U(s)} = \frac{-\omega_n^2(s-1)}{s^2 + 2\varsigma\omega_n s + \omega_n^2}$$

Comment on how the adding RHP zero affects the rise time, overshoot, and settling time.

P3.6a: Consider a system with transfer function

$$\frac{X(s)}{R(s)} = G(s) = \frac{4}{s^2 + 3s + 2}$$

and let $r(t)$ and $x(t)$ be the inverse Laplace transforms of $R(s)$ and $X(s)$, respectively. Find the differential equation corresponding to the transfer function $G(s)$.

P3.6b: Find the characteristic equation and the poles of the system.

P3.6c: Find the damping ratio ς, the natural frequency ω_n, and the steady-state step response x_{ss} of the system.

P3.6d: Is the system overdamped? critically damped? underdamped? or undamped?

P3.6e: Assume the initial conditions $x(0) = 0$ and $\dot{x}(0) = 0$, and let the input $r(t)$ be a unit step function. Find the output response $x(t)$.

P3.6f: Plot the constant term, the two exponential terms of $x(t)$ and the sum of these three terms versus t on the same graph. Discuss how these two exponential terms relate to the system poles, and how the constant term relates to x_{ss}.

P3.7a: Consider a system with transfer function

$$\frac{X(s)}{R(s)} = G(s) = \frac{20}{s^2 + 2s + 10}$$

and let $r(t)$ and $x(t)$ be the inverse Laplace transform of $R(s)$ and $X(s)$, respectively. Find the differential equation corresponding to the transfer function $G(s)$.

P3.7b: Find the characteristic equation and the poles of the system.

P3.7c: Find the damping ratio ς, the natural frequency ω_n, and the steady-state step response x_{ss} of the system.

P3.7d: Is the system overdamped? critically damped? underdamped? or undamped?

P3.7e: Assume the initial conditions $x(0) = 0$ and $\dot{x}(0) = 0$, and let the input $r(t)$ be a unit step function. Find the output response $x(t)$.

P3.7f: Plot the constant term, the decaying sinusoidal term of $x(t)$ and the sum of these two terms versus t on the same graph. Discuss how the decaying sinusoidal term relates to the system poles, and how the constant term relates to x_{ss}.

P3.8a: Consider a system with transfer function

$$\frac{X(s)}{R(s)} = G(s) = \frac{x_{ss}\omega_n^2}{s^2 + 2\varsigma\omega_n s + \omega_n^2}$$

where $0 < \varsigma < 1$. Let $r(t)$ and $x(t)$ be the inverse Laplace transforms of $R(s)$ and $X(s)$, respectively. Assume $r(t)$ is a unit step function, and the step response of the system can be found as,

$$x(t) = x_{ss}\left(1 - \frac{e^{-\alpha t}}{\sqrt{1-\varsigma^2}}\sin(\omega t + \theta)\right), \text{ where } \alpha = \varsigma\omega_n, \; \omega = \omega_n\sqrt{1-\varsigma^2}, \; \theta = \cos^{-1}\varsigma \qquad (3.90)$$

Let $\varsigma = 0.4$, $\omega_n = 1$ rad/s, $x_{ss} = 1$. Find the differential equation corresponding to the transfer function $G(s)$.

P3.8b: Find the characteristic equation and the poles of the system.

P3.8c: Assume the initial conditions $x(0) = 0$ and $\dot{x}(0) = 0$, and let the input $r(t)$ be a unit step function. Find the output response $x(t)$ using Equation 3.90.

P3.8d: Verify the value $x(0) = 0$ and $\dot{x}(0) = 0$ using the result of P3.8c, $\lim_{t\to 0} x(t)$ and $\lim_{t\to 0} \dot{x}(t)$.

P3.8e: Verify the steady-state step response $\lim_{t\to\infty} x(t)$, which should be x_{ss}.

P3.8f: Compute the sinusoidal oscillation frequency $\omega = \omega_n\sqrt{1-\varsigma^2}$ and the period $T = 2\pi/\omega$ of the step response $x(t)$.

P3.8g: Compute the peak time $t_p = \pi/\omega$ at which the maximum overshoot occurs. Note that t_p is half of the period T.

P3.8h: Compute the values of $x(kt_p) = x_{ss}(1 + e^{-\alpha kt_p})$ for $k = 1, 3, 5$ and $x(kt_p) = x_{ss}(1 - e^{-\alpha kt_p})$ for $k = 2, 4, 6$. These values provide the information regarding the locations of the peaks and valleys of the step response $x(t)$.

P3.8i: Use the above information obtained from the results of P3.8d, e, f, g, h to construct the step response graph $x(t)$ versus t.

P3.8j: Verify the step response graph using MATLAB command `plot` to plot the $x(t)$ obtained in P3.8c.

P3.8k: Use the above step response graph $x(t)$ to compute the maximum overshoot according to the following formula: $OS = (x(t_p) - x_{ss})/x_{ss}$.

P3.8l: Use the formula $OS = e^{-\varsigma\pi/\sqrt{1-\varsigma^2}}$ to compute the maximum overshoot, and verify it with the result of P3.8k.

4

Modeling of Mechanical Systems

IN the previous two chapters we have employed some simple physical systems: mass-friction system, RC low-pass filter, DC motor, mass–damper–spring system, resister–inductor–capacitor circuit, and motor position control system, to demonstrate fundamental systems and control concept, analysis, and design. It is clear that a meaningful control system design begins with a trustworthy dynamics model of the physical system to be controlled. In this chapter, we will focus on the dynamics modeling of fundamental translational and rotational mechanical systems using *the Newtonian approach* and *the Lagrange approach*. Both approaches eventually will lead to exactly the same dynamic model equations. However, they have completely different road maps to reach the same destination. **The Newtonian approach involves the geometry and vector relationship of each component in the mechanical system. On the other hand, the Lagrange approach only needs the information of the kinetic energy, the potential energy, the power dissipation, and the external forces, but it requires differential calculus computations.**

Both have advantages and disadvantages, but interestingly they complement each other perfectly: the disadvantage of one is the advantage of the other, and vice versa. The Newtonian approach is more intuitive, providing clear picture of the interactions among components inside the system, but the modeling process can be tedious, especially for larger multi-body systems. Conversely, the Lagrange approach is more elegant without the need to worry about the directions of vectors and detailed interconnection of components, but it allows virtually no insight of the interactions among components within the system.

The Lagrange approach is not included in most of the undergraduate control and dynamics textbooks. Part of the reasons may be due to its lack of intuitiveness and insight. Actually, learning the Lagrange approach together with the Newtonian approach will be more effective, and will not necessarily require more learning hours. We will apply both approaches to almost all mechanical systems in this chapter so that the students can learn both approaches together and compare their results. It is easy, especially for the beginners, to miss hidden reaction forces or commit sign errors using the Newtonian approach. It is also very possible to miss some energy and power dissipation terms or commit differential calculus computation errors using the Lagrange approach. **However, it is rare for these two approaches to have same errors in their end results. Hence, employing both approaches for system modeling not only enables the students to understand the system better from two different prospectives, but also provides additional assurance on modeling correctness.**

4.1 Translational Mechanical Systems

To analyze the behavior or to obtain a mathematical model of a translational mechanical system, the first step is to understand the force-velocity or the force-displacement relationship of the three fundamental translational mechanical elements—damper, spring, and mass. As shown in Figure 4.1, the force-velocity relationship of the damper is $f_{fri} = -Bv = -B\dot{x}$, in which the negative sign means that the viscous friction force is always in the opposite direction of the velocity. The units for the force f, velocity v, displacement x, and friction coefficient B are Newton (N), meter/sec (m/s), meter (m), and Ns/m, respectively. The force-displacement relationship of the spring is described by Hooke's law, $f_{spr} = -Kx$, where the spring force is proportional to the magnitude of the displacement but its direction is in the opposite direction of the displacement. The unit of the spring constant K is N/m.

The force-velocity or the force-displacement relationship of the mass is described by Newton's second law of motion, $f_{net} = M\dot{v} = M\ddot{x} = -f_{ine}$, where f_{net} and f_{ine} are the physical *net force* and the *inertial force*, respectively. The unit of the mass or inertia M is kilogram (kg). Note that the physical net force needs to have the same magnitude of the inertial force to keep the mass M moving with acceleration $\ddot{x}$. The magnitude of the inertial force is proportional to the acceleration. **Strictly speaking, the inertial force is not a physical force. It is even called as** *fictitious force* **in some dynamics books, yet it plays an essential role leading to the key concept of the famous** *d'Alembert's principle*, which will be addressed in the next subsection. The characteristics of these three translational mechanical system elements are summarized in Figure 4.1.

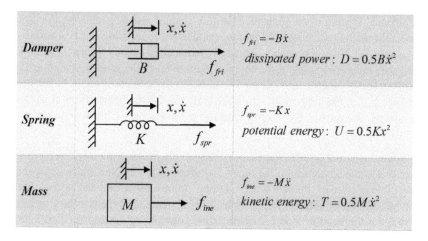

Fig. 4.1: Basic translational mechanical system elements.

4.1.1 d'Alembert's Principle

Recall that in the beginning of Chapter 3, we considered a simple mass–damper–spring mechanical system, which is shown again here on the left-hand side of Figure 4.2. The mathematical model of this simple mechanical system can be derived based on Newton's second law of motion, $f_{net} = M\ddot{x}$, where f_{net} is the net physical force, M is the mass or inertia, and $\ddot{x}$ is the acceleration, which we learned from physics courses in high school. For the simple MBK system shown in Figure 4.2, f_{net} is the physical net force applied to the mass M, which is the algebraic sum of the applied force $f_a(t)$, the spring force $-Kx(t)$, and the damper friction force $-B\dot{x}(t)$, and therefore we have the following:

$$f_{net} = f_a + (-B\dot{x}) + (-Kx) = M\ddot{x} \qquad (4.1)$$

This is exactly the same governing dynamics equation of the *MBK* system we had in Equation 3.1.

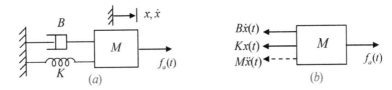

Fig. 4.2: A simple mass–damper–spring (MBK) system and the associated free-body diagram.

The direct Newton's $f = Ma$ method of assembling the equation of motion works well for simple systems, but will become more confusing and difficult to manage for complicated multi-body systems. In a multi-body system, its subsystems may be interconnected each other to constrain relative motions in a complicated way. **This disadvantage can be eliminated by employing** *d'Alembert's principle* that allows the system to be systematically partitioned into several isolated free bodies to make it easier to assemble the equations of motion. The central idea is to consider the mass times acceleration, $M\ddot{x}$, as simply another force called the *inertial force* that acts opposite to the direction of acceleration.

Theorem 4.1 (d'Alembert's Principle)

Assume all the inertial forces and physical forces in the system are considered. Then the algebraic sum of all forces acting at any point in the system is zero.

$$f_{sum} = \sum_i f_i = 0 \qquad (4.2)$$

∎

Note that this principle can be applied in each admissible direction of motion. The significance of d'Alembert's principle is far greater than a simple restatement of Newton's second law, as explained in depth by Lanczos [Lanczos, 1970].

For example, the algebraic sum of the forces acting onto a point between the spring K and the mass M in the MBK system shown in Figure 4.2 is zero since the two forces on this point are in opposite directions with equal magnitude of Kx. For another example, if the term $M\ddot{x}$ in Equation 4.1 is moved from the right-hand side of the equation to the left-hand side, the equation will become the following:

$$f_a + (-B\dot{x}) + (-Kx) + (-M\ddot{x}) = 0 \qquad (4.3)$$

This equation fulfills d'Alembert's principle if the term $-M\ddot{x}$ is considered as a force.

Equation 4.3 is mathematically equivalent to Equation 4.1, which was derived from the well-known Newton's second law of motion, but **the significance of d'Alembert's principle is more than just a restatement of Newton's laws of motion. It provides an important** *dynamic equilibrium* **concept that allows complicated multi-body system dynamics to be broken down into several free-body diagrams and make it much easier to construct the dynamics model for mechanical systems.**

Remark 4.2 (Dynamic Equilibrium)

For any mechanical system, if the algebraic sum of all the physical forces acting on the system is zero there would be no acceleration for the system, and the system is said to be at equilibrium since it will remain at rest if the initial condition of the system is at rest. Now, for the MBK system, the algebraic sum of all the three physical forces, which is the net force, acting on the system is usually nonzero. The nonzero net force will keep the mass in motion with the acceleration $\ddot{x}(t)$; hence, the system is not at equilibrium in the general sense of static equilibrium.

However, according to Equation 4.3 or d'Alembert's principle, the algebraic sum of all the four forces acting on the system is zero if the inertial force term, $-M\ddot{x}(t)$, is considered as a force. Then the system is at an equilibrium, a special kind of equilibrium called *dynamic equilibrium***, for time $t \geq 0$. Although $x(t)$ may change, the algebraic sum of these four forces remains zero all the time.** The dynamic equilibrium concept has made it easier to construct the equations of motion, especially for complicated multi-body systems.   ■

Example 4.3 (Newtonian Approach Modeling of the Simple MBK System)

Consider the mass–damper–spring (MBK) system in Figure 4.2, where $f_a(t)$ is the applied force and the variable of interest is the displacement of mass $x(t)$. The origin reference (the position of $x = 0$) is chosen at the equilibrium condition when the spring is neither stretched nor compressed, and the reference of direction of motion is assumed positive if it points to the right. For example, a positive displacement $x(t)$ means the mass is at the right-hand side of the equilibrium position and a negative velocity $\dot{x}(t)$ indicates that the mass is moving towards the left. Now, the objective is to find the dynamics model of the system, which is a differential equation describing the relationship between the input $f_a(t)$ and the output $x(t)$, using the Newtonian approach and d'Alembert's principle.

Solution:

In general, for a complicated system, it may require several free-body diagrams to assemble the equations of motion for the system. But for the simple MBK system, only one free-body diagram is needed. The free-body diagram is drawn based on the schematic diagram of the MBK system shown on the left of Figure 4.2. It can be seen that there are three physical forces acting on the mass M. Since the applied force $f_a(t)$ is assumed to point to the right when it is positive, a right directional arrow with label $f_a(t)$ should be drawn on the free-body diagram. **Note that both the arrow direction and the label sign are relevant.** A left directional arrow together with a negative sign label $-f_a(t)$ can also represent the applied force on the free-body diagram. Since both the friction force $-B\dot{x}(t)$ and the spring force $-Kx(t)$ have negative signs, they should be represented by left directional arrows with labels $B\dot{x}(t)$ and $Kx(t)$, respectively, on the free-body diagram.

Since the inertial force $-M\ddot{x}(t)$ is not a physical force, it is represented by a *dashed-line arrow* **instead of a solid-line arrow on the free-body diagram. The inertial force also has a negative sign; therefore, its representation on the free-body diagram should be a left directional dashed-line arrow with label $M\ddot{x}(t)$.**

Now, with the completed free-body diagram in Figure 4.2 and d'Alembert's principle, the algebraic sum of the four forces on M should be zero, and we have the following dynamics model of the mass–damper–spring system:

$$M\ddot{x}(t) + B\dot{x}(t) + Kx(t) = f_a(t) \tag{4.4}$$

■

Remark 4.4 (Tips to Avoid Errors in Free-Body Diagrams)

The key step in the Newtonian approach is to draw a correct free-body diagram. Students seldom make mistakes on the magnitude of the forces, but it takes only one force direction or sign error in the free-body diagram to void the effort of constructing the dynamics model of the system. **The first tip to avoid confusion and mistakes is to follow conventional rules** if they are available. For example, the

Cartesian coordinate system with the origin located at an equilibrium position can be employed to serve as a reference for all vectors in the system so that a positive horizontal vector is pointing to the right and a positive vertical vector is in the up direction.

The second tip is not to have negative sign on any label so that the direction of each vector on the free-body diagram is purely determined by its arrow direction. For the MBK system shown in Figure 4.2, the positive motion direction is assumed to point to the right and all labels of the four force vectors, $f_a(t)$, $B\dot{x}(t)$, $Kx(t)$, and $M\ddot{x}(t)$ are with no negative sign attached to them. Therefore, the vector arrow of $f_a(t)$ points to the right, but the vector arrows of the other three forces are in the left direction.   ∎

This mechanical system dynamics model construction approach is a Newtonian approach, which is mainly based on detailed geometry and interactions among the component vectors. The Lagrange approach, on the other hand, is basically a scalar function approach involving energy and power functions without the need of knowing the detailed system configuration and interactions among the components. As mentioned in the beginning of this chapter, **these two approaches actually complement each other very well. Learning these two approaches at the same time certainly will enhance students' learning experience.** Both Newtonian and Lagrange approaches will be employed to derive the equations of motion for almost every mechanical systems discussed in this chapter.

4.1.2 A Brief Introduction of the Lagrange Approach

Unlike the Newtonian approach, **the Lagrange approach is a scalar- and energy-based approach requiring the kinetic energy function, the potential energy functions, and the dissipated power functions.** It does not need free-body diagrams, but it requires differential calculus computations involving the following *Lagrange equation*:

$$\frac{d}{dt}\left(\frac{\partial \mathscr{L}}{\partial \dot{q}}\right) - \frac{\partial \mathscr{L}}{\partial q} + \frac{\partial D}{\partial \dot{q}} = Q \tag{4.5}$$

In the equation, q and $\dot{q}$ are *generalized coordinate vector* and *generalized velocity vector*, respectively. $\mathscr{L}(\dot{q},q)$ represents the *Lagrangian* function, which is defined as

$$\mathscr{L}(\dot{q},q) = T(\dot{q},q) - U(q) \tag{4.6}$$

where $T(\dot{q},q)$ is the *kinetic energy* function of the system, and $U(q)$ is the *potential energy* function. $D(\dot{q})$ is the *dissipated power* function of the system, and Q is the *generalized external force vector* acting on the system.

Example 4.5 (Lagrange's Approach Modeling of the Simple MBK System)

Consider the same simple MBK dynamics modeling problem shown in Example 4.3 but find the dynamics model of the system using the Lagrange approach.

Solution:

For the simple MBK system shown on the left-hand side of Figure 4.2, the generalized coordinate and velocity are simply x and $\dot{x}$. The kinetic energy of the system is stored in the mass as $T = 0.5M\dot{x}^2$, the potential energy of the system is stored in the spring as $U = 0.5Kx^2$, and the power dissipated in the damper is $D = 0.5B\dot{x}^2$. Hence, **the Lagrangian function is** $\mathscr{L} = T - U = 0.5M\dot{x}^2 - 0.5Kx^2$. Then the key differentials in the Lagrange equation can be found as,

$$\frac{\partial \mathscr{L}}{\partial \dot{x}} = \frac{\partial\left(0.5M\dot{x}^2 - 0.5Kx^2\right)}{\partial \dot{x}} = M\dot{x}, \quad \frac{\partial D}{\partial \dot{x}} = \frac{\partial\left(0.5B\dot{x}^2\right)}{\partial \dot{x}} = B\dot{x}$$

$$\frac{\partial \mathscr{L}}{\partial x} = \frac{\partial\left(0.5M\dot{x}^2 - 0.5Kx^2\right)}{\partial x} = -Kx, \quad Q = f_a \tag{4.7}$$

Now, from Equation 4.5, the Lagrange equation, we have the dynamics model equation:

$$\frac{d}{dt}\left(\frac{\partial \mathscr{L}}{\partial \dot{x}}\right) - \frac{\partial \mathscr{L}}{\partial x} + \frac{\partial D}{\partial \dot{x}} = Q \quad \rightarrow \quad M\ddot{x}(t) + Kx(t) + B\dot{x}(t) = f_a(t) \tag{4.8}$$

which is exactly the same as that obtained using the Newtonian approach shown in Equation 4.4.

■

Remark 4.6 (Differences Between the Two Approaches)

After working on the same modeling problem of the simple MBK system using the Newtonian and Lagrange approaches, we have observed some differences between the two approaches. The Newtonian approach relies on the free-body diagram that depicts the force interactions among the components and the applied force. On the other hand, the Lagrange approach does not need to know how the components of the system interact with each other. Instead, it only requires the information of the kinetic energy function, the potential energy function, the power dissipation function, and the external force. These two approaches are very different, but amazingly the end results are identical.

■

4.1.3 A Quarter-Car Suspension System

A simplified quarter-car suspension system is shown in Figure 4.3. In the figure, M_2 represents quarter of the mass of the car body, B_2 is the friction coefficient of the shock absorber (damper), K_2 is the spring constant of the strut, M_1 represents the mass of the wheel, and K_1 is the spring constant of the tire. **The displacements, $x_2(t)$, $x_1(t)$, and** $d(t)$ of the masses, M_2, M_1, and the tire, respectively, **are measured from their equilibrium conditions.** The equilibrium conditions are assumed not affected by gravity, and both springs K_2 and K_1 are neither stretched nor compressed. Thus, the gravity forces will be incorporated in the free-body diagram and appear on the dynamics model. In case that the equilibrium positions are chosen to offset according to the gravity effect, then the two gravity forces $M_1 g$ and $M_2 g$ should not appear on the free-body diagram or the dynamics model.

The car is assumed moving to the right, and it may encounter uneven road conditions with disturbance $d(t)$. **The objective of the study here is to find the dynamics model of the system that describes how the disturbance input $d(t)$ would affect the output variables $x_1(t)$ and $x_2(t)$. The dynamics model also can be employed to choose the desired values of the strut spring constant K_2 and the damper friction coefficient B_2 so that the suspension system has a desired performance.**

Example 4.7 (Newtonian Approach Modeling of the Quarter-Car Suspension System)

Consider the quarter-car suspension system shown on the right-hand side of Figure 4.3. Note that we follow the Cartesian coordinate convention to choose the up direction as the positive direction for all vectors in the system and that the displacements $x_1(t)$, $x_2(t)$, and $d(t)$ are measured from their respective equilibrium positions. **Find the dynamics model of the system, which is a set of differential equations describing the relationship between the input $f_a(t)$ and the outputs $x_1(t)$ and $x_2(t)$, using the Newtonian approach and d'Alembert's principle.**

Solution:

Since there are two masses, M_1 and M_2, the free-body diagram is broken down into two parts: the M_2 free-body diagram on the top and the M_1 free-body diagram at bottom, as shown on the left-hand side of Figure 4.3. **There are four forces acting on the mass M_2 and five forces acting on the mass M_1.**

The two gravitational forces of M_2 and M_1 always point down to the center of the Earth; hence, they are represented by the two downward arrows with labels $M_2 g$ and $M_1 g$, respectively, on the top and the bottom free-body diagrams. **The inertia forces for M_2 and M_1 are opposite to the conventional positive up direction, so they are represented by the two downward arrows, respectively, with labels $M_2\ddot{x}_2$ and $M_1\ddot{x}_1$ on the top and the bottom free-body diagrams.**

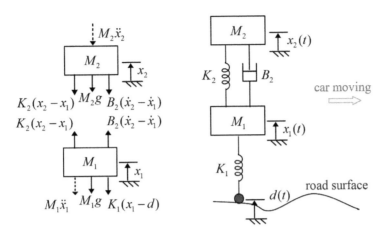

Fig. 4.3: A quarter-car suspension system and the associated free-body diagram.

Based on d'Alembert's principle or Newton's third law of motion, the two forces at both ends of the spring K_2 should have the same magnitude but in opposite directions. If $x_2 = x_1$, the spring is neither stretched nor compressed, and the forces at both ends are zero. **If $x_2 > x_1$, the spring will be stretched but the recoil spring force will resist the elongation of the spring. In other words, the same spring force $K_2(x_2 - x_1)$ will pull M_2 down and at the same time pull up M_1.** Similarly, the same friction force $B_2(\dot{x}_2 - \dot{x}_1)$ is resisting the motions of M_1 and M_2 from increasing the gap between them. For the spring force on K_1, if $x_1 > d$, the spring will stretch and the recoil spring force at the lower end of M_1 will go downward with the label $K_1(x_1 - d)$.

Now, with the completed free-body diagrams on the left-hand side of Figure 4.3, we will obtain two differential equations by summing up the four forces on M_2 and the five forces on M_1,

$$M_1\ddot{x} - B_2(\dot{x}_2 - \dot{x}_1) - K_2(x_2 - x_1) + K_1(x_1 - d) + M_1 g = 0$$
$$M_2\ddot{x} + B_2(\dot{x}_2 - \dot{x}_1) + K_2(x_2 - x_1) + M_2 g = 0 \tag{4.9}$$

which can be rewritten in the following matrix form:

$$\begin{bmatrix} M_1 & 0 \\ 0 & M_2 \end{bmatrix}\begin{bmatrix} \ddot{x}_1 \\ \ddot{x}_2 \end{bmatrix} + \begin{bmatrix} B_2 & -B_2 \\ -B_2 & B_2 \end{bmatrix}\begin{bmatrix} \dot{x}_1 \\ \dot{x}_2 \end{bmatrix} + \begin{bmatrix} K_1 + K_2 & -K_2 \\ -K_2 & K_2 \end{bmatrix}\begin{bmatrix} x_1 \\ x_2 \end{bmatrix} = \begin{bmatrix} K_1 \\ 0 \end{bmatrix} d + \begin{bmatrix} -M_1 \\ -M_2 \end{bmatrix} g \tag{4.10}$$

■

Example 4.8 (Lagrange's Approach Modeling of the Quarter-Car Suspension System)

Consider the same quarter-car suspension system dynamics modeling problem shown in Example 4.7, but find the dynamics model of the system using the Lagrange approach.

Solution:

For the quarter-car suspension system shown on the right-hand side of Figure 4.3, the generalized coordinate and velocity are $\begin{bmatrix} x_1 & x_2 \end{bmatrix}^T$ and $\begin{bmatrix} \dot{x}_1 & \dot{x}_2 \end{bmatrix}^T$, respectively. The kinetic energy of the system is stored in the two masses M_1 and M_2 as $T = 0.5(M_1\dot{x}_1^2 + M_2\dot{x}_2^2)$, the potential energy of the system is stored in the springs K_1, K_2 and in the gravity field as $U = 0.5[K_2(x_2 - x_1)^2 + K_1(x_1 - d)^2] + M_1gx_1 + M_2gx_2$, and the power dissipated in the damper B_2 is $D = 0.5B_2(\dot{x}_1 - \dot{x}_2)^2$. Hence, the Lagrangian function is

$$\mathcal{L} = T - U = 0.5(M_1\dot{x}_1^2 + M_2\dot{x}_2^2) - 0.5[K_2(x_2 - x_1)^2 + K_1(x_1 - d)^2] - M_1gx_1 - M_2gx_2 \qquad (4.11)$$

Then the key differentials in the Lagrange equation can be found as,

$$\frac{\partial \mathcal{L}}{\partial \dot{x}} = \begin{bmatrix} \partial \mathcal{L}/\partial \dot{x}_1 \\ \partial \mathcal{L}/\partial \dot{x}_2 \end{bmatrix} = \begin{bmatrix} M_1\dot{x}_1 \\ M_2\dot{x}_2 \end{bmatrix}, \quad \frac{\partial D}{\partial \dot{x}} = \begin{bmatrix} \partial D/\partial \dot{x}_1 \\ \partial D/\partial \dot{x}_2 \end{bmatrix} = \begin{bmatrix} B_2(\dot{x}_1 - \dot{x}_2) \\ -B_2(\dot{x}_1 - \dot{x}_2) \end{bmatrix}$$

$$\frac{\partial \mathcal{L}}{\partial x} = \begin{bmatrix} \partial \mathcal{L}/\partial x_1 \\ \partial \mathcal{L}/\partial x_2 \end{bmatrix} = \begin{bmatrix} K_2(x_2 - x_1) - K_1(x_1 - d) - M_1g \\ -K_2(x_2 - x_1) - M_2g \end{bmatrix}, \quad Q = 0 \qquad (4.12)$$

Then from the Lagrange equation Equation 4.5 we have the dynamics model equation:

$$\begin{bmatrix} M_1\ddot{x}_1 \\ M_2\ddot{x}_2 \end{bmatrix} - \begin{bmatrix} K_2(x_2 - x_1) - K_1(x_1 - d) - M_1g \\ -K_2(x_2 - x_1) - M_2g \end{bmatrix} + \begin{bmatrix} B_2(\dot{x}_1 - \dot{x}_2) \\ -B_2(\dot{x}_1 - \dot{x}_2) \end{bmatrix} = \begin{bmatrix} 0 \\ 0 \end{bmatrix} \qquad (4.13)$$

which can be rewritten in the following matrix form:

$$\begin{bmatrix} M_1 & 0 \\ 0 & M_2 \end{bmatrix} \begin{bmatrix} \ddot{x}_1 \\ \ddot{x}_2 \end{bmatrix} + \begin{bmatrix} B_2 & -B_2 \\ -B_2 & B_2 \end{bmatrix} \begin{bmatrix} \dot{x}_1 \\ \dot{x}_2 \end{bmatrix} + \begin{bmatrix} K_1 + K_2 & -K_2 \\ -K_2 & K_2 \end{bmatrix} \begin{bmatrix} x_1 \\ x_2 \end{bmatrix} = \begin{bmatrix} K_1 \\ 0 \end{bmatrix} d + \begin{bmatrix} -M_1 \\ -M_2 \end{bmatrix} g \qquad (4.14)$$

This is exactly the same as that obtained using the Newtonian approach shown in Equation 4.10. ∎

Remark 4.9 (Equilibrium Offset Due to Gravity)

The differential equations in Equation 4.10 or Equation 4.14 can be considered as a special case of the generalized MBK system matrix equation of this form, $M\ddot{x} + B\dot{x} + Kx = F_d + F_g$, where F_g is a constant gravitational force vector and F_d is a disturbance input vector. Note that the equilibrium occurs at $x_e = K^{-1}F_g$. Define $\hat{x} = x - K^{-1}F_g$, then the generalized MBK matrix equation will become $M\ddot{\hat{x}} + B\dot{\hat{x}} + K\hat{x} = F_d$ and the equilibrium occurs at $\hat{x}_e = 0$. ∎

4.2 Rotational Mechanical Systems

As engineers, we may encounter more rotational systems than translational systems since almost all of the translational motions are driven by rotational systems like wheels, pulleys, motors, and engines. Just like the translational mechanical system, the rotational mechanical system also has three fundamental rotational mechanical elements: rotational damper, torsional spring, and moment of inertia. As shown in Figure 4.4, the torque-angular velocity relationship of the rotational damper is $\tau_{fri} = -B\omega = -B\dot{\theta}$, in which the negative sign means that the viscous friction torque is always in the opposite direction of the angular velocity $\dot{\theta}$. The units for the torque τ, angular velocity ω, angular displacement θ, and friction coefficient B are Newton (N-m), radian/sec (rad/s), radian (rad), and Nms/rad, respectively. The torque-angular displacement relationship of the torsional spring is described by Hooke's law $\tau_{spr} = -K\theta$, where the spring torque is proportional to the magnitude of the angular displacement θ but its direction is in the opposite rotation direction of the angular displacement.

The unit of the torsional spring coefficient K is Nm/rad. The torque-angular velocity or the torque-angular displacement relationship of the moment of inertia is described by Newton's second law of motion, $\tau_{net} = J\dot{\omega} = J\ddot{\theta} = -\tau_{ine}$, where τ_{net} and τ_{ine} are the *net torque* and the *inertial torque*, respectively. Note that the net torque needs to have the same magnitude of the inertial torque to move the moment of inertia J with angular acceleration $\ddot{\theta}$. The magnitude of the inertial torque is proportional to the angular acceleration $\ddot{\theta}$. The unit of the moment of inertia J is kgm^2 or Nms^2/rad. The characteristics of these three rotational mechanical system elements are summarized in Figure 4.4.

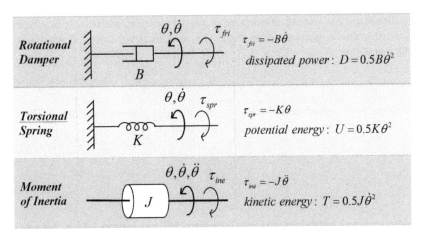

Fig. 4.4: Basic rotational mechanical system elements.

4.2.1 d'Alembert's Principle in Rotational Systems

It can be easily seen that there exists an analogy between the rotational system and the translational system. That means the concept and the dynamics modeling approaches we learned in the previous section can be applied to rotational systems with little modifications. We will see that the single torsional pendulum system in Figure 4.5 is mathematically equivalent to the simple MBK system in Figure 4.2. In addition, these two systems are analogous to each other.

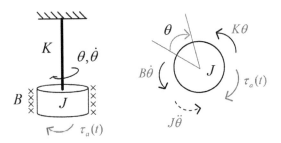

Fig. 4.5: A single torsional pendulum.

Recall that the rotational version of Newton's Second Law of Motion is described by the equation, $\tau_{net} = J\alpha = J\ddot{\theta}$, where τ_{net} is the net physical torque, J is the moment of inertia, and $\alpha = \ddot{\theta}$ is the angular acceleration. For the single torsional pendulum system shown in Figure 4.5, τ_{net} is the physical net torque applied to the moment of inertia J, which is the algebraic sum of the applied torque $\tau_a(t)$, the spring torque $-K\theta(t)$, and the friction torque $-B\dot{\theta}(t)$, and therefore we have the following:

$$\tau_{net} = \tau_a + (-B\dot{\theta}) + (-K\theta) = J\ddot{\theta} \tag{4.15}$$

This equation is analogous to the governing dynamics equation of the MBK system we had in Equation 3.1.

The direct (Newton's $\tau = J\alpha$) method of assembling the equation of motion works well for simple systems, but will become more complicated and difficult to manage for large multi-body systems. **This disadvantage can be eliminated if the** *d'Alembert's principle* **is employed to make it easier to assemble the equations of motion.** The rotational version of d'Alembert's principle is described in the following.

Theorem 4.10 (d'Alembert's Principle for Rotational Systems)

Assume all the inertial torques and physical torques in the system are considered. Then, the algebraic sum of all torques acting at any point in a multi-body system is zero.

$$\tau_{sum} = \sum_i \tau_i = 0 \tag{4.16}$$

■

For the single torsional pendulum system, if the term $J\ddot{\theta}$ in Equation 4.15 is moved from the right-hand side of the equation to the left-hand side, the equation will become the following:

$$\tau_a + (-B\dot{\theta}) + (-K\theta) + (-J\ddot{\theta}) = 0 \tag{4.17}$$

This equation fulfills d'Alembert's principle if the term $-J\ddot{\theta}$ is considered as a torque.

As in the translational systems, d'Alembert's principle provides an important concept of *dynamic equilibrium* **that allows complicated multi-body rotational system dynamics to be broken down into several free-body diagrams and makes it much easier to construct the dynamics model.**

Example 4.11 (Modeling of the Single Torsional Pendulum System by Newtonian Approach)

The rotational mechanical system shown in Figure 4.5 is a single torsional pendulum. The link between the disk, which has moment of inertia J, and the fixture at top is a flexible shaft with torsional spring constant K. When the system is in motion, there is a viscous friction torque with friction coefficient B. **The positive rotation direction is chosen according to the right-hand rule with the thumb pointing down at the center of the disk, or it is in the clockwise direction viewing from the top. The angular displacement θ of the disk J is measured from the equilibrium position at which the torsional spring torque is zero. In this example, the Newtonian approach with d'Alembert's principle will be employed to find the dynamics model of the system, which is a differential equation describing the relationship between the input $\tau_a(t)$ and the output $\theta(t)$.**

Solution:

The free-body diagram is shown on the right-hand side of Figure 4.5. **This diagram shows the same top view of the disk. The positive rotation direction is in the clockwise direction.** This free-body diagram should consist of four torques: the applied torque τ_a, the friction torque $\tau_{fri} = -B\dot{\theta}$, the spring torque $\tau_{spr} = -K\theta$, and the inertial torque $\tau_{ine} = -J\ddot{\theta}$. The applied torque τ_a obviously is in the clockwise direction, but the other three torques are all with negative signs, **as shown in Figure 4.4. Therefore, $B\dot{\theta}$, $K\theta$, and $J\ddot{\theta}$ should all be in the counterclockwise direction.**

We utilize the signs in the torque equations to determine the torque directions in the free-body diagram. The torque direction determination can also be validated by some simple virtual experiment, for example, if θ is positive, which means the disk has been rotated clockwise away from equilibrium. **Just imagine your hand is holding the disk at this displaced position; you would feel the recoiled torque from the torsional spring attempting to go back to the equilibrium, which verifies the torsional spring torque is indeed in the opposite direction of θ.** Similarly, the friction torque is always in the opposite direction of the angular velocity; hence, $B\dot{\theta}$ should be in the counterclockwise direction.

The negative inertial torque, $-\tau_{ine} = J\ddot{\theta}$ and its direction on the free-body diagram may be confusing. The confusion is understandable since $J\ddot{\theta}$ actually is equal to the net torque required to perform the rotational motion to move J with acceleration $\ddot{\theta}$ toward the same direction of θ according to Newton's second law of motion. Then why, in the free-body diagram, is $\ddot{\theta}$ shown in the opposite direction of θ? This confusion can be resolved using the following explanation of d'Alembert's principle. It is easy to see that the following equations are correct:

$$\begin{aligned} \tau_{net}(t) &= J\ddot{\theta}(t) \\ \tau_{net}(t) &= \tau_a(t) - B\dot{\theta}(t) - K\theta(t) \end{aligned} \quad \rightarrow \quad \tau_a(t) - B\dot{\theta}(t) - K\theta(t) - J\ddot{\theta}(t) = 0 \qquad (4.18)$$

The above equation on the left is obviously the result of Newton's second law of motion, and the equation on the right verifies d'Alembert's Principle that the algebraic sum of all torques acting on J is zero. **This equation clearly shows that $J\ddot{\theta}$ is in the same direction with $B\dot{\theta}$ and $K\theta$. Therefore, on the free-body diagram, $J\ddot{\theta}$ is always in the opposite direction of the assumed positive rotation direction.** For this example, $J\ddot{\theta}$ should be in the counterclockwise direction.

Once the free-body diagram is completed, as shown on the right-hand side of Figure 4.5, it is easy to see that the sum of the torques in the counterclockwise direction should be equal to the sum of the torques in the clockwise direction:

$$J\ddot{\theta}(t) + B\dot{\theta}(t) + K\theta(t) = \tau_a(t) \qquad (4.19)$$

which is the dynamics model equation for the single torsional pendulum system shown on the left-hand side of Figure 4.5. **Note that the equation is mathematically equivalent and analogous to that of the simple mass–damper–spring system shown in Figure 4.2.** ■

4.2.2 The Lagrange Approach for Rotational Systems

As discussed in the previous section, the Newtonian and the Lagrange approaches have their advantages and disadvantages, but they complement each other very well. Students are urged to apply these two approaches to every mechanical system dynamics modeling problem. Doing so not only enhances learning experience, but also greatly reduces the probability of obtaining incorrect modeling results. These two approaches are very different—one relies on the vectors and their geometrical relationship and the other is based on the scalar energy and power functions. Therefore, it is rare for these two approaches to lead to same errors.

The application of the Lagrange approach to the rotational system is similar to the translational system. **For a more complicated system that involves both translational and rotational subsystems, the Lagrange approach may be less complicated than the Newtonian approach since the Newtonian approach requires separate free-body diagrams for translational and rotational subsystems while for the Lagrange approach the rotational energy functions and the translational energy functions can be simply combined together.**

The Lagrange equation is basically the same as follows:

$$\frac{d}{dt}\left(\frac{\partial \mathscr{L}}{\partial \dot{q}}\right) - \frac{\partial \mathscr{L}}{\partial q} + \frac{\partial D}{\partial \dot{q}} = Q \qquad (4.20)$$

The only difference is that the generalized coordinate q vector and the generalized velocity $\dot{q}$ vector will be rotational system variables.

Example 4.12 (Modeling of the Single Torsional Pendulum by the Lagrange Approach)

In this example, we will employ the Lagrange approach to find the dynamics model for the same single torsional pendulum system considered in Example 4.11.

Solution:

For the single torsional pendulum system shown on the left-hand side of Figure 4.5, the generalized coordinate and velocity are θ and $\dot{\theta}$, respectively. The kinetic energy of the system is stored in the moment of inertia J as $T = 0.5J\dot{\theta}^2$, the potential energy of the system is stored in the torsional spring K as $U = 0.5K\theta^2$, and the power dissipated with friction coefficient B is $D = 0.5B\dot{\theta}^2$. Hence, the Lagrangian function is $\mathscr{L} = T - U = 0.5J\dot{\theta}^2 - 0.5K\theta^2$. The key differentials in Lagrange's equation can be found as,

$$\partial\mathscr{L}/\partial\dot{\theta} = \partial\left(0.5J\dot{\theta}^2 - 0.5K\theta^2\right)/\partial\dot{\theta} = J\dot{\theta}, \quad \partial D/\partial\dot{\theta} = \partial\left(0.5B\dot{\theta}^2\right)/\partial\dot{\theta} = B\dot{\theta}$$

$$\partial\mathscr{L}/\partial\theta = \partial\left(0.5J\dot{\theta}^2 - 0.5K\theta^2\right)/\partial\theta = -K\theta, \quad Q = \tau_a$$

(4.21)

Then from Lagrange's equation we have the dynamics model equation in the following,

$$\frac{d}{dt}\left(\frac{\partial\mathscr{L}}{\partial\dot{\theta}}\right) - \frac{\partial\mathscr{L}}{\partial\theta} + \frac{\partial D}{\partial\dot{\theta}} = Q \quad\rightarrow\quad J\ddot{\theta}(t) + B\dot{\theta}(t) + K\theta(t) = \tau_a(t)$$

(4.22)

which is exactly the same as that obtained using the Newtonian approach shown in Equation 4.19. ∎

4.2.3 A Two-Rotor/One-Shaft Rotational System

A two-rotor/one-shaft rotational system is shown in Figure 4.6. In the figure, J_1 and J_2 represent the two rotors with moment of inertia J_1 and J_2, respectively. B_1 and B_2 are the rotational friction coefficients of the two rotors, respectively. These two rotors are connected with a shaft whose stiffness (the torsional spring constant) is K. **The positive rotation direction is chosen according to the right-hand rule with the thumb pointing from the left side of the figure at the center of the two rotors, or in the clockwise direction viewing from the left of the figure. The angular displacements θ_1 and θ_2 of the two rotors are measured respectively from the equilibrium positions at which the torsional spring torque is zero.**

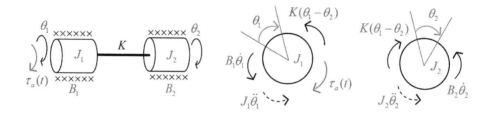

Fig. 4.6: A two-rotor/one-shaft rotational system.

Example 4.13 (The Two-Rotor/One-Shaft Rotational System by Newtonian Approach)

Consider the two-rotor/one-shaft rotational system shown on the left side of Figure 4.6. In this example, the Newtonian approach with d'Alembert's principle will be employed to find the dynamics model of the system, which is a set of differential equations that govern the relationship between the input $\tau_a(t)$ and the two outputs $\theta_1(t)$ and $\theta_2(t)$.

Solution:

The free-body diagram is shown on the right-hand side of Figure 4.6. This diagram shows the same left side view of the two rotors. The positive rotation direction for all vectors in the system is in the clockwise direction viewed from the left side. Since there are two rotors, J_1 and J_2, the free-body diagram is broken down into two parts side by side: the J_1 free-body diagram on the left and the J_2 free-body diagram on the right, as shown on the right-hand side of Figure 4.6.

There are four torques acting on the rotor J_1, and three torques on the rotor J_2. Since the applied torque τ_a is in the chosen positive rotation direction when it is positive, it is represented by a clockwise (CW) arrow with label $\tau_a(t)$ on the J_1 free-body diagram. The friction torques $B_1\dot{\theta}_1$ and $B_2\dot{\theta}_2$ are always against their respective rotor motion; hence, they are represented by counter clockwise (CCW) arrows, respectively, on the J_1 and the J_2 free-body diagrams. For the same reason, the inertial torques $J_1\ddot{\theta}_1$ and $J_2\ddot{\theta}_2$ are drawn as CCW dashed arrows on the J_1 and the J_2 free-body diagrams, respectively.

According to d'Alembert's principle or Newton's third law of motion, the spring torques at both ends of the torsional spring K should have the same magnitude but in opposite rotation directions. These two are labeled the same with $K(\theta_1 - \theta_2)$, but their rotation direction are opposite—the one with the J_1 free-body diagram is CCW and the other with J_2 free-body diagram is in CW. The reason that $K(\theta_1 - \theta_2)$ is CCW on the J_1 rotor is explained as follows: If the label $K(\theta_1 - \theta_2)$ is positive, (i.e., $\theta_1 > \theta_2$), the torsional spring K is twisted clockwise, which will cause the spring to recoil. Hence, the recoiled spring torque is CCW, in the opposite rotation direction. Note that if the spring torques are labeled differently as $K(\theta_2 - \theta_1)$, then their rotation directions on the free-body diagrams need to be reversed!

Now the free-body diagrams are completed, as shown on the right-hand side of Figure 4.6, and we can obtain two differential equations by summing up the four torques on the J_1 free-body diagram and the three torques on the J_2 free-body diagram, respectively.

$$J_1\ddot{\theta}_1 + B_1\dot{\theta}_1 + K(\theta_1 - \theta_2) = \tau_a$$
$$J_2\ddot{\theta}_2 + B_2\dot{\theta}_2 - K(\theta_1 - \theta_2) = 0$$

(4.23)

which can be rewritten in the following matrix form:

$$\begin{bmatrix} J_1 & 0 \\ 0 & J_2 \end{bmatrix}\begin{bmatrix} \ddot{\theta}_1 \\ \ddot{\theta}_2 \end{bmatrix} + \begin{bmatrix} B_1 & 0 \\ 0 & B_2 \end{bmatrix}\begin{bmatrix} \dot{\theta}_1 \\ \dot{\theta}_2 \end{bmatrix} + \begin{bmatrix} K & -K \\ -K & K \end{bmatrix}\begin{bmatrix} \theta_1 \\ \theta_2 \end{bmatrix} = \begin{bmatrix} 1 \\ 0 \end{bmatrix}\tau_a$$

(4.24)

∎

Example 4.14 (The Two-Rotor/One-Shaft Rotational System by the Lagrange Approach)

In this example, we will employ the Lagrange approach to find the dynamics model of the same two-rotor/one-shaft rotational system considered in Example 4.13.

Solution:

For the two-rotor/one-shaft rotational system shown in the left-hand side of Figure 4.6, the generalized coordinate and velocity are $\begin{bmatrix} \theta_1 & \theta_2 \end{bmatrix}^T$ and $\begin{bmatrix} \dot{\theta}_1 & \dot{\theta}_2 \end{bmatrix}^T$, respectively. The kinetic energy of the system is stored in the moments of inertia, J_1 and J_2, as $T = 0.5(J_1 \dot{\theta}_1^2 + J_2 \dot{\theta}_2^2)$, the potential energy of the system is stored in the torsional spring K as $U = 0.5K(\theta_1 - \theta_2)^2$, and the power dissipated in frictions, B_1 and B_2, is $D = 0.5(B_1 \dot{\theta}_1^2 + B_2 \dot{\theta}_2^2)$. Hence, the Lagrangian function is

$$\mathcal{L} = T - U = 0.5(J_1 \dot{\theta}_1^2 + J_2 \dot{\theta}_2^2) - 0.5K(\theta_1 - \theta_2)^2 \tag{4.25}$$

Then the key differentials in Lagrange's equation can be found as,

$$\frac{\partial \mathcal{L}}{\partial \dot{\theta}} = \begin{bmatrix} \partial \mathcal{L}/\partial \dot{\theta}_1 \\ \partial \mathcal{L}/\partial \dot{\theta}_2 \end{bmatrix} = \begin{bmatrix} J_1 \dot{\theta}_1 \\ J_2 \dot{\theta}_2 \end{bmatrix}, \quad \frac{\partial D}{\partial \dot{\theta}} = \begin{bmatrix} \partial D/\partial \dot{\theta}_1 \\ \partial D/\partial \dot{\theta}_2 \end{bmatrix} = \begin{bmatrix} B_1 \dot{\theta}_1 \\ B_2 \dot{\theta}_2 \end{bmatrix}$$

$$\frac{\partial \mathcal{L}}{\partial \theta} = \begin{bmatrix} \partial \mathcal{L}/\partial \theta_1 \\ \partial \mathcal{L}/\partial \theta_2 \end{bmatrix} = \begin{bmatrix} -K(\theta_1 - \theta_2) \\ K(\theta_1 - \theta_2) \end{bmatrix}, \quad Q = \begin{bmatrix} \tau_a \\ 0 \end{bmatrix} \tag{4.26}$$

Now, from Lagrange's equation Equation 4.20 we have the dynamics model equation

$$\begin{bmatrix} J_1 \ddot{\theta}_1 \\ J_2 \ddot{\theta}_2 \end{bmatrix} - \begin{bmatrix} -K(\theta_1 - \theta_2) \\ K(\theta_1 - \theta_2) \end{bmatrix} + \begin{bmatrix} B_1 \dot{\theta}_1 \\ B_2 \dot{\theta}_2 \end{bmatrix} = \begin{bmatrix} \tau_a \\ 0 \end{bmatrix} \tag{4.27}$$

which can be rewritten in the following general matrix form:

$$\begin{bmatrix} J_1 & 0 \\ 0 & J_2 \end{bmatrix} \begin{bmatrix} \ddot{\theta}_1 \\ \ddot{\theta}_2 \end{bmatrix} + \begin{bmatrix} B_1 & 0 \\ 0 & B_2 \end{bmatrix} \begin{bmatrix} \dot{\theta}_1 \\ \dot{\theta}_2 \end{bmatrix} + \begin{bmatrix} K & -K \\ -K & K \end{bmatrix} \begin{bmatrix} \theta_1 \\ \theta_2 \end{bmatrix} = \begin{bmatrix} 1 \\ 0 \end{bmatrix} \tau_a \tag{4.28}$$

This equation is exactly the same as that obtained using the Newtonian approach shown in Equation 4.24. ∎

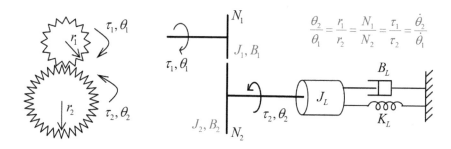

Fig. 4.7: A rotational system with a gear train.

4.3 A Rotational System with a Gear Train

A gear train is an important mechanical device widely used in almost any power driving system to provide the best power matching between a motor or an engine and the system to be driven. A simple rotational system with a gear train is shown in Figure 4.7. **An ideal case is considered at this moment, assuming the inertia J_1, J_2 and friction B_1, B_2 of the gears are negligible and the power transferred from the input gear to the output gear is lossless.**

For the lossless special case, the work done by the input gear, $\tau_1 \theta_1$, is equal to that by the output gear, $\tau_2 \theta_2$.

$$\tau_1 \theta_1 = \tau_2 \theta_2 \tag{4.29}$$

where τ_1 and θ_1 are the torque and the angular displacement associated with the input gear, and τ_2 and θ_2 are associated with the output gear. Since the arc length traveled by the input gear should be the same as that traveled by the output gear, we have

$$r_1 \theta_1 = r_2 \theta_2 \tag{4.30}$$

where r_1 and r_2 are the radii of the input gear and output gear, respectively.

With Equation 4.29, Equation 4.30, and the fact that gear ratio should be equal to the radius ratio, the relationships between the input and output gear variables are summarized as follows:

$$\frac{\theta_2}{\theta_1} = \frac{r_1}{r_2} = \frac{N_1}{N_2} = \frac{\tau_1}{\tau_2} = \frac{\dot{\theta}_2}{\dot{\theta}_1} \tag{4.31}$$

The dynamics model equation of the rotational system in Figure 4.7 **without** the gear train can be easily obtained using the Newtonian or the Lagrange approach as follows,

$$J_L \ddot{\theta}_2(t) + B_L \dot{\theta}_2(t) + K_L \theta_2(t) = \tau_2(t) \tag{4.32}$$

which is mathematically equivalent to Equation 4.19. Due to the angular velocity and torque relationships between the input and output gears shown in Equation 4.31, we have

$$\theta_2 = \frac{N_1}{N_2}\theta_1, \quad \dot{\theta}_2 = \frac{N_1}{N_2}\dot{\theta}_1, \quad \ddot{\theta}_2 = \frac{N_1}{N_2}\ddot{\theta}_1, \quad \tau_2 = \frac{N_2}{N_1}\tau_1 \tag{4.33}$$

Then the dynamics model equation of the rotational system in Figure 4.7 **with** the gear train can be found as

$$J_L\left(\frac{N_1}{N_2}\right)^2 \ddot{\theta}_1(t) + B_L\left(\frac{N_1}{N_2}\right)^2 \dot{\theta}_1(t) + K_L\left(\frac{N_1}{N_2}\right)^2 \theta_1(t) = \tau_1(t) \tag{4.34}$$

This equation can be further rewritten in terms of the equivalent moment of inertia J_e, the equivalent rotational friction coefficient B_e, and the equivalent torsional spring constant K_e as follows:

$$J_e \ddot{\theta}_1(t) + B_e \dot{\theta}_1(t) + K_e \theta_1(t) = \tau_1(t) \tag{4.35}$$

where

$$J_e = \left(\frac{N_1}{N_2}\right)^2 J_L, \quad B_e = \left(\frac{N_1}{N_2}\right)^2 B_L, \quad K_e = \left(\frac{N_1}{N_2}\right)^2 K_L \tag{4.36}$$

If the gears are chosen so that the gear ratio $N_2/N_1 = 4$, the torque required to drive the system from the input gear side will be four times smaller. Furthermore, the moment of inertia, the friction coefficient, and the spring constant of the load observed from the input gear side will all become sixteen times smaller.

Remark 4.15 (A Realistic Gear with Moment of Inertia and Friction)

Consider the same rotational system with a gear train whose moments of inertia J_1, J_2, and frictions B_1, B_2 are not negligible. In this more general case, the dynamics model equation of the rotational system can still be described in the same form of Equation 4.35,

$$J_e\ddot{\theta}_1(t) + B_e\dot{\theta}_1(t) + K_e\theta_1(t) = \tau_1(t) \tag{4.37}$$

but with modified equivalent moment of inertia J_e and equivalent friction coefficient B_e as follows:

$$J_e = J_1 + \left(\frac{N_1}{N_2}\right)^2 (J_2 + J_L), \quad B_e = B_1 + \left(\frac{N_1}{N_2}\right)^2 (B_2 + B_L), \quad K_e = \left(\frac{N_1}{N_2}\right)^2 K_L \tag{4.38}$$

■

4.4 A Simple Inverted Pendulum

In this section, the Newtonian and Lagrange approaches will be employed to derive the nonlinear dynamics model of a simple inverted pendulum system in the form of nonlinear differential equation. By defining the angular displacement and angular velocity of the pendulum as *state variables*, the nonlinear differential equation can be converted into a *state space model* that consists of two first-order differential equations, which can be packaged into a matrix form called the *state equation*.

Then the nonlinear state equation can be utilized to determine the *equilibriums* and the local linear state-space model of the pendulum system at each equilibrium. We will investigate the behavior of the system at the vicinity of the equilibrium of interest and use the linear state-space models to design a *feedback controller* to stabilize the system or to improve the performance of the closed-loop system.

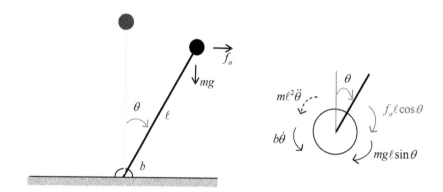

Fig. 4.8: A simple inverted pendulum system.

4.4.1 Modeling the Simple Inverted Pendulum

Newtonian Approach

As shown in Figure 4.8, the angular displacement θ is assumed zero when the pendulum is at the upright position. The length of the stick is ℓ(m), but the weight of the stick is assumed negligible compared with the mass m(kg) of the black ball, which is attached to one end of the stick. The other end of the stick is connected to the pivot. **The rotational friction coefficient is assumed b(Nms/rad) and the moment of inertia of the black ball is $m\ell^2$. The black ball is subjected to the gravitational force mg and the applied control force f_a(N), which is perpendicular to the gravity. Since the angular displacement**

θ is a variable, the torque due to the gravity is $mg\ell\sin\theta$ and the torque generated by the control force is $f_a\ell\cos\theta$.

The dynamics model of the simple inverted pendulum system can be obtained using the Newtonian approach with the free-body diagram in Figure 4.8 as follows:

$$m\ell^2\ddot{\theta} + b\dot{\theta} - mg\ell\sin\theta = f_a\ell\cos\theta \tag{4.39}$$

Lagrange's Approach

Note that the system is a nonlinear system. The dynamics model can also be derived using the Lagrange approach. The kinetic energy, the potential energy, and the power dissipated in the system are $T = 0.5m\ell^2\dot{\theta}^2$, $U = -mg\ell(1 - \cos\theta)$, and $D = 0.5b\dot{\theta}^2$, respectively. Hence, the Lagrangian is

$$\mathscr{L} = T - U = 0.5m\ell^2\dot{\theta}^2 + mg\ell(1 - \cos\theta)$$

and the differentials in Lagrange's equation can be found as

$$\frac{\partial\mathscr{L}}{\partial\dot{\theta}} = \frac{\partial\left(0.5m\ell^2\dot{\theta}^2 + mg\ell(1-\cos\theta)\right)}{\partial\dot{\theta}} = m\ell^2\dot{\theta}, \quad \frac{\partial D}{\partial\dot{\theta}} = \frac{\partial\left(0.5b\dot{\theta}^2\right)}{\partial\dot{\theta}} = b\dot{\theta}$$

$$\frac{\partial\mathscr{L}}{\partial\theta} = \frac{\partial\left(0.5m\ell^2\dot{\theta}^2 + mg\ell(1-\cos\theta)\right)}{\partial\theta} = mg\ell\sin\theta, \quad Q = f_a\ell\cos\theta$$

Now, from Lagrange's equation,

$$\frac{d}{dt}\left(\frac{\partial\mathscr{L}}{\partial\dot{\theta}}\right) - \frac{\partial\mathscr{L}}{\partial\theta} + \frac{\partial D}{\partial\dot{\theta}} = Q$$

we have the dynamics model

$$m\ell^2\ddot{\theta} + b\dot{\theta} - mg\ell\sin\theta = f_a\ell\cos\theta$$

which is exactly the same as Equation 4.39, obtained by Newtonian approach.

4.4.2 Equilibriums and Linearization

The dynamics model equation of the simple inverted pendulum can be slightly rearranged as follows:

$$\ddot{\theta} + \frac{b}{m\ell^2}\dot{\theta} - \frac{g}{\ell}\sin\theta = \frac{1}{m\ell}\cos\theta f_a \tag{4.40}$$

Nonlinear State-Space Model

In order to identify the equilibriums of the system and to find a linearized model for each equilibrium of interest, we will first convert the nonlinear differential equation into a state equation. Although there are infinite many choices in defining the state variables, usually the state variables are selected based on two considerations. One is to associate the state variables with physical variables in reality like displacements, velocities, voltages, and currents. The other is to choose state variables so that the state-space model is in a special form for the purpose of analysis or design.

In the following, the angular displacement θ and the angular velocity $\dot{\theta}$ are chosen to be the state variables. Let

$$x_1 = \theta, \quad x_2 = \dot{\theta}, \quad \text{and} \quad u = f_a$$

where u is used to represent f_a since u is a common notation for control input. Then we have the state equation in matrix form:

$$\begin{bmatrix} \dot{x}_1 \\ \dot{x}_2 \end{bmatrix} = \begin{bmatrix} x_2 \\ \frac{g}{\ell}\sin x_1 - \frac{b}{m\ell^2}x_2 + \frac{1}{m\ell}\cos x_1 \cdot u \end{bmatrix}$$

Assume $g = 9.8$ m/s^2, $\ell = 1.089$ m, $m = 0.918$ kg, and $b = 0.551$ Ns,

$$\frac{g}{\ell} = 9, \quad \frac{b}{m\ell^2} = 0.6, \quad \frac{1}{m\ell} = 1$$

Therefore, we have the following nonlinear state-space model to represent the simple inverted pendulum system:

$$\dot{x} = \begin{bmatrix} \dot{x}_1 \\ \dot{x}_2 \end{bmatrix} = \begin{bmatrix} x_2 \\ 9\sin x_1 - 0.6x_2 + \cos x_1 \cdot u \end{bmatrix} = f(x,u) = \begin{bmatrix} f_1(x_1,x_2,u) \\ f_2(x_1,x_2,u) \end{bmatrix} \tag{4.41}$$

Finding Equilibriums

Let the control input u be zero, and then the equilibriums of the system can be found by solving the state equations with the derivative of the state variables set to zero. Now, we have

$$u = 0, \quad \begin{bmatrix} \dot{x}_1 \\ \dot{x}_2 \end{bmatrix} = 0 \quad \rightarrow \quad \begin{array}{l} x_2 = 0 \\ \frac{g}{\ell}\sin x_1 - \frac{b}{m\ell^2}x_2 = 0 \end{array} \quad \rightarrow \quad \begin{bmatrix} x_1^* \\ x_2^* \end{bmatrix} = \begin{bmatrix} 0 \\ 0 \end{bmatrix} \quad \text{or} \quad \begin{bmatrix} \pi \\ 0 \end{bmatrix}$$

The system has two equilibriums: One is $x_U^* = \begin{bmatrix} 0 & 0 \end{bmatrix}^T$, which represents the upright stick position $\theta = 0$, and the other is $x_D^* = \begin{bmatrix} \pi & 0 \end{bmatrix}^T$, which represents the downward stick position $\theta = \pi$.

Linearized State-Space Model at the Unstable Equilibrium

Next, we will find a linearized state-space model for each of the two equilibriums. At the upright equilibrium $x_U^* = \begin{bmatrix} 0 & 0 \end{bmatrix}^T$, we have the state-space model

$$\dot{x}(t) = A_U x(t) + B_U u(t) \tag{4.42}$$

where the matrices A_U and B_U are computed via Jacobian matrices J_x and J_u, respectively, as follows (see appendix C):

$$A_U = J_x = \left[\frac{\partial f}{\partial x}\right]_{x^*} = \begin{bmatrix} \partial f_1/\partial x_1 & \partial f_1/\partial x_2 \\ \partial f_2/\partial x_1 & \partial f_2/\partial x_2 \end{bmatrix}_{x^*=\begin{bmatrix} 0 \\ 0 \end{bmatrix}} = \begin{bmatrix} 0 & 1 \\ 9\cos x_1 & -0.6 \end{bmatrix}_{x^*=\begin{bmatrix} 0 \\ 0 \end{bmatrix}} = \begin{bmatrix} 0 & 1 \\ 9 & -0.6 \end{bmatrix}$$

$$B_U = J_u = \left[\frac{\partial f}{\partial u}\right]_{x^*} = \begin{bmatrix} \partial f_1/\partial u \\ \partial f_2/\partial u \end{bmatrix}_{x^*=\begin{bmatrix} 0 \\ 0 \end{bmatrix}} = \begin{bmatrix} 0 \\ \cos x_1 \end{bmatrix}_{x^*=\begin{bmatrix} 0 \\ 0 \end{bmatrix}} = \begin{bmatrix} 0 \\ 1 \end{bmatrix}$$

Note that the eigenvalues of A_U are 2.715 and -3.315, which shows that the equilibrium is unstable.

Linearized State-Space Model at the Stable Equilibrium

On the other hand, at the downward equilibrium $x_D^* = \begin{bmatrix} \pi & 0 \end{bmatrix}^T$, let $\bar{x}(t) = x(t) - x_D^*$, and we have the state-space model

$$\dot{\bar{x}}(t) = A_D\bar{x}(t) + B_D u(t) \tag{4.43}$$

where the matrices A_D and B_D are computed via Jacobian matrices J_x and J_u, respectively, as follows:

$$A_D = J_x = \begin{bmatrix} \frac{\partial f}{\partial x} \end{bmatrix}_{x^*} = \begin{bmatrix} \partial f_1/\partial x_1 & \partial f_1/\partial x_2 \\ \partial f_2/\partial x_1 & \partial f_2/\partial x_2 \end{bmatrix}_{x^* = \begin{bmatrix} \pi \\ 0 \end{bmatrix}} = \begin{bmatrix} 0 & 1 \\ 9\cos x_1 & -0.6 \end{bmatrix}_{x^* = \begin{bmatrix} \pi \\ 0 \end{bmatrix}} = \begin{bmatrix} 0 & 1 \\ -9 & -0.6 \end{bmatrix}$$

$$B_D = J_u = \begin{bmatrix} \frac{\partial f}{\partial u} \end{bmatrix}_{x^*} = \begin{bmatrix} \partial f_1/\partial u \\ \partial f_2/\partial u \end{bmatrix}_{x^* = \begin{bmatrix} \pi \\ 0 \end{bmatrix}} = \begin{bmatrix} 0 \\ \cos x_1 \end{bmatrix}_{x^* = \begin{bmatrix} \pi \\ 0 \end{bmatrix}} = \begin{bmatrix} 0 \\ -1 \end{bmatrix}$$

Note that the eigenvalues of A_D are $-0.3 \pm j2.985$, which verifies that the equilibrium is stable. These eigenvalues also reveal that the damping ratio and the natural frequency of the system around the downward equilibrium are $\varsigma = 0.1$ and $\omega_n = 3$ rad/s, respectively.

Open-Loop Simulation Using Nonlinear Simulink Model

A Simulink computer simulation program built based on the nonlinear state-space model Equation 4.41 will be employed to conduct simulations for the simple inverted pendulum. This Simulink file name is `SIPmodel.mdl`, which will be called by either `CSD_fig4p10_SIPmainOL.m` for open-loop simulation or `CSD_fig4p11_SIPmainCL.m` for closed-loop simulation.

The block diagram of the Simulink model is shown in Figure 4.9. Since the system has two state variables, there are two integrator s^{-1} blocks. The output of the integrator blocks are: x_1, the angular displacement, and x_2, the angular velocity, respectively. The initial conditions $x_1(0)$ and $x_2(0)$ can be set by clicking the integrator block to type x10 and x20 in the Initial condition boxes for Integrator1 and Integrator2, respectively. The values of x10 and x20 will be given in the main m-file program.

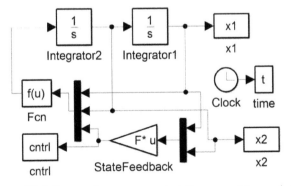

Click the integrator blocks to type x10 and x20 as initial condtitions for Integrator1 and Integrator2, respectively.

Click the ToWorkplace blocks x1, x2, time, and cntrl, type x1, x2, t, and cntrl as variable names, and select Array in Save format box.

Click F*u, and type F and select Matrix(K*u).

Click Fcn, and type `9*sin(u(1))-0.6*u(2)+cos(u(1))*u(3)` in the Expression box.

Fig. 4.9: The nonlinear Simulink model, `SIPmodel.mdl`, of the simple inverted pendulum system will be employed to conduct both open-loop and closed-loop simulations.

Click the ToWorkplace blocks: x1, x2, time, and cntrl, type x1, x2, t, and cntrl as Variable names, and select Array in Save Format box. The simulation results are recorded simultaneously on these arrays x1, x2, t, and cntrl, and can be plotted after the simulation is completed. Click the Gain block, F*u, and type F as the gain and select Matrix(K*u) in Multiplication box. In the Fcn block, you need to type the nonlinear function,

```
9*sin(u(1))-0.6*u(2)+cos(u(1))*u(3)
```

where u(1), u(2), and u(3) represent the state variables x_1, x_2, and the control input u, respectively.

We will run the following MATLAB program: CSD_fig4p10_SIPmainOL.m, which will automatically call the Simulink model program SIPmodel.mdl, to conduct the open-loop simulation. The MATLAB code is listed as follows:

```
% CSD_Fig_4.10_SIPmainOL.m, Simple Inverted Pendulum Open-loop Simulation
% BC Chang, Drexel University, on 3/11/2020
% MATLAB R2015a or later versions
% Run CSD_fig4p10_SIPmainOL.m, which will automatically call SIPmodel.mdl
% x1_dot=x2, x2_dot=9*sinx1-0.6*x2+cosx1*u
% Initial Conditions
 x10_deg = 15, x10=x10_deg*pi/180, x20=0,
% Use this for open-loop response. At the down XD equilibrium:
 A=[0  1; -9  -0.6], B=[0; 1], eig(A), F=[0  0];
% Part 2 Simulation
 sim_time = 20 %  for open-loop simulation
 sim_options=simset('SrcWorkspace', 'current', 'DstWorkspace', 'current');
 open('SIPmodel'), sim('SIPmodel', [0, sim_time], sim_options);
% Part3 Plot the simulation results
 figure(41), plot(t,x1,'b-',t,x2,'r-'), grid on, grid minor,
 xlabel('t, sec'), ylabel('x1 rad and x2 rad/s'), legend ('x1','x2'),
 figure(42), plot(t,cntrl,'r-'), grid on, grid minor,
 xlabel('t,sec'), ylabel('cntrl'), figure(43), plot(x1,x2),
 grid on, grid minor, xlabel('x1'), ylabel('x2')
```

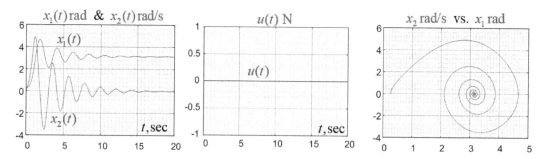

Fig. 4.10: Time responses and phase plane trajectory of the uncompensated nonlinear simple pendulum system, which converge into the stable downward equilibrium.

The result of the open-loop inverted pendulum system simulation is shown in Figure 4.10. As expected, without control action (i.e., $u(t) = 0$), the pendulum will always spiral into the downward stable equilibrium at $x_D^* = \begin{bmatrix} \pi & 0 \end{bmatrix}^T$ despite where the initial condition is. Figure 4.10 shows that the pendulum with initial condition $x(0) = \begin{bmatrix} 0.26 & 0 \end{bmatrix}^T$ would depart from the nearby unstable upward equilibrium $x_U^* = \begin{bmatrix} 0 & 0 \end{bmatrix}^T$, move toward and overshoot passing the downward equilibrium x_D^*, oscillate around several times, and eventually settle at the equilibrium after about 15 seconds. **The high overshoot oscillation is caused by the low damping property of the system with $\varsigma = 0.1$ and $\omega_n = 3$ rad/s.**

4.4.3 State Feedback Controller Design to Stabilize a Simple Inverted Pendulum

In the following, a simple state-feedback controller will be designed to stabilize the simple inverted pendulum at the upright position (i.e., to convert the originally unstable equilibrium $x_U^* = \begin{bmatrix} 0 & 0 \end{bmatrix}^T$ to a stable one). Moreover, the closed-loop system poles can be placed at desired locations on the complex plane to obtain a desired closed-loop performance. For ease of reference, the linearized state-space model at the upright equilibrium obtained in Equation 4.42 is repeated here:

$$\dot{x}(t) = A_U x(t) + B_U u(t) = \begin{bmatrix} 0 & 1 \\ 9 & -0.6 \end{bmatrix} x(t) + \begin{bmatrix} 0 \\ 1 \end{bmatrix} u(t)$$

Since the controllability matrix

$$\begin{bmatrix} B_U & A_U B_U \end{bmatrix} = \begin{bmatrix} 0 & 1 \\ 1 & -0.6 \end{bmatrix}$$

is nonsingular, there exists a state-feedback control strategy, $u(t) = Fx(t)$, so that the closed-loop system poles or the eigenvalues of $A_U + B_U F$ can be placed anywhere in the complex plane as long as the control-input constraints are satisfied. The definition of controllability matrix and controllability theory will be discussed in Chapter 10.

Let the state-feedback matrix be $F = \begin{bmatrix} F_1 & F_2 \end{bmatrix}$. Then the closed-loop system characteristic equation will be

$$\det \begin{bmatrix} sI - (A_U + B_U F) \end{bmatrix} = s^2 + (0.6 - F_2)s - 9 - F_1 = 0 \tag{4.44}$$

The desired closed-loop characteristic equation can be chosen as

$$s^2 + 2\varsigma \omega_n s + \omega_n^2 = 0$$

with damping ratio $\varsigma = 0.8$ and $\omega_n = 5$ rad/s, which is

$$s^2 + 8s + 25 = 0 \tag{4.45}$$

Comparing the coefficients of Equations 4.44 and 4.45, we have $F_1 = -34$ and $F_2 = -7.4$. Hence, the state-feedback controller is designed as

$$u(t) = F_1 x_1(t) + F_2 x_2(t) = -34 x_1(t) - 7.4 x_2(t)$$

Now, with the state-feedback controller, the closed-loop system state equation at the upright equilibrium becomes

$$\dot{x}(t) = (A_U + B_U F)x(t) = \begin{bmatrix} 0 & 1 \\ -25 & -8 \end{bmatrix} x(t) \tag{4.46}$$

Note that the eigenvalues of $A_U + B_U F$ are $-4 \pm j3$, which verifies that the originally unstable upright equilibrium is now stable and has a desired transient response characterized by its damping ratio $\varsigma = 0.8$ and natural frequency $\omega_n = 5$ rad/s.

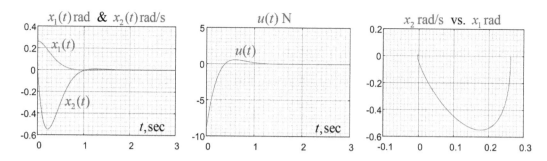

Fig. 4.11: With control compensation, the originally unstable upright equilibrium is stabilized.

Closed-Loop Simulation Using Nonlinear Simulink Model

The same Simulink simulation program, SIPmodel.mdl, will be employed to work together with the closed-loop stabilization program, CSD_fig4p11_SIPmainCL.m, to conduct the closed-loop control simulation. **Figure 4.11 shows that the pendulum with initial condition** $x(0) = \begin{bmatrix} 0.26 & 0 \end{bmatrix}^T$ **would move toward and settle at the upright equilibrium after just about one second without much overshoot and oscillation. This desired transient response is the direct result of the choice of damping ratio and natural frequency as** $\varsigma = 0.8$ **and** $\omega_n = 5$ **rad/s, respectively.**

The simulation results showed in Figure 4.11 are obtained from running the MATLAB program CSD_fig4p11_SIPmainCL.m with the Simulink nonlinear inverted pendulum model, SIPmodel.mdl, shown in Figure 4.9. The MATLAB code of is listed as follows:

```
% filename: CSD_fig4p11_SIPmainCL.m,  Simple Inverted Pendulum
% BC Chang, Drexel University, on 8/11/2018
% MATLAB R2015a or later versions
% Run CSD_fig4p11_SIPmainCL.m, which will aoutomatically call
% SIPmodel.mdl
% x1_dot=x2, x2_dot=9*sinx1-0.6*x2+cosx1*u
% Initial Conditions
 x10_deg = 15, x10=x10_deg*pi/180, x20=0,
% Use this for closed-loop stabiliztion. At the up XU equilibrium:
 A=[0 1; 9 -0.6], B=[0; 1], eig(A), ze=0.8, wn=5,
 F=[-9-wn^2 0.6-2*ze*wn], Acl=A+B*F,  eig(Acl),
% Part 2 Simulation
 sim_time=3    % for closed-loop simulation
 sim_options=simset('SrcWorkspace', 'current', 'DstWorkspace', 'current');
 open('SIPmodel'), sim('SIPmodel', [0, sim_time], sim_options);
% Part3 Plot the simulation results
 figure(41), plot(t,x1,'b-',t,x2,'r-'), grid on, grid minor,
 xlabel('t, sec'), ylabel('x1 rad and x2 rad/s'), legend ('x1','x2'),
 figure(42), plot(t,cntrl,'r-'), grid on, grid minor,
 xlabel('t,sec'), ylabel('cntrl'), figure(43), plot(x1,x2),
 grid on, grid minor, xlabel('x1'), ylabel('x2')
```

Although the controller was designed based on the linearized model at the upright equilibrium, this linear state-feedback controller not only performs satisfactorily within the linearized region, it actually is capable of bringing the pendulum from a wide range of initial positions to the upright equilibrium at $x_U^* = \begin{bmatrix} 0 & 0 \end{bmatrix}^T$, as shown in Figure 4.12. The graph at the right shows the 14 phase trajectories of the closed-loop system with the initial pendulum positions from $-10°$ to $-70°$ and from $10°$ to $70°$. Within the range of $-70°$ and $70°$, the controller only requires a small amount of effort to quickly bring the pendulum to the upright equilibrium.

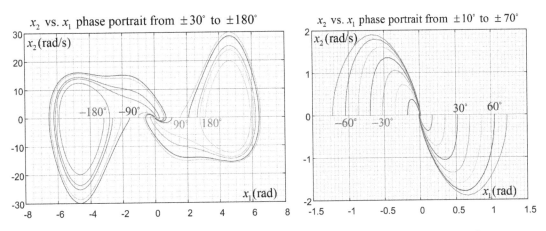

Fig. 4.12: Phase portraits of the simple inverted pendulum with feedback control.

Since the control-input force $u(t)$ can only work in the horizontal direction, the effective control-input torque is $u\ell\cos\theta$, which gets smaller as θ moves closer to $90°$. When θ becomes greater than $90°$, the effective control-input torque $u\ell\cos\theta$ will change sign and join the gravity force to push the pendulum ball down and swing it to the other side. The pendulum will continue to swing up and may change swing direction several times before reaching the top to swing back through almost one full revolution to the upright equilibrium $x_U^* = \begin{bmatrix} 0 & 0 \end{bmatrix}^T$. Therefore, for the phase trajectories with the initial position beyond $80°$ the controller would need to make more effort and travel a longer distance to bring the pendulum to the upright equilibrium as shown on the left graph of the figure.

Now, the state-feedback controller $u(t) = F_1 x_1(t) + F_2 x_2(t) = -34x_1(t) - 7.4x_2(t)$ has successfully converted the originally unstable upright equilibrium to a stable one. We may want to know how the same controller affect the downward equilibrium at $x_D^* = \begin{bmatrix} \pi & 0 \end{bmatrix}^T$. Recall that state equation of the linearized state-space model at this equilibrium is

$$\dot{\bar{x}}(t) = A_D \bar{x}(t) + B_D u(t) = \begin{bmatrix} 0 & 1 \\ -9 & -0.6 \end{bmatrix} \bar{x}(t) + \begin{bmatrix} 0 \\ -1 \end{bmatrix} u(t)$$

Hence, the closed-loop system state equation at the downward equilibrium is

$$\dot{\bar{x}}(t) = (A_D + B_D F) \bar{x}(t) = \begin{bmatrix} 0 & 1 \\ 25 & 6.8 \end{bmatrix} \bar{x}(t) \qquad (4.47)$$

Note that the eigenvalues of $A_D + B_D F$ are 9.4465 and -2.6465, which verifies that the originally stable downward equilibrium is now unstable.

Remark 4.16 (Radian and Degree)

The common units for angles and angular displacements are radian and degree. It seems that *degree* is more intuitive to humans, but in engineering analysis and design we have to use *radian* instead of *degree*. It is not only because *radian* has become a standard convention; **there are several practical reasons why we should use** *radian* **instead of** *degree* **in engineering and scientific computations.** One of the practical reasons is relevant to the linearization process we employed to obtain the linearized model at the upward pendulum equilibrium. For instance, $\sin\theta = 0.2571$ is approximately equal to θ for $\theta = 0.26$ rad when the unit used is radian. But it is not the case for $\theta = 15°$ when the unit used is degree.   ∎

4.5 Cart-Inverted Pendulum System

The cart-inverted pendulum control system is one of the most well-known benchmark control problems that has been extensively studied for decades. The problem is so intriguing—it is inherently unstable, nonlinear, and under actuated—that almost all available control design approaches have been employed to solve the problem.

The main objective of this section is to derive the nonlinear dynamics model of the cart-inverted pendulum system using both the Newtonian and the Lagrange approaches. Once the nonlinear dynamics model is derived, it can be employed to analyze the nonlinear system behavior around the unstable equilibrium, to obtain a linearized dynamics model at the unstable equilibrium, and to utilize the information of the linearized model to design a controller so that the unstable equilibrium can be converted to a stable one.

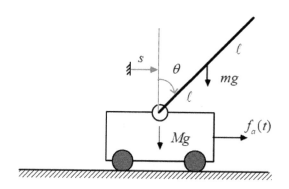

Fig. 4.13: A cart-inverted pendulum system.

A schematic diagram of a typical linear-rail inverted pendulum system is shown in Figure 4.13. The cart has mass M kilograms and is driven by a force f_a Newtons, which can be generated by a DC motor inside the cart. The displacement of the cart is represented by s meters measuring from the center of the rail to the right. A positive s means the cart is at the right side of the rail. On the other hand, a negative s indicates a position on the other side of the rail. The direction of the force is defined accordingly so that a positive force f_a would move the cart forward to the right, and a negative f_a would go reverse to the left. The friction coefficient of the translational motion is assumed a constant B_s.

The stick with mass m kilograms and length 2ℓ meters is hinged to the cart with a pivot so that the stick can rotate freely and make a whole 360-degree swing in either clockwise or counter clockwise direction. The friction coefficient of the rotational motion is assumed as a constant B_θ. **The angular** displacement is represented by θ radians, measuring from the upward reference in the clockwise direction. A positive θ means the stick is tilted to the right side of the pivot.

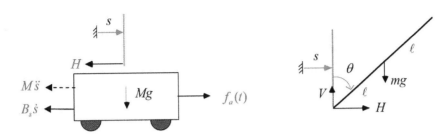

Fig. 4.14: Free-body diagrams of the cart-inverted pendulum system.

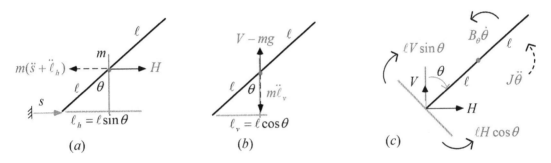

Fig. 4.15: More detailed free-body diagrams for the stick subsystem: (a) horizontal translational motion of the stick, (b) vertical translational motion of the stick, (c) rotational motion of the stick.

4.5.1 The Newtonian Approach Modeling of the Cart-Inverted Pendulum System

Translational Motion Equation of the Cart:

The cart-inverted pendulum system consists of the cart subsystem and the stick subsystem. The free-body diagrams of the stick and the cart are shown in Figure 4.14. **V and H are the vertical and horizontal reaction forces at the pivot, respectively.** There are four forces acting on the cart, and the algebraic sum of these forces is zero according to d'Alembert's principle,

$$M\ddot{s} + B_s\dot{s} + H - f_a = 0 \tag{4.48}$$

Horizontal Translational Motion Equation of the Stick CG:

Unlike the cart subsystem, the stick subsystem involves two translational motions—horizontal and vertical, and one rotational motion. To make it easier to establish the three equations of motion for the stick subsystem, **the stick free-body diagram needs to be further decomposed into three more**

detailed free-body diagrams, shown in Figure 4.15.

Figure 4.15(a) shows the free-body diagram for the horizontal translational motion of the center of gravity (CG) of the stick. Note that the mass of the stick is m, and the horizontal displacement of the CG is $s + \ell_h$, where $\ell_h = \ell \sin \theta$. At the CG, there are two forces: the horizontal reaction force H pointing to the right and the negative inertia force, $m(\ddot{s} + \ddot{\ell}_h)$, which is always in the opposite direction of s. According to d'Alembert's principle, the horizontal translational equation of motion for the CG is obtained as

$$H = m\left(\ddot{s} + \frac{d^2\left(\ell \sin \theta\right)}{dt^2}\right) = m\left(\ddot{s} + \ell \cos \theta \, \ddot{\theta} - \ell \sin \theta \, \dot{\theta}^2\right) \tag{4.49}$$

Vertical Translational Motion Equation of the Stick CG:

Figure 4.15(b) shows the free-body diagram for the vertical translational motion of the center of gravity of the stick. Note that the vertical displacement of the CG is ℓ_v, where $\ell_v = \ell \cos \theta$, and there are three forces acting on the CG. Apparently the vertical reaction force V is in the up direction, while the gravitational force mg is always pointing down. Since the up direction is assumed positive, the inertia force, $m\ddot{\ell}_v$, should point down on the free-body diagram since it is always in the opposite direction of the positive reference direction. According to d'Alembert's principle, the vertical translational equation of motion for the CG is obtained as

$$V - mg = m\frac{d^2\left(\ell \cos \theta\right)}{dt^2} = -m\ell\left(\sin \theta \, \ddot{\theta} + \cos \theta \, \dot{\theta}^2\right) \tag{4.50}$$

Rotational Motion Equation of the Stick:

Figure 4.15(c) shows the free-body diagram for the rotational motion of the stick about the CG of the stick. Note that the torques about the CG due to the vertical reaction force V and the horizontal reaction force H are $\ell V \sin \theta$ and $\ell H \cos \theta$, respectively. The torque $\ell V \sin \theta$ is in the clockwise direction while $\ell H \cos \theta$ is in the opposite, the CCW direction. The friction torque $B_\theta \dot{\theta}$ and the inertial torque $J\ddot{\theta}$ are also in the CCW direction. Hence, the rotational equation of motion for the CG is obtained as

$$\ell V \sin \theta - \ell H \cos \theta - B_\theta \dot{\theta} - J\ddot{\theta} = 0 \tag{4.51}$$

where B_θ is the rotational friction coefficient of the stick, which usually is very small or negligible and J is the moment of inertia of the stick about the CG, which is

$$J = m\ell^2/3 \tag{4.52}$$

and ℓ is half of the length of the stick.

Nonlinear Equation of Motion of the Cart-Inverted Pendulum:

After eliminating the internal reaction forces V and H from Equations 4.48, 4.49, 4.50, and 4.51, we have the following nonlinear governing differential equations for the cart-inverted pendulum system:

$$(M + m)\ddot{s} + B_s \dot{s} - m\ell \sin \theta \, \dot{\theta}^2 + m\ell \cos \theta \, \ddot{\theta} = f_a$$
$$(J + m\ell^2)\ddot{\theta} + B_\theta \dot{\theta} - mg\ell \sin \theta + m\ell \cos \theta \, \ddot{s} = 0 \tag{4.53}$$

Note that the translational dynamics of the cart and the rotational/translational dynamics of the stick are coupled in a nonlinear fashion. In the next subsection, the Lagrange approach will be employed to derive the equation of motion for the same cart-inverted pendulum system.

4.5.2 Lagrange's Approach Modeling of the Cart-Inverted Pendulum System

For the cart-inverted pendulum system shown in Figure 4.13, the generalized coordinate and velocity are $q = \begin{bmatrix} s & \theta \end{bmatrix}^T$ and $\dot{q} = \begin{bmatrix} \dot{s} & \dot{\theta} \end{bmatrix}^T$, respectively. The kinetic energy of the system is stored in the masses M and m and in the moment of inertia J as

$$T = 0.5M\dot{s}^2 + 0.5m\left[\left(\dot{s} + \ell\dot{\theta}\cos\theta\right)^2 + \left(\ell\dot{\theta}\sin\theta\right)^2\right] + 0.5J\dot{\theta}^2 \tag{4.54}$$

where the first, the second, and the third terms of the kinetic energy are due to the translational motion of the cart, the translational motion of the stick, and the rotational motion of the stick, respectively. In the second term, $\dot{s} + \ell\dot{\theta}\cos\theta$ is the horizontal translational velocity of the CG of the stick and $-\ell\dot{\theta}\sin\theta$ is the vertical translational velocity of the CG of the stick. The potential energy of the system is stored in the gravitational field as

$$U = mg\ell\cos\theta \tag{4.55}$$

where $\ell\cos\theta$ is the vertical displacement of the CG of the stick. The power dissipated in the frictions are $D = 0.5B_s\dot{s}^2 + 0.5B_\theta\dot{\theta}^2$. Hence, the Lagrangian function is

$$\mathcal{L} = T - U = 0.5M\dot{s}^2 + 0.5m\left[\left(\dot{s} + \ell\dot{\theta}\cos\theta\right)^2 + \left(\ell\dot{\theta}\sin\theta\right)^2\right] + 0.5J\dot{\theta}^2 - mg\ell\cos\theta \tag{4.56}$$

Then the key differentials in Lagrange's equation can be found as,

$$\frac{\partial\mathcal{L}}{\partial\dot{q}} = \begin{bmatrix} \partial\mathcal{L}/\partial\dot{s} \\ \partial\mathcal{L}/\partial\dot{\theta} \end{bmatrix} = \begin{bmatrix} M\dot{s} + m(\dot{s} + \ell\dot{\theta}\cos\theta) \\ m\ell\cos\theta\dot{s} + m\ell^2\dot{\theta} + J\dot{\theta} \end{bmatrix}, \quad \frac{\partial D}{\partial\dot{q}} = \begin{bmatrix} \partial D/\partial\dot{s} \\ \partial D/\partial\dot{\theta} \end{bmatrix} = \begin{bmatrix} B_s\dot{s} \\ B_\theta\dot{\theta} \end{bmatrix}$$

$$\frac{\partial\mathcal{L}}{\partial q} = \begin{bmatrix} \partial\mathcal{L}/\partial s \\ \partial\mathcal{L}/\partial\theta \end{bmatrix} = \begin{bmatrix} 0 \\ -m\ell\dot{s}\dot{\theta}\sin\theta + mg\ell\sin\theta \end{bmatrix}, \quad Q = \begin{bmatrix} f_a \\ 0 \end{bmatrix} \tag{4.57}$$

Now, from Lagrange's equation,

$$\frac{d}{dt}\left(\frac{\partial\mathcal{L}}{\partial\dot{q}}\right) - \frac{\partial\mathcal{L}}{\partial q} + \frac{\partial D}{\partial\dot{q}} = Q \tag{4.58}$$

we have the dynamics model equation

$$\begin{bmatrix} (M+m)\ddot{s} + B_s\dot{s} - m\ell\sin\theta\dot{\theta}^2 + m\ell\cos\theta\ddot{\theta} \\ (J+m\ell^2)\ddot{\theta} + B_\theta\dot{\theta} - mg\ell\sin\theta + m\ell\cos\theta\ddot{s} \end{bmatrix} = \begin{bmatrix} f_a \\ 0 \end{bmatrix} \tag{4.59}$$

which is identical to the dynamics model equation derived using the Newtonian approach shown in Equation 4.53.

This nonlinear dynamics model described by the two coupled second-order differential equations will be employed in Section 7.6 for further investigation of the cart-inverted pendulum system regarding nonlinear state-space model construction, equilibriums, linear state-space models, and stabilization controller design and analysis.

4.6 Exercise Problems

P4.1a: Consider the double MBK (mass–damper–spring) system shown in Figure 4.16, where $M_1 = M_2 = 1$ kg, $K_1 = K_2 = 2$ N/m, $B_1 = B_2 = 0$ Ns/m, and the initial conditions of the system are $x_1(0) = x_{10}$,

$\dot{x}_1(0) = 0$, $x_2(0) = x_{20}$, and $\dot{x}_2(0) = 0$. Verify the following governing equations of the system by Newtonian approach.

$$\ddot{x}_1(t) + 4x_1(t) - 2x_2(t) = 0$$
$$-2x_1(t) + \ddot{x}_2(t) + 2x_2(t) = 0$$

And show that the Laplace transform of these equations are:

$$s^2 X_1(s) - sx_{10} + 4X_1(s) - 2X_2(s) = 0$$
$$-2X_1(s) + s^2 X_2(s) - sx_{20} + 2X_2(s) = 0$$

P4.1b: Repeat P4.1a using the Lagrange approach.

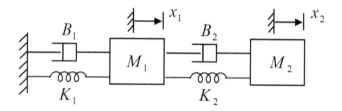

Fig. 4.16: A double MBK system.

P4.1c: Solve for $X_1(s)$ and $X_2(s)$ as

$$X_1(s) = \frac{A_1 s}{s^2 + 0.76393} + \frac{A_3 s}{s^2 + 5.23607}$$
$$X_2(s) = \frac{C_1 s}{s^2 + 0.76393} + \frac{C_3 s}{s^2 + 5.23607}$$

and find A_1, A_3, C_1, and C_3 as functions of the initial conditions x_{10} and x_{20}.

P4.1d: Choose initial conditions x_{10} and x_{20} so that $A_3 = 0$ and $C_3 = 0$, and show that the two masses M_1 and M_2 will exhibit in-phase harmonic motions at the frequency $\omega_L = \sqrt{0.76393}\,\text{rad}/\text{s}$.

P4.1e: Under the initial conditions given in P4.1d, find the inverse Laplace transform of $X_1(s)$ and $X_2(s)$ to obtain $x_1(t)$ and $x_2(t)$. Plot $x_1(t)$ and $x_2(t)$ and use the graphs to verify the in-phase harmonic motions and the oscillation frequency obtained in P4.1d.

P4.1f: Choose initial conditions x_{10} and x_{20} so that $A_1 = 0$ and $C_1 = 0$, and show that the two masses M_1 and M_2 will exhibit 180-degree out-of-phase harmonic motions at the frequency $\omega_H = \sqrt{5.23607}\,\text{rad}/\text{s}$.

P4.1g: Under the initial conditions given in P4.1f, find the inverse Laplace transform of $X_1(s)$ and $X_2(s)$ to obtain $x_1(t)$ and $x_2(t)$. Plot $x_1(t)$ and $x_2(t)$, and use the graphs to verify the 180-degree out-of-phase harmonic motions and the oscillation frequency obtained in P4.1f.

P4.1h: Randomly choose a set of the initial conditions, x_{10} and x_{20}, and then find the inverse Laplace transform of $X_1(s)$ and $X_2(s)$ to obtain $x_1(t)$ and $x_2(t)$. Plot $x_1(t)$ and $x_2(t)$, and comment on the motion of the system.

P4.2: Consider the simple pendulum positioning system shown in Figure 4.17. Unlike the simple inverted pendulum control problem, the objective of this project is not to stabilize the pendulum at the upright unstable equilibrium. Instead, it is an angular position tracking/regulation control problem for a lightly damped pendulum system.

As shown in the figure, one end of the pendulum stick is connected to the pivot under the ceiling, and the other end attaching to a black ball with mass m kg. The pendulum stick's length is ℓ m, and its mass is assumed negligible. The gravity $g = 9.81$ m/s^2, and the control force is u N, whose direction is assumed always perpendicular to the pendulum stick. The friction torque of the system is proportional to the angular velocity with friction coefficient b Nm/rad/s.

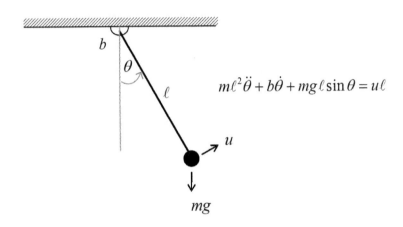

Fig. 4.17: A simple pendulum positioning system.

P4.2a: Show that the governing differential equation for the pendulum system is

$$m\ell^2\ddot{\theta}(t) + b\dot{\theta}(t) + mg\ell\sin\theta = u\ell$$

using the Newtonian approach.

P4.2b: Verify the result of P4.2a using the Lagrange approach.

P4.2c: Define the state variables $x_1 = \theta$, $x_2 = \dot{\theta}$ and then find the nonlinear state equation of the system.

P4.2d: Assume $\frac{g}{\ell} = 16$, $\frac{b}{m\ell^2} = 0.6$, $\frac{1}{m\ell} = 2$, and then rewrite the nonlinear state equation with these numerical values.

P4.2e: Show that $x_D^* = \begin{bmatrix} 0 & 0 \end{bmatrix}^T$ is the *static equilibrium* of the system associated with the downward pendulum positions. A static equilibrium is an equilibrium of the system when the input $u(t)$ is zero.

P4.2f: Find the linearized state equation associated with the downward equilibrium in the form of $\dot{x}(t) = A_D x(t) + B_D u(t)$ and show that the equilibrium $x_D^* = \begin{bmatrix} 0 & 0 \end{bmatrix}^T$ is stable based on the eigenvalues of A_D.

P4.2g: Find the characteristic equation associated with this equilibrium, and use it to determine the pole locations $-\alpha \pm j\omega$, the damping ratio ς, and the natural frequency ω_n. Discuss how α, ω, ς, and ω_n will affect the time response of the system around this equilibrium. Predict the maximum overshoot and the oscillation frequency based on the information of α, ω, ς, and ω_n.

P4.2h: Build a Simulink/MATLAB program based on the nonlinear state equation obtained in P4.2d, and use it to conduct an initial state response simulation with $x_1(0) = 0.26$ rad and $x_2(0) = 0$ rad/s. You will see that the downward equilibrium $x_D^* = \begin{bmatrix} 0 & 0 \end{bmatrix}^T$ is stable, but the response is oscillatory with large overshoot.

P4.2i: Measure the maximum overshoot and the oscillation frequency from the initial state response graph obtained from the simulation in P4.2h, and compare the simulation results with your predictions in P4.2g.

P4.3: As we learned from Problem P4.2a – Problem 4.2i, the system near x_D^*, the downward equilibrium, is stable; however, the time response is oscillatory with large overshoot. The performance of the system can be improved using feedback control. Consider the state equation,

$$\dot{x}(t) = A_D x(t) + B_D u(t)$$

With the state-feedback control, $u(t) = Fx(t)$, the state equation of the closed-loop system will become

$$\dot{x}(t) = (A_D + B_D F)x(t)$$

and the poles of the closed-loop system will be the eigenvalues of $A_D + B_D F$.

P4.3a: Design a state-feedback controller $u(t) = Fx(t) = F_1 x_1(t) + F_2 x_2(t)$ so that the closed-loop system has damping ratio $\varsigma = 0.7$ and natural frequency at $\omega_n = 4$ rad/s. After closing the loop, determine the pole locations, and discuss how the pole locations, the damping ratio and the natural frequency will affect the time response of the system around this equilibrium. Predict the maximum overshoot and the oscillation frequency based on the information of the closed-loop poles and their corresponding damping ratio and natural frequency.

P4.3b: Modify the Simulink/MATLAB program you used in P4.2h to incorporate the state-feedback controller you designed in P4.3a. Conduct simulations to verify that the time response performance has been greatly improved.

P4.3c: Measure the maximum overshoot and the oscillation frequency from the initial state response graph obtained from the simulation in P4.3b, and compare the simulation results with your predictions in P4.3a.

P4.4: As mentioned in P4.2e, a static equilibrium is an equilibrium when the input $u(t)$ is zero. In contrast, a *dynamic equilibrium* is an equilibrium when the input $u(t)$ is a nonzero constant. Many practical systems are required to work at a dynamic equilibrium, or to switch from one equilibrium to another. For example, an aircraft cruise level straight flight maintains a constant speed with a constant thrust.

P4.4a: In this problem, we are interested in investigating the behavior of the pendulum system at the dynamic equilibrium $x^* = \begin{bmatrix} 0.26 & 0 \end{bmatrix}^T$, which means the angular displacement is $\theta = 15$ degree and the angular velocity $\dot{\theta}$ is zero. Use the nonlinear state-space model obtained in P4.2d to determine the input u^* at this equilibrium.

P4.4b: Find a linearized state-space model of the pendulum system at the dynamic equilibrium chosen in P4.4a. The linearized state-space model should be of the following form:

$$\dot{\bar{x}}(t) = A\bar{x}(t) + B\bar{u}(t), \quad \text{where} \quad \bar{x}(t) = x(t) - x^* \quad \text{and} \quad \bar{u}(t) = u(t) - u^*$$

Note that $x(t)$ and $u(t)$ are the actual state vector and the actual control input, respectively; x^* and u^* are the values of the state vector and the control input at the equilibrium; and $\bar{x}(t)$ and $\bar{u}(t)$ are the deviations of the state vector and the control input, respectively, from the equilibrium values.

P4.4c: Find the characteristic equation associated with this equilibrium, and use it to determine the pole locations $-\alpha \pm j\omega$, the damping ratio ς, and the natural frequency ω_n. Discuss how α, ω, ς, and ω_n will affect the time response of the system in the vicinity of this equilibrium. Predict the maximum overshoot and the oscillation frequency.

P4.4d: Build a Simulink/MATLAB program, similar to what you did in P4.2h, based on the nonlinear state equation obtained in P4.2a, and use it to conduct an initial state response simulation with $x_1(0) = 0$ rad, $x_2(0) = 0$ rad/s, and $u(t) = u^*$. Observe if the time response converges to the new dynamic equilibrium chosen in P4.4a.

P4.4e: Measure the maximum overshoot and the oscillation frequency from the initial state response graph obtained from the simulation in P4.4d, and compare the simulation results with your predictions based on the pole locations, damping ratio, and natural frequency obtained in P4.4c.

P4.5: As we learned from Problem P4.4a – Problem P4.4e, the system around the (x^*, u^*), the dynamic equilibrium chosen in P4.4a, is stable; however, the time response is oscillatory with large overshoot. The performance of the system can be improved using feedback control. Consider the state equation,

$$\dot{\bar{x}}(t) = A\bar{x}(t) + B\bar{u}(t)$$

With the state-feedback control, $\bar{u}(t) = F\bar{x}(t)$, the state equation of the closed-loop system will be

$$\dot{\bar{x}}(t) = (A + BF)\bar{x}(t)$$

and the poles of the closed-loop system at the dynamic equilibrium will become the eigenvalues of $A + BF$.

P4.5a: Design a state-feedback controller $\bar{u}(t) = F\bar{x}(t) = F_1\bar{x}_1(t) + F_2\bar{x}_2(t)$ so that the closed-loop system has damping ratio $\varsigma = 0.7$ and natural frequency at $\omega_n = 4$rad/s. After closing the loop, determine the pole locations, and discuss how the pole locations, the damping ratio and the natural frequency will affect the time response of the system in the vicinity of this equilibrium. Predict the maximum overshoot and the oscillation frequency.

P4.5b: Modify the Simulink/MATLAB program you used in P4.4d to incorporate the state-feedback controller you designed in P4.5a. Since $\bar{x} = x - x^*$ and $\bar{u} = u - u^*$, the state-feedback control law $\bar{u}(t) = F\bar{x}$ needs to be replaced by $u = F(x - x^*) + u^*$ in the simulation. Conduct simulation to verify if the time response performance is improved.

P4.5c: Measure the maximum overshoot and the oscillation frequency from the initial state response graph obtained from the simulation in P4.5b, and compare the simulation results with your predictions based on the pole locations, damping ratio, and natural frequency of the closed-loop system.

5

Modeling of Electrical Systems

RECALL that in Chapter 2 and Chapter 3, we started with a few simple mechanical, electrical, and electromechanical systems and their associated mathematical model equations. These models were employed in the analysis to understand how systems work and in a few simple design examples to achieve desired time-domain and frequency-domain performance. Since mathematical system modeling is essential in the analysis and design of control systems, two chapters are allocated in the book to address the fundamental modeling approaches for mechanical systems, electrical circuits, and electromechanical systems.

In Chapter 4, we have learned how to employ the Newtonian approach, d'Alembert's principle, and the Lagrange approach to assemble the governing dynamics equations as mathematical models for mechanical systems. Electrical circuits or systems are a little bit different, but there are close relationships between the mechanical and electrical systems. For the MBK mechanical system and the electrical RLC circuit we discussed in the beginning of Chapter 3, their governing dynamics equations shown in the following clearly reveal that the two systems are mathematically equivalent and their physical component properties are analogous to each other:

$$M\ddot{y}(t) + B\dot{y}(t) + Ky(t) = f_a(t)$$
$$L\ddot{q}(t) + R\dot{q}(t) + (1/C)q(t) = e_a(t)$$

(5.1)

The mechanical system is driven by the applied force $f_a(t)$, which is analogous to the voltage source $e_a(t)$. The voltage source was called electromotive force (emf) when the electricity era had just started. This term is still used on some occasions since the voltage source serves as a means to drive the electrical system. The resistance R and the friction coefficient B are analogous to each other because their dissipated powers are of the same form, with $0.5R\dot{q}^2$ and $0.5B\dot{y}^2$, respectively. The inductor L and the inverse capacitance $1/C$ are analogous to M and K, respectively, since L and M have the same form of kinetic energy, $0.5L\dot{q}^2$ and $0.5M\dot{y}^2$, respectively, and $1/C$ and K have the form of potential energy $(0.5/C)q^2$ and $0.5Ky^2$, respectively.

In Chapter 2 and Chapter 3 we briefly reviewed the characteristics of the three basic passive electric elements, resistor, inductor, and capacitor, and used the component relations together with Kirchhoff's current law and voltage law to derive the governing dynamics equations for a simple first-order RC circuit and a typical second-order RLC system. In this chapter, we will explain in detail how to assemble the governing dynamic equations for electric circuits using several different approaches. Although electric circuits seem less tangible than mechanical systems, the electrical system modeling is more straightforward than the mechanical system since the geometry of the electric circuit is, in a sense, more limited.

Resistor	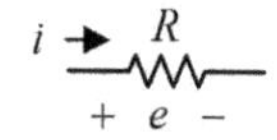 $i \rightarrow \overset{R}{\wedge\wedge\wedge}$ $+ \quad e \quad -$	$e = R\,i$, where $i = dq/dt$ dissipated power: $D = 0.5R\dot{q}^2$
Inductor	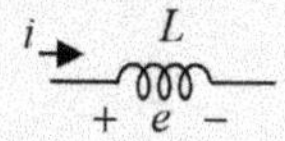 $i \rightarrow \overset{L}{\text{—m—}}$ $+ \quad e \quad -$	$e = L\,di/dt$ or $d\Phi = L\,di$, where $e = d\Phi/dt$ kinetic energy: $T = 0.5L\dot{q}^2$
Capacitor	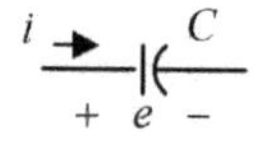 $i \rightarrow \overset{C}{—||—}$ $+ \quad e \quad -$	$i = C\,de/dt$ or $dq = C\,de$ potential energy: $U = (0.5/C)q^2$
Independent Voltage Source	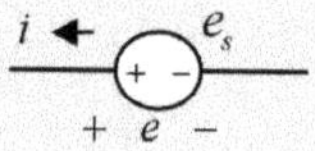 $i \leftarrow \overset{e_s}{(+\,-)}$ $+ \quad e \quad -$	$e = e_s$ for any i
Independent Current Source	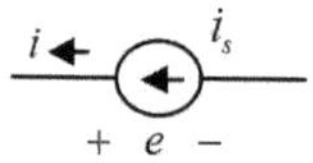 $i \leftarrow \overset{i_s}{(\bullet)}$ $+ \quad e \quad -$	$i = i_s$ for any e
Dependent Voltage Source	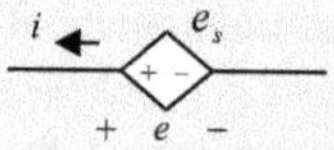 $i \leftarrow \overset{e_s}{\langle+\,-\rangle}$ $+ \quad e \quad -$	$e = e_s$ for any i, where the value of e_s is determined by some parameter in the circuit
Dependent Current Source	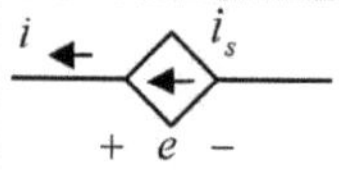 $i \leftarrow \overset{i_s}{\langle\bullet\rangle}$ $+ \quad e \quad -$	$i = i_s$ for any e, where the value of i_s is determined by some parameter in the circuit
Open Circuit	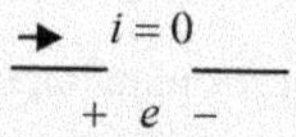 $\rightarrow \quad i = 0$ $+ \quad e \quad -$	$i = 0$ for any e
Short Circuit	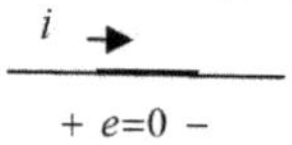 $i \rightarrow$ $+ \quad e = 0 \quad -$	$e = 0$ for any i

Fig. 5.1: Symbols and characteristics of fundamental two-terminal electrical elements.

5.1 Basic Electrical Circuit Elements and Circuit Conventions

To analyze the behavior or to obtain a mathematical model of an electrical system, the first step is to understand the **voltage-current relationships** of the three fundamental passive electrical elements, *resistor, capacitor, inductor*—just like we did in Chapter 4 for mechanical systems about the **force-velocity relationships** of the three mechanical elements, *damper, spring, mass*. As shown in Figure 5.1, the *e-i* relationship of the resistor is $e = Ri$, which is the well-known Ohm's law. **The units for the voltage e, current i, charge q, and resistance R are volt, ampere, coulomb, and ohm, respectively.** The *e-i* relationship of the capacitor is $i = Cde/dt$, where **the unit of the capacitance C is Farad.** The *e-i* relationship of the inductor is $e = Ldi/dt$ or $d\Phi = Ldi$, where **the units of the inductance L and the magnetic flux Φ are Henry and Weber, respectively.**

Note that **the voltage polarity and the current flow direction need to be consistent: The current always** *flows into* **the positive terminal of every passive element.** Although in reality, especially in a complicated circuit, we may not know the actual polarity of the elements before the circuit analysis is completed, it is a common practice to specify voltage and current with polarity for each element of interest in the circuit. For the simple circuit in Figure 5.2, the voltages and currents with polarity and flow direction are specified as shown. Since the specified current direction needs to be consistent with the specified voltage polarity, **only either one of them, voltage or current, needs to be specified.** The polarity can be arbitrarily chosen, but once the specified voltage and current variables are selected they should stay unchanged during the whole circuit analysis process.

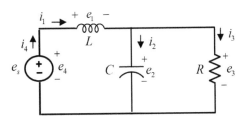

Fig. 5.2: The convention of voltage polarity and current direction in an RLC circuit.

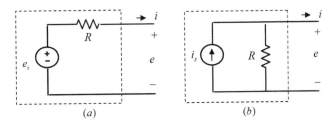

Fig. 5.3: (a) Thevenin and (b) Norton equivalent circuits.

The voltage of the voltage source and the current of the current source are prespecified, and **the current always** *flows out of* **the positive terminal of the source element.** Behold, this is different from the three passive electrical elements R, L, and C; with them the current always *flows into* the positive terminal. The voltage and current sources are classified into two categories: independent and dependent voltage/current sources. The independent ones represent the independent power sources whose supplied voltages or currents do not depend on any parameters of the circuit. On the other hand, the dependent sources represent some active devices like transistors or operational amplifiers whose supplied voltages or currents are dependent on some parameters in the circuit. The voltage/current sources listed in Figure 5.1 are ideal sources. **Although there exists no ideal voltage/current source in the real world, most of the real signals and power sources can be modeled as a combination of an ideal voltage/current source together with passive electrical components.** For example, a signal source or a battery can be modeled as a Thevenin or a Norton equivalent circuit, as shown in Figure 5.3.

5.2 Basic Time-Domain Circuit Modeling Approaches and Kirchhoff's Laws

As mentioned earlier, the mathematical modeling of mechanical systems is essential, since without it it would be difficult or even impossible to achieve optimal mechanical design and feedback control system design for performance enhancement, including precision, reliability, safety, and automation. The mathematical modeling of electrical systems is even more important since electronic devices and electromechanical systems have been embedded in almost all systems that impact our daily life. We will start from the basic time-domain circuit modeling approach. This approach includes three variations: (1) the $2k$ **equations approach, (2) the node–to–datum (NTD) voltages approach, and (3) the mesh currents approach.**

5.2.1 Circuit Modeling Using the $2k$ Equations Approach

For the electrical system or circuit with k two-terminal elements that include at least one independent voltage or current source, the dynamic system model should have the capability of exhibiting the cause-effect relationship and the interactions among all the k elements. Since there is one pair of voltage and current variables associated with each element, in total there are $2k$ variables, and therefore $2k$ independent equations are required to solve these variables. Based on the e-i relationship of the passive elements and the voltage/current information for the voltage/current sources, as described in Figure 5.1, k equations can be easily set up. The other k equations must be obtained using Kirchhoff's voltage law (KVL) and current law (KCL) according to the interconnection of the elements in the circuit.

Recall that voltage was defined as the energy required to bring a positive unit charge from one point to another in a conservative electric field. Based on the conservation of energy law, the energy required for a charge to travel around a closed path back to the starting point is zero, and **the algebraic sum of the voltages around any closed path is zero**, which is exactly the statement of Kirchhoff's voltage law (KVL),

$$\sum_i e_i = 0 \tag{5.2}$$

On the other hand, Kirchhoff's current law (KCL) is derived from Conservation of Charge law. At any junction of elements, called *node*, charge can neither be destroyed nor created, and therefore **the algebraic sum of the currents entering any node is zero**. Thus,

$$\sum_j i_j = 0 \tag{5.3}$$

Example 5.1 (*2k* **Equations Approach**)

For the electric circuit shown in Figure 5.2, there are $k = 4$ elements, including one each of inductor L, capacitor C, resistor R, and voltage source e_s. Apparently, we have the following $k = 4$ equations from the e-i relationship of the L, C, and R elements and the value of the voltage source e_s:

$$e_1 = L\frac{di_1}{dt}, \quad i_2 = C\frac{de_2}{dt}, \quad e_3 = R_3 i_3, \quad \text{and} \quad e_4 = e_s \tag{5.4}$$

As specified on the circuit elements in Figure 5.2, there are $2k$ variables: $i_1, e_1, i_2, e_2, i_3, e_3, i_4, e_4$. It is clear that $k = 4$ more independent equations are needed to determine the voltages and currents for all the $k = 4$ elements. These $k = 4$ equations must be obtained using KVL and KCL according to the interconnection of the $k = 4$ elements. It can be seen that the circuit has $m = 2$ meshes, where a mesh is a loop in the circuit that does not contain any other loop, and therefore $m = 2$ mesh equations can be obtained by applying KVL around the two meshes:

$$-e_4 + e_1 + e_2 = 0, \quad \text{and} \quad -e_2 + e_3 = 0 \tag{5.5}$$

There are $n = 3$ nodes in the circuit, but they can only provide $n - 1 = 2$ independent node equations by applying KCL to any 2 nodes:

$$i_4 - i_1 = 0 \quad \text{and} \quad i_1 - i_2 - i_3 = 0 \tag{5.6}$$

The $2k$ equations approach described is conceptually straightforward; however, it is tedious computationally. As a matter of fact, the system model equations do not need to include all the $2k$ variables. For example, in the circuit shown in Figure 5.2, if we know the voltage across the capacitor, e_2, then we have the voltage across the resistor, $e_3 = e_2$, and the voltage across the inductor, $e_1 = e_s - e_2$, simply by inspection. With the knowledge of the voltages for the three L, C, R elements, the currents i_1, i_2, and i_3 can be easily computed based on the simple e-i relationship of each element, and finally, by inspection again, we have $i_4 = i_1$ and $e_4 = e_s$. Hence, the system model needs only one equation that can be employed to solve for e_2.   ■

From this discussion, certainly there exists at least one electric circuit modeling approach that is more efficient than the $2k$ equations approach.

5.2.2 The Node–To–Datum (NTD) Voltages Approach

The first step of the node–to–datum (NTD) voltages approach is to select one node as the datum, which will serve as the common reference point. The selection is arbitrary, but the negative terminal of a voltage or current source is a good choice. The next step is to assign a node–to–datum (NTD) voltage variable for each node of the circuit except the positive terminal of voltage sources. Then the final step is to apply KCL to all assigned nodes to set up equations with only the NTD voltages as variables.

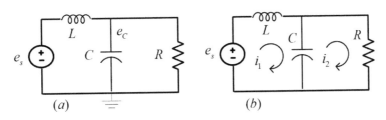

Fig. 5.4: (a) The NTD voltages approach, (b) The mesh currents approach.

Example 5.2 (NTD Voltages Approach)

The circuit in Figure 5.4(a) is exactly the same as the one in Figure 5.2, which was considered in Example 5.1. The difference here is that by using the NTD approach only one voltage variable, instead of $2k$ variables, needs to be assigned. The node connecting to the negative terminal of the voltage source is selected as the datum, and one NTD voltage variable e_C is assigned at the node connecting to the three elements L, C, and R. The third node is connecting to the positive terminal of the voltage source, and its NTD voltage is obviously given as e_s. Therefore, only one NTD voltage variable is required to be assigned. Now we apply Kirchhoff's current law to the assigned node to obtain the following KCL equation:

$$C\frac{de_C}{dt} + \frac{e_C}{R} + (1/L)\int(e_C - e_s)dt = 0 \tag{5.7}$$

Note that the first term, the second term, and the third term of the equation are the currents flowing out of the node through the capacitor, the resistor, and the inductor, respectively. This equation describes the unique relationship between the voltage source voltage e_s and the voltage at the assigned node, e_C. The voltage e_C will be determined by solving the equation if e_s is given, and once e_C is known, all the voltages and currents in the circuit can be easily determined.

Meanwhile, by taking Laplace transform of Equation 5.7, we have the following transfer function:

$$sCE_C + \frac{E_C}{R} + \frac{E_C - E_s}{sL} = 0 \quad \rightarrow \quad \frac{E_C(s)}{E_s(s)} = \frac{R}{RLCs^2 + Ls + R}$$

■

5.2.3 The Mesh Currents Approach

The circuit in Figure 5.4(b) will be employed in the following example to demonstrate how to assemble dynamic equations of the circuit using the mesh current approach. This circuit is exactly the same as those of Figure 5.2 and Figure 5.4(a), considered in Example 5.1 and Example 5.2, respectively.

Example 5.3 (Mesh Currents Approach)

First we assign a mesh current variable to each mesh. There are two meshes in the circuit shown in Figure 5.4(b). The first mesh is the loop consisting of the voltage source e_s, the inductor L, and the capacitor C, and the second mesh is the loop composed of the capacitor C and the resistor R. These two mesh current variables are denoted as i_1 and i_2, respectively, and both mesh currents are in the clockwise direction. **Then** we **apply Kirchhoff's voltage law to the two meshes** to obtain the following two KVL equations:

$$-e_s + L\frac{di_1}{dt} + \frac{1}{C}\int (i_1 - i_2)dt = 0 \qquad (5.8a)$$

$$\frac{1}{C}\int (i_2 - i_1)dt + Ri_2 = 0 \qquad (5.8b)$$

The left side of the first KVL equation in Equation 5.8a is the algebraic sum of the voltage drops around *mesh 1* **clockwise, starting from the negative terminal of the voltage source.** The first term $-e_s$, the second term Ldi_1/dt, and the third term $(1/C)\int (i_1 - i_2)dt$ are the voltage drops of the voltage source, the inductor, and the capacitor, respectively. **Similarly, the left side of the second KVL equation, Equation 5.8b, is the algebraic sum of the voltage drops around** *mesh 2* **clockwise, starting from the bottom terminal of the capacitor.** The mesh current variables i_1 and i_2 can be determined by solving the two equations if e_s is given; and, once i_1 and i_2 are known, all the voltages and currents in the circuit can be easily determined.   ∎

For this particular circuit, the mesh currents approach employs two mesh current variables requiring two equations while the NTD voltages approach needs only one NTD voltage variable that only requires one equation. It seems that the NTD voltages approach is simpler than the mesh currents approach, but this is not always the case. For some circuits, the mesh currents approach may require less equations than the NTD voltages approach.

5.3 Basic Impedance Circuit Modeling Approaches

Recall that the *e-i* relationships of the resistor, inductor, and capacitor, respectively are

$$e_R(t) = Ri_R(t), \quad e_L(t) = L\frac{di_L(t)}{dt}, \quad i_C(t) = C\frac{de_C(t)}{dt} \qquad (5.9)$$

After the Laplace transform, the voltage-current relationships of the resistor, inductor, and capacitor, respectively, will be described by the following algebraic equations:

$$E_R(s) = RI_R(s), \quad E_L(s) = sLI_L(s), \quad \text{and} \quad I_C(s) = sCE_C(s) \qquad (5.10)$$

These equations can be further rewritten in the form of E-I relationship, described by *generalized Ohm's law* :

$$E_R(s) = Z_R(s)I_R(s), \quad E_L(s) = Z_L(s)I_L(s), \quad E_C(s) = Z_C(s)I_C(s) \qquad (5.11)$$

where

Resistor	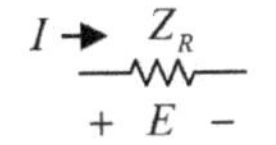 $I \rightarrow \ Z_R$ $+\ E\ -$	$E = Z_R I$, where $Z_R = R$
Inductor	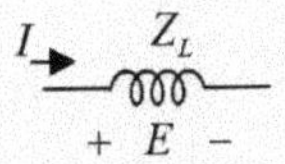 $I \rightarrow \ Z_L$ $+\ E\ -$	$E = Z_L I$, where $Z_L = sL$
Capacitor	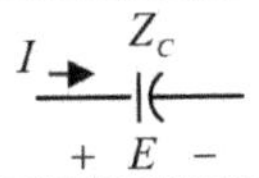 $I \rightarrow \ Z_C$ $+\ E\ -$	$E = Z_C I$, where $Z_C = 1/sC$
Independent Voltage Source	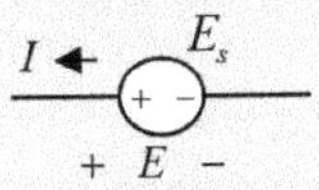 $I \leftarrow \ E_s$ $+\ E\ -$	$E = E_s$ for any I
Independent Current Source	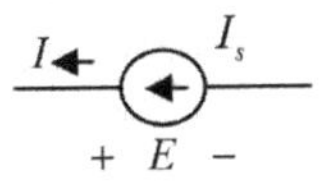 $I \leftarrow \ I_s$ $+\ E\ -$	$I = I_s$ for any E

Fig. 5.5: E-I relationship of fundamental two-terminal electrical elements in frequency domain.

$$Z_R(s) = R, \quad Z_L(s) = sL, \quad Z_C(s) = 1/sC \tag{5.12}$$

are called the *impedance* **of the resistor, inductor, and capacitor.** The frequency-domain E-I characteristics of the fundamental two-terminal electrical elements are summarized in Figure 5.5.

The impedance circuit modeling approaches are basically the frequency-domain counterparts of the NTD voltages and the mesh currents approaches described in the previous section. The difference is that the impedance circuit modeling approaches are carried out in the frequency domain while those in the previous section are done in the time domain. The frequency-domain approach with the impedance concept is more versatile in which the inductors, the capacitors, and the resistors are treated the same following the generalized Ohm's law.

Example 5.4 (Find the Transfer Function $E_C(s)/E_s(s)$ Using Impedance Manipulations)

Consider the circuit in Figure 5.6(a). It can be seen that if $E_C(s)$ is known, all the voltages and currents in the circuit can be easily derived. In the next subsection, we will use the impedance NTD voltages approach to solve for $E_C(s)$. But, here, we would like to show that the same objective can be achieved by applying a couple of simple impedance manipulations.

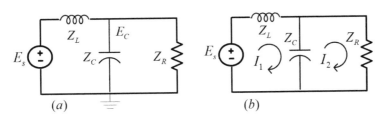

Fig. 5.6: (a) Impedance NTD voltages approach, (b) Impedance mesh currents approach.

First combine the Z_C and Z_R into one impedance as Z_{RC} according to the parallel combination law of impedances:

$$\frac{1}{Z_{RC}} = \frac{1}{Z_R} + \frac{1}{Z_C} = \frac{1}{R} + sC = \frac{RCs+1}{R} \quad \rightarrow \quad Z_{RC} = \frac{R}{RCs+1} \tag{5.13}$$

Then the voltage divider law can be applied to obtain the transfer function E_C/E_s as follows:

$$\frac{E_C(s)}{E_s(s)} = \frac{Z_{RC}}{Z_{RC} + Z_L} = \frac{\frac{R}{RCs+1}}{\frac{R}{RCs+1} + sL} = \frac{R}{sL(RCs+1) + R} = \frac{R}{RLCs^2 + Ls + R} \tag{5.14}$$

Note that the transfer function of the circuit is mathematically equivalent to the typical second-order system discussed in Chapter 3.

A Quiz Problem: Find a set of values for the inductor, capacitor, and resistor so that the system has a damping ratio $\varsigma = 0.7$ with natural frequency $\omega_n = 100$ rad/s.   ∎

5.3.1 The Impedance NTD Voltages Approach

The impedance NTD voltages approach basically is the same as the time-domain NTD voltages approach we learned in Section 5.2.2. The only difference is that the impedance approach is much easier, requiring only algebraic computation without the need to deal with integrations or differentiations. The circuit considered in Example 5.2 will be employed in the following example to demonstrate the advantage of the impedance approach.

Example 5.5 (NTD Voltages Approach)

Consider the circuit in Figure 5.6(a), which is exactly the same as the one we studied using the time-domain NTD voltages approach in Example 5.2. **The procedure of setting up equations is almost identical, but all variables are in frequency domain as functions of s and all equations are algebraic.**

As shown in Figure 5.6(a), the circuit has three nodes, and one of the three nodes, the negative terminal of the voltage source E_s, is chosen as the datum. The voltage at the upper-left node is known as E_s since the node is the positive terminal of the voltage source E_s. Hence, the only unknown NTD voltage is E_C, the voltage at the node that connects to Z_L, Z_C and Z_R.

Applying Kirchhoff's current law to the assigned NTD node, the algebraic sum of the three currents leaving the node should be zero:

$$\frac{E_C}{Z_C} + \frac{E_C}{Z_R} + \frac{E_C - E_s}{Z_L} = 0 \quad \rightarrow \quad \left(sC + \frac{1}{R} + \frac{1}{sL}\right)E_C = \frac{1}{sL}E_s \tag{5.15}$$

Note that the currents flowing out of the NTD node into the capacitor C, the resistor R, and the inductor L are E_C/Z_C, E_C/Z_R and $(E_C - E_s)/Z_L$, respectively, according to the generalized Ohm's law. Plugging the impedances, $Z_C = 1/sC$, $Z_R = R$, and $Z_L = sL$ into the KCL equation and moving the E_s term to the right-hand side of the equation, we obtain the new equation on the right-hand side of the arrow sign. This new equation leads to the following transfer function:

$$\frac{E_C(s)}{E_s(s)} = \frac{R}{RLCs^2 + Ls + R}$$

This transfer function is exactly the same as the one obtained by taking Laplace transform of Equation 5.7 in Example 5.2. It is also identical to the result obtained in Equation 5.14 based on simple impedance manipulations.   ∎

5.3.2 The Impedance Mesh Currents Approach

The impedance mesh currents approach basically is the same as the time-domain mesh currents approach we learned in Section 5.2.3. **The only difference is that the impedance approach is much easier, requiring only algebraic computation without the need to deal with integrations or differentiations.** The circuit considered in Example 5.3 will be employed in the following example to demonstrate the advantage of the impedance approach.

Example 5.6 (Impedance Mesh Currents Approach)

Consider the circuit in Figure 5.6(b), which is exactly the same as the one we studied using the time-domain mesh currents approach in Example 5.3. The procedure of setting up equations is almost identical, but all variables are in frequency domain as functions of s and all equations are algebraic.

As shown in Figure 5.6(b), the circuit has two meshes; hence, two clockwise mesh currents I_1 and I_2 are assigned. **The first mesh is the loop consisting of the voltage source E_s, the inductor impedance Z_L, and the capacitor impedance Z_C, and the second mesh is the loop composed of the capacitor impedance Z_C and the resistor impedance Z_R.** Now we apply Kirchhoff's voltage law to the two meshes to obtain two KVL equations:

$$Z_L I_1 + Z_C (I_1 - I_2) - E_s = 0$$
$$Z_C (I_2 - I_1) + Z_R I_2 = 0$$

(5.16)

which can be rewritten in matrix form as

$$\begin{bmatrix} Z_L + Z_C & -Z_C \\ -Z_C & Z_C + Z_R \end{bmatrix} \begin{bmatrix} I_1 \\ I_2 \end{bmatrix} = \begin{bmatrix} E_s \\ 0 \end{bmatrix} \rightarrow \begin{bmatrix} sL + \frac{1}{sC} & \frac{-1}{sC} \\ \frac{-1}{sC} & \frac{1}{sC} + R \end{bmatrix} \begin{bmatrix} I_1 \\ I_2 \end{bmatrix} = \begin{bmatrix} E_s \\ 0 \end{bmatrix}$$

(5.17)

To solve this matrix equation for I_1 and I_2,

$$\begin{bmatrix} I_1 \\ I_2 \end{bmatrix} = \begin{bmatrix} sL + \frac{1}{sC} & \frac{-1}{sC} \\ \frac{-1}{sC} & \frac{1}{sC} + R \end{bmatrix}^{-1} \begin{bmatrix} E_s \\ 0 \end{bmatrix} = \frac{1}{RLCs^2 + Ls + R} \begin{bmatrix} RCs + 1 \\ 1 \end{bmatrix} E_s$$

(5.18)

It is easy to verify that $E_C = I_2 Z_R = I_2 R$. **Hence, the result is consistent with those shown in Equation 5.14 and Equation 5.15, obtained using the impedance manipulations and the impedance NTD voltages approach, respectively.** ∎

5.4 The Lagrange Approach for Circuit Modeling

As discussed in Chapter 4, the Lagrange approach provides an elegant and efficient way of constructing dynamic equations in the mechanical system modeling process. The Lagrange approach can also be applied to electrical systems in which the electric charge q and its derivative $\dot{q}$ (the electric current) are considered as configuration variables.

Recall that the *Lagrangian* $\mathscr{L}(\dot{q}, q)$ is defined as

$$\mathscr{L}(\dot{q}, q) = T(\dot{q}, q) - U(q)$$

(5.19)

where $T(\dot{q}, q)$ and $U(q)$ are the total kinetic energy and the total potential energy in the system, respectively. For electrical systems, $T(\dot{q}, q)$ **is the total kinetic energy stored in inductors, and $U(q)$ is the total potential energy stored in capacitors.** In addition to the energy stored in the inductors and capacitors, the energy delivered by the voltage/current sources and the dissipated power in resistors are represented by δW, **which is the total** *virtual work* **done by all forces action through** δq, a variation of the generalized coordinate vector:

$$\delta W = Q^T \cdot \delta q \quad \text{or} \quad Q = \partial(\delta W)/\partial(\delta q) \tag{5.20}$$

where Q is the *generalized force vector*. With the Lagrangian $\mathscr{L}(\dot{q}, q)$ and the generalized force vector Q defined, the **Lagrange equation** is given as

$$\frac{d}{dt}\frac{\partial \mathscr{L}(\dot{q}, q)}{\partial \dot{q}} - \frac{\partial \mathscr{L}(\dot{q}, q)}{\partial q} = Q \tag{5.21}$$

In the following, we will use the same circuit in Figure 5.2 or Figure 5.4, which is redrawn in Figure 5.7, to demonstrate how the Lagrange approach can be employed to derive dynamic equations in electrical system modeling.

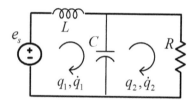

Fig. 5.7: Circuit modeling using the Lagrange approach.

As shown in Figure 5.7, the electric charges traveling around mesh 1 and mesh 2 are q_1 and q_2, respectively, and their corresponding mesh currents are denoted by $\dot{q}_1$ and $\dot{q}_2$. The generalized coordinate and velocity vectors are $q = \begin{bmatrix} q_1 & q_2 \end{bmatrix}^T$ and $\dot{q} = \begin{bmatrix} \dot{q}_1 & \dot{q}_2 \end{bmatrix}^T$, respectively. The total kinetic energy $T(\dot{q}, q) = 0.5L\dot{q}_1^2$ is the kinetic energy stored in the inductor L, and the total potential energy $U(q) = (0.5/C)(q_1 - q_2)^2$ is the potential energy stored in the capacitor C. The **total virtual work** through δq from the contribution of the voltage source and the dissipation in the resistor will be

$$\delta W = e_s \delta q_1 - R\dot{q}_2 \delta q_2 \tag{5.22}$$

The **generalized force vector** is computed according to Equation 5.20 as

$$Q = \frac{\partial(\delta W)}{\partial(\delta q)} = \begin{bmatrix} e_s \\ -R\dot{q}_2 \end{bmatrix} \tag{5.23}$$

Now the Lagrangian is

$$\mathscr{L}(\dot{q}, q) = T(\dot{q}, q) - U(q) = 0.5L\dot{q}_1^2 - (0.5/C)(q_1 - q_2)^2 \tag{5.24}$$

Then according to the Lagrange equation in Equation 5.21, we have the following:

$$\begin{bmatrix} L\ddot{q}_1 + (1/C)(q_1 - q_2) \\ -(1/C)(q_1 - q_2) \end{bmatrix} = \begin{bmatrix} e_s \\ -R\dot{q}_2 \end{bmatrix} \tag{5.25}$$

Since $\dot{q}_1 = i_1$ and $\dot{q}_2 = i_2$, Equation 5.25 can be rewritten as the following:

$$Ldi_1/dt + (1/C)\int(i_1 - i_2)dt = e_s$$
$$(1/C)\int(i_1 - i_2)dt = Ri_2$$

(5.26)

which is exactly the same as **Equation 5.8**, the dynamic equation obtained using the mesh currents approach for the same circuit.

Remark 5.7 (An Alternative Way of Addressing the Dissipated Power in Lagrange's Equation)

Note that the Lagrangian used in the Lagrange equation, Equation 5.21, consists of only the total kinetic energy and the total potential energy of the system. The consideration of the dissipated energy is included in the virtual work described in Equation 5.20 and appears in Equation 5.21 as part of the generalized force vector Q on the right-hand side of the equation.

An alternative way of addressing this issue is to add one dissipated power term D to represent the total power dissipated in the system. Then the Lagrange equation will be slightly modified to:

$$\frac{d}{dt}\left(\frac{\partial\mathscr{L}}{\partial\dot{q}}\right) - \frac{\partial\mathscr{L}}{\partial q} + \frac{\partial D}{\partial\dot{q}} = Q_s$$

(5.27)

where Q_s **is the generalized external force vector** acting on the system.   ∎

Example 5.8 (Use of the Modified Lagrange Equation With the Dissipated Power Term D)

Here we will employ the same circuit in Figure 5.7, to demonstrate how to utilize the modified Lagrange equation, Equation 5.27 to assemble the dynamics system model for electric circuits.

The generalized coordinate and velocity vectors are still $q = \begin{bmatrix} q_1 & q_2 \end{bmatrix}^T$ and $\dot{q} = \begin{bmatrix} \dot{q}_1 & \dot{q}_2 \end{bmatrix}^T$, respectively. The Lagrangian is also the same:

$$\mathscr{L}(\dot{q},q) = T(\dot{q},q) - U(q) = 0.5L\dot{q}_1^2 - (0.5/C)(q_1 - q_2)^2$$

The difference is the term $\partial D/\partial\dot{q}$ added to the left-hand side of the equation, and the Q_s term on the right-hand side now only consists of the generalized external force vector acting on the system without including the forces that cause the dissipated power.

The total dissipated power of the system is the power dissipated in the resistor R, $D = 0.5R\dot{q}_2^2$. The generalized external force vector is $Q_s = \begin{bmatrix} e_s & 0 \end{bmatrix}^T$. Since the current $\dot{q}_1$ flows out of the positive terminal of the voltage source, the positive voltage e_s is located at the first entry of the vector Q_s corresponding to q_1, $\dot{q}_1$. Now, with the following key Lagrange differentials,

$$\frac{\partial\mathscr{L}}{\partial\dot{q}} = \begin{bmatrix} \partial\mathscr{L}/\partial\dot{q}_1 \\ \partial\mathscr{L}/\partial\dot{q}_2 \end{bmatrix} = \begin{bmatrix} L\dot{q}_1 \\ 0 \end{bmatrix}, \quad \frac{\partial D}{\partial\dot{q}} = \begin{bmatrix} \partial D/\partial\dot{q}_1 \\ \partial D/\partial\dot{q}_2 \end{bmatrix} = \begin{bmatrix} 0 \\ R\dot{q}_2 \end{bmatrix}$$
$$\frac{\partial\mathscr{L}}{\partial q} = \begin{bmatrix} \partial\mathscr{L}/\partial q_1 \\ \partial\mathscr{L}/\partial q_2 \end{bmatrix} = \begin{bmatrix} -(1/C)(q_1 - q_2) \\ (1/C)(q_1 - q_2) \end{bmatrix}, \quad Q_s = \begin{bmatrix} e_s \\ 0 \end{bmatrix}$$

(5.28)

Then, from the Lagrange equation, Equation 5.27, **we have the dynamics model equation for the circuit as follows:**

$$\begin{bmatrix} L\ddot{q}_1 + (1/C)(q_1 - q_2) \\ -(1/C)(q_1 - q_2) + R\dot{q}_2 \end{bmatrix} = \begin{bmatrix} e_s \\ 0 \end{bmatrix}$$

(5.29)

As expected, the result is identical to that shown in Equation 5.25, which was obtained based on the regular Lagrange's equation, Equation 5.21.   ∎

In the following, we will work on two more circuit modeling examples using the Lagrange approach. The first is the circuit on Figure 5.8a, which consists of four nodes, two meshes, one voltage source, one resistor, one inductor, and two capacitors. There are many ways to assemble a dynamics model for the electrical system. If we choose to use the NTD voltages approach, we would select the node connecting to the negative terminal of the voltage source as the datum, and assign the two capacitor voltages as the two NTD voltages. Then Kirchhoff's current law will be applied to these two NTD nodes to yield two KCL equations by which the two NTD voltage variables can be solved. Once these two NTD voltages are found, the voltage and current of each element in the circuit can be easily derived.

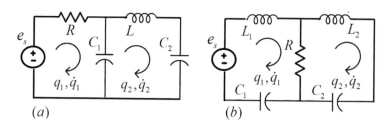

Fig. 5.8: More examples on circuit modeling using the Lagrange's equation approach.

If the mesh currents approach is selected, we would assign a mesh current variable for each mesh, and apply Kirchhoff's voltage law to assemble two KVL equations in terms of these two variables. After solving these two equations to obtain the two mesh currents, all the voltages and currents can be easily computed.

Both of the NTD voltages approach and the mesh currents approach are carried out based on the circuit geometry and the interactions among the components, like the Newtonian approach for mechanical systems modeling. The Lagrange approach is quite different. It is energy based that does not require detailed information of the geometry and interactions among the components. It does require differential calculus computations, but they are quite straightforward.

Two versions of the Lagrange equations are included in this Chapter. These two versions are basically identical. The only difference is in how the dissipated power and the generalized force vector Q are included in the equation. The dissipated power term $\partial D/\partial \dot{q}$ and the generalized force vector Q are explicitly included in Equation 5.27, while in Equation 5.21 the information of power dissipation and the generalized force vector Q is included in the virtual work. Either version will do the job.

Example 5.9 (Apply the Lagrange Approach to the Circuit on Figure 5.8a)

There are two meshes in the circuit. Assume mesh 1 is on the left and mesh 2 is on the right. The electric charges traveling around mesh 1 and mesh 2 are q_1 and q_2, respectively, and their corresponding mesh currents are denoted by $\dot{q}_1$ and $\dot{q}_2$. Both mesh currents are assumed in clockwise direction. Although the mesh current direction can be assigned arbitrarily, it is better to follow the convention whenever possible to avoid confusions. Since the positive current direction is assumed flowing out of the positive terminal of voltage source according to the convention rules shown in Figure 5.1, the mesh 1 current should be in the clockwise direction.

The generalized coordinate and velocity vectors are $q = \begin{bmatrix} q_1 & q_2 \end{bmatrix}^T$ and $\dot{q} = \begin{bmatrix} \dot{q}_1 & \dot{q}_2 \end{bmatrix}^T$, respectively. The total kinetic energy is stored in the inductor L, which is $T = 0.5L\dot{q}_2^2$. Total potential energy of the system is $U = 0.5(1/C_1)(q_1-q_2)^2 + 0.5(1/C_2)q_2^2$ in which the first term is contributed by the capacitor

C_1 and the second term is by C_2. Hence the Lagrangian is

$$\mathscr{L} = T - U = 0.5L\dot{q}_2^2 - 0.5(1/C_1)(q_1 - q_2)^2 - 0.5(1/C_2)q_2^2 \tag{5.30}$$

The total power dissipation is from the resistor R, which is $D = 0.5R\dot{q}_1^2$. The differentials and the generalized force vector involved in the Lagrange equation can be found as

$$\frac{\partial\mathscr{L}}{\partial\dot{q}} = \begin{bmatrix} \partial\mathscr{L}/\partial\dot{q}_1 \\ \partial\mathscr{L}/\partial\dot{q}_2 \end{bmatrix} = \begin{bmatrix} 0 \\ L\dot{q}_2 \end{bmatrix}, \quad \frac{\partial D}{\partial\dot{q}} = \begin{bmatrix} \partial D/\partial\dot{q}_1 \\ \partial D/\partial\dot{q}_2 \end{bmatrix} = \begin{bmatrix} R\dot{q}_1 \\ 0 \end{bmatrix}$$

$$\frac{\partial\mathscr{L}}{\partial q} = \begin{bmatrix} \partial\mathscr{L}/\partial q_1 \\ \partial\mathscr{L}/\partial q_2 \end{bmatrix} = \begin{bmatrix} -(1/C_1)(q_1 - q_2) \\ (1/C_1)(q_1 - q_2) - (1/C_2)q_2 \end{bmatrix}, \quad Q_s = \begin{bmatrix} e_s \\ 0 \end{bmatrix} \tag{5.31}$$

Then, according to the Lagrange equation in Equation 5.27, we have the following dynamics model for the electric circuit:

$$\begin{bmatrix} (1/C_1)(q_1 - q_2) + R\dot{q}_1 \\ L\ddot{q}_2 - (1/C_1)(q_1 - q_2) + (1/C_2)q_2 \end{bmatrix} = \begin{bmatrix} e_s \\ 0 \end{bmatrix} \tag{5.32}$$

This equation can be rewritten in terms of the mesh currents i_1 and i_2 as follows:

$$\begin{bmatrix} Ri_1 + (1/C_1)\int (i_1 - i_2)dt \\ -(1/C_1)\int (i_1 - i_2)dt + L\frac{di_2}{dt} + (1/C_2)\int i_2 dt \end{bmatrix} = \begin{bmatrix} e_s \\ 0 \end{bmatrix} \tag{5.33}$$

∎

The next circuit to be considered is shown in Figure 5.8b, which consists of five nodes, two meshes, one voltage source, one resistor, two inductors, and two capacitors. Since there are five nodes, if the NTD voltages approach were chosen to solve the circuit problem, then three NTD voltage variables need to be assigned and three KCL equations would have to be set up and solved. On the other hand, the circuit has two meshes that requires only two KVL equations. Hence, for this particular circuit, the mesh currents approach will be more efficient than the NTD voltages approach.

Example 5.10 (Apply the Lagrange Approach to the Circuit on Figure 5.8b)

There are two meshes in the circuit. Assume mesh 1 is on the left and mesh 2 is on the right. The electric charges traveling around mesh 1 and mesh 2 are q_1 and q_2, respectively, and their corresponding mesh currents are denoted by $\dot{q}_1$ and $\dot{q}_2$. Mesh 1 current direction is assigned to be in the clockwise direction to match the polarity of the voltage source. Mesh 2's current direction is also assumed to be in the clockwise direction.

The generalized coordinate and velocity vectors are $q = \begin{bmatrix} q_1 & q_2 \end{bmatrix}^T$ and $\dot{q} = \begin{bmatrix} \dot{q}_1 & \dot{q}_2 \end{bmatrix}^T$, respectively. The total kinetic energy stored in the two inductors L_1 and L_2 is $T = 0.5L_1\dot{q}_1^2 + 0.5L_2\dot{q}_2^2$. The total potential energy of the system is $U = 0.5(1/C_1)q_1^2 + 0.5(1/C_2)q_2^2$. Hence, the Lagrangian is

$$\mathscr{L} = T - U = 0.5L_1\dot{q}_1^2 + 0.5L_2\dot{q}_2^2 - 0.5(1/C_1)q_1^2 - 0.5(1/C_2)q_2^2 \tag{5.34}$$

The total virtual work done by the generalized forces, including the applied power sources and the internal ones to cause power dissipation, are

$$\delta W = e_s\delta q_1 - R(\dot{q}_1 - \dot{q}_2)(\delta q_1 - \delta q_2) \tag{5.35}$$

The differentials and the generalized force vector involved in the Lagrange equation can be found as

$$\frac{\partial \mathscr{L}}{\partial \dot{q}} = \begin{bmatrix} \partial \mathscr{L}/\partial \dot{q}_1 \\ \partial \mathscr{L}/\partial \dot{q}_2 \end{bmatrix} = \begin{bmatrix} L\dot{q}_1 \\ L\dot{q}_2 \end{bmatrix}, \quad \frac{\partial \mathscr{L}}{\partial q} = \begin{bmatrix} \partial \mathscr{L}/\partial q_1 \\ \partial \mathscr{L}/\partial q_2 \end{bmatrix} = \begin{bmatrix} -(1/C_1)q_1 \\ -(1/C_2)q_2 \end{bmatrix}$$

$$Q = \frac{\partial(\delta W)}{\partial(\delta q)} = \begin{bmatrix} \partial(\delta W)/\partial(\delta q_1) \\ \partial(\delta W)/\partial(\delta q_2) \end{bmatrix} = \begin{bmatrix} e_s - R(\dot{q}_1 - \dot{q}_2) \\ R(\dot{q}_1 - \dot{q}_2) \end{bmatrix}$$

(5.36)

Then **according to the Lagrange equation in Equation 5.21**, we have the following dynamics model for the electric circuit.

$$\begin{bmatrix} L_1\ddot{q}_1 + (1/C_1)q_1 \\ L_2\ddot{q}_2 + (1/C_2)q_2 \end{bmatrix} = \begin{bmatrix} e_s - R(\dot{q}_1 - \dot{q}_2) \\ R(\dot{q}_1 - \dot{q}_2) \end{bmatrix}$$

(5.37)

This equation can be rewritten in terms of the mesh currents i_1 and i_2 as follows,

$$\begin{bmatrix} L_1 di_1/dt + R(i_1 - i_2) + (1/C_1)\int i_1 dt \\ L_2 di_2/dt - R(i_1 - i_2) + (1/C_2)\int i_2 dt \end{bmatrix} = \begin{bmatrix} e_s \\ 0 \end{bmatrix}$$

(5.38)

∎

5.5 Circuit Modeling Using the State-Space Approach

Dynamic systems can be described by differential equations, transfer functions, or state-space representations. Due to the recent rapid advancement of computing tools and the state-space control systems theory, more and more sophisticated control systems are required to be analyzed and designed using state-space approaches, and therefore the state-space representation of systems has become increasingly important. Although a state-space representation can be obtained from differential equations or transfer functions, it is more favorable if a state-space representation can be directly constructed in the modeling process when the meaningful physical variables like displacements and velocities can be easily selected as state variables.

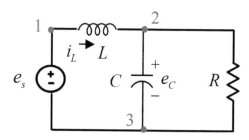

Fig. 5.9: Circuit modeling using the state-space approach.

For electrical systems, **the order of the system or the number of state variables in the system is determined by the number of energy-storing elements in the circuit.** As mentioned earlier, inductors store kinetic energy $T = 0.5Li_L^2$ in magnetic fields, and capacitors store potential energy $U = 0.5Ce_C^2$ in electric field. Hence, **it is natural to select the currents of inductors and the voltages of capacitors as state variables.** The circuit shown in Figure 5.9 has been employed several times to demonstrate the NTD voltages approach, the mesh currents approach, and the Lagrange approach. We will also use this circuit to demonstrate how to assemble state-space models for electrical systems by directly using the state-space modeling approach.

Example 5.11 (State-Space Modeling of the Circuit on Figure 5.9)

The circuit in Figure 5.9 has three nodes, marked as red dots with numbers 1, 2, and 3 for ease of reference. There is one inductor L between node 1 and node 2, a parallel combination of one capacitor C, and one resistor R connected between nodes 2 and 3, and finally one voltage source between nodes 1 and 3 with node 1 as the positive terminal. **The current i_L of the inductor L and the voltage e_C of the capacitor C are chosen as the two state variables of the system.** To construct the state equations associated with the inductor current i_L, Kirchhoff's voltage law is employed to obtain a KVL equation around the loop 1-2-3-1, consisting of the inductor L. According to Kirchhoff's voltage law, the algebraic sum of the voltage drops around the loop 1-2-3-1 is zero. That means the voltage drop from node 1 to node 2, $L di_L/dt$, should be equal to the algebraic sum of the voltage drops along the other path 1-3-2, which is $e_s - e_C$. Hence, we have **the KVL equation** in the following,

$$L\frac{di_L(t)}{dt} = -e_C(t) + e_s(t)$$

Meanwhile, Kirchhoff's current law is applied to give a KCL equation at node 2, which is connected to the capacitor C. According to Kirchhoff's current law, the algebraic sum of the currents of all the three branches leaving node 2 is zero. That means the current leaving node 2 via capacitor C, $C de_C/dt$, should be equal to the algebraic sum of the currents entering node 2 via the inductor L and via the resistor R, which is $i_L + (-e_C)/R$. Hence, we have **the KCL equation** in the following:

$$C\frac{de_C(t)}{dt} = i_L(t) - \frac{1}{R}e_C(t)$$

These KVL and KCL equations can be rewritten as follows in the standard matrix form of state equation,

$$\begin{bmatrix} di_L/dt \\ de_C/dt \end{bmatrix} = \begin{bmatrix} 0 & -1/L \\ 1/C & -1/(RC) \end{bmatrix} \begin{bmatrix} i_L \\ e_C \end{bmatrix} + \begin{bmatrix} 1/L \\ 0 \end{bmatrix} e_s \qquad (5.39)$$

In general, the state-space representation or state-space model of a system is described by

$$\dot{x}(t) = Ax(t) + Bu(t)$$
$$y(t) = Cx(t) + Du(t) \qquad (5.40)$$

where the first equation is called the state equation, and the second is the output equation. The vectors $x(t)$ and $u(t)$ are the state vector and the input vector of the system, respectively, and $y(t)$ is the output vector consisting of the variables of interest. For the circuit example considered above, the state vector, input vector, the A and B matrices are

$$x(t) = \begin{bmatrix} i_L(t) \\ e_C(t) \end{bmatrix}, \quad u(t) = e_s(t), \quad A = \begin{bmatrix} 0 & -1/L \\ 1/C & -1/(RC) \end{bmatrix}, \quad B = \begin{bmatrix} 1/L \\ 0 \end{bmatrix} \qquad (5.41)$$

If $e_C(t)$ is the variable of interest (i.e., $y(t) = e_C(t)$) then the C and D matrices in the state-space model will be $C = \begin{bmatrix} 0 & 1 \end{bmatrix}$ and $D = 0$. The state-space model described in Equation 5.40 in many cases is referred as (A, B, C, D) for convenience. ∎

In the following, we will work on two more circuit modeling examples using the state-space modeling approach.

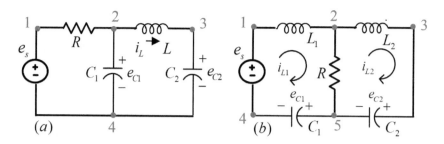

Fig. 5.10: More state-space modeling approach examples.

Example 5.12 (State-Space Modeling of the Circuit on Figure 5.10a)

The circuit in Figure 5.10(a) has four nodes, marked as red dots with numbers 1, 2, 3, and 4 for ease of reference. There is one inductor L between node 2 and node 3, and two capacitors with C_1 between node 2 and node 4, and C_2 between node 3 and node 4. There also exists one resistor R connected between nodes 1 and 2, and one voltage source between nodes 1 and 4 with node 1 as the positive terminal.

The current i_L of the inductor L and the voltages e_{C1} and e_{C2} of the capacitor C_1 and C_2, respectively, are chosen as the three state variables of the system. To construct the state equations associated with the inductor current i_L, Kirchhoff's Voltage law is employed to obtain a KVL equation around the loop 2-3-4-2, consisting of the inductor L, the capacitor C_2, and another capacitor C_1. According to Kirchhoff's Voltage law, the algebraic sum of the voltage drops around the loop 2-3-4-2 is zero. That means the voltage drop from node 2 to node 3, $L di_L/dt$, should be equal to the algebraic sum of the voltage drops along the other path 2-4-3, which is $e_{C1} - e_{C2}$. Hence, we have **the KVL equation** in the following:

$$L\frac{di_L(t)}{dt} = e_{C1}(t) - e_{C2}(t)$$

Meanwhile, Kirchhoff's current law is applied to give two KCL equations: one at node 2, which connects to C_1, and another at node 3, which is connected to the capacitor C_2. According to Kirchhoff's current law, the algebraic sum of the currents of all the three branches leaving node 2 is zero. That means the current leaving node 2 via capacitor C_1, $C_1 de_{C1}/dt$, should be equal to the algebraic sum of the currents entering node 2 via the inductor L and via the resistor R, which is $-i_L + (e_s - e_{C1})/R$. Hence, we have **the KCL equation** in the following:

$$C_1\frac{de_{C1}(t)}{dt} = -i_L(t) + \frac{e_s(t) - e_{C1}(t)}{R}$$

Similarly, the algebraic sum of the currents of all the two branches leaving node 3 is zero. That means the current leaving node 3 via capacitor C_2, $C_2 de_{C2}/dt$, should be equal to the current entering node 3 via the inductor L, which is simply i_L. Hence, we have **the KCL equation** in the following:

$$C_2\frac{de_{C2}(t)}{dt} = i_L(t)$$

The one KVL equation and two KCL equations can now be combined into one state equation in matrix form:

$$\begin{bmatrix} di_L/dt \\ de_{C1}/dt \\ de_{C2}/dt \end{bmatrix} = \begin{bmatrix} 0 & 1/L & -1/L \\ -1/C_1 & -1/(RC_1) & 0 \\ 1/C_2 & 0 & 0 \end{bmatrix} \begin{bmatrix} i_L \\ e_{C1} \\ e_{C2} \end{bmatrix} + \begin{bmatrix} 0 \\ 1/(RC_1) \\ 0 \end{bmatrix} e_s \qquad (5.42)$$

■

The next circuit to be considered is shown in Figure 5.10(b), which consists of five nodes, two meshes, one voltage source, one resistor, two inductors, and two capacitors.

Example 5.13 (State-Space Modeling of the Circuit on Figure 5.10(b))

The circuit in Figure 5.10(b) has five nodes, marked as red dots with numbers 1, 2, 3, 4, and 5 for ease of reference. There are two inductors with L_1 between node 1 and node 2, and L_2 between node 2 and node 3. At the bottom of the diagram, there are two capacitors with C_1 between node 4 and node 5, and C_2 between node 5 and node 3. There also exist one resistor R connected between nodes 2 and 5, and one voltage source between nodes 1 and 4 with node 1 as the positive terminal.

The two currents i_{L1} and i_{L2} of the inductors L_1 and L_2, respectively, and the two voltages e_{C1} and e_{C2} of the capacitor C_1 and C_2, respectively, are chosen as the four state variables of the system. To construct the state equation associated with the inductor current i_{L1}, Kirchhoff's voltage law is employed to obtain a KVL equation around the loop 1-2-5-4-1, consisting of the inductor L_1, the resistor R, the capacitor C_1, and the voltage source e_s. According to Kirchhoff's voltage law, the algebraic sum of the voltage drops around the loop 1-2-5-4-1 is zero. That means the voltage drop from node 1 to node 2, $L_1 di_{L1}/dt$, should be equal to the algebraic sum of the voltage drops along the other path 1-4-5-2, which is $e_s - e_{C1} + (i_{L2} - i_{L1})R$. Hence, we have **the first KVL equation** in the following:

$$L_1 \frac{di_{L1}(t)}{dt} = -Ri_{L1}(t) + Ri_{L2}(t) - e_{C1}(t) + e_s(t)$$

To construct the state equation associated with the inductor current i_{L2}, Kirchhoff's voltage law is employed to obtain a KVL equation around the loop 2-3-5-2, consisting of the inductor L_2, the capacitor C_2, and the resistor R. According to Kirchhoff's voltage law, the algebraic sum of the voltage drops around the loop 2-3-5-2 is zero. That means the voltage drop from node 2 to node 3, $L_2 di_{L2}/dt$, should be equal to the algebraic sum of the voltage drops along the other path 2-5-3, which is $R(i_{L1} - i_{L2}) - e_{C2}$. Hence, we have **the second KVL equation** in the following:

$$L_2 \frac{di_{L2}(t)}{dt} = Ri_{L1}(t) - Ri_{L2}(t) - e_{C2}(t)$$

Meanwhile, Kirchhoff's current law is applied to give two KCL equations: one at node 4, which connects to C_1, and another at node 3, which is connected to the capacitor C_2. According to Kirchhoff's current law, the current entering node 4 via capacitor C_1, $C_1 de_{C1}/dt$, should be equal to the current leaving node 4 for the voltage source e_s, which is i_{L1}. Similarly, the current flowing through the capacitor C_2, $C_2 de_{C2}/dt$, should be equal to the current through L_2, which is i_{L2}. Hence, we have **the two KCL equations** in the following:

$$C_1 \frac{de_{C1}(t)}{dt} = i_{L1}(t), \quad C_2 \frac{de_{C2}(t)}{dt} = i_{L2}(t)$$

The two KVL and two KCL equations can now be combined into one state equation in matrix form:

$$\begin{bmatrix} di_{L1}/dt \\ di_{L2}/dt \\ de_{C1}/dt \\ de_{C2}/dt \end{bmatrix} = \begin{bmatrix} -R/L_1 & R/L_1 & -1/L_1 & 0 \\ R/L_2 & -R/L_2 & 0 & 1/L_1 \\ 1/C_1 & 0 & 0 & 0 \\ 0 & 1/C_2 & 0 & 0 \end{bmatrix} \begin{bmatrix} i_{L1} \\ i_{L2} \\ e_{C1} \\ e_{C2} \end{bmatrix} + \begin{bmatrix} 1/L_1 \\ 0 \\ 0 \\ 0 \end{bmatrix} e_s \qquad (5.43)$$

∎

Remark 5.14 (Significance of the State-Space Model)

As mentioned early in the beginning of this section, the state-space representation of systems has become increasingly important due to the recent rapid advancement of computing tools and the state-space control systems theory. Although we have not yet officially introduced the fundamental theory regarding the state-space concept, state equation solutions, and state-space control system analysis and design, we did start to employ the state-space models to conduct stability analysis, stabilizing controller design, and computer simulations for the simple inverted pendulum system in the previous chapter, Chapter 4. **It is clear that the state-space model control system analysis and design is important and will be one of the main emphases of the book.**   ∎

5.6 Operational Amplifier Circuits

The operational amplifier, usually called op amp, is an almost ideal electronic amplifier due to its large voltage gain, high input impedance, and low output impedance. These properties are significant in two aspects. First, it virtually has **no loading effect**, which makes the op amp circuit a perfect building block in an interconnected system. The op amp circuit will preserve its performance in any normally operating interconnected system. Secondly, these three properties are the foundation that lead to the development of the *virtual short concept* approach for the op amp circuit analysis and design.

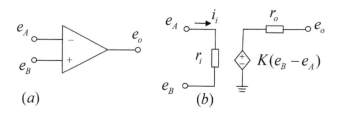

Fig. 5.11: Equivalent circuit of the op amp.

The virtual-short concept approach has made it possible to greatly simplify the analysis and design of op amp circuits, which otherwise would be extremely complicated. Due to these two reasons, the op amp has become one of the most versatile and widely used electronic devices. **The op amp circuits can perform a variety of functions** like signal addition, substraction, integration, detection, amplification, filtering, binary–to–decimal conversion, decimal–to–binary conversion, and common-mode disturbance cancelation, and so on.

The symbol of the op amp in Figure 5.11 shows that **the op amp has two inputs, e_A and e_B, and one output, e_o.** Note that the common reference terminal and the DC power supply do not show on the symbol. The real circuit inside the op amp chip consists of numerous transistors and other components; however, it is not a concern for users. A much simpler *equivalent circuit* is shown on the right-hand side of the figure. The op amp is basically a four-terminal device. One terminal is the common reference, or the ground. The voltages at the input terminals A and B are represented by e_A and e_B, respectively. **The input impedance between the two input terminals is r_i, and the positive input current i_i direction is assumed flowing into terminal A. The output terminal is marked with e_o as the output voltage** at the terminal with respect to the ground. Between the output terminal and the ground there is a series combination of a dependent voltage source, $K(e_B - e_A)$, and the output resistor, r_o, where K is the voltage gain.

If we follow the traditional circuit analysis and design approach, we would use the equivalent circuit in Figure 5.11 as a model of the op amp and set up KVL and KCL equations using the NTD voltages, mesh currents, or the state-space modeling approaches. The equations would be complicated even for a simple circuit, but they can be greatly simplified by letting $K \to \infty$, $r_i \to \infty$, and $r_o \to 0$. **The virtual short concept approach also utilizes the approximations, but the difference is that it will carry out approximations before the equations are set up.**

Now, from the equivalent circuit in Figure 5.11, with the accompanied approximations, $K \to \infty$, $r_i \to \infty$, and $r_o \to 0$, we will see the following intriguing properties of the op amp.

Theorem 5.15 (Virtual Short Concept)

From the equivalent circuit in Figure 5.11, it is easy to deduct the following statement:

$$If \quad r_i \cong \infty, \quad r_o \cong 0, \quad K \cong \infty, \quad then \quad i_i \cong 0 \quad and \quad e_A \cong e_B \tag{5.44}$$

If the input impedance r_i is virtually infinity, then the current flowing through r_i is virtually zero, which means the circuit between the two input terminals A and B is virtually open circuit. Meanwhile, on the right side of the equivalent circuit, the output impedance r_o is virtually zero; hence, the output voltage e_o will be virtually equal to $K(e_B - e_A)$. Since the voltage gain K is virtually infinity and the output voltage e_o is finite at the same time, the only possibility is that $(e_B - e_A)$ has to be virtually zero. That is, the circuit between the two input terminals A and B is virtually short circuit. Therefore, the circuit between the two input terminals A and B is virtually open circuit and short circuit at the same time! ∎

The virtual short concept seems to be a paradox because it is impossible for a circuit to be open circuit and short circuit at the same time. However, it is true that the circuit between the two input terminals A and B of the op amp is virtually open circuit and virtually short circuit at the same time.

Remark 5.16 (A Subtle but Big Difference Between Short Circuit and Virtual Short Circuit)

It is easy to get confused with these two terms, virtual short circuit and short circuit. Short circuit means that the voltages of the two terminals A and B are equal and at the same time **the resistance between these two terminals is zero.** On the other hand, virtual short circuit simply means that the electric potentials, or the voltages, e_A and e_B, are virtually identical, but **the resistance between terminals A and B is virtually infinite. The difference is big, although it seems subtle.** ∎

In this section, we will employ a few op amp circuits to demonstrate how to utilize the virtual short concept to assemble equations for modeling op amp circuits. The first example is the general inverting amplifier circuit shown in Figure 5.12.

Example 5.17 (Virtual Short Concept Approach for the Inverting Amplifier Circuit)

The op amp circuit in Figure 5.12 is a general inverting amplifier, where the two impedances blocks $Z_1(s)$ and $Z_2(s)$ can be any combination of capacitors, inductors, and resistors. Owing to the virtual short concept, **the current i_A flowing into terminal A of the op amp is virtually zero**; hence, according to Kirchhoff's current law, the algebraic sum of the two currents flowing into terminal A should be zero. Hence

$$I_1(s) + I_2(s) = 0 \tag{5.45}$$

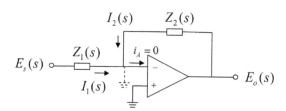

Fig. 5.12: General op amp inverting amplifier.

Based on the virtual short concept again, **the two voltages e_A and e_B are virtually identical, which means terminal A is virtually connected to the ground as shown in the figure by a dotted ground sign.** Hence, the current I_2 is E_o/Z_2 according to the generalized Ohm's law. Similarly, $I_1 = E_s/Z_1$. Therefore, we have the following transfer function of the circuit:

$$\frac{E_s(s)}{Z_1(s)} + \frac{E_o(s)}{Z_2(s)} = 0 \quad \rightarrow \quad \frac{E_o(s)}{E_s(s)} = \frac{-Z_2(s)}{Z_1(s)} \tag{5.46}$$

■

We have just experienced the effectiveness of the virtual short concept approach and were surprised by **how ridiculously simple the problem had become.** It seems that we had done something unlawful to connect terminal A to the ground and ignored the existence of the op amp. Of course, **the virtual short concept has been proved and the procedure is legitimate.** To be more sure about this, we can employ another approach to the same circuit problem to double check the result. In the next example, we will employ the traditional equivalent circuit approach to assemble the equations and obtain the transfer function for the same circuit of Figure 5.12.

Example 5.18 (**Traditional Approach for the Inverting Amplifier Circuit**)

After replacing the op amp in the inverting amplifier circuit of Figure 5.12 by its equivalent circuit shown on the right-hand side of Figure 5.11, we have the circuit diagram shown in Figure 5.13. We will **set up the equations without applying approximations until the last step.**

The circuit shown in Figure 5.13 has three meshes. If the mesh current approach were selected to assemble the equations for the circuit, we would have to set up three KVL mesh equations to solve for three mesh current variables. On the other hand, the circuit has five nodes: (1) The one at the bottom of the diagram is selected as the ground reference; (2) Two are the positive terminals of the input voltage source E_s and the dependent voltage source $K(e_B - e_A)$; and (3) There are **only two NTD voltage variables needed to be assigned, and only two KCL NTD equations are required to solve for these two unknown voltage variables.** These two NTD voltages are E_o, the output, and E_A, the voltage at terminal A.

Applying Kirchhoff's current law at terminal A will yield the following KCL equation:

$$\frac{E_s - E_A}{Z_1} + \frac{E_o - E_A}{Z_2} = \frac{E_A}{r_i}$$

Similarly, at the output terminal O we have **another KCL equation** as

$$\frac{E_o - E_A}{Z_2} + \frac{E_o - K(0 - E_A)}{r_o} = 0$$

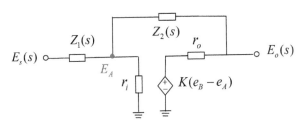

Fig. 5.13: Equivalent circuit of the general op amp inverting amplifier.

Note that the terminal B is connected to the ground; hence, E_B has been replaced by zero in the equation. After eliminating E_A, the two equations will reduce to the following:

$$\frac{E_s}{Z_1} + \frac{E_o}{Z_2} = \left(\frac{1}{Z_1} + \frac{1}{Z_2} + \frac{1}{r_i}\right)\left(\frac{r_o + Z_2}{r_o - KZ_2}\right)E_o$$

Now, apply approximations letting $K \to \infty$, $r_i \to \infty$, **and** $r_o \to 0$. Then we have

$$\frac{E_s(s)}{Z_1(s)} + \frac{E_o(s)}{Z_2(s)} = 0 \quad \to \quad \frac{E_o(s)}{E_s(s)} = \frac{-Z_2(s)}{Z_1(s)} \qquad (5.47)$$

As expected, the result matches the one obtained using the virtual short concept approach. The only difference is that the traditional approach is more tedious and complicated. ∎

Example 5.19 (Inverting Amplifier and Integrator Circuits)

As mentioned earlier, the Z_2 and Z_1 impedance blocks of the general inverting amplifier circuit shown in Figure 5.12 can be any combination of resistors, capacitors, and inductors. If the impedances blocks are chosen to be $Z_2 = R_2$ and $Z_1 = R_1$, then the output voltage will be equal to

$$E_o(s) = \frac{-R_2}{R_1}E_s(s) \quad \to \quad e_o(t) = \frac{-R_2}{R_1}e_s(t) \qquad (5.48)$$

The circuit can serve as a voltage amplifier if R_2 is chosen to be larger than R_1.

If the impedances blocks are chosen to be $Z_2 = 1/(sC)$ **and** $Z_1 = R$, then the input-output voltage relationship will be

$$E_o(s) = \frac{-(1/sC)}{R}E_s(s) = \frac{-1}{sRC}E_s(s) \quad \to \quad e_o(t) = \frac{-1}{RC}\int e_s(t)dt \qquad (5.49)$$

It is clear that the circuit performs integration. ∎

The general inverting amplifier circuit can also be employed to implement a PID analog controller.

Example 5.20 (PID Analog Controller Circuits)

In Figure 5.12, assume the impedance block Z_2 **is a series combination of a resistor** R_2 **and a capacitor** C_2. Meanwhile, Z_1 **is a parallel combination of a resistor** R_1 **and a capacitor** C_1. Thus, we have the impedances Z_2 and Z_1 as follows:

$$Z_2 = R_2 + \frac{1}{sC_2} = \frac{R_2 C_2 s + 1}{sC_2} \quad \text{and} \quad \frac{1}{Z_1} = \frac{1}{R_1} + sC_1 = \frac{R_1 C_1 s + 1}{R_1}$$

Then combine the two equations together with Equation 5.46 and we have

$$\frac{E_o}{E_s} = \frac{-Z_2}{Z_1} = -\left(\frac{R_1 C_1 + R_2 C_2}{R_1 C_2} + \frac{1}{R_1 C_2 s} + R_2 C_1 s \right) := -\left(K_P + K_I \frac{1}{s} + K_D s \right) \tag{5.50}$$

That is,

$$e_o(t) = -\left(K_P e_s(t) + K_I \int e_s(t) dt + K_D \frac{de_s(t)}{dt} \right)$$

Therefore, the circuit can be employed to implement the function of proportional, integral, and derivative control. ∎

Note that for those circuits constructed using the inverting amplifier structure, there always is a sign change, which may not be favorable. This issue can be fixed by cascading the circuit by another inverting amplifier with unit gain. It is also possible to design a noninverting amplifier based on the op amp circuit configuration shown in Figure 5.14.

Example 5.21 (General Non-Inverting Amplifier Circuit)

The op amp circuit in Figure 5.14 is a general noninverting amplifier, where the two impedances blocks $Z_1(s)$ and $Z_2(s)$ can be any combination of capacitors, inductors, and resistors.

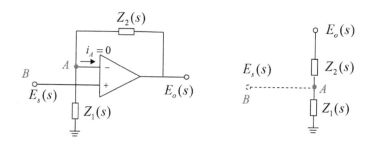

Fig. 5.14: General op amp noninverting amplifier.

Owing to the virtual short concept, the current i_A flowing into terminal A of the op amp is virtually zero; hence, according to Kirchhoff's current law, **the current flowing into terminal** A **via** Z_2 **should be the same as the current leaving terminal** A **via** Z_1 **into the ground.** Meanwhile, the virtual short concept implies that **the voltage at terminal** A **is virtually equal to** E_s, **which is connecting to the terminal** B. Thus, we have

$$\frac{E_o - E_s}{Z_2} = \frac{E_s}{Z_1} \quad \rightarrow \quad \frac{E_o}{Z_2} = \frac{E_s}{Z_1} + \frac{E_s}{Z_2} = \frac{Z_1 + Z_2}{Z_1 Z_2} E_s$$

and the transfer function from $E_s(s)$ to $E_o(s)$ is

$$\frac{E_o(s)}{E_s(s)} = \left(1 + \frac{Z_2(s)}{Z_1(s)}\right) \tag{5.51}$$

■

The next op amp circuit to be considered is a summing amplifier, which can perform the addition and substraction of signals.

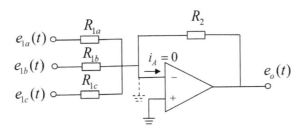

Fig. 5.15: Op amp summing amplifier.

Example 5.22 (Summing Amplifier Circuit)

Consider the op amp summing amplifier circuit in Figure 5.15. The terminal A of the op amp is connected to four resistors, R_2, R_{1a}, R_{1b}, and R_{1c}. In addition, it is also virtually connected to the ground according to the virtual short concept condition. Since the current flowing into the terminal A of the op amp is virtually zero, **the algebraic sum of the four currents from the four resistors entering into the terminal A node (the ground) is zero** according to Kirchhoff's current law.

$$\frac{e_o}{R_2} + \frac{e_{1a}}{R_{1a}} + \frac{e_{1b}}{R_{1b}} + \frac{e_{1c}}{R_{1c}} = 0$$

Therefore, **the output $e_o(t)$ is the algebraic sum of the three incoming weighted signals,**

$$e_o(t) = -R_2 \left(\frac{e_{1a}(t)}{R_{1a}} + \frac{e_{1b}(t)}{R_{1b}} + \frac{e_{1c}(t)}{R_{1c}}\right) \tag{5.52}$$

■

The following op amp circuit is a differential amplifier, which can be employed to eliminate the common-mode disturbances during signal transmission. There are two input signals, but only the difference of the two signals will affect the output.

Example 5.23 (Differential Amplifier Circuit)

Consider the op amp differential amplifier circuit in Figure 5.16. On the upper half of the circuit diagram, the terminal A of the op amp is connected to the first input e_1 and the output e_o via resistors R_1 and R_2, respectively. On the bottom half of the circuit diagram, the terminal B of the op amp is

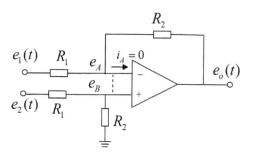

Fig. 5.16: Op amp differential amplifier.

connected to the second input e_2 and the ground via another set of resistors R_1 and R_2, respectively. According to the virtual short concept, the current flowing into terminal A or out of terminal B of the op amp is virtually zero. Hence, **the algebraic sum of the two currents from e_1 and from e_o entering the terminal A node is zero,**

$$\frac{e_1 - e_A}{R_1} + \frac{e_o - e_A}{R_2} = 0 \quad \rightarrow \quad \frac{e_1}{R_1} - \left(\frac{1}{R_1} + \frac{1}{R_2}\right) e_A + \frac{e_o}{R_2} = 0$$

Similarly, the algebraic sum of the two currents from e_2 and from the ground entering the terminal B node is zero,

$$\frac{e_2 - e_B}{R_1} + \frac{-e_B}{R_2} = 0 \quad \rightarrow \quad \frac{e_2}{R_1} - \left(\frac{1}{R_1} + \frac{1}{R_2}\right) e_B = 0$$

From the two equations and the fact that **the two voltages e_A and e_B are virtually equal, we have the following differential amplifier input-output relationship:**

$$e_o(t) = \frac{R_2}{R_1} \left(e_2(t) - e_1(t)\right) \tag{5.53}$$

∎

5.7 DC Motor

Recall that in Figure 2.1, the DC motor system was considered as one of the three typical first-order dynamic system examples. Some students might have been wondering how it can be possible since the DC motor seems to be a complicated system, consisting of an electric circuit and a rotational mechanical system. Indeed, the internal structure and the detailed theory explaining how it works may be a little bit complicated, but **in most of the applications the relationship between the angular velocity and the input control voltage can be described by a first-order differential equation.**

A schematic diagram of a DC motor system is shown in Figure 5.17. On the right-hand side of the diagram is a rotational mechanical system including the gear train and the load that consists of the moment of inertia J_ℓ and the rotational damper B_ℓ. On the left-hand side of the diagram is the **DC motor, whose dynamic behavior will be determined by a circuit equation involving e_a, L_a, R_a, and e_b, and a mechanical equation of motion involving τ_m, J_m, and B_m.** Before we start to assemble the equations, we will digress a little bit to refresh our memory on some relevant fundamental electromagnetism we learned from high school physics courses.

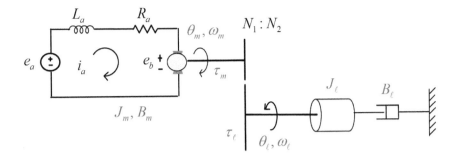

Fig. 5.17: DC motor system.

5.7.1 Ampere's Force Law and Faraday's Law of Induction

The first relevant electromagnetism law is **Ampere's force law regarding the interaction between two electric wires with currents.** Should this sound familiar with the name *Ampere*? Yes, it is the unit of electric current named after Andre-Marie Ampere, one of the greatest pioneers in electromagnetism. Ampere's force law was discovered in 1825, which revealed that the two parallel electric wires would experience forces after being energized with electric currents. The forces would either attract the two wires to each other or do the opposite, expel each other, depending on the relative current directions. It was a great discovery that manifested the possibility of converting electrical energy into mechanical energy.

The DC motor is equipped with two wound-up electric coils. The first coil is called the field coil that is fixed in the structure and is driven by a constant current I_f to generate a constant magnetic flux $\Phi_f = k_f I_f$. The second coil, called the armature coil, is wound around the motor rotor, which is designed to be able to rotate inside the magnetic field provided by Φ_f. The rotor will rotate when the armature coil is energized. **The rotor torque is proportional to both the magnetic flux Φ_f and the armature current $i_a(t)$,**

$$\tau_m(t) = c_1 \Phi_f i_a(t) := K_m i_a(t) \quad \rightleftarrows \quad T_m(s) = K_m I_a(s) \tag{5.54}$$

where $T_m(s)$ and $I_a(s)$ are the Laplace transforms of $\tau_m(t)$ and $i_a(t)$, respectively. This constant K_m is called the *torque constant*, which usually is available on the data sheet of the DC motor.

The second relevant electromagnetism law we need to review is **Michael Faraday's law of electromagnetic induction, which in the year of 1831 revealed how the variation of magnetic flux will produce an electromotive force (EMF).** This discovery is as significant as Ampere's force law, if not greater. The law of induction is the underlying principle of the AC electric generators that convert mechanical power like steam, hydraulic, or even nuclear power into electric power. **In addition, many other important inventions like the AC voltage transformers, the AC electric power transmissions, the inductors, the induction motors, the solenoids, and radio wireless communications, would not be possible without the knowledge of electromagnetic induction.**

Now, back to the DC motor schematic diagram in Figure 5.17, there is a back EMF (electromotive force) voltage e_b developed across the two terminals of the DC motor. This back EMF is caused by the variation of the magnetic flux the armature coil has received. Although the field magnetic flux Φ_f is constant, **the magnetic flux received by the armature coil is a function of time** since the motor rotor is moving. The back EMF voltage e_b is proportional to Φ_f and the angular velocity of the rotor, $\omega_m(t)$,

$$e_b(t) = c_2 \Phi_f \omega_m(t) := K_b \omega_m(t) \quad \rightleftarrows \quad E_b(s) = K_b \Omega_m(s) \tag{5.55}$$

where $E_b(s)$ and $\Omega_m(s)$ are the Laplace transforms of $e_b(t)$ and $\omega_m(t)$, respectively. This constant K_b is called the *back EMF constant*, which is usually available on the data sheet of the DC motor.

5.7.2 Assembling Equations for the DC Motor System

In the schematic diagram of the motor system in Figure 5.17, there is an electric circuit loop on the left-hand side of the diagram. This loop includes the control-input voltage source $e_a(t)$, the inductor L_a, the resistor R_a, and the back EMF voltage $e_b(t)$. Applying Kirchhoff's voltage law, we have the following KVL equation:

$$L_a \frac{di_a(t)}{dt} + R_a i_a(t) + e_b(t) = e_a(t)$$

Taking Laplace transform, this equation becomes

$$sL_a I_a(s) + R_a I_a(s) + E_b(s) = E_a(s) \tag{5.56}$$

Now, on the right-hand side of the diagram in Figure 5.17, we can see that the torque generated by the DC motor is employed to drive a rotational mechanical system via the gear train. Based on the discussion of gear train in Section 4.3, we have the equivalent moment of inertia J_e and the equivalent rotational friction coefficient B_e from the perspective of τ_m as follows:

$$J_e = J_m + \left(\frac{N_1}{N_2}\right)^2 J_\ell, \quad B_e = B_m + \left(\frac{N_1}{N_2}\right)^2 B_\ell \tag{5.57}$$

Then the equation for the rotational motion is given by

$$(J_e s + B_e)\Omega_m(s) = T_m(s) \tag{5.58}$$

where $\Omega_m(s)$ and $T_m(s)$ are the Laplace transforms of $\omega_m(t)$ and $\tau_m(t)$, respectively.

The electrical circuit equation, Equation 5.56, and the mechanical rotational motion equation, Equation 5.58, are coupled to each other via the torque equation, Equation 5.54 and the back EMF equation, Equation 5.55. These four equations are combined to yield the following:

$$sL_a I_a(s) + R_a I_a(s) + K_b \Omega_m(s) = E_a(s)$$
$$(J_e s + B_e)\Omega_m(s) = K_m I_a(s) \tag{5.59}$$

In many applications, the impedance of the inductor sL_a is negligible since it is very small compared to the impedance of the resistor, R; hence, the first equation of Equation 5.59 can be rewritten as

$$I_a(s) = \frac{E_a(s) - K_b \Omega_m(s)}{R_a} \tag{5.60}$$

Substitute this expression for $I_a(s)$ in the second equation of Equation 5.59 to yield the following transfer function between the control-input voltage source $E_a(s)$ and the angular velocity of the DC motor system, $\Omega_m(s)$.

$$\frac{\Omega_m(s)}{E_a(s)} = \frac{K_m}{R_a J_e s + B_e R_a + K_m K_b} = \frac{b}{s+a} = \frac{\omega_{ss}}{\tau s + 1} \tag{5.61}$$

where the parameters a, b, time constant τ, and the steady-state step response ω_{ss}, are given as follows:

$$a = \frac{B_e R_a + K_m K_b}{R_a J_e} = \frac{B_e}{J_e} + \frac{K_m K_b}{R_a J_e}, \quad b = \frac{K_m}{R_a J_e}, \quad \tau = \frac{1}{a}, \quad \omega_{ss} = \frac{b}{a} \tag{5.62}$$

5.7.3 Torque-Speed Relationship

Some DC motor manufactures may include the torque-speed relationships or graphs on the data sheet of the DC motor. The torque-speed graph will look like the one shown in Figure 5.18.

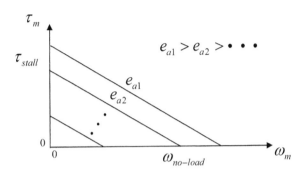

Fig. 5.18: Torque-angular velocity graph for the DC motor.

From the torque equation, Equation 5.54, we have $I_a(s) = T_m(s)/K_m$. Substituting it into Equation 5.60 will yield the following *torque-speed equation*:

$$T_m(s) + \frac{K_m K_b}{R_a} \Omega_m(s) = \frac{K_m}{R_a} E_a(s) \quad \rightleftarrows \quad \tau_m(t) + \frac{K_m K_b}{R_a} \omega_m(t) = \frac{K_m}{R_a} e_a(t) \tag{5.63}$$

At the steady state with a constant voltage input, we have the following algebraic relationship among the torque τ_m, angular velocity ω_m, and the input voltage e_a:

$$\tau_m = \frac{-K_m K_b}{R_a} \omega_m + \frac{K_m}{R_a} e_a \tag{5.64}$$

When $\omega_m = 0$, we have

$$\tau_{stall} = \frac{K_m}{R_a} e_a \quad \rightarrow \quad \frac{K_m}{R_a} = \frac{\tau_{stall}}{e_a} \tag{5.65}$$

On the other hand, when $\tau_m = 0$, we have

$$\omega_{no-load} = \frac{1}{K_b} e_a \quad \rightarrow \quad K_b = \frac{e_a}{\omega_{no-load}} \tag{5.66}$$

From the torque-speed relationship, we can compute the parameters K_m/R_a and K_b required in Equations 5.61 and 5.62.

5.7.4 A DC Micromotor Example

The DC micromotor to be considered is a Faulhaber 2230.012S micromotor with 1:14 gear head. First, we will read the data sheet and associate the data sheet values with the DC motor model equations shown in Equations 5.61 and 5.62. A partial data sheet with values of the micromotor is given in Figure 5.19. The data values shown here are fundamentally identical to those on the manufacturer's data sheet. We only slightly revise the no-load speed from 9,500 rpm to 9,550 rpm and the stall torque from 13.2 mNm to 13.3 mNm in order to exactly match the values of the torque constant K_m and the back EMF constant K_b. The small discrepancies among the data sheet values most likely were caused by rounding errors.

The manufacturer's data sheet only shows rpm (revolutions per minute) as the unit for rotational speed. The unit rpm is more intuitive for humans than the rad/s unit. However, in dynamics system analysis, design, and computation, we have to use the unit rad/s to avoid unit inconsistencies and errors. In Remark 4.16, we had a brief discussion on a similar issue regarding degrees and radians. On many occasions, we have no choice but to use both units, one for display to humans and another for computation in machine. Hence, in Figure 5.19, we showed both units, rpm and rad/s, for the angular velocity ω.

Nominal voltage	e_a	12 V
Armature resistance	R_a	10.8 Ohms
No-load speed	$\omega_{no-load}$	9550 rpm or 1000 rad/s
Stall torque	τ_{stall}	13.3 mNm
Back EMF constant	K_b	1.25 mV/rpm or 12 mV/rad/s
Torque constant	K_m	12 mNm/A
Rotor inductance	L_a	420 μH
Rotor inertia	J_m	2.7 gcm^2 or 2.7×10^{-7} kgm^2
Maximum speed	ω_{max}	11000 rpm or 1152 rad/s

Fig. 5.19: Partial data sheet values of Faulhaber micromotor 2230.012S.

In the analysis, computation, and design, we will use, for the following data values of $\omega_{no-load}$ and ω_{max} in rad/s, and K_b in mV/rad/s:

$$\omega_{no-load} = 1,000 \text{ rad/s}, \quad \omega_{max} = 1,152 \text{ rad/s}, \quad \text{and} \quad K_b = 12 \text{ mV/rad/s}$$

instead of those in rpm or in mV/rpm on the manufacturer's data sheet:

$$\omega_{no-load} = 9,550 \text{ rpm}, \quad \omega_{max} = 11,000 \text{ rpm}, \quad \text{and} \quad K_b = 1.25 \text{ mV/rpm}$$

The back EMF constant K_b was 1.25 in old mV/rpm unit, and now K_b equals to 12 in the new mV/rad/s unit. Note that now the back EMF constant, $K_b = 12$ mV/rad/s, and the torque constant, $K_m = 12$ mNm/A have the same value, 12. It is not a coincidence. There is a significant physical meaning behind the equivalency of these two constants. $K_b = K_m$ means that the electric power $e_b i_a$ into the DC motor equals to the mechanical power $\tau_m \omega_m$ out of the DC motor. That means the power transfer is lossless. In most cases, the loss of this electric power to mechanical power conversion is negligible. Therefore, these two constants should be very close, if not equal. If the units used were not consistent, the equivalency of these two constants would not be revealed.

The inductance of the armature inductor, $L_a = 430$ μH, and the rotation frequency of the rotor is less than $\omega_{max} = 1,152$ rad/s; hence, the magnitude of the impedance of the inductor will be less than $|j\omega_{max}L_a| = 0.495$ Ω, which is negligible compared to the armature resistance $R_a = 10.8$ Ω. This verifies the underlying assumption in the previous subsection that the impedance of the inductor sL_a is negligible.

The manufacturer's data sheet not only provides the values of torque constant K_m, the back EMF constant K_b, and the armature resistance R_a, but also gives the information of the no-load speed $\omega_{no-load}$ and stall torque τ_{stall} shown in Figure 5.20. We will verify that all these data values are consistent. As it can be seen from the graph, when the input voltage is kept at 12 V, the relationship between the torque τ_m and the angular velocity ω_m is described by the straight line connecting these two points (1000,0) and (0,13.3). From Equations 5.65 and 5.66, we can compute the values of K_m and K_b based on the information of the stall torque and no-load speed as follows:

$$K_m = \frac{\tau_{stall}}{e_a} R_a = \frac{13.3}{12} 10.8 = 12 \text{ mNm}/\text{A}, \quad K_b = \frac{e_a}{\omega_{no-load}} = \frac{12}{1000} = 12 \text{ mV}/\text{rad}/\text{s}$$

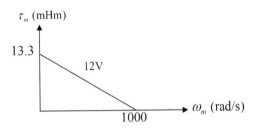

Fig. 5.20: A torque-speed graph of Faulhaber micromotor 2230.012S.

Now, we have all the parameters relevant to the DC motor dynamics except the rotor moment of inertia J_m and rotor friction coefficient B_m. **The rotor friction is negligible, but the rotor moment of inertia is $J_m = 2.7 \times 10^{-7}$ kgm^2.**

In the following, we will consider the dynamics of the DC motor, only without the gear train and the external load.

Example 5.24 (Analysis of the DC Motor Without Load)

The transfer function of the DC motor system without the external load can be obtained from Equations 5.61 and 5.62,

$$\frac{\Omega_m(s)}{E_a(s)} = \frac{b}{s+a} = \frac{\omega_{ss}}{\tau s + 1}$$

where the parameters a and b are

$$a = \frac{K_m K_b}{R_a J_e} = \frac{12 \cdot 12 \cdot 10^{-6}}{10.8 \cdot 2.7 \cdot 10^{-7}} = 49.38, \quad b = \frac{K_m}{R_a J_e} = \frac{12 \cdot 10^{-3}}{10.8 \cdot 2.7 \cdot 10^{-7}} = 4115$$

and the time constant τ and the steady-state step response value ω_{ss} are

$$\tau = \frac{1}{49.38} = 0.0203 \text{ s}, \quad \omega_{ss} = \frac{b}{a} = 83.33 \text{ rad}/\text{s}$$

That is,

$$\frac{\Omega_m(s)}{E_a(s)} = \frac{4115}{s + 49.38} = \frac{83.33}{0.0203s + 1} \tag{5.67}$$

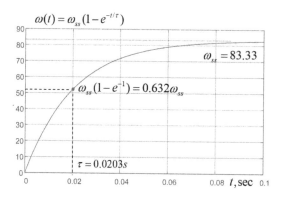

Fig. 5.21: Step response of the DC micromotor without gear train or external load.

Remember what we learned in Chapter 2? If the input $e_a(t)$ is a unit step function (i.e., $E_a(s) = 1/s$), we can solve for $\omega(t)$ by using the Laplace transform approach. We can even draw the response graph and write down the solution without any computation just by inspection and reasoning. The first-order system step response graph is determined by only three points: the initial condition at $t = 0$, the final steady-state response as $t \to \infty$, and the time response at $t = \tau$. For this problem, the initial condition is zero when $t = 0$ and the final steady-state response is ω_{ss}, which is 83.33 rad/s, as $t \to \infty$. The response curve in between is an exponentially rising curve, which has to be in the form $A(1 - e^{-t/\tau})$, where τ is the time constant, and A is the steady-state value. Therefore, the step response of the system is

$$\omega_m(t) = \omega_{ss}\left(1 - e^{-t/\tau}\right)$$

and its associated step response graph is shown in Figure 5.21. **Note that** $\omega_m(\tau) = \omega_{ss}(1 - e^{-1}) = 0.632\omega_{ss}$. **The time constant is** $\tau = 20.3$ ms. The response is very fast. If the input is a step function with amplitude 12 (i.e., $E_a(s) = 12/s$), then the waveform shape will be the same but the steady-state value will be 12 times as large; ω_{ss} will be 1,000 rad/s.   ∎

Example 5.25 (Analysis of the DC Motor with Gear Train and Load)

Consider the same DC micromotor, but **the motor will drive an external load via a 1:14 gear train.** The moment of inertia and the rotational friction coefficient of the external load are

$$J_\ell = 5.4 \times 10^{-5} \text{ kgm}^2, \quad \text{and} \quad B_\ell = 2 \text{ mNm/rad/s}$$

respectively. Then the equivalent moment of inertial J_e and the equivalent rotational friction coefficient B_e are

$$J_e = J_m + \left(\frac{1}{14}\right)^2 J_\ell = 5.455 \times 10^{-7}, \quad B_e = \left(\frac{1}{14}\right)^2 B_\ell = 1.02 \times 10^{-5}$$

The transfer function of the DC motor system with gear train and the external load can be obtained from Equations 5.61 and 5.62

$$\frac{\Omega_m(s)}{E_a(s)} = \frac{b}{s+a} = \frac{\omega_{ss}}{\tau s + 1}$$

where **the parameters** a **and** b **are**

$$a = \frac{B_e}{J_e} + \frac{K_m K_b}{R_a J_e} = 18.7 + 24.44 = 43.14, \quad b = \frac{K_m}{R_a J_e} = \frac{12 \cdot 10^{-3}}{10.8 \cdot 5.455 \cdot 10^{-7}} = 2037$$

and the time constant τ and the steady-state step response value ω_{ss} are

$$\tau = \frac{1}{43.14} = 0.0232 \text{ s}, \quad \omega_{ss} = \frac{b}{a} = 47.22 \text{ rad/s}$$

That is,

$$\frac{\Omega_m(s)}{E_a(s)} = \frac{2037}{s + 43.14} = \frac{47.22}{0.0232s + 1} \quad \text{or} \quad \frac{\Omega_\ell(s)}{E_a(s)} = \frac{145.5}{s + 43.14} = \frac{3.373}{0.0232s + 1} \tag{5.68}$$

The step response of the system for $\omega_\ell(t)$, the angular velocity of the load can be found as

$$\omega_\ell(t) = 3.373(1 - e^{-t/0.0232}) \text{ rad/s} = 32.21(1 - e^{-t/0.0232}) \text{ rpm} \tag{5.69}$$

The time constant is $\tau = 0.0232s$, which is not much different from the no-load dynamics time constant, $\tau = 0.0203s$. However, the steady-state angular speed has dropped tremendously, from 83.3rad/s to 3.373rad/s, which is about only 4% of its no-load angular speed. The reduction of speed mainly comes from the 1:14 gear ratio. The heavy load, whose moment of inertia is about 200 times of that of the motor rotor, also contributes to slow down the rotation speed of the motor. **The loss of 96% of the no-load speed seems terrible, but it is certainly worthwhile for the gain in 14 times more torque and ability to handle a heavy load with 200 times more moment of inertia than the motor itself. Even at 4% of the no-load speed, the motor system still can move the load up to the speed of 380 rpm, which is enough in many applications.** ∎

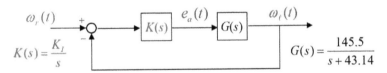

Fig. 5.22: Feedback speed control of the DC motor system using integral control.

In the following, we will design a feedback speed control system based on the dynamics model obtained from Example 5.25.

Example 5.26 (Speed Control of the DC Motor System Using Integral Controller)

The block diagram of the feedback control system is shown in Figure 5.22. On the left-hand side of the diagram, the reference input signal $\omega_r(t)$ is fed into a little circle with + and − signs, which is called the summer, a device that can add or subtract signals. The output signal $\omega_\ell(t)$, which is the angular velocity to be controlled, is fed back into the same summer with a negative sign so that the output signal of the summer is the difference of the two incoming signals $\omega_r(t) - \omega_\ell(t)$. This difference signal in turn becomes the input signal to the controller $K(s)$. The controller will process the information, make decisions, and send out a control signal $e_a(t)$ to either increase or decrease the speed of the motor until $\omega_\ell(t)$ is equal to $\omega_r(t)$.

In general, the controller $K(s)$ is to be designed so that the closed-loop system is stable, the steady-state error is zero if possible, and the transient error is as small as possible. Detailed discussion on stability will be given in later chapters. **Roughly speaking,** *stability* **means that no signals within the system will grow without bound, and** *zero steady-state error* **implies** $\omega_\ell(t)$ **will be equal to** $\omega_r(t)$ **at a steady state.** A minimization of the tracking error represents a requirement to reach the goal as quickly as possible without much overshoot or oscillations. There are many ways to design a tracking controller like this one. In this example, we will use a very simple design approach without much mathematics.

The first step is to find the overall transfer function of the closed-loop system between the reference input $\Omega_r(s)$ and the output $\Omega_\ell(s)$. The relationships among signals in frequency domain are all algebraic and can be easily manipulated. Just by inspection of the diagram, we have following two equations:

$$\Omega_\ell(s) = G(s)E_a(s) \quad \text{and} \quad E_a(s) = K(s)\left[\Omega_r(s) - \Omega_\ell(s)\right]$$

These two equations can be combined into one by eliminating the internal variable $E_a(s)$. Then, with a few moving around terms within the equation, we have the following transfer function:

$$\frac{\Omega_\ell(s)}{\Omega_r(s)} = \frac{G(s)K(s)}{1 + G(s)K(s)} \tag{5.70}$$

Plugging the expressions of $K(s) = K_i/s$ and $G(s)$ into the closed-loop transfer function, we have

$$\frac{\Omega_\ell(s)}{\Omega_r(s)} = \frac{\frac{145.5K_i}{s(s+43.14)}}{1 + \frac{145.5K_i}{s(s+43.14)}} = \frac{145.5K_i}{s^2 + 43.14s + 145.5K_i} = \frac{\omega_n^2}{s^2 + 2\varsigma\omega_n s + \omega_n^2} \tag{5.71}$$

Note that this closed-loop transfer function belongs to the category of the typical second-order system we studied in Chapter 3. Recall that the dynamic behavior of the typical second-order system is characterized by the damping ratio ς and the natural frequency ω_n. From Equation 5.71, we have the following two equations that relate the damping ratio ς and the natural frequency ω_n to the integral constant K_i:

$$\omega_n^2 = 145.5K_i \quad \text{and} \quad 2\varsigma\omega_n = 43.14$$

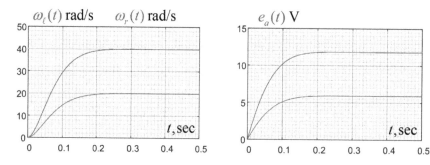

Fig. 5.23: Simulation results of the feedback speed control of the DC motor system using integral control.

Due to the restriction of the integral control structure that there is only one design parameter K_i to be determined, we only have one degree of freedom in choosing the damping ratio and the natural frequency. **If we choose the damping ratio to be 0.9, $\varsigma = 0.9$, then the natural frequency will be $\omega_n = 43.14/1.8 = 23.97$ rad/s and the integral gain should be $K_i = 3.95$.**

With the integral control constant determined, the block diagram in Figure 5.22 can be employed to build a simulation program and conduct simulations of the feedback speed control of the DC motor system using the integral control approach. The simulation results are shown in Figure 5.23. With the damping ratio chosen to be $\varsigma = 0.9$, there will be, as expected, an almost undetectable overshoot and virtually no oscillations. The step response reaches steady state with no steady-state error shortly after $t = 0.2$ s. **The rise time can be faster if there is another degree of freedom to select a higher natural frequency in the design process. We will revisit this problems later in Chapter 6. A dual-loop feedback control structure with two design parameters will be employed in Example 6.1 to achieve a better performance.**

The control-input plots are also shown in Figure 5.23. It can be seen that when the angular speed of the load, $\omega_\ell(t)$ reaches 20 rad/s, the control input $e_a(t)$ is around 6 volts voltage. Similarly, when $\omega_\ell(t)$ follows another reference input $\omega_r(t) = 40$ rad/s to get up to 40 rad/s, it requires about 12 volts from the voltage source. **The control inputs always have their limitations in magnitude or in rate of change. The system needs to work within the capability of the control inputs; otherwise, the system may perform poorly or become unstable.** ∎

5.8 Exercise Problems

P5.1a: Find the transfer function $G_1(s) = E_o(s)/E_s(s)$ of the op amp circuit shown in Figure 5.24(a) and explain the function and application of this circuit.

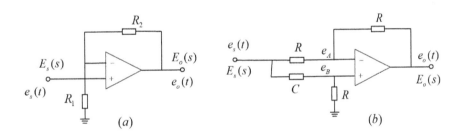

Fig. 5.24: Op amp circuits.

P5.1b: Find the transfer function $G_2(s) = E_o(s)/E_s(s)$ of the op amp circuit shown in Figure 5.24(b). Then compute the magnitude and phase of $G_2(j\omega)$ and explain the frequency-domain behavior of the system.

P5.2: Assume the DC motor is Faulhaber micromotor 2230.012S. You can find the data sheet values of this DC motor from Figure 5.19. The DC motor system under consideration is shown in Figure 5.17. Let the gear ratio be $N_1/N_2 = 1/10$, and $J_\ell = 2 \times 10^{-5}$ kgm^2, $B_\ell = 1$ mNm/rad/s. Find the transfer function $G(s) = \Omega_\ell(s)/E_a(s)$.

P5.3: Use the transfer function $G(s) = \Omega_\ell(s)/E_a(s)$ you obtained in Problem P5.2. Design an integral controller $K(s) = \frac{K}{s}$ so that the closed-loop system shown in Figure 5.25 has its characteristic equation with damping ratio $\varsigma = 0.8$. Then evaluate the performance of the closed-loop system by conducting computer simulations with the reference input $\omega_r(t) = 40u_s(t)$ rad/s. Plot the output response $\omega_\ell(t)$ and the control input $e_a(t)$, and give your comments based on the simulation results.

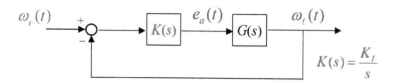

Fig. 5.25: A DC motor speed control system.

P5.4: Consider the circuit shown in Figure 5.26, where $e_o(t)$ and $e_s(t)$ are the output and the input, respectively. Assign e_C and i_L as state variables, then find the state-space model of the electrical system.

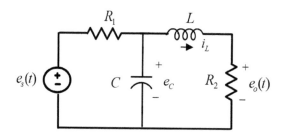

Fig. 5.26: Find a state-space model of the RLC circuit.

P5.5: Consider the circuit shown in Figure 5.26, where $e_o(t)$ and $e_s(t)$ are the output and the input, respectively. Let $E_o(s)$ and $E_s(s)$ be the Laplace transforms of $e_o(t)$ and $e_s(t)$, respectively. Find the transfer function $E_o(s)/E_s(s)$ Using the NTD voltages approach.

P5.6: Repeat Problem **P5.5** using the mesh currents approach.

P5.7: Repeat Problem **P5.5** using the Lagrange approach.

P5.8: For the circuit shown in Figure 5.26, which has just been considered in Problems P5.5, P5.6, and P5.7, assume the component values of the resistors, the capacitor, and the inductor are: $R_1 = 1k\Omega$, $R_2 = 10\Omega$, $L = 2H$, and $C = 100\mu F$. Find the transfer function $E_o(s)/E_s(s)$, and the damping ratio ς and the natural frequency ω_n of the system.

6

Systems Representations and Interconnected Systems

T HERE is no question that mathematical dynamics models are essential in the study of dynamic systems analysis, design, and control. **Without a clear and truthful description of a dynamic system it would be very difficult or even impossible to understand how the system works, how to fix problems if some engineering issues arise, or how to design and build a better system.** For this reason, we have to understand how physical dynamic systems are described by their mathematical dynamic model equations. On the other hand, for every equation, engineering law, or scientific theory we learn, we should associate them with some technical reasoning, experience, lab works, or virtual experiment for verification.

As we learn from the previous chapters, although the dynamic system model equations can be derived using different approaches, the end results are essentially identical. However, dynamic system representations are not unique. For example, the simple *RC* circuit discussed in Chapter 2 can be represented by a first-order differential equation in the time domain or by its corresponding frequency-domain description as a transfer function. These two representations provide different aspects of the same system. **In the time domain, the differential equation reveals the charging and discharging activities of the system, while the frequency-domain transfer function helps us understand the low-pass filtering property of the system.**

It seems that the time-domain behavior and properties are more intuitive than their counterparts in the frequency domain; one would think the time-domain approaches would dominate the development of the control system theory and technology in earlier years. But history showed the opposite: Most of the classical control theory, analysis, and design tools were developed in frequency domain during the period of almost a hundred years since James Clerk Maxwell's historic flyball stability analysis paper published in 1868 until late 1950s when the optimal control theory and the state-space approach started to emerge.

Due to the advancement of the state-space control theory, the matrix computing algorithms, and the evolving computer technology, the time-domain state-space approach based on the state-space representation has become more significant, especially in its ability of handling the more complicated multivariable control systems. The frequency-domain multivariable control approach also made tremendous progress in 1970s and 1980s in addressing the robust stability and robust performance issues based on the transfer function matrix representation. The manipulation of the transfer function matrices requires polynomial matrix computations, which is more tedious than the constant matrix computations in the state-space approach.

The polynomial matrix computation issue was eliminated in the late 1980s by converting the underlying transfer function matrix representation into the state-space representation and re-deriving the optimal robust control solution in state space. **Hence, the state-space control systems approach to-day is not a purely time-domain approach. It is a merged time-domain and frequency-domain approach on the state-space framework for efficient and reliable computation, yet allows both of the frequency-domain and time-domain components to be considered in the analysis and design process.**

In this chapter, we will present an overview of the common systems representations, including the differential equations, the transfer functions, the state-space representations, the simulation diagrams, the block diagrams, and the signal flow graphs. We will discuss the relationship among the system representations, and explain how to find the transfer function or the state-space representation of an interconnected system of interest that are usually required in analysis or design.

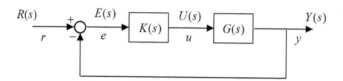

Fig. 6.1: A simple block diagram with feedback structure.

6.1 Block Diagrams

Even before we officially define the term *block diagram* we had used it on two occasions: one in Figure 3.15 for DC motor position control, and another in Figure 5.22 for DC motor speed control. These two block diagrams look similar to the one shown in Figure 6.1. Assume the plant, which means the system to be controlled, is a typical first-order system $G(s)$ representing the transfer function of a DC motor whose output is the angular velocity, the input is a control voltage signal, and the PI (proportional plus integral) controller $K(s)$ are given in

$$G(s) = \frac{b}{s+a} \quad \text{and} \quad K(s) = K_p + \frac{K_i}{s}$$

respectively, where b and a are given constants, and K_p and K_i are the proportional and integral constants in the controller to be designed.

A block diagram is an effective graphical representation of an interconnected system that shows the interconnection relationship among the subsystems and components in the system. The block diagram in Figure 6.1 shows that the output $y(t)$ of the plant $G(s)$ is the variable (the motor speed in this case) to be controlled. The reference input $r(t)$ represents the desired motor speed fed into the summer, which is represented by a little circle with $+$ and $-$ signs around it for addition or substraction. The actual speed variable $y(t)$ is fed back into the negative terminal of the summer so that the difference signal $e(t) = r(t) - y(t)$ will be sent to the controller $K(s)$. The controller $K(s)$ will follow the controller law (the PI control law in this case) based on the difference input to make decisions and send out the control-input signal to either increase or decrease the speed of the motor system until the actual speed equals the desired speed commanded by the reference input.

In the design and analysis of the feedback control system, we may need to find the closed-loop transfer function $Y(s)/R(s)$, or any other representation describing the relationship between the reference input $r(t)$ and the output $y(t)$. If the transfer function of each block is available, the computation of the overall transfer function will be fairly straightforward since it only involves algebraic manipulations. For this example, from the block diagram in Figure 6.1, we have the following two algebraic equations,

$$Y(s) = G(s)U(s) \quad \text{and} \quad U(s) = K(s)\left[R(s) - Y(s)\right]$$

Then these two equations can be combined into the following transfer function by eliminating the internal variable $U(s)$:

$$\frac{Y(s)}{R(s)} = \frac{G(s)K(s)}{1 + G(s)K(s)} = \frac{\frac{b}{s+a}\frac{K_p s + K_i}{s}}{1 + \frac{b}{s+a}\frac{K_p s + K_i}{s}} = \frac{bK_p s + bK_i}{s^2 + (a + bK_p)s + bK_i}$$

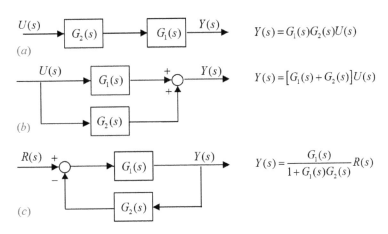

Fig. 6.2: Common basic block diagram connections: (a) cascade connection, (b) parallel connection, (c) feedback connection.

Block diagram connections are pretty self-explanatory. They consist of several blocks that represent subsystems or components. Each block is assumed to have an input terminal to receive an incoming signal and an output terminal to send an outgoing signal. Signals are represented by arrows with arrowheads on their tips showing the signal flow directions. Signals can be added or subtracted to form a new signal using a summer, which is represented by a little circle with $+$ and $-$ signs around it to determine whether the sign of the incoming signal needs to be changed before entering the summer. A signal also can be tapped to create a new branch to send exactly the same signal to another block or summer. Unlike the split of water flow or electric current, the tapping here is just a sharing of information—the signal magnitude won't be affected.

Three common basic block diagram connections are shown in Figure 6.2. The block diagram in (a) is a cascade connection in which U is the input signal for the G_2 block, whose output will be $G_2 U$. Similarly, the output of the G_1 block is G_1 multiplied by its input signal, $G_2 U$. Therefore, the output of the G_1 block is $G_1 G_2 U$. The block diagram (b) is a parallel connection of G_1 and G_2. The output Y is the sum of the two incoming signals of the summer, which are $G_1 U$ and $G_2 U$, respectively. Therefore, $Y = G_1 U + G_2 U = (G_1 + G_2)U$. The block diagram (c) is a feedback connection with its forward path gain G_1 and the loop gain $-G_1 G_2$. The output of the summer is $R - G_2 Y$, which yields $Y = G_1(R - G_2 Y)$. By moving the term $-G_1 G_2 Y$ to the other side, we have the following:

$$Y + G_1 G_2 Y = G_1 R \quad \rightarrow \quad Y = \frac{G_1}{1 + G_1 G_2}R$$

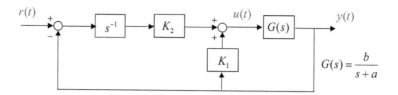

Fig. 6.3: A dual-loop feedback tracking control design.

In the following example, we will revisit the DC motor speed control problem using a new controller with *dual-loop feedback* structure. First, we will use this opportunity to practice how to find the transfer function of the closed-loop system block diagram in a speed control design problem. The block diagram is a little bit more complicated than the previous integral control case considered in Example 5.26, but the new control system structure provides two degrees of freedom in the controller design that allows us to choose the damping ratio and the natural frequency of the closed-loop dynamics independently.

Example 6.1 (Revisit the DC Motor Speed Control System Using Dual-Loop Feedback)

The block diagram of the dual-loop feedback control system is shown in Figure 6.3. On the left-hand side of the diagram, the reference input signal $r(t)$ is fed into the summer. The output signal $y(t)$, which is the angular speed of the motor to be controlled, is fed back into the same summer with a negative sign so that the output signal of the summer is the difference, $r(t) - y(t)$, of the two incoming signals. This difference signal in turn becomes the input signal to the integrator $1/s$. There are two controller parameters to be determined—one is K_2, which is the integrator gain, and the other is K_1 in the second feedback loop.

The first step is to find the overall transfer function of the closed-loop system between the reference input $R(s)$, which is the Laplace transform of $r(t)$, and the output $Y(s)$, the Laplace transform of $y(t)$. By inspection of the diagram, we have following equation:

$$Y = GK_1Y + GK_2(1/s)(R-Y)$$

Then move all the Y terms to the left-hand side and substitute G by $b/(s+a)$ into the equation

$$\left(1 - GK_1 + \frac{GK_2}{s}\right)Y = \frac{GK_2}{s}R \quad \rightarrow \quad \left(1 - \frac{bK_1}{s+a} + \frac{bK_2}{s(s+a)}\right)Y = \frac{bK_2}{s(s+a)}R$$

which can be simplified to

$$\left(s^2 + (a_1 - bK_1)s + bK_2\right)Y = bK_2R$$

and we have the closed-loop transfer function as follows:

$$\frac{Y}{R} = \frac{bK_2}{s^2 + (a - bK_1)s + bK_2} \tag{6.1}$$

Using the DC micromotor dynamics data obtained in Equation 5.68, we have $b = 145.5$ and $a = 43.14$. Then the closed-loop transfer function of the dual-loop feedback DC micromotor speed control system will be

$$\frac{Y(s)}{R(s)} = \frac{145.5K_2}{s^2 + (43.14 - 145.5K_1)s + 145.5K_2} = \frac{\omega_n^2}{s^2 + 2\varsigma\omega_n s + \omega_n^2} \tag{6.2}$$

Note that this closed-loop transfer function belongs to the category of the typical second order system we studied in Chapter 3. Since the dynamic behavior of the typical second-order system is characterized by the damping ratio ς and the natural frequency ω_n, from Equation 6.2, we have the following two equations that relate the **damping ratio** $\varsigma = 0.9$ and the **natural frequency** $\omega_n = 50$ **rad/s** to the controller parameters K_1 and K_2:

$$\omega_n^2 = 145.5K_2 = 50^2 \quad \text{and} \quad 2\varsigma\omega_n = 2(0.9)\omega_n = 43.14 - 145.5K_1$$

Hence, $K_1 = -0.322$ and $K_2 = 17.18$.

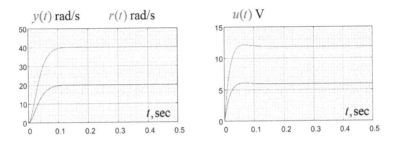

Fig. 6.4: Simulation result of the tracking control design using dual-loop feedback.

After the dual-loop feedback controller constants K_1 and K_2 are determined, the block diagram in Figure 6.3 can be employed to build a simulation program to conduct simulations of the DC motor speed control system. The simulation results are shown on Figure 6.4. **With the damping ratio chosen to be** $\varsigma = 0.9$**, there are no oscillations and the overshoot is almost invisible. The step response reaches steady state with zero steady-state error shortly after** $t = 0.1$**s, which is two times faster than the one with integral control shown in Figure 5.23.** The faster response is due to the dual-loop feedback's ability to choose a higher natural frequency, $\omega_n = 50$ rad/s, compared to $\omega_n = 23.97$ rad/s in the integral control case.

The control-input plots are also shown in Figure 6.4. It can be seen that when the angular speed of the load, $y(t)$ reaches 20 rad/s, the control input $u(t)$ is around 6 volts voltage. Similarly, when $y(t)$ follows the reference input $r(t) = 40$ rad/s to get up to 40 rad/s, it requires about 12.5 volts from the voltage source, only a slight increase than the integral control case. ∎

In this section, we have experienced the effectiveness of the frequency-domain block diagram/transfer function approach in obtaining the overall system model. Just imagine how much harder the work would be if we had to find the differential equation of the overall system in time domain by combining a group of differential equations. However, for a more complicated interconnected system, solving a set of algebraic equations can still be time-consuming. Some block diagram reduction techniques may help, but the graphic reduction procedure can still be tedious. **One of the most efficient ways to compute the overall transfer function (or gains) of a large system is Mason's gain formula.**

Although Mason's gain formula can be applied to the block diagram, it is more intuitive for it to work together with the *signal flow graph*. **The signal flow graph is virtually equivalent to the block diagram, but it looks neater and shows the signal flow path more clearly than its counterpart.**

6.2 Signal Flow Graphs and Mason's Gain Formula

6.2.1 Signal Flow Graphs

In signal flow graphs, signals are represented by circular dots, called *nodes*, **and the transfer functions or gains of systems between signals are represented by** *directional branches*, **with the arrowhead in the** *middle* **of the branch showing the signal flow direction.** Each node may connect with several incoming and outgoing branches, but the value of the signal at each node (except the input nodes) is only determined by the signals via the incoming branches. That is, the signal at each node equals the algebraic sum of all incoming signals via the incoming branches, and it has nothing to do with the outgoing branches. Note that the nodes with no incoming branches are regarded as input nodes. Similarly, the nodes without outgoing branches are considered output nodes, although some output nodes in general may still have outgoing branches.

Four basic signal flow graph connections are shown in Figure 6.5. The signal flow graph (a) is trivial in which the node $Y(s)$ has only one incoming branch, and the signal coming from node $U(s)$ via branch $G(s)$ is the product, $G(s)U(s)$. For the cascade connection in (b), it is easy to see that $Y = G_1E$ and $E = G_2U$; hence, we have $Y = G_1G_2U$. Unlike the parallel connection in the block diagram, we do not need a summer in the signal flow graph (c). To perform an addition operation, it only requires feeding signals via two or more incoming branches into a node. For the parallel connection in (c), the output node Y has two incoming branches, G_1 and G_2, and these two branches are connected to the same signal source, $U(s)$. Hence, $Y = G_1U + G_2U$, which is $Y = (G_1 + G_2)U$.

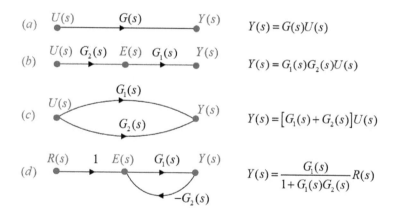

Fig. 6.5: Basic signal flow graph connections: (a) two nodes one branch, (b) cascade connection, (c) parallel connection, (d) feedback connection.

The feedback connection consists of three nodes, the input node R on the left, the output node Y on the right, and the error signal node E in the middle. The input node R has one outgoing branch to node E, but has no incoming branch. The error signal node E has two incoming branches, 1 and $-G_2$ connected to R and Y, respectively. Hence, the signal at node E is

$$E = 1 \cdot R - G_2Y = R - G_2Y$$

The output node has one incoming signal from node E via branch G_1; hence, the signal at the output node is

$$Y = G_1 E$$

Combine the two equations by eliminating the intermediate variable E to yield the following transfer function from R to Y:

$$Y = G_1(R - G_2 Y) \quad \rightarrow \quad Y + G_1 G_2 Y = G_1 R \quad \rightarrow \quad \frac{Y}{R} = \frac{G_1}{1 + G_1 G_2}$$

6.2.2 Mason's Gain Formula

As mentioned a while ago, Mason's gain formula is one of the most efficient ways to compute the overall transfer function (or overall gain) of a large system. The formula will be given in the following. The general description of the formula may seem long and complicated. However, almost all the students will find the formula is straightforward and easy after working on a few examples.

Theorem 6.2 (Mason's Gain Formula)

Consider a system represented by a signal flow graph, in which the relationships among signals and systems are all algebraic. Then the transfer function from the input U to the output Y is

$$\frac{Y}{U} = \sum_{n=1}^{N} \frac{F_n \Delta_n}{\Delta} \tag{6.3}$$

where

$N = $ *total number of forward paths*

$F_n = $ *the n-th forward path gain*

$M = $ *total number of loops*

$\ell_i = $ *the i-th loop gain*

$\Delta = 1 - \sum_{i}^{M} \ell_i + \sum_{i,j}^{NT} \ell_i \ell_j - \sum_{i,j,k}^{NT} \ell_i \ell_j \ell_k + \cdots \cdots$

The superscript NT means nontouching.

$\sum_{i,j}^{NT} \ell_i \ell_j$ *is the sum of the products of two nontouching loop gains.*

$\sum_{i,j,k}^{NT} \ell_i \ell_j \ell_k$ *is the sum of the products of three nontouching loop gains.*

$\Delta_n :$ *same as the Δ, but only the loops that do NOT touch the n-th forward path are considered.* ∎

Example 6.3 (Mason's Gain Formula for the Basic Feedback System)

Consider the feedback connection signal flow graph in Figure 6.5(d). The transfer function of the closed-loop system Y/R can be obtained just by inspection using Mason's gain formula.

The signal flow graph has one forward path and the forward path gain is $F_1 = G_1$. There is one loop with loop gain $\ell_1 = -G_1 G_2$, which is touching the forward path. Hence, we have

$$\Delta = 1 - \ell_1 = 1 + G_1 G_2, \quad \Delta_1 = 1, \quad F_1 = G_1 \quad \rightarrow \quad \frac{Y}{R} = \frac{F_1 \Delta_1}{\Delta} = \frac{G_1}{1 + G_1 G_2}$$

Example 6.4 (Mason's Gain Formula for the Dual-Loop Feedback Control System)

The signal flow graph shown in Figure 6.6 is equivalent to the block diagram shown in Figure 6.3, where a dual-loop feedback controller was employed to achieve a desirable DC motor speed control. In Example 6.1, algebraic equations were first set up according to the interrelationships among the subsystems and signals within the system, and then some algebraic manipulations were performed to obtain the overall transfer function of the system. Now, we will apply Mason's gain formula to this signal flow graph to determine the transfer function from R to Y.

The signal flow graph from R to Y has one forward path and two loops. The forward path gain and the two loop gains are

$$F_1 = 1 \cdot (1/s) \cdot K_2 \cdot G = K_2 G/s$$

and

$$\ell_1 = GK_1, \quad \ell_2 = -1 \cdot (1/s) \cdot K_2 \cdot G = -K_2 G/s$$

Hence, the Δ and Δ_1 will be

$$\Delta = 1 - (\ell_1 + \ell_2) = 1 - GK_1 + K_2 G/s, \quad \Delta_1 = 1$$

since both loops are touching the forward path. Therefore, the transfer function is

$$\frac{Y}{R} = \frac{F_1 \Delta_1}{\Delta} = \frac{K_2 G/s}{1 - GK_1 + K_2 G/s} = \frac{\frac{bK_2}{s(s+a)}}{1 - \frac{bK_1}{s+a} + \frac{bK_2}{s(s+a)}} = \frac{bK_2}{s^2 + (a - bK_1)s + bK_2}$$

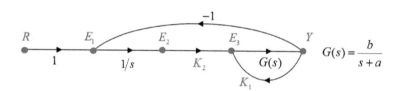

Fig. 6.6: Signal flow graph for the DC motor dual-loop feedback speed control system.

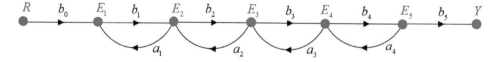

Fig. 6.7: Signal flow graph of a four-loop system.

Example 6.5 (Mason's Gain Formula for a System with Four Loops)

The signal flow graph shown in Figure 6.7 has one forward path and four loops. This example is employed to demonstrate how to compute the Δ terms when there are multiple nontouching pairs of loops. The forward path gain and the four loop gains are

$$F_1 = b_0 b_1 b_2 b_3 b_4 b_5$$

and

$$\ell_1 = b_1 a_1, \; \ell_2 = b_2 a_2, \; \ell_3 = b_3 a_3, \; \ell_4 = b_4 a_4$$

Hence, the Δ and Δ_1 are

$$\Delta = 1 - (\ell_1 + \ell_2 + \ell_3 + \ell_4) + (\ell_1 \ell_3 + \ell_1 \ell_4 + \ell_2 \ell_4), \quad \Delta_1 = 1$$

Note that there are three nontouching pairs of loops for the third term in the Δ equation and there exists no nontouching trio of loops in the signal flow graph. Δ_1 is 1 because all the four loops touch the forward path. Therefore, the transfer function Y/R is

$$\frac{Y}{R} = \frac{F_1 \Delta_1}{\Delta} = \frac{b_0 b_1 b_2 b_3 b_4 b_5}{1 - b_1 a_1 - b_2 a_2 - b_3 a_3 - b_4 a_4 + b_1 a_1 b_3 a_3 + b_1 a_1 b_4 a_4 + b_2 a_2 b_4 a_4}$$

If the conventional algebraic approach were employed to solve the problem, six equations would have to be set up, and the five intermediate variables E_1, E_2, E_3, E_4, and E_5 would need to be eliminated before the transfer function can be found. ∎

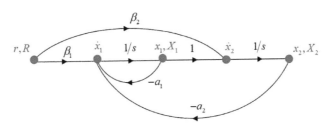

Fig. 6.8: Signal flow graph of a state diagram.

Example 6.6 (Mason's Gain Formula for a State Diagram)

The signal flow graph shown in Figure 6.8 will serve for two purposes. One is to demonstrate the construction of Δ_n when there exists a loop that does not touch the n-th forward path. In this example, if X_2 is considered as the output, we will see that the signal flow graph has two forward paths:

$$F_1 = \beta_1 \cdot (1/s) \cdot 1 \cdot (1/s) = \beta_1/s^2, \; F_2 = \beta_2/s$$

and two loops:

$$\ell_1 = -a_1 \cdot (1/s) = -a_1/s, \quad \ell_2 = -a_2 \cdot (1/s) \cdot 1 \cdot (1/s) = -a_2/s^2$$

Note that the two loops are touching each other; i.e., there is no nontouching pair of loops. Hence, the Δ is

$$\Delta = 1 - (\ell_1 + \ell_2) = 1 + \frac{a_1}{s} + \frac{a_2}{s^2} = \frac{s^2 + a_1 s + a_2}{s^2}$$

Since these two loops are also touching the forward path F_1, they are not counted in the construction of Δ_1. However, the loop ℓ_1 should be counted in the construction of Δ_2 because it is not touching the forward path F_2. Thus, Δ_1, Δ_2 are:

$$\Delta_1 = 1, \quad \Delta_2 = 1 - \ell_1 = \frac{s + a_1}{s}$$

Therefore, the transfer function from R to X_2 is

$$\frac{X_2}{R} = \frac{F_1\Delta_1 + F_2\Delta_2}{\Delta} = \frac{s^2}{s^2 + a_1s + a_2}\left(\frac{\beta_1}{s^2} + \frac{\beta_2}{s} \cdot \frac{s + a_1}{s}\right) = \frac{\beta_2 s + a_1\beta_2 + \beta_1}{s^2 + a_1s + a_2}$$

The second purpose of this signal flow graph is to show that signal flow graph can also be employed to represent a graphical representation of a state-space representation, called the *state diagram*. We can see that two of the nodes are labeled as x_1 and x_2, which are the state variables of the system. Furthermore, we can obtain the state equation from this diagram as follows:

$$\begin{bmatrix} \dot{x}_1 \\ \dot{x}_2 \end{bmatrix} = \begin{bmatrix} -a_1 & -a_2 \\ 1 & 0 \end{bmatrix} \begin{bmatrix} x_1 \\ x_2 \end{bmatrix} + \begin{bmatrix} \beta_1 \\ \beta_2 \end{bmatrix} r$$

6.3 State-Space Model

In Section 4.4.2, we informally introduced the state-space approach to convert the nonlinear coupled second-order differential equation of the simple inverted pendulum system into a state equation that consists of two first-order differential equations. **This conversion has made it much easier to conduct analysis, linearization, controller design, and simulations.** A state-space representation, called a state-space model, can always be obtained by converting an existing dynamic system differential equation or transfer function. It also can be constructed directly from the dynamic system modeling process as described in Section 5.5, where we usually assign inductor current and capacitor voltage as state variables for electrical systems. Similarly, displacement and velocity are usually assigned as state variables for mechanical systems.

The transfer function frequency-domain approach played an essential role in early control systems theory development due to its ability to simplify systems manipulations and to conduct frequency-domain analysis and design. However, its application is restricted to linear time-invariant systems with single input and single output. On the other hand, the state-space approach can handle multi-input/multi-output systems that are nonlinear and time-varying. In fact, **the state-space model is a more complete description of dynamic systems, since it not only describes the input-output relationship, but also reveals the information of the internal states. Furthermore, the analysis, design, and simulation in state space involve only constant matrices, which are more efficient on digital computers than those involve complicated polynomial manipulations.**

The state-space model usually is represented in the compact matrix form

$$\begin{aligned} \dot{x}(t) &= Ax(t) + Bu(t) \\ y(t) &= Cx(t) + Du(t) \end{aligned} \tag{6.4}$$

where the vectors $x \in R^n$, $u \in R^m$, and $y \in R^p$ are the $n \times 1$ state vector, the $m \times 1$ input vector, and the $p \times 1$ output vector, respectively. The matrices $A \in R^{n\times n}$, $B \in R^{n\times m}$, $C \in R^{p\times n}$, and $D \in R^{p\times m}$ are the $n \times n$ A matrix, the $n \times m$ B matrix, the $p \times n$ C matrix, and the $p \times m$ D matrix, respectively. The state-space model in expanded matrix form will look like the following:

$$\begin{bmatrix} \dot{x}_1 \\ \dot{x}_2 \\ \vdots \\ \dot{x}_n \end{bmatrix} = \begin{bmatrix} a_{11} & a_{12} & \cdots & a_{1n} \\ a_{21} & a_{22} & \cdots & a_{2n} \\ \vdots & \vdots & \ddots & \vdots \\ a_{n1} & a_{n2} & \cdots & a_{nn} \end{bmatrix} \begin{bmatrix} x_1 \\ x_2 \\ \vdots \\ x_n \end{bmatrix} + \begin{bmatrix} b_{11} & b_{12} & \cdots & b_{1m} \\ b_{21} & b_{22} & \cdots & b_{2m} \\ \vdots & \vdots & \ddots & \vdots \\ b_{n1} & b_{n2} & \cdots & b_{nm} \end{bmatrix} \begin{bmatrix} u_1 \\ u_2 \\ \vdots \\ u_m \end{bmatrix} \tag{6.5a}$$

$$\begin{bmatrix} y_1 \\ y_2 \\ \vdots \\ y_p \end{bmatrix} = \begin{bmatrix} c_{11} & c_{12} & \cdots & c_{1n} \\ c_{21} & c_{22} & \cdots & c_{2n} \\ \vdots & \vdots & \ddots & \vdots \\ c_{p1} & c_{p2} & \cdots & c_{pn} \end{bmatrix} \begin{bmatrix} x_1 \\ x_2 \\ \vdots \\ x_n \end{bmatrix} + \begin{bmatrix} d_{11} & d_{12} & \cdots & d_{1m} \\ d_{21} & d_{22} & \cdots & d_{2m} \\ \vdots & \vdots & \ddots & \vdots \\ d_{p1} & d_{p2} & \cdots & d_{pm} \end{bmatrix} \begin{bmatrix} u_1 \\ u_2 \\ \vdots \\ u_m \end{bmatrix} \tag{6.5b}$$

The number of the state variables or the dimension of the A matrix is the order of the state-space model. In general, the order of the state-space model is the same as that of its associated differential equation or transfer function. For example, the equation of motion for the simple inverted pendulum system discussed in Section 4.4.2 is a second-order differential equation; hence, the order of its state-space model is $n = 2$.

Example 6.7 (Find a State-Space Model for the Simple MBK System)

Assume we have a simple mass–damper–spring mechanical system, shown in Figure 6.9; what information do we need at any time instant, $t = t_0$, in order to predict the motion of the system for $t > t_0$? We would need to know both of the displacement and velocity values at $t = t_0$ and the applied external force $f_a(t)$ for $t \geq t_0$. Hence, the displacement x and velocity $\dot{x}$ are perfect candidates to serve as state variables. Let the state variables be

$$x_1(t) = x(t) \quad \text{and} \quad x_2(t) = \dot{x}(t)$$

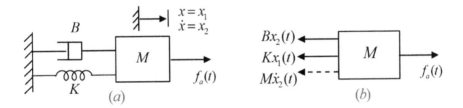

Fig. 6.9: Find a state-space model for the simple mass–damper–spring (MBK) system.

From the definition of the state variables, we immediately have the first state equation as

$$\dot{x}_1(t) = x_2(t)$$

Then from the free-body diagram in Figure 6.9, we have

$$M\dot{x}_2(t) + Bx_2(t) + Kx_1(t) = f_a(t) \quad \rightarrow \quad \dot{x}_2(t) = \frac{-K}{M}x_1(t) + \frac{-B}{M}x_2(t) + \frac{1}{M}f_a(t)$$

Combine the two state equations into one state equation in matrix form and choose the displacement variable as the output; then we have the following state-space model for the mass–damper–spring system:

$$\begin{bmatrix} \dot{x}_1(t) \\ \dot{x}_2(t) \end{bmatrix} = \begin{bmatrix} 0 & 1 \\ -K/M & -B/M \end{bmatrix} \begin{bmatrix} x_1(t) \\ x_2(t) \end{bmatrix} + \begin{bmatrix} 0 \\ 1/M \end{bmatrix} f_a(t)$$

$$y(t) = \begin{bmatrix} 1 & 0 \end{bmatrix} \begin{bmatrix} x_1(t) \\ x_2(t) \end{bmatrix} \tag{6.6}$$

■

The state diagram associated with the state-space model of the simple MBK system given by Equation 6.6 is shown in Figure 6.10, which is a graphical representation of the state-space model. The graphical tool can be either a signal flow graph or a block diagram. In the diagram, s^{-1} represents an integrator, and the constants M, B, and K are the mass, the friction coefficient, and the spring constant of the system, respectively. The signal at each node (blue dot) can be represented by a time-domain variable in lower-case blue or by a frequency-domain variable in capital-case red. That means the same state diagram can be employed for analysis in both time domain and frequency domain. **But caution needs to be taken to not mix up the time-domain and the frequency-domain signals. For example, the initial state for the state variable $x_1(t)$ to be used in a simulation (time-domain) should be just the constant x_{10} instead of x_{10}/s, the integral of x_{10}. On the other hand, to find the transfer function from x_{10} to $X_1(s)$, we would need to compute the transfer function from $X_{10}(s)$ to $X_1(s)$ first. Then we have**

$$X_1(s) = G(s)X_{10}(s) = G(s)\frac{1}{s}x_{10}$$

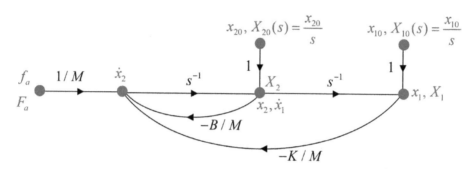

Fig. 6.10: The state diagram associated with the state-space model of the simple mass–damper–spring (MBK) system.

Example 6.8 (Simulation of the Simple MBK System Using the State Diagram)

In this example we will conduct a simulation using a simulation diagram based on the state diagram shown in Figure 6.10. In this simulation, the applied force input $f_a(t)$ is assumed zero. The initial velocity of the system $\dot{x}_1(0) = x_2(0) = x_{20}$ is also assumed zero. But the initial displacement of the system $x_1(0) = x_{10}$ is assumed to be $x_{10} = 0.5$ m. This initial condition can be implemented in the lab. Assume the left end of the spring and damper are fixed to a wall as the schematic suggested in Figure 6.9. Imagine you are holding the mass and gradually moving it away from its equilibrium toward the right. You will feel that both of the friction and spring reaction forces are against the motion. The spring reaction force, especially, will get stronger as you move the mass further away from the equilibrium. As the mass reaches the 50 cm mark, you will stop moving but continue to hold the mass at position. Then you may want to know how the mass will move after the mass is released.

We will conduct the simulation two times using different sets of mass, spring, and damper. In the first run, the mass, spring, and damper are chosen so that $M = 0.1$ kg, $K = 0.1$ N/m, and $B = 0.05$ Ns/m. Since this simple MBK system is a typical second-order system, the following two characteristic equations should be equivalent, as discussed in Section 3.5:

$$s^2 + (B/M)s + (K/M) = 0 \quad \rightleftarrows \quad s^2 + 2\varsigma\omega_n s + \omega_n^2 = 0$$

Hence, the damping ratio and natural frequency of the system corresponding to the chosen MBK values will be

$$\varsigma = 0.5B/\sqrt{MK} = (0.5)(0.05)/0.1 = 0.25, \quad \omega_n = \sqrt{K/M} = \sqrt{0.1/0.1} = 1 \text{ rad/s}$$

With this low damping ratio $\varsigma = 0.25$ and slow natural frequency $\omega_n = 1$ rad/s, we expect the response will be underdamped with high overshoot and oscillations with frequency,

$$\omega = \omega_n \sqrt{1 - \varsigma^2} = 0.968 \text{ rad/s}$$

which is equivalent to oscillation period = 6.49 sec.

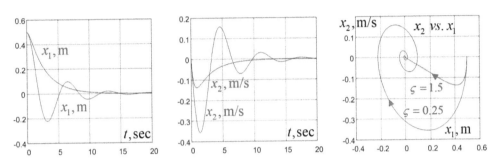

Fig. 6.11: Simulation using the state-space model of the simple mass–damper–spring (MBK) system.

The simulation results are shown in Figure 6.11. The first round simulation results ($\varsigma = 0.25$) are shown in blue lines, and the second round responses are in red ($\varsigma = 1.5$). The left graph records both of the blue and the red displacements $x_1(t)$, and the middle graph shows the velocities $x_2(t)$ for both blue and red cases. For the blue (lightly damped with $\varsigma = 0.25$) case, the mass moves from the initial 0.5 m position to the left overshooting by more than 50%, then oscillates several times before converging to the equilibrium shortly after 15 seconds. Both the displacement curve $x_1(t)$ and the velocity curve $x_2(t)$ show the same oscillation period approximately equals 6.5 sec. On the right-hand side of the figure is the phase plane trajectory on the x_2 versus x_1 plot spiraling from the initial (0.5,0) point on the (x_1, x_2) coordinates to eventually converge to the equilibrium (0,0).

In the second round of the simulation, the values of the mass M and the spring constant K remain the same, but the friction coefficient B is changed from $B = 0.05$ Ns/m to $B = 0.3$ Ns/m. This increase of the friction coefficient does not affect the natural frequency, but it changes the damping ratio from $\varsigma = 0.25$ to $\varsigma = 1.5$. Hence, the initial state response will become overdamped with no overshoot or oscillation. The x_2 versus x_1 plot on the right-hand side of the figure showed that the phase plane trajectory just monotonically moves toward the equilibrium without much spiral motion.

■

The simulation results in Figure 6.11 are generated using the following MATLAB code:

```
% CSD Fig6.11 MBK initial response due to x=[0.5 0]'
  t=linspace(0,20,201); X0=[0.5 0]', M=0.1, K=0.1, c=[1 0], b=[0;1/M],d=0,
  B=0.05, A=[0 1; -K/M -B/M], G=ss(A,b,c,d), [y,t,X]=initial(G,X0,t);
  x1=X(:,1); x2=X(:,2); subplot(1,3,1), plot(t,x1,'b-'), grid, hold on,
  subplot(1,3,2), plot(t,x2,'b-'), grid, hold on, subplot(1,3,3),
  plot(x1,x2,'b-'),grid, hold on, B=0.3, A=[0 1; -K/M -B/M], G=ss(A,b,c,d),
  [y,t,X]=initial(G,X0,t); x1=X(:,1); x2=X(:,2); subplot(1,3,1),
  plot(t,x1,'r-'), grid, hold on, subplot(1,3,2), plot(t,x2,'r-'), grid,
  hold on, subplot(1,3,3), plot(x1,x2,'r-'), grid
```

6.4 State Transition Matrix

The state-space model include a state equation and an output equation as shown in Equation 6.4. For ease of reference, these equations are repeated:

$$\dot{x}(t) = Ax(t) + Bu(t)$$
$$y(t) = Cx(t) + Du(t)$$

Recall that $x(t)$, $u(t)$, and $y(t)$ are the state vector, the input vector, and the output vector, respectively, and A, B, C, and D in general are all real constant matrices. The output equation is just an algebraic equation. If the state vector $x(t)$ is known, the output vector will become known accordingly. Hence, to investigate the behavior of the system described by the state-space model the main task is solving the state equation.

The state equation is a first-order differential equation. The procedures required to solve a first-order differential equation are less complicated than those involved in high-order differential equations. However, the state equations in general require matrix manipulations and computations. Owing to the advancement of matrix computing algorithms and computer technology in the last six decades, the digital tools for matrix computations and manipulations are now efficient and reliable.

Just like other differential equations, the solution to the state equation includes two parts: the *homogeneous solution* and the *particular solution*. We will find the homogeneous solution first and consider the particular solution later. The homogeneous solution does not depend on the input vector $u(t)$. Hence, only the following state equation with initial conditions is considered for now:

$$\dot{x}(t) = Ax(t), \qquad x(0) = x_0 \tag{6.7}$$

To get a clue on how to solve this equation in general matrix form, we will first consider the scalar case of this equation,

$$\dot{x}(t) = ax(t), \qquad x(0) = x_0$$

which we already have a solution,

$$x(t) = e^{at}x_0$$

Then, let us try to extend the scalar solution to the general matrix case and assume the solution can be written as follows:

$$x(t) = e^{At}x_0 \tag{6.8}$$

Note that this notation e^{At} is created by just replacing the a in e^{at} with A. At this moment, we still do not know what this notation e^{At} would represent except that it is an $n \times n$ matrix and $x(t) = e^{At}x_0$ must satisfy Equation 6.7. Now, by substituting $x(t) = e^{At}x_0$ into Equation 6.7, we have the following equation in question:

$$\dot{x}(t) = \frac{de^{At}x_0}{dt} \quad ? =? \quad Ae^{At}x_0 = Ax(t)$$

6.4.1 Theorems and Properties of the State Transition Matrix

In the previous discussion **the notation e^{At} can be replaced by an $n \times n$ matrix $\Phi(t)$, and $x(t) = \Phi(t)x_0$ is a solution of Equation 6.7 if and only if $\frac{d\Phi(t)}{dt} = A\Phi(t)$.** This fact is summarized in the following theorem and this matrix $\Phi(t)$ or e^{At} is called the *state transition matrix* of the system described by Equation 6.7.

Definition 6.9 (State Transition Matrix)

The $n \times n$ matrix $\Phi(t)$ that satisfies the following differential equation is called the state transition matrix associated with the A matrix.

$$\frac{d\Phi(t)}{dt} = A\Phi(t) \tag{6.9}$$

■

Theorem 6.10 (State Equation Homogeneous Solution)

If $\Phi(t)$ is the state transition matrix for the system described by Equation 6.7, then $x(t) = \Phi(t)x_0$ is a solution of Equation 6.7.

Proof:

If $\Phi(t)$ satisfies Equation 6.9, then we have

$$\dot{x}(t) = \frac{d\Phi(t)x_0}{dt} = A\Phi(t)x_0 = Ax(t)$$

which completes the proof.

■

Theorem 6.11 (State Transition Matrix Expression)

The state transition matrix $\Phi(t)$ can be expressed as follows,

$$\Phi(t) = e^{At} = I + At + \frac{A^2t^2}{2!} + \frac{A^3t^3}{3!} + \frac{A^4t^4}{4!} + \frac{A^5t^5}{5!} + \cdots \cdots \tag{6.10}$$

Proof:

It is straightforward to show that

$$\frac{de^{At}}{dt} = 0 + A + A^2t + \frac{A^3t^2}{2!} + \frac{A^4t^3}{3!} + \cdots = A\left(I + At + \frac{A^2t^2}{2!} + \frac{A^3t^3}{3!} + \cdots\right) = Ae^{At}$$

■

Theorem 6.12 (Properties of State Transition Matrix)

Some properties of the state transition matrix $\Phi(t)$ are summarized in the following:

- $\Phi(0) = I$
- $\Phi^{-1}(t) = \Phi(-t)$
- $\Phi(t_1)\Phi(t_2) = \Phi(t_1 + t_2) = \Phi(t_2)\Phi(t_1)$
- $\Phi(t_2 - t_1)\Phi(t_1 - t_0) = \Phi(t_2 - t_0)$

Proof:

Use $\Phi(t) = e^{At}$.

■

Remark 6.13 (Significance of the State Transition Matrix)

For $x(t) = \Phi(t)x_0$ to be a solution of the state equation

$$\dot{x}(t) = Ax(t), \qquad x(0) = x_0$$

the matrix $\Phi(t)$ has to be the state transition matrix that satisfies Equation 6.9. Note that the solution can be rewritten in the general form

$$x(t_2) = \Phi(t_2 - t_1)x(t_1)$$

which depicts the transition of the state of the system from $x(t_1)$ to $x(t_2)$, where t_1 and t_2 can be any time instant. ∎

Theorem 6.14 (State Transition Matrix Expression in Frequency Domain)

The state transition matrix $\Phi(t)$ is the inverse Laplace transform of

$$\Phi(s) = (sI - A)^{-1} \tag{6.11}$$

Proof:

Let $X(s)$ be the Laplace transform of $x(t)$, then taking the Laplace transform of Equation 6.7 will yield the following,

$$sX(s) - x_0 = AX(s) \quad \rightarrow \quad (sI - A)X(s) = x_0$$

Then we have

$$X(s) = (sI - A)^{-1}x_0 \quad \rightarrow \quad x(t) = \mathcal{L}^{-1}\left[(sI - A)^{-1}\right]x_0$$

∎

6.4.2 Computing the State Transition Matrix

To compute the state transition matrix, we can use either one of the following two formulas:

$$\Phi(t) = e^{At} = \sum_{k=0}^{\infty} \frac{1}{k!}A^k t^k = I + At + \frac{A^2 t^2}{2!} + \frac{A^3 t^3}{3!} + \frac{A^4 t^4}{4!} + \frac{A^5 t^5}{5!} + \cdots \tag{6.12}$$

or

$$\Phi(t) = \mathcal{L}^{-1}\left[(sI - A)^{-1}\right] \tag{6.13}$$

The first formula, Equation 6.12, works well for machine computing, but it is not suitable for analytic work due to its infinite series expression. However, based on the Cayley-Hamilton theorem, this infinite-series formula can be converted into a closed-form expression convenient for analytic work. The second formula, Equation 6.13, is a Laplace transform approach that provides closed-form solutions via matrix inversion and inverse Laplace transform manipulations. In the following, we will first introduce the Cayley-Hamilton approach and then use second-order examples to demonstrate the procedure. Shortly after that, the same examples will be employed to illustrate the Laplace transform approach.

Theorem 6.15 (The Cayley-Hamilton Theorem)

Consider an $n \times n$ matrix A. Assume $\lambda_1, \lambda_2, \cdots, \lambda_n$ are the eigenvalues of the A matrix, which means they are the roots of the following characteristic equation:

$$f(\lambda) := \det(\lambda I - A) = 0$$

Then

$$f(\lambda_i) = 0, \quad i = 1, 2, ..., n \quad \text{if and only if} \quad f(A) = 0$$

■

Based on the Cayley-Hamilton theorem, the state transition matrix of Equation 6.12 can be rewritten as follows:

$$e^{At} = \sum_{i=0}^{n-1} \alpha_i(t)A^i = \alpha_0(t)I + \alpha_1(t)A + \alpha_2(t)A^2 + \cdots + \alpha_{n-1}(t)A^{n-1} \tag{6.14}$$

Note that the state transition matrix now has only n terms, but the coefficients,

$$\alpha_i(t), \quad i = 0, 1, 2, ..., n-1$$

are required to be determined. These time-dependent coefficients can be solved from

$$e^{\lambda_\ell t} = \sum_{i=0}^{n-1} \alpha_i(t)\lambda_\ell^i, \quad \ell = 1, 2, ..., n \tag{6.15}$$

where λ_ℓ, $\ell = 1, 2, ..., n$ are the eigenvalues of the A matrix.

To make it more clear regarding the coefficient equations of Equation 6.15, without loss of generality we will use an $n = 3$ case to illustrate how to solve for the coefficients in these sets of equations. **Assume the A matrix has three distinct eigenvalues λ_1, λ_2, and λ_3.** The case of multiple eigenvalues will be addressed shortly after this. Then the third-order version of Equation 6.15 will be

$$e^{\lambda_1 t} = \alpha_0(t) + \alpha_1(t)\lambda_1 + \alpha_2(t)\lambda_1^2$$
$$e^{\lambda_2 t} = \alpha_0(t) + \alpha_1(t)\lambda_2 + \alpha_2(t)\lambda_2^2 \tag{6.16}$$
$$e^{\lambda_3 t} = \alpha_0(t) + \alpha_1(t)\lambda_3 + \alpha_2(t)\lambda_3^2$$

Since these three eigenvalues are distinct, the three equations are linearly independent; hence, the three coefficients $\alpha_0(t)$, $\alpha_1(t)$, and $\alpha_2(t)$ can be uniquely determined. Therefore, the state transition matrix of the 3rd-order system will be

$$e^{At} = \sum_{i=0}^{3-1} \alpha_i(t)A^i = \alpha_0(t)I + \alpha_1(t)A + \alpha_2(t)A^2 \tag{6.17}$$

Now, let us consider **the case with multiple eigenvalues. Assume $\lambda_2 = \lambda_1$;** then the second and the first equations of Equation 6.16 are identical. We have to **remove the second equation and replace it by a new equation obtained by taking derivative of a copy of the first equation with respect to λ_1.** In other words, Equation 6.16 is replaced by the following new coefficient equations:

$$e^{\lambda_1 t} = \alpha_0(t) + \alpha_1(t)\lambda_1 + \alpha_2(t)\lambda_1^2$$
$$te^{\lambda_1 t} = \alpha_1(t) + 2\alpha_2(t)\lambda_1 \tag{6.18}$$
$$e^{\lambda_3 t} = \alpha_0(t) + \alpha_1(t)\lambda_3 + \alpha_2(t)\lambda_3^2$$

which are now linearly independent; hence, the three coefficients $\alpha_0(t)$, $\alpha_1(t)$, and $\alpha_2(t)$ can be uniquely determined.

Example 6.16 (Find a State Transition Matrix Using the Cayley-Hamilton Approach)

Consider the matrix $A = \begin{bmatrix} 0 & 1 \\ -2 & -3 \end{bmatrix}$, whose eigenvalues can be found, $\lambda_1 = -1$ and $\lambda_2 = -2$. Based on the Cayley-Hamilton theorem, the state transition matrix associated with this A matrix can be written as

$$e^{At} = \alpha_0(t)I + \alpha_1(t)A$$

From Equation 6.15 or Equation 6.16 we have the coefficient equations:

$$e^{\lambda_1 t} = \alpha_0(t) + \alpha_1(t)\lambda_1$$

$$e^{\lambda_2 t} = \alpha_0(t) + \alpha_1(t)\lambda_2$$

Substitute $\lambda_1 = -1$ and $\lambda_2 = -2$ into these two equations to get

$$e^{-t} = \alpha_0(t) - \alpha_1(t)$$

$$e^{-2t} = \alpha_0(t) - 2\alpha_1(t)$$

and solve these two equations to yield the two coefficients

$$\alpha_0(t) = 2e^{-t} - e^{-2t}$$

$$\alpha_1(t) = e^{-t} - e^{-2t}$$

Then we have the state transition matrix as follows:

$$e^{At} = (2e^{-t} - e^{-2t})I + (e^{-t} - e^{-2t})A = \begin{bmatrix} 2e^{-t} - e^{-2t} & e^{-t} - e^{-2t} \\ -2e^{-t} + 2e^{-2t} & -e^{-t} + 2e^{-2t} \end{bmatrix}$$

∎

Example 6.17 (Cayley-Hamilton Approach for the Case with Multiple Eigenvalues)

Consider the matrix $A = \begin{bmatrix} 0 & 1 \\ -1 & -2 \end{bmatrix}$, whose two eigenvalues are identical as $\lambda_1 = -1$ and $\lambda_2 = -1$. Based on the Cayley-Hamilton theorem, the state transition matrix associated with this A matrix can be written as

$$e^{At} = \alpha_0(t)I + \alpha_1(t)A$$

Since the two eigenvalues are identical, Equation 6.15 or Equation 6.16 can provide only one coefficient equation in the following:

$$e^{\lambda_1 t} = \alpha_0(t) + \alpha_1(t)\lambda_1$$

One more coefficient equation is required to solve for the two coefficient variables. Following the same procedure as we did to obtain Equation 6.18, we can obtain the supplemental coefficient equation by taking derivative of the above equation with respective to λ_1. Now we have the supplemental coefficient equation

$$te^{-t} = \alpha_1(t)$$

Together with the regular coefficient equation

$$e^{-t} = \alpha_0(t) - \alpha_1(t)$$

we obtain the two coefficients

$$\alpha_0(t) = e^{-t} + te^{-t}$$

$$\alpha_1(t) = te^{-t}$$

Then we have the state transition matrix as follows:

$$e^{At} = (e^{-t} + te^{-t})I + te^{-t}A = \begin{bmatrix} e^{-t} + te^{-t} & te^{-t} \\ -te^{-t} & e^{-t} - te^{-t} \end{bmatrix}$$

∎

In the following we will employ the same example matrices to illustrate the procedure of the Laplace transform approach using the formula

$$\Phi(t) = \mathcal{L}^{-1}\left[(sI - A)^{-1}\right]$$

Example 6.18 (Find a State Transition Matrix Using the Laplace Transform Approach)

Consider the matrix $A = \begin{bmatrix} 0 & 1 \\ -2 & -3 \end{bmatrix}$, whose eigenvalues can be found, $\lambda_1 = -1$ and $\lambda_2 = -2$. In order to apply the formula shown, the first step is to compute the inverse of the matrix $sI - A$ and perform partial fraction expansion of each entry of the matrix in the following:

$$(sI - A)^{-1} = \begin{bmatrix} s & -1 \\ 2 & s+3 \end{bmatrix}^{-1} = \frac{1}{s^2 + 3s + 2}\begin{bmatrix} s+3 & 1 \\ -2 & s \end{bmatrix}$$

$$= \begin{bmatrix} \frac{s+3}{(s+1)(s+2)} & \frac{1}{(s+1)(s+2)} \\ \frac{-2}{(s+1)(s+2)} & \frac{s}{(s+1)(s+2)} \end{bmatrix} = \begin{bmatrix} \frac{2}{s+1} + \frac{-1}{s+2} & \frac{1}{s+1} + \frac{-1}{s+2} \\ \frac{-2}{s+1} + \frac{2}{s+2} & \frac{-1}{s+1} + \frac{2}{s+2} \end{bmatrix}$$

Then we have the state transition matrix as

$$\Phi(t) = \mathcal{L}^{-1}\left[(sI - A)^{-1}\right] = \begin{bmatrix} 2e^{-t} - e^{-2t} & e^{-t} - e^{-2t} \\ -2e^{-t} + 2e^{-2t} & -e^{-t} + 2e^{-2t} \end{bmatrix}$$

∎

Example 6.19 (Laplace Transform Approach for the Case with Multiple Eigenvalues)

Consider the matrix $A = \begin{bmatrix} 0 & 1 \\ -1 & -2 \end{bmatrix}$, whose two eigenvalues are identical as $\lambda_1 = -1$ and $\lambda_2 = -1$. The same Laplace transform approach shown in Example 6.18 can be employed for the case with multiple eigenvalues to compute the inverse of the matrix $sI - A$ and perform partial fraction expansion of each entry of the matrix before conducting the inverse Laplace transform.

$$(sI - A)^{-1} = \begin{bmatrix} s & -1 \\ 1 & s+2 \end{bmatrix}^{-1} = \frac{1}{s^2 + 2s + 1}\begin{bmatrix} s+2 & 1 \\ -1 & s \end{bmatrix}$$

$$= \begin{bmatrix} \frac{s+2}{(s+1)^2} & \frac{1}{(s+1)^2} \\ \frac{-1}{(s+1)^2} & \frac{s}{(s+1)^2} \end{bmatrix} = \begin{bmatrix} \frac{1}{s+1} + \frac{1}{(s+1)^2} & \frac{1}{(s+1)^2} \\ \frac{-1}{(s+1)^2} & \frac{1}{s+1} + \frac{-1}{(s+1)^2} \end{bmatrix}$$

Then we have the state transition matrix as

$$\Phi(t) = \mathcal{L}^{-1}\left[(sI - A)^{-1}\right] = \begin{bmatrix} e^{-t} + te^{-t} & te^{-t} \\ -te^{-t} & e^{-t} - te^{-t} \end{bmatrix}$$

∎

6.5 Solution of the State Equation

Consider the state equation,

$$\dot{x}(t) = Ax(t) + Bu(t) \tag{6.19}$$

where A, B, $x(0) = x_0$, and $u(t)$, $t \geq 0$ are given. The problem is to find $x(t)$ for $t \geq 0$.

Let $X(s)$ and $U(s)$ be the Laplace transforms of the state vector $x(t)$ and the input vector $u(t)$, respectively. Taking the Laplace transform on the state equation yields the following frequency-domain equation:

$$sX(s) - x_0 = AX(s) + BU(s)$$

Since the objective is to find the state response, the state vector terms are moved to the left-hand side of the equation while keeping or moving the input and the initial state vector to the right-hand side:

$$(sI - A)X(s) = x_0 + BU(s)$$

Multiplying $(sI - A)^{-1}$ to both sides of the equation from the left, we obtain the solution of the state equation in the frequency domain:

$$X(s) = (sI - A)^{-1}x_0 + (sI - A)^{-1}BU(s) \tag{6.20}$$

Then we have the state response $x(t)$, which is the inverse Laplace transform of $X(s)$,

$$x(t) = \mathscr{L}^{-1}\left[(sI - A)^{-1}\right]x_0 + \mathscr{L}^{-1}\left[(sI - A)^{-1}BU(s)\right] \tag{6.21}$$

Recall that the inverse Laplace transform of $(sI - A)^{-1}$ is the state transition matrix $\Phi(t)$:

$$\mathscr{L}^{-1}\left[(sI - A)^{-1}\right] = \Phi(t)$$

Thus, Equation 6.21 can be rewritten in terms of the state transition matrix as follows:

$$x(t) = \Phi(t)x_0 + \int_0^t \Phi(t - \tau)Bu(\tau)d\tau := x_h(t) + x_p(t) \tag{6.22}$$

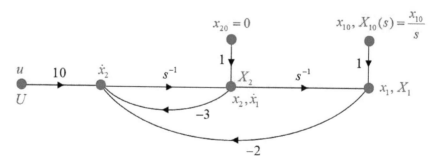

Fig. 6.12: State diagram for the simple MBK system time response simulation.

The convolution theorem (Theorem 2.24) was employed in the inverse Laplace transform manipulations, and the second term of the above state response is a convolution integral. Also note that **the first** term of the response $x_h(t)$ is the homogeneous solution due to the initial state vector x_0 and the second term of the response $x_p(t)$ is the particular solution due to the input $u(t)$.

In the following, we will employ the simple MBK system again to illustrate how to compute the time responses in both time and frequency domains and verify the computational results with the simulation results. The Simulink simulation diagram, $CSD\_fig6p13\_StateModel.mdl$, shown on the top of Figure 6.13 is constructed based on the state diagram in Figure 6.12. This simulation diagram is similar to that shown in Figure 6.10. The difference is that this time we will consider overall time responses of all states due to the initial condition and the input while in the previous simulation we only considered the output response due to the initial condition. The mass, damper, and spring are are chosen as $M = 0.1$ kg, $B = 0.3$ Ns/m, and $K = 0.2$ N/m. This change causes the damping ratio and natural frequency of the system to become $\varsigma = 1.06$ and $\omega_n = 1.414$ rad/s, respectively. The response will be faster and less damped than the previous overdamped case simulation in Example 6.8.

The simulation will be conducted three times, one for the homogeneous solution $x_h(t)$, the response due to the initial state x_0; the second one for the particular solution $x_p(t)$, the response due to the input $u(t)$; and finally the complete solution $x(t)$, the total response due to the combined effort of x_0 and $u(t)$. The initial conditions for the displacement state and the velocity state are assumed $x_1(0) = 0.5$ m and $x_2(0) = 0$ m/s, respectively. The applied force input is assumed $u(t) = 0.05$ N for $t \geq 0$.

We will run the following MATLAB program: $CSD\_fig6p13.m$, which will automatically call the Simulink model program $CSDfig6p13SM.mdl$, to conduct the simulation. The MATLAB code is listed as follows:

```
% Filename: CSD_fig6p13.m     May 4, 2020   initial & step response
% Run this CSD_fig6p13.m program to automatically call the Simulink file:
% CSDfig6p13SM.mdl and plot_1Blue.m, plot_2Red.m, plot_3Black.m,
% Nominal plant
 M=0.1, K=0.2,  B=0.3,
%% Simulation 1
 u=0, x10=0.5, sim_time=10,
 sim_options=simset('SrcWorkspace', 'current', 'DstWorkspace ', 'current');
 open('CSDfig6p13SM'), sim('CSDfig6p13SM', [0, sim_time], sim_options);
 run('plot_1Blue')
%% Simulation 2
 u=0.05, x10=0, sim_time=10,
 sim_options=simset('SrcWorkspace', 'current', 'DstWorkspace', 'current');
 open('CSDfig6p13SM'), sim('CSDfig6p13SM', [0, sim_time], sim_options);
 run('plot_2Red')
%% Simulation 3
 u=0.05, x10=0.5, sim_time=10,
 sim_options=simset('SrcWorkspace', 'current', 'DstWorkspace', 'current');
 open('CSDfig6p13SM'), sim('CSDfig6p13SM', [0, sim_time], sim_options);
 run('plot_3Black')
```

Before running this program, make sure to include the Simulink file $CSDfig6p13SM.mdl$, and the three plotting files: $plot\_1Blue.m$, $plot\_2Red.m$, and $plot\_3black.m$ in the same folder. Only one of the plot files is given. The other two are the same except the color.

```
% filename: plot_1Blue.m    plot after running simulink file:
 figure(1)
 subplot(1,3,1), plot(t,x1,'b-'), grid on, grid minor, title('x1'), hold on,
 subplot(1,3,2), plot(t,x2,'b-'), grid on, grid minor, title('x2'), hold on,
 subplot(1,3,3), plot(x1,x2,'b-'), grid on, grid minor, title('x2 vs x1'),
 hold on,
```

The simulation results are shown in Figure 6.13. The response graph for x_1 on the left shows three displacement response curves: (1) x_{1h}: the displacement response due to the initial state x_0 only, (2) x_{1p}: the displacement response due to the input $u(t)$ only, and (3) x_1: the displacement response due to both x_0 and $u(t)$ acting at the same time. It is observed that $x_1(t) = x_{1h}(t) + x_{1p}(t)$.

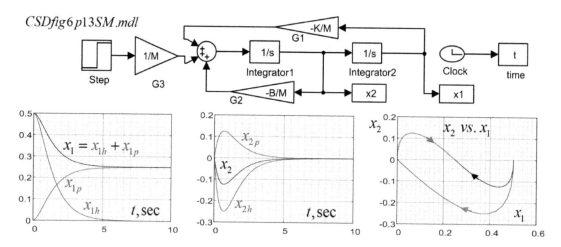

Fig. 6.13: Simple MBK system time response simulation results.

Similarly, the response graph for x_2 in the middle shows three velocity response curves: (1) x_{2h}: the velocity response due to the initial state x_0 only, (2) x_{2p}: the velocity response due to the input $u(t)$ only, and (3) x_2: the response due to both x_0 and $u(t)$ acting at the same time. It is observed that $x_2(t) = x_{2h}(t) + x_{2p}(t)$.

The response graph on the right of Figure 6.13 exhibits the phase plane trajectories of the three responses displayed on the left and the middle graphs. The homogeneous solution motion (in blue) would move the state from (0.5,0) towards the origin (0,0) if there was no input. On the other hand, the particular solution motion (in red) would move the state from the origin (0,0) towards its intended destination (0.25,0) if the state conditions were zero. Actually the real motion (in black) is the combination of both actions that together move the state from (0.5,0) to (0.25,0).

Example 6.20 (Computation of the Homogeneous and Particular Solutions of the State Equation in Time Domain)

In the state diagram of the simple MBK (mass–damper–spring) system shown in Figure 6.12, there is one integrator between the x_1 node and the x_2 node, implying $\dot{x}_1 = x_2$. By summing up the three incoming signals at the $\dot{x}_2$ node, we have another first-order differential equation $\dot{x}_2 = -2x_1 - 3x_2 + 10u$. Hence, we have the state equation of the system:

$$\begin{bmatrix} \dot{x}_1(t) \\ \dot{x}_2(t) \end{bmatrix} = \begin{bmatrix} 0 & 1 \\ -2 & -3 \end{bmatrix} \begin{bmatrix} x_1(t) \\ x_2(t) \end{bmatrix} + \begin{bmatrix} 0 \\ 10 \end{bmatrix} u(t), \qquad x(0) = x_0 = \begin{bmatrix} x_{10} \\ 0 \end{bmatrix}$$

where the initial displacement state is assumed $x_{10} = 0.5$ m, and the applied force input $u(t)$ is a step input with magnitude 0.05N. The objective of this example is to find the homogeneous solution and the particular solution of the state equation. These solutions can be found using the time-domain approach via Equation 6.22, which are:

$$x_h(t) = \Phi(t)x_0, \quad \text{and} \quad x_p(t) = \int_0^t \Phi(t-\tau)Bu(\tau)d\tau$$

The state transition matrix $\Phi(t)$ in the above two equations can be obtained using the Cayley-Hamilton approach or the Laplace transform approach described in Section 6.4.2.

In Example 6.16 we had applied the Cayley-Hamilton approach to the same A matrix to obtain its state transition matrix, which is

$$\Phi(t) = \begin{bmatrix} 2e^{-t} - e^{-2t} & e^{-t} - e^{-2t} \\ -2e^{-t} + 2e^{-2t} & -e^{-t} + 2e^{-2t} \end{bmatrix}$$

Thus, we have the homogeneous solution as follows:

$$x_h(t) = \Phi(t)x_0 = \begin{bmatrix} 2e^{-t} - e^{-2t} & e^{-t} - e^{-2t} \\ -2e^{-t} + 2e^{-2t} & -e^{-t} + 2e^{-2t} \end{bmatrix} \begin{bmatrix} 0.5 \\ 0 \end{bmatrix} = \begin{bmatrix} e^{-t} - 0.5e^{-2t} \\ -e^{-t} + e^{-2t} \end{bmatrix}$$

The computation of the particular solution $x_p(t)$ is a little bit more complicated since it involves convolution integral.

$$x_p(t) = \int_0^t \Phi(t-\tau)Bu(\tau)d\tau = \int_0^t \Phi(t-\tau) \begin{bmatrix} 0 \\ 10 \end{bmatrix} 0.05u_s(\tau)d\tau$$

Note that the variable τ, instead of t, is the integration variable. When carrying out the integration, t should be temporarily treated as a constant parameter. According to the convolution theorem, the convolution integral can be rewritten as the following:

$$x_p(t) = \int_0^t \Phi(\tau) \begin{bmatrix} 0 \\ 0.5 \end{bmatrix} u_s(t-\tau)d\tau$$

Since $u_s(t-\tau)$ is 1 when $\tau < t$ and 0 elsewhere, the value of $u_s(t-\tau)$ is 1 inside the integration range; hence, the above integral can further be simplified as follows:

$$x_p(t) = \int_0^t \Phi(\tau) \begin{bmatrix} 0 \\ 0.5 \end{bmatrix} d\tau = 0.5 \int_0^t \begin{bmatrix} e^{-\tau} - e^{-2\tau} \\ -e^{-\tau} + 2e^{-2\tau} \end{bmatrix} d\tau = 0.5 \begin{bmatrix} -e^{-\tau} + 0.5e^{-2\tau} \\ e^{-\tau} - e^{-2\tau} \end{bmatrix}_0^t$$

Then we have the particular solution of the state equation as

$$x_p(t) = 0.5 \begin{bmatrix} -e^{-t} + 0.5e^{-2t} - (-1+0.5) \\ e^{-t} - e^{-2t} - (1-1) \end{bmatrix} = \begin{bmatrix} -0.5e^{-t} + 0.25e^{-2t} + 0.25 \\ 0.5e^{-t} - 0.5e^{-2t} \end{bmatrix}$$

■

Next, we will apply the Laplace transform approach to compute the homogeneous and particular solutions of the same state equation.

Example 6.21 (Computation of the Homogeneous and Particular Solutions of the State Equation Using the Laplace Transform Approach)

The state equation to be considered is repeated here for convenience.

$$\begin{bmatrix} \dot{x}_1(t) \\ \dot{x}_2(t) \end{bmatrix} = \begin{bmatrix} 0 & 1 \\ -2 & -3 \end{bmatrix} \begin{bmatrix} x_1(t) \\ x_2(t) \end{bmatrix} + \begin{bmatrix} 0 \\ 10 \end{bmatrix} u(t), \quad x(0) = x_0 = \begin{bmatrix} x_{10} \\ 0 \end{bmatrix}$$

where the initial displacement state is assumed $x_{10} = 0.5$ m, and the applied force input $u(t)$ is a step input with magnitude 0.05 N.

The state transition matrix associated with the A matrix had been computed in Example 6.18 using the Laplace transform as the following:

$$\Phi(t) = \mathcal{L}^{-1}\left[(sI-A)^{-1}\right] = \begin{bmatrix} 2e^{-t} - e^{-2t} & e^{-t} - e^{-2t} \\ -2e^{-t} + 2e^{-2t} & -e^{-t} + 2e^{-2t} \end{bmatrix}$$

Thus, the homogeneous solution is

$$x_h(t) = \Phi(t)x_0 = \begin{bmatrix} 2e^{-t} - e^{-2t} & e^{-t} - e^{-2t} \\ -2e^{-t} + 2e^{-2t} & -e^{-t} + 2e^{-2t} \end{bmatrix}\begin{bmatrix} 0.5 \\ 0 \end{bmatrix} = \begin{bmatrix} e^{-t} - 0.5e^{-2t} \\ -e^{-t} + e^{-2t} \end{bmatrix}$$

Since the Laplace transform of the particular solution is $(sI-A)^{-1}BU(s)$, we have

$$X_p(s) = (sI-A)^{-1}BU(s) = \begin{bmatrix} \frac{s+3}{(s+1)(s+2)} & \frac{1}{(s+1)(s+2)} \\ \frac{-2}{(s+1)(s+2)} & \frac{s}{(s+1)(s+2)} \end{bmatrix}\begin{bmatrix} 0 \\ 10 \end{bmatrix}\frac{0.05}{s} = \begin{bmatrix} \frac{0.5}{s(s+1)(s+2)} \\ \frac{0.5s}{s(s+1)(s+2)} \end{bmatrix}$$

Then the particular solution of the state equation can be obtained by finding the inverse Laplace transform of the previous matrix,

$$x_p(t) = \mathcal{L}^{-1}[X_p(s)] = \mathcal{L}^{-1}\begin{bmatrix} \frac{0.25}{s} + \frac{-0.5}{s+1} + \frac{0.25}{s+2} \\ \frac{0.5}{s+1} + \frac{-0.5}{s+2} \end{bmatrix} = \begin{bmatrix} 0.25 - 0.5e^{-t} + 0.25e^{-2t} \\ 0.5e^{-t} - 0.5e^{-2t} \end{bmatrix}$$

∎

6.6 State-Space Models and Transfer Functions

Systems can be represented by differential equations, transfer functions, state-space models, or state diagrams. In many analysis and design cases, we may need to convert from one representation to another. In this section, we will discuss how to do it correctly and efficiently. Since we have just utilized the Laplace transform approach to solve a state equation in the previous section, we will first discuss how to find the transfer function of a system from a given state-space model of the system.

6.6.1 Find Transfer Function from State-Space Model

Consider the following state-space model:

$$\dot{x}(t) = Ax(t) + Bu(t)$$
$$y(t) = Cx(t) + Du(t)$$

Let $X(s)$, $U(s)$, and $Y(s)$ be the Laplace transforms of the state vector $x(t)$, the input vector $u(t)$, and the output vector $y(t)$, respectively. Recall that the solution $X(s)$ of the transformed state equation was given by Equation 6.20 as

$$X(s) = (sI-A)^{-1}x_0 + (sI-A)^{-1}BU(s)$$

Plugging this solution into the transformed output equation of the state-space model,

$$Y(s) = CX(s) + DU(s)$$

we will have the following output response:

$$Y(s) = C(sI - A)^{-1}x_0 + \left[C(sI - A)^{-1}B + D \right] U(s) \tag{6.23}$$

Note that the first term is the output response due to the initial state x_0, and the second term is the output response due to the input $U(s)$. Therefore, **the transfer function from the input $U(s)$ to the output $Y(s)$ is**

$$\frac{Y(s)}{U(s)} := G(s) = C(sI - A)^{-1}B + D \tag{6.24}$$

Example 6.22 (State-Space Model $\rightarrow$ Transfer Function)

For the simple MBK system considered in Example 6.7, if the system parameters are chosen to be $M = 0.1$ kg, $B = 0.3$ Ns/m, and $K = 0.2$ N/m, the system dynamics can be described by the state-space model.

$$\dot{x}(t) = Ax(t) + Bu(t)$$
$$y(t) = Cx(t) + Du(t)$$

where

$$A = \begin{bmatrix} 0 & 1 \\ -2 & -3 \end{bmatrix}, B = \begin{bmatrix} 0 \\ 10 \end{bmatrix}, C = \begin{bmatrix} 1 & 0 \end{bmatrix}, D = 0$$

The transfer function of the system can be obtained using Equation 6.24 as follows:

$$G(s) = C(sI - A)^{-1}B + D = \begin{bmatrix} 1 & 0 \end{bmatrix} \begin{bmatrix} s & -1 \\ 2 & s+3 \end{bmatrix}^{-1} \begin{bmatrix} 0 \\ 10 \end{bmatrix}$$

Since

$$\begin{bmatrix} s & -1 \\ 2 & s+3 \end{bmatrix}^{-1} = \frac{1}{\Delta} \begin{bmatrix} s+3 & 1 \\ -2 & s \end{bmatrix} \quad \text{where} \quad \Delta = s(s+3) + 2$$

we have the transfer function as follows:

$$G(s) = \frac{1}{\Delta} \begin{bmatrix} 1 & 0 \end{bmatrix} \begin{bmatrix} s+3 & 1 \\ -2 & s \end{bmatrix} \begin{bmatrix} 0 \\ 10 \end{bmatrix} = \frac{10}{\Delta} = \frac{10}{s^2 + 3s + 2}$$

■

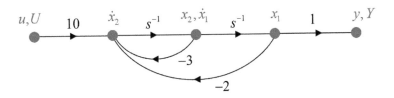

Fig. 6.14: Using the state diagram of a state-space model to find the transfer function.

Example 6.23 (State-Space Model → State Diagram → Transfer Function)

In this example, we will demonstrate how to use the state diagram to find the transfer function. The state diagram associated with the state-space model considered in Example 6.22 can be constructed as shown in Figure 6.14. **Since the state diagram is a signal flow graph, Mason's gain formula can be employed to find the transfer function from U to Y.** By inspection, we can see there are two loops and one forward path in the diagram. The two loop gains and one forward path gain are

$$\ell_1 = -3s^{-1}, \quad \ell_2 = -2s^{-2}, \quad \text{and} \quad F_1 = 10s^{-2}$$

so that Δ and Δ_1 are

$$\Delta = 1 - (\ell_1 + \ell_2) = 1 + 3s^{-1} + 2s^{-2}, \quad \Delta_1 = 1$$

Therefore, the transfer function $G(s)$ is

$$G(s) := \frac{Y(s)}{U(s)} = \frac{F_1 \Delta_1}{\Delta} = \frac{10s^{-2}}{1 + 3s^{-1} + 2s^{-2}} = \frac{10}{s^2 + 3s + 2}$$

∎

Given a state-space model (A, B, C, D), we can find the transfer function using the direct formula $C(sI - A)^{-1}B + D$ or utilizing the state diagram together with Mason's gain formula. It seems that the state diagram approach requires more steps. **But in many cases, especially when the order of the system is higher, the computation involved in the state diagram approach is easier than that in the direct formula approach.**

6.6.2 Construct a State-Space Model in Companion Form Using Direct Realization

As we know, we cannot have two different transfer functions for a given system, but there exist infinitely many state-space models for the same system since state variables can be defined in infinitely many differently ways. For this reason, give a state-space model, we will obtain the same transfer function despite using different approaches. Conversely we may not get the same state-space model from a given transfer function. The transfer function of a system is unique, but the state-space model is not.

There are many ways to assign state variables. Sometimes we would like the state variables to associate with the physical variables in the real world, like the displacements, the velocities in mechanical systems and the inductor currents, the capacitor voltages in electric circuits. On the other hand, in many analysis and design cases we may need a state-space model in some special form. One of the commonly used forms of state-space models is called *companion form*, which is also named the controller canonical form, or the phase variable canonical form.

Without loss of generality, we assume the transfer function is a third-order strictly proper rational function as shown:

$$\frac{Y(s)}{U(s)} := G(s) = \frac{b_2 s^2 + b_1 s + b_0}{s^3 + a_2 s^2 + a_1 s + a_0} \tag{6.25}$$

Here, *strictly proper* means that the degree of the numerator polynomial is less than that of the denominator polynomial. **If both degrees are equal, a division needs to be performed to convert the transfer function into two terms: one strictly proper rational function and the other a constant.** Recall that the corresponding differential equation of the transfer function is

$$\dddot{y}(t) + a_2 \ddot{y}(t) + a_1 \dot{y}(t) + a_0 y(t) = b_2 \ddot{u}(t) + b_1 \dot{u}(t) + b_0 u(t)$$

In the equation, $\dddot{y}$ and $\ddot{y}$ represents the third and second derivatives of y, respectively. Note that the Laplace transform s variable can be regarded as a differentiation operator in the conversion between transfer function and differential equation.

The first step toward the construction of the companion form state-space model is to multiply a new variable $X(s)$ to both the numerator and the denominator of the transfer function in Equation 6.25 as follows:

$$\frac{Y(s)}{U(s)} = \frac{b_2 s^2 + b_1 s + b_0}{s^3 + a_2 s^2 + a_1 s + a_0} \frac{X(s)}{X(s)}$$

Split the numerator and denominator to get the following two equations:

$$
\begin{aligned}
Y(s) &= b_2 s^2 X(s) + b_1 s X(s) + b_0 X(s) \quad \rightleftarrows \quad y = b_2 \ddot{x} + b_1 \dot{x} + b_0 x \\
U(s) &= s^3 X(s) + a_2 s^2 X(s) + a_1 s X(s) + a_0 X(s) \quad \rightleftarrows \quad u = \dddot{x} + a_2 \ddot{x} + a_1 \dot{x} + a_0 x
\end{aligned}
\tag{6.26}
$$

The second equation can be rearranged to the following,

$$\dddot{x} = -a_2 \ddot{x} - a_1 \dot{x} - a_0 x + u \tag{6.27}$$

Including the input u, the output y, the variable x and its three derivative variables, six nodes are required in the state diagram. They are labeled as u, $\dddot{x}$, $\ddot{x}$, $\dot{x}$, x, and y. **Based on Equation 6.27, the node $\dddot{x}$ shall receive the four incoming branches from nodes u, $\ddot{x}$, $\dot{x}$, and x. Similarly according to the first equation of Equation 6.26, three incoming branches from nodes $\ddot{x}$, $\dot{x}$, and x will feed to the output node y.** Thus, we have the state diagram shown in Figure 6.15.

Now, we are ready to assign state variables. The rule is to assign a state variables at each integrator's output. Although no specific order of the state variables is required, we would follow the companion form convention to assign node x as x_1, node $\dot{x}$ as x_2, and node $\ddot{x}$ as x_3, as shown in the state diagram. Then, according to the state diagram, we can easily write down the state equation and the output equation in the following:

$$
\begin{bmatrix} \dot{x}_1(t) \\ \dot{x}_2(t) \\ \dot{x}_3(t) \end{bmatrix} = \begin{bmatrix} 0 & 1 & 0 \\ 0 & 0 & 1 \\ -a_0 & -a_1 & -a_2 \end{bmatrix} \begin{bmatrix} x_1(t) \\ x_2(t) \\ x_3(t) \end{bmatrix} + \begin{bmatrix} 0 \\ 0 \\ 1 \end{bmatrix} u(t), \qquad y(t) = \begin{bmatrix} b_0 & b_1 & b_2 \end{bmatrix} \begin{bmatrix} x_1(t) \\ x_2(t) \\ x_3(t) \end{bmatrix} \tag{6.28}
$$

This state-space model is said to be in the companion form. Note that the A matrix has the following three features: (1) The entries right above the main diagonal are all 1's; (2) the entries at the bottom row are the denominator coefficients of the transfer function with sign change; and (3) the rest of the A matrix entries are all 0's. The column vector B has all 0's except the bottom entry, which is 1. The row vector C is constructed using the numerator coefficients.

Example 6.24 (Construct a Companion-Form State-Space Model Using Direct Realization)

In this example, we will simply follow the companion form construction procedure to draw a state diagram like Figure 6.15, and then use this state diagram to find the state-space model in the companion form as shown in Equation 6.28.

Consider the transfer function

$$G(s) = \frac{s+3}{s^2 + 3s + 2}$$

The first step is to multiply a new variable $X(s)$ to both the numerator and the denominator of the transfer function as follows:

$$\frac{Y(s)}{U(s)} = \frac{s+3}{s^2 + 3s + 2} \frac{X(s)}{X(s)}$$

Split the numerator and denominator to get the following two equations:

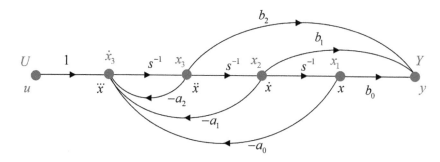

Fig. 6.15: Construction of a state-space model in companion form via a state diagram.

$$Y(s) = sX(s) + 3X(s) \quad \rightleftarrows \quad y = \dot{x} + 3x$$
$$U(s) = s^2 X(s) + 3sX(s) + 2X(s) \quad \rightleftarrows \quad u = \ddot{x} + 3\dot{x} + 2x \quad \rightleftarrows \quad \ddot{x} = -3\dot{x} - 2x + u$$

Including the input u, the output y, the variable x, and its two derivative variables, five nodes are required in the state diagram. They are labeled as u, $\ddot{x}$, $\dot{x}$, x, and y, as shown in Figure 6.16.

According to the second of the two equations, $\ddot{x} = -3\dot{x} - 2x + u$, the node $\ddot{x}$ shall receive the three incoming branches from nodes u, $\dot{x}$, and x with gains 1, -3, and -2, respectively. Similarly, based on the other equation, $y = \dot{x} + 3x$, the two incoming branches from nodes $\dot{x}$, and x with gains 1 and 3 feed to the output node y. **Thus, we have the state diagram shown in Figure 6.16.**

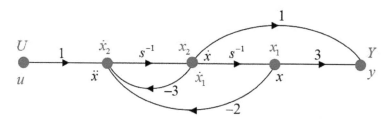

Fig. 6.16: Construct a companion form state-space model from a transfer function.

Now, we are ready to assign state variables. The rule is to assign state variables at the output of each integrator. Although no specific order of the state variables is required, we would follow the companion form convention to assign node x as x_1, and node $\dot{x}$ as x_2, as shown in the state diagram. Then we have the state equation and the output equation as follows:

$$\begin{bmatrix} \dot{x}_1(t) \\ \dot{x}_2(t) \end{bmatrix} = \begin{bmatrix} 0 & 1 \\ -2 & -3 \end{bmatrix} \begin{bmatrix} x_1(t) \\ x_2(t) \end{bmatrix} + \begin{bmatrix} 0 \\ 1 \end{bmatrix} u(t), \qquad y(t) = \begin{bmatrix} 3 & 1 \end{bmatrix} \begin{bmatrix} x_1(t) \\ x_2(t) \end{bmatrix}$$

∎

6.6.3 Construct a State-Space Model from Interconnected Systems

In the following, we will use three examples to illustrate how to construct state diagrams, and consequently state-space models, respectively, from a cascade connection of two transfer functions, a parallel connection of two transfer functions, and a feedback connection with plant and controller transfer functions.

In the following example, we will consider the **construction of a state-space model from a cascade connection of two transfer functions.** That is, the input-output relationship of the system is described by

$$Y(s)/U(s) = G_1(s)G_2(s)$$

where $G_1(s)$ and $G_2(s)$ can be from a decomposition of a given transfer function or they can be from two different subsystems.

Example 6.25 (Construct a State-Space Model from Cascaded Subsystems)

Consider a system, which is composed of two subsystems $G_1(s)$ and $G_2(s)$ with the following transfer functions:

$$\frac{Y_1(s)}{U_1(s)} = G_1(s) = \frac{s+3}{s+1} = 1 + \frac{2}{s+1}, \quad \frac{Y_2(s)}{U_2(s)} = G_2(s) = \frac{1}{s+2}$$

The relationship of the overall system $G(s)$ and its subsystems is described by $G(s) = G_1(s)G_2(s)$. Of course, we could combine the two rational functions into one, and then construct a state-space model based on the combined system. However, for practical reasons, we **should keep the state variables of the subsystems if possible.**

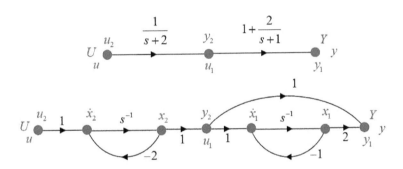

Fig. 6.17: Construct a state-space model from a cascade connection of two subsystems.

Hence, we will construct state-space models separately for all subsystems and then combine them together to form a state-space model for the overall system. The state-space models of the two subsystems can be constructed as follows:

$$\frac{Y_1}{U_1} = 1 + \frac{2}{s+1} \cdot \frac{X_1}{X_1} \quad \rightleftarrows \quad \begin{array}{l} \dot{x}_1 = -x_1 + u_1 \\ y_1 = 2x_1 + u_1 \end{array}, \quad \text{and} \quad \frac{Y_2}{U_2} = \frac{1}{s+2} \cdot \frac{X_2}{X_2} \quad \rightleftarrows \quad \begin{array}{l} \dot{x}_2 = -2x_2 + u_2 \\ y_2 = x_2 \end{array}$$

where x_1 and x_2 are the state variables of the subsystems G_1 and G_2, respectively.

Let $y(t)$ and $u(t)$ be the output and input of the combined cascade system, respectively. According to the cascade connection, we have $y(t) = y_1(t)$, $y_2(t) = u_1(t)$, and $u(t) = u_2(t)$. **Based on the state-space models of subsystems and the above connection information, the state diagram for the overall system can be completed as shown in Figure 6.17.**

The subsystems state variables $x_1(t)$ and $x_2(t)$ are of course the state variable of the combined system. The state vector of the overall system is defined as $x = \begin{bmatrix} x_1 & x_2 \end{bmatrix}^T$. **Then according to the state diagram in Figure 6.17, we have the following state-space model for the overall system:**

$$\begin{bmatrix} \dot{x}_1(t) \\ \dot{x}_2(t) \end{bmatrix} = \begin{bmatrix} -1 & 1 \\ 0 & -2 \end{bmatrix} \begin{bmatrix} x_1(t) \\ x_2(t) \end{bmatrix} + \begin{bmatrix} 0 \\ 1 \end{bmatrix} u(t), \qquad y(t) = \begin{bmatrix} 2 & 1 \end{bmatrix} \begin{bmatrix} x_1(t) \\ x_2(t) \end{bmatrix}$$ ∎

In the following example, we will consider the construction of a state-space model from a parallel connection of two subsystems. That is, the input-output relationship of the system is described by

$$Y(s)/U(s) = G_1(s) + G_2(s)$$

where $G_1(s)$ and $G_2(s)$ can be obtained from a decomposition of a given transfer function, or they can come from two different systems.

Example 6.26 (Construct a State-Space Model from a Parallel Connection of Two Subsystems)

Assume the relationship of the overall system $G(s)$ and its subsystems $G_1(s)$ and $G_2(s)$ is described by

$$\frac{Y(s)}{U(s)} = \frac{Y_1(s)}{U_1(s)} + \frac{Y_2(s)}{U_2(s)} = G_1(s) + G_2(s) = \frac{2}{s+1} + \frac{-1}{s+2}$$

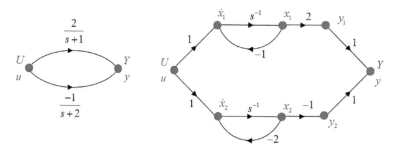

Fig. 6.18: Construct a state-space model from a parallel connection of two subsystems.

With the inputs and outputs of the subsystems G_1 and G_2 being denoted by U_1, U_2, and Y_1, Y_2, respectively, and the given transfer functions of the subsystems, we can **construct the state-space models for each of the two subsystems** as follows:

$$\frac{Y_1}{U_1} = \frac{2}{s+1} \cdot \frac{X_1}{X_1} \quad \rightleftharpoons \quad \begin{matrix} \dot{x}_1 = -x_1 + u_1 \\ y_1 = 2x_1 \end{matrix}, \quad \text{and} \quad \frac{Y_2}{U_2} = \frac{-1}{s+2} \cdot \frac{X_2}{X_2} \quad \rightleftharpoons \quad \begin{matrix} \dot{x}_2 = -2x_2 + u_2 \\ y_2 = -x_2 \end{matrix}$$

Based on the above state-space models of the two subsystems, and the fact of $u_1 = u_2 = u$ and $y = y_1 + y_2$ due to the parallel connection, the combined state diagram can be completed as shown in Figure 6.18. Note that the G_1 subsystem state diagram is drawn on the top side and the G_2 subsystem state diagram is at the bottom side. Both subsystems are driven by the same input $u(t)$, and the output of the overall system is the sum of the two subsystems' outputs.

Now, assign the outputs of the integrators as state variables x_1 and x_2 as shown in the state diagram. Let $x = \begin{bmatrix} x_1 & x_2 \end{bmatrix}^T$ be the state vector of the overall system, where x_1 and x_2 are the state variables of the subsystems G_1 and G_2, respectively. Then according to the state diagram in Figure 6.18, we have the following state-space model for the overall system:

$$\begin{bmatrix} \dot{x}_1(t) \\ \dot{x}_2(t) \end{bmatrix} = \begin{bmatrix} -1 & 0 \\ 0 & -2 \end{bmatrix} \begin{bmatrix} x_1(t) \\ x_2(t) \end{bmatrix} + \begin{bmatrix} 1 \\ 1 \end{bmatrix} u(t), \qquad y(t) = \begin{bmatrix} 2 & -1 \end{bmatrix} \begin{bmatrix} x_1(t) \\ x_2(t) \end{bmatrix}$$

∎

In the following example, we will consider the construction of a state-space model from a feedback connection with both the plant and the controller transfer functions. That is, the input-output relationship of the system is described by

$$\frac{Y(s)}{R(s)} = \frac{G(s)K(s)}{1+G(s)K(s)}$$

where $G(s)$ is the plant, which is the system to be controlled, and $K(s)$ is the controller.

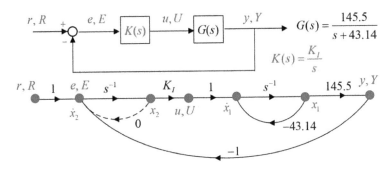

Fig. 6.19: Construct a state-space model from a feedback connection.

Example 6.27 (Construct a State-Space Model from a Feedback Connection)

Assume the feedback connection is depicted by the block diagram shown on the top of Figure 6.19, which means the feedback control system is described by the following three equations:

$$Y(s) = G(s)U(s), \quad U(s) = K(s)E(s), \quad \text{and} \quad E(s) = R(s) - Y(s)$$

Here, $G(s)$ represents the transfer function of the DC motor we studied in Example 5.25, and $K(s)$ is an integral controller to be designed. We will first **build an individual state diagram for each of the plant and the controller transfer functions** as follows:

$$\frac{Y}{U} = \frac{145.5}{s+43.14} \cdot \frac{X_1}{X_1} \quad \rightleftharpoons \quad \begin{array}{c} \dot{x}_1 = -43.14x_1 + u \\ y_1 = 145.5x_1 \end{array}, \quad \text{and} \quad \frac{U}{E} = \frac{K_I}{s} \cdot \frac{X_2}{X_2} \quad \rightleftharpoons \quad \begin{array}{c} \dot{x}_2 = 0x_2 + e \\ u = K_I x_2 \end{array}$$

The $G(s)$ and $K(s)$ subsystem state diagrams are built and shown on the right-hand and the left-hand sides, respectively, in Figure 6.19, and then are connected together **based on the feedback connection** $e = r - y$ **to complete the feedback system state diagram**. Now, after assigning the outputs of the integrators as state variables x_1 and x_2, we have the state equation and the output equation as follows:

$$\begin{bmatrix} \dot{x}_1(t) \\ \dot{x}_2(t) \end{bmatrix} = \begin{bmatrix} -43.14 & K_I \\ -145.4 & 0 \end{bmatrix} \begin{bmatrix} x_1(t) \\ x_2(t) \end{bmatrix} + \begin{bmatrix} 0 \\ 1 \end{bmatrix} u(t), \quad y(t) = \begin{bmatrix} 145.4 & 0 \end{bmatrix} \begin{bmatrix} x_1(t) \\ x_2(t) \end{bmatrix}$$

Once the state-space model or the state diagram is obtained for the feedback control system, we can use them for simulation, for analysis, and for design.

The characteristic equation of the closed-loop system can be computed from the A matrix of the state-space model as follows:

$$|sI - A| = \begin{vmatrix} s+43.14 & -K_I \\ 145.4 & s \end{vmatrix} = s^2 + 43.14s + 145.4K_I = 0$$

Recall that the second-order characteristic equation can be written in terms of the damping ratio ς and the natural frequency ω_n as follows:

$$s^2 + 2\varsigma\omega_n s + \omega_n^2 = 0$$

Hence, we can relate the integral constant K_I to the damping ratio and the natural frequency by the following equations:

$$2\varsigma\omega_n = 43.14, \quad \text{and} \quad \omega_n^2 = 145.4K_I$$

If the damping ratio is chosen to be $\varsigma = 0.9$, the system response is underdamped with a very small overshoot and almost undetectable oscillations. Then the natural frequency and the integral constant will be $\omega_n = 23.97$ rad/s and $K_I = 3.95$, respectively.

We can conduct a computer simulation of the DC motor speed control system based on this state diagram or state-space model, and the results will be the same as those shown in Figure 5.23. The closed-loop transfer function can be computed either using the Laplace transform formula or by using the state diagram together with Mason's gain formula. The Laplace transform approach will give

$$G_{closedloop}(s) = C(sI - A)^{-1}B = \begin{bmatrix} 145.4 & 0 \end{bmatrix} \begin{bmatrix} s+43.14 & -3.95 \\ 145.4 & s \end{bmatrix}^{-1} \begin{bmatrix} 0 \\ 1 \end{bmatrix}$$

$$= \frac{1}{\Delta}\begin{bmatrix} 145.4 & 0 \end{bmatrix} \begin{bmatrix} s & 3.95 \\ -145.4 & s+43.14 \end{bmatrix}\begin{bmatrix} 0 \\ 1 \end{bmatrix} = \frac{574.7}{s^2+43.14s+574.7}$$

If the state diagram is employed together with **Mason's gain formula** to compute the closed-loop transfer function, we will find two loops and one forward path in the state diagram. The loop gains and the forward path gains are

$$\ell_1 = -43.14s^{-1}, \quad \ell_2 = -574.7s^{-2}, \quad \text{and} \quad F_1 = 574.7s^{-2}$$

which leads to

$$\Delta = 1 - (\ell_1 + \ell_2) = 1 + 43.14s^{-1} + 574.7s^{-2} \quad \text{and} \quad \Delta_1 = 1$$

Therefore, the closed-loop transfer function is

$$G_{closedloop}(s) = \frac{F\Delta_1}{\Delta} = \frac{574.7s^{-2}}{1+43.14s^{-1}+574.7s^{-2}} = \frac{574.7}{s^2+43.14s+574.7}$$

6.7 Exercise Problems

P6.1a: Consider the PI (proportional and integral) feedback control system shown in Figure 6.20. Let $K_p = 0$ (i.e., the controller is an integral controller $K(s) = K_i/s$). Determine the value of K_i so that the closed-loop system has damping ratio $\varsigma = 0.707$.

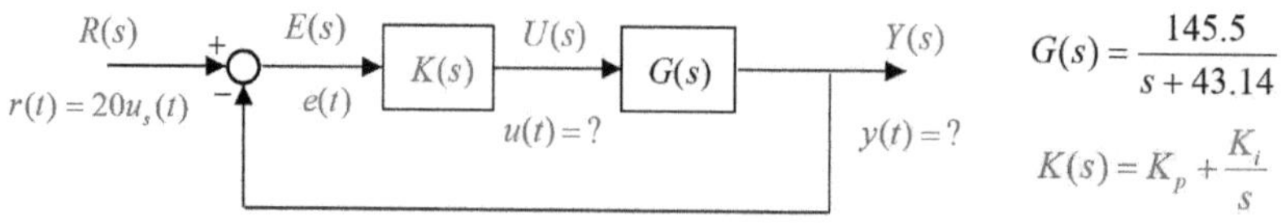

Fig. 6.20: PI feedback control system.

P6.1b: With the controller $K(s)$ chosen in P6.1a, find the natural frequency ω_n and the transfer functions $Y(s)/R(s)$ and $U(s)/R(s)$ of the closed-loop system.

P6.1c: Plot the output response $y(t)$ and control input $u(t)$ due to the reference input $r(t) = 20u_s(t)$ on separate graphs using the two transfer functions obtained in P6.1b and the MATLAB step command.

P6.2a: Consider the PI (proportional and integral) feedback control system shown in Figure 6.20. Let $K_i = 0$ (i.e., the controller is a proportional controller $K(s) = K_p$). Determine the value of K_p so that the closed-loop system has steady-state error smaller than 10%.

P6.2b: With the controller $K(s)$ chosen in P6.2a, find the time constant τ and the transfer functions $Y(s)/R(s)$ and $U(s)/R(s)$ of the closed-loop system.

P6.2c: Plot the output response $y(t)$ and control input $u(t)$ due to the reference input $r(t) = 20u_s(t)$ on separate graphs using the two transfer functions obtained in P6.2b and the MATLAB step command. Comment on the limitation of the proportional control system.

P6.3a: Consider the feedback control system shown in Figure 6.20, where the controller is a PI controller (proportional and integral controller) $K(s) = K_p + (K_i/s)$. Determine the values of K_p and K_i so that the closed-loop system has damping ratio $\varsigma = 0.707$ and natural frequency $\omega_n = 50\text{rad/s}$.

P6.3b: With the controller $K(s)$ chosen in P6.3a, find the transfer functions $Y(s)/R(s)$ and $U(s)/R(s)$ of the closed-loop system.

P6.3c: Plot the output response $y(t)$ and control input $u(t)$ due to the reference input $r(t) = 20u_s(t)$ on separate graphs using the two transfer functions obtained in P6.3b and the MATLAB step command.

P6.4a: Consider the dual-loop feedback control system shown in Figure 6.21. Determine the values of K_1 and K_2 so that the closed-loop system has damping ratio $\varsigma = 0.707$ and natural frequency $\omega_n = 50$ rad/s.

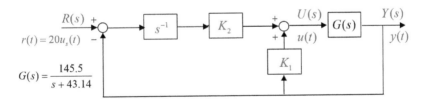

Fig. 6.21: A dual-loop feedback control system.

P6.4b: With the values of K_1 and K_2 chosen in P6.4a, find the transfer functions $Y(s)/R(s)$ and $U(s)/R(s)$ of the closed-loop system.

P6.4c: Plot the output response $y(t)$ and control input $u(t)$ due to the reference input $r(t) = 20u_s(t)$ on separate graphs using the MATLAB step command and the two transfer functions $Y(s)/R(s)$ and $U(s)/R(s)$ obtained in P6.4b.

P6.5: Compare the closed-loop system performances of the above four controllers obtained in P6.1, P6.2, P6.3, and P6.4, respectively, and give your comments. Remember that the objective of the feedback control is to find a controller so that the closed-loop system is stable and the difference between the reference input and the output is as small as possible, subject to the control-input magnitude constrains.

P6.6a: Consider a system described by the following state equation:

$$\begin{bmatrix} \dot{x}_1(t) \\ \dot{x}_2(t) \end{bmatrix} = \begin{bmatrix} -2 & -2 \\ 2 & 3 \end{bmatrix} \begin{bmatrix} x_1(t) \\ x_2(t) \end{bmatrix} + \begin{bmatrix} -1 \\ 1 \end{bmatrix} u(t)$$

Is the system stable? Explain the reasoning behind your answer.

P6.6b: Design a state-feedback controller $u(t) = \begin{bmatrix} F_1 & F_2 \end{bmatrix} \begin{bmatrix} x_1(t) \\ x_2(t) \end{bmatrix}$ so that the closed-loop system is stable, and the characteristic equation of the closed-loop system is $s^2 + 2\varsigma\omega_n s + \omega_n^2 = 0$ with damping ratio $\varsigma = 0.866$ and natural frequency $\omega_n = 4$ rad/s.

P6.6c: Build a Simulink program to conduct the closed-loop system simulation with initial state $x_1(0) = 2$, $x_2(0) = 0$. Plot $x_1(t)$, $x_2(t)$ on the same graph and $u(t)$ on a separate graph using MATLAB plot command.

P6.7a: Consider the three state diagrams shown in Figure 6.22(a), Figure 6.22(b), and Figure 6.22(c), respectively. Find the state-space model associated with each of the three state diagrams.

P6.7b: Use Mason's gain formula to find the transfer function $Y(s)/U(s)$ associated with each of the three state diagrams shown in Figure 6.22(a), Figure 6.22(b), and Figure 6.22(c), respectively.

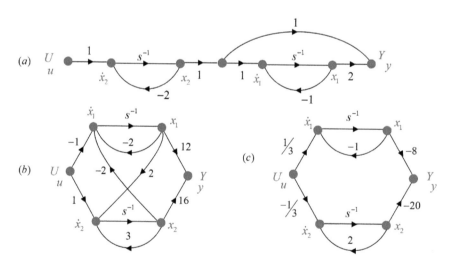

Fig. 6.22: State diagrams.

Part II

Linear Control System Design

Fundamentals of Feedback Control Systems

I N Chapters 2 and 3, we learned that the frequency-domain approach not only transforms the differential equations into the algebraic ones to make them easier to solve, but also reveals the valuable frequency-domain properties and provides convenient, easy-to-use tools for the analysis and design of control systems. Note that the frequency-domain and the time-domain properties are closely related via an easily crossed bilateral bridge: the Laplace transform. As shown in the typical second-order system step response graph in Figure 3.11, the time-domain attributes, like the maximum overshoot, the oscillation frequency, the rise time, and settling time of the step response, are mainly characterized by the frequency-domain poles.

Despite the success of the frequency-domain approach based on transformed transfer functions, it only applies to linear, time-invariant SISO (single-input/single-output) systems. Recall that in Chapter 4, we obtained a dynamics model of the simple inverted pendulum system, which was described by a nonlinear differential equation. In order to investigate the properties of the system, we would have to introduce the concept of equilibriums, and explain how to find a linear local model for each equilibrium of interest. Although there exists other ad hoc ways of locating the equilibriums and finding local linear models, the most systematic and efficient approach is to carry out the linearization process in state space.

For this purpose, in Section 4.4.2, we introduced the state-space analysis approach the first time in the book. First, the original nonlinear differential equation was converted into a nonlinear state equation, in which the state variables were chosen to be the angular displacement and the angular velocity of the pendulum. The nonlinear state equation was then employed to systematically determine the equilibrium points, and to assemble a linearized state-space local model at the equilibrium of interest. The linear state-space model associated with the upright equilibrium has a pole in the right half of the complex plane, which verifies the instability of the upright equilibrium.

Furthermore, in Section 4.4.3, students were guided to utilize the local linear state-space model to design a state-feedback controller based on a simple pole placement concept so that the closed-loop systems poles are in the left half of the complex plane. A computer simulation was conducted to validate that the linear state-feedback controller, designed based on the linear model, was capable of stabilizing the originally unstable nonlinear system. This state-feedback controller design turned out to be the first feedback control system design project the students would learn from the book.

In addition to this state-feedback controller design experience, students had also learned how to design an integral feedback controller and a dual-loop feedback controller in Section 5.7.4 and Section 6.1, respectively. In both of these design examples, the frequency-domain approach based on transformed transfer functions was employed to place the closed-loop system poles according to the desired closed-loop system damping ratio and natural frequencies.

Feedback controllers can be designed in state space or in frequency domain. Either approach has its strength and limitations. Fortunately, the advancement of control theory and digital computing technology in the past three decades has made it possible to integrate these two approaches together. For example, the frequency-domain MIMO (multi-input/multi-output) system robustness measure can be blended into the cost function (or performance index) of the state-space H_2 and H_∞ optimization formulation process. On the other hand, the state-space LQR or LQG approaches can work together with the root locus design approach to achieve a best possible performance.

The main objective of this chapter is to provide the fundamentals for the discussion of feedback control systems in later chapters. We will first address basic features of feedback control systems, which include the advantages and the limitations. Then, after a brief review of system representations and commonly used terminologies, we will introduce stability, similarity transformations, Routh-Hurwitz stability criterion, and basic pole-placement control systems designs.

7.1 Features of Feedback Control

The discovery of feedback control seems not as well recognized as the great inventions of the steam engine and aircraft. The steam engine was the main power force behind the Industrial Revolution at the turn of the 19th century. About a hundred years later, the invention of aircraft by the Wright Brothers created the aerospace industry and opened up a new era of aviation transportation that shrinks the world and makes the people all over the world more connected than before. However, **it was James Watt's flyball governor control system that transformed the inefficient, unsafe, sometimes even explosive steam engines into controllable, reliable, and efficient ones so that the steam engine could be widely employed and become the main power source for the Industrial Revolution.**

For the flight control of aircraft, Wilber Wright envisioned that "**the age of flying**" will have arrived when "**this one feature (the ability to balance and steer)**" had been worked out, for all other difficulties are of minor importance. The age of flying certainly has arrived, and the implementation of feedback control theory has greatly improved the ability to balance and steer and has enhanced the safety, quality, and performance of the flight. **Feedback control technology have been embedded in almost all aerospace vehicles, ships, manufacturing processes, power grids systems, automobiles, and a variety of machines/devices that require automation, optimization, precision, stability, safety, reliability, and performance enhancement.** In the following, we will briefly discuss the features of feedback control and its limitations.

7.1.1 A Demonstrative Feedback Control System

Instead of just listing the features of the feedback control, we would associate these features with some tangible feedback control system that we can experience in the lab or in computer simulations. The simple motor speed control system we designed in Example 6.1 will be employed to demonstrate some features of feedback control. The block diagram of the motor speed control system of Figure 6.3 is redrawn in Figure 7.1. We add the disturbance input $d(t)$ to the block diagram in order to study the system response due to the disturbance. The plant $G(s)$ will be altered so that the effect of the plant perturbations on the system can be observed and analyzed.

In Figure 7.1, $G(s)$ is the mathematical model of the plant, including the Faulhaber 2230.012S micromotor, the 1:14 gear head, and the external load J_ℓ and B_ℓ, described in Example 5.25. The transfer function $G(s)$ is

$$G(s) = \frac{x_{ss}}{\tau s + 1} \tag{7.1}$$

where $\tau = 0.02318$ sec and $x_{ss} = 3.3727$ rad/s as given in Equation 5.68. Recall that the objective of the speed control system is to design a controller $K(s)$ or K_1 and K_2 so that the closed-loop system is stable and the steady-state tracking error is zero (i.e., $\lim_{t \to \infty} e(t) = 0$), and the transient error response is as small as possible.

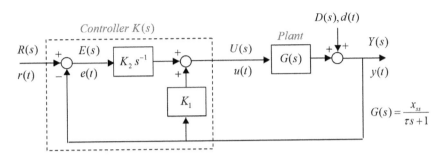

Fig. 7.1: A speed tracking feedback control system.

The controller was designed in Example 6.1, $K_1 = -0.322$ and $K_2 = 17.18$. With the added disturbance input, the closed-loop system now has two inputs: the reference input $r(t) = \mathcal{L}^{-1}[R(s)]$, together with the disturbance input $d(t) = \mathcal{L}^{-1}[D(s)]$, and one output $y(t) = \mathcal{L}^{-1}[Y(s)]$, which represents the angular speed of the load moment of inertia, J_ℓ. Applying Mason's gain formula to the block diagram of Figure 7.1, we can find the transfer functions $G_R(s)$ from $R(s)$ to $Y(s)$, and $G_D(s)$ from $D(s)$ to $Y(s)$, respectively,

$$G_R(s) = \frac{K_2 x_{ss}}{\tau s^2 + (1 - K_1 x_{ss})s + K_2 x_{ss}}, \quad G_D(s) = \frac{\tau s^2 + s}{\tau s^2 + (1 - K_1 x_{ss})s + K_2 x_{ss}} \tag{7.2}$$

and therefore, the output $Y(s)$ has two parts: one due to the reference input $R(s)$ and the other due to the disturbance input $D(s)$.

$$Y(s) = G_R(s)R(s) + G_D(s)D(s) := Y_R(s) + Y_D(s) \tag{7.3}$$

Assume the reference input $r(t)$ and the disturbance input $d(t)$ are step functions with arbitrary magnitude. That is, $R(s) = R/s$ and $D(s) = D/s$, where R and D are arbitrary constants. According to Theorem 2.27, which is the final-value theorem, and Equations 7.2 and 7.3, we have

$$\lim_{t \to \infty} y_R(t) = \lim_{s \to 0} sY_R(s) = \lim_{s \to 0} G_R(s)R = R, \quad \lim_{t \to \infty} y_D(t) = \lim_{s \to 0} sY_D(s) = \lim_{s \to 0} G_D(s)D = 0 \tag{7.4}$$

These final values of $y_D(t)$ and $y_R(t)$ reveal that at steady state the effect of the disturbance $d(t)$ on the output $y(t)$ will be zero, and the output $y(t)$ will perfectly follow the reference input $r(t)$. Note that the steady-state response analysis is conducted completely in frequency domain. Similarly, the transient response of the system also can be characterized without an explicit time-domain expression of $y(t)$.

It can be seen from Equation 7.2 that the characteristic equation of the closed-loop system is

$$\tau s^2 + (1 - K_1 x_{ss})s + K_2 x_{ss} = 0 \tag{7.5}$$

With the plant parameters τ, x_{ss} and the controller constants K_1, K_2, the characteristic equation becomes

$$s^2 + 90s + 2500 = s^2 + 2\varsigma\omega_n s + \omega_n^2 = 0 \tag{7.6}$$

Hence, the damping ratio, the natural frequency, and the pole locations of the closed-loop system are

$$\varsigma = 0.9, \quad \omega_n = 50 \text{ rad/s}, \quad \begin{matrix} p_1 \\ p_2 \end{matrix} = -\alpha \pm j\omega = -45 \pm j21.795 \tag{7.7}$$

The transfer function $G_R(s)$ in Equation 7.2 and the damping ratio $\varsigma = 0.9$ reveal that the closed-loop system is an underdamped typical second-order system. Thus, the formulas listed in Section 3.4.3 can be employed here to compute the rise time, the settling time, the peak time, the maximum over-shoot, and other local peak and valley points of the step response. Since the oscillation frequency is $\omega = 21.795$ rad/s, the period of the decaying sinusoidal step response is $T = 2\pi/\omega = 0.288$ s. Hence, the peak time $t_p = T/2 = 0.144$ s, and $y(t_p) = R(1 + e^{-45t_p}) = R(1 + 0.0015)$ imply that the maximum overshoot is $OS = 0.15\%$. Note that the maximum overshoot is so small that the maximum peak point is already within $\pm 2\%$ of the steady-state value, which implies the settling time is less than the peak time t_p. It is verified by the settling time formula, $t_s = -\ln(0.02\sqrt{1-\varsigma^2})/\omega = 0.105$ s.

Therefore, the feedback control not only achieves perfect disturbance rejection and reference track-ing at steady state, it also provides excellent transient response, allowing fast, smooth convergence to the steady state.

7.1.2 Performance Verification by Time-Domain Simulation

The ability to envision the time-domain response based on the frequency-domain attributes like transfer function, pole-zero pattern, damping ratio, and natural frequency, is essential, especially in the phase of feedback control design since the explicit expression of the time-domain response is not available until the design is completed. However, after a controller is designed on the drafting board, it is a necessity for the controller to undergo a thorough time-domain simulation verification to determine if the control system has fulfilled all the required closed-loop system performance.

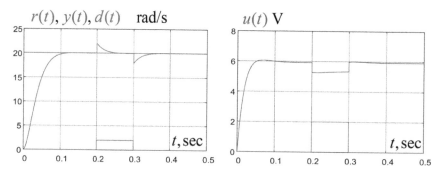

Fig. 7.2: Effect of the disturbance $d(t)$ on $y(t)$ and $u(t)$.

A Simulink simulation based on the speed tracking feedback control system block diagram shown in Figure 7.1 was conducted to verify the disturbance response reduction capability and the reference tracking performance of the system. The simulation results are shown in Figure 7.2. The reference input $r(t) = 20u_s(t)$ (in green color) is a step function intending to command the motor to increase its angular velocity $y(t)$ from 0 to 20 rad/s. The output $y(t)$ (in blue color), following the command, would rise quickly and smoothly to $20 \times 98\% = 19.6$ rad/s in 0.105 s (the settling time), to pass the desired speed 20 rad/s at $t = 0.123$ s, and reach its maximum speed 20.03 rad/s (0.15% maximum overshoot) at the peak time $t_p = 0.144$ s. The continued sinusoidal fluctuations of $y(t)$ around the reference speed 20 rad/s will decay quickly to negligible shortly after the peak time.

To demonstrate how the feedback control system reacts to a disturbance, a disturbance pulse $d(t)$ (in red color) is assumed to occur between $t = 0.2$ s and $t = 0.3$ s. It can be observed that the feedback control system takes immediate action to quickly reduce the influence of the disturbance $d(t)$ on $y(t)$ to about zero in 0.06 s.

On the right-hand side of Figure 7.2 is the graph of the control input $u(t)$ versus time t. It can be seen from the motor transfer function $G(s)$ that to sustain the desired motor speed 20 rad/s at steady state, the control-input voltage $u(t)$ needs to be $u(t) = 5.93$ V at steady state. The graph in Figure 7.2 shows exactly what we expect after the system reaches the steady state shortly after $t = 0.144$ s. The graph also shows that upon the sudden step change of the reference input $r(t)$ from 0 to 20 rad/s at $t = 0$ s, the control input $u(t)$ immediately shoots up from 0 V to about 6 V in 0.05 s, then a little overshoot, and converges to the new equilibrium at $u(t) = 5.93$ V.

When the disturbance $d(t)$ jumps from 0 to 2 rad/s at $t = 0.2$ s, the control input responds right away to drop about 0.7 V and continues to adjust its value to counter the effect of the disturbance and bring the motor speed back to the equilibrium 20 rad/s. At $t = 0.3$ s when the disturbance recedes to 0, the control input $u(t)$ again reacts accordingly to reduce the effect of the disturbance to zero in about 0.05 s, and brings the system back to the equilibrium, $y(t) = 20$ rad/s and $u(t) = 5.93$ V, at the steady state.

The next simulation examines the robustness of the motor speed tracking feedback control system against the uncertainties in the plant $G(s)$. The mathematical model we employ in the design process usually is not exactly the same as the real physical system it represents. The discrepancy may be caused by the modeling inaccuracies and the variations of the system parameters that are functions of environmental conditions like temperature, pressure, and gravity. Hence, it is important for a system to be capable of accommodating the unmodeled dynamics or the perturbations of the system parameters.

The graphs in Figure 7.3 record the results of three motor speed tracking simulations. The reference input is assumed to be $r(t) = 20u_s(t)$ rad/s (in green color), and the objective of the feedback control system is to make the output $y(t)$, the motor speed, to follow the reference input $r(t)$ as closely as possible, subject to the control-input constraints.

The first simulation is for the nominal case when the plant parameters τ and x_{ss} are the same as the nominal values $\tau = 0.02318$ s and $x_{ss} = 3.3727$ rad/s, respectively. The tracking response $y(t)$ is shown in red on the left graph of Figure 7.3. The corresponding control-input response $u(t)$, also in red, is shown on the right graph of the figure. These nominal responses $y(t)$ and $u(t)$ are the same as those shown in Figure 7.2.

In the second simulation, the plant parameter τ remains the same but **the parameter x_{ss} is reduced 20% to $x_{ss} = (0.8)(3.3727)$ rad**. The characteristic equation of the perturbed closed-loop system will become $s^2 + 80.6216s + 1999.76 = 0$, and the damping ratio and the natural frequency will change to $\varsigma = 0.901$ and $\omega_n = 44.72$ rad/s, respectively. The tracking response $y(t)$ is shown in black on the left graph of Figure 7.3, slightly below the red nominal response. The transient response is a little bit slower than the nominal one, but **the steady-state response is identical to the nominal one, still at the desired 20 rad/s**. The corresponding control-input response $u(t)$, also in black, is shown on the right graph of the figure. **Note that the control input $u(t)$ is very different from the nominal one: it has to increase by 25% (since 1/0.8=1.25) to** 7.41 **V at steady state to accommodate the 20% decrease of the plant parameter x_{ss}.**

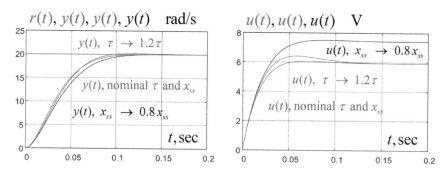

Fig. 7.3: Effect of the perturbations of τ and x_{ss} on $y(t)$ and $u(t)$.

In the third simulation, the plant parameter x_{ss} remains the same, but **the parameter τ is increased 20% to $\tau = (1.2)(0.02318)$ s.** The characteristic equation of the perturbed closed-loop system will become $s^2 + 75s + 2083.33 = 0$, and the damping ratio and the natural frequency will change to $\varsigma = 0.822$ and $\omega_n = 45.64$ rad/s, respectively. The tracking response $y(t)$ is shown in blue on the left graph of Figure 7.3, slightly above the red nominal response. The transient response has a little bit more overshoot than the nominal one, but **the steady-state response is identical to the nominal one, at the desired 20 rad/s.** The corresponding control-input response $u(t)$, also in blue color, is shown on the right graph of the figure. **Note that $u(t)$ is different from the nominal one since it has to adjust to minimize the effect on $y(t)$ due to the change of the plant parameter τ.**

In summary, the feedback control mechanism in the motor speed tracking feedback control system shown in Figure 7.1 provides excellent robustness against the parameter variations in the plant $G(s)$. The steady-state tracking performance is perfectly robust, and the effect of the plant parameter variations on the transient tracking performance is very small—almost negligible. The feedback control mechanism is also capable of performing perfect steady-state step command tracking and arbitrary constant disturbance rejection to achieve fast convergent transient response.

7.1.3 Advantages and Limitations of Feedback Control

From the analysis and simulation verification of the motor speed tracking control system discussed in Sections 7.1.1 and 7.1.2, we have witnessed the advantages brought forth by the feedback control theory in dealing with the important systems and control issues including disturbance rejection, precision command tracking, robust stability, and performance against plant uncertainties.

We will first summarize the advantages of feedback control, and then briefly discuss the limitations and caution items in feedback control applications. The basic feedback control block diagram shown in Figure 7.1 will continue to be employed in interpreting the functions of feedback control, but the plant $G(s)$ is not restricted to be the DC motor, and the controller $K(s)$ may represent more general control strategy.

Advantages of Feedback Control

1. **Automatic Control**

   Feedback control is a naturally perfect mechanism for automatic control. There probably exists no better way to achieve automatic control than using feedback control. The basic feedback control block diagram shown in Figure 7.1 has been employed to achieve automatic speed control of a DC motor. The same feedback control principle can be applied to design the automobile cruise control system or can be extended to address the 3D trajectory tracking issues relevant to aircraft guidance/navigation, missile defense and satellite positioning systems. In a feedback control system, the control input $u(t)$ is not obtained by any complicated micro management process. Instead, it is automatically generated in real time by the controller according to the control strategy $K(s)$ and the real-time values of the reference input $r(t)$ and the output $y(t)$. The control strategy is predesigned to achieve perfect reference tracking at steady state, and optimize the closed-loop performance subject to control-input constraints.

2. **Ability to Modify the Dynamic Characteristics via Pole Placement**

The dynamics behavior of a system is mainly determined by its pole locations; therefore, through feedback control the closed-loop system poles can be placed at desired locations to improve the performance of the system. Recall that the poles of the unstable uncompensated simple inverted pendulum system in Section 4.4.2 were at 2.715 and −3.315, which are the eigenvalues of the A_U matrix. With a state-feedback controller, the compensated system's poles are placed at $-4 \pm j3$, which are the eigenvalues of $A_U + B_U F$, as shown in Equation 4.46. The new poles are all in the left half of the complex plane to ensure the stability of the compensated cart-inverted pendulum. For another example, the motor speed tracking control system in Figure 7.1, the damping ratio and the natural frequency of the closed-loop system were purposely selected as $\varsigma = 0.9$ and $\omega_n = 50\,\text{rad}/\text{s}$, respectively, to achieve a desired performance with small maximum overshoot and fast rise time.

3. **Steady-State Disturbance Response Rejection**

A feedback controller can be designed to achieve steady-state disturbance response rejection for certain types of disturbances, including step disturbances with arbitrary magnitude, ramp disturbances with arbitrary slope, and sinusoidal disturbances with arbitrary amplitude and phase. For the motor speed tracking control system example, the controller was designed to achieve steady-state disturbance response rejection for the step disturbances with arbitrary magnitude. It was shown in Equation 7.4 that the steady-state disturbance response is zero, $\lim_{t\to\infty} y_D(t) = 0$. The steady-state disturbance response rejection was also verified in the simulation shown in Figure 7.2.

4. **Steady-State Reference Input Tracking**

Steady-state reference input tracking and steady-state disturbance response rejection are mathematically the same problem. A feedback controller can be designed to achieve steady-state reference input tracking for certain types of reference inputs, including step references with arbitrary magnitude, ramp references with arbitrary slope, and sinusoidal references with arbitrary amplitude and phase. For the motor speed tracking control system example, the controller was designed to achieve steady-state reference input tracking for the step reference inputs with arbitrary magnitude. It was shown in Equation 7.4 that the steady-state output response is the same as the reference input at steady state, $\lim_{t\to\infty} y_R(t) = R$. The steady-state reference input tracking was also verified in the simulations shown in Figure 7.2 and Figure 7.3.

5. **Robust Performance Against Plant Uncertainties**

For an uncompensated system, whatever variations occurs in the plant dynamics will pass on to directly affect the output response. Feedback control provides an effective mechanism to tremendously reduce the effect of the plant uncertainties and variations on the output. For the motor speed tracking control system example, it can be seen from the simulation results on Figure 7.3 that the 20% variations of the plant parameters τ and x_{ss} have no effect on the output $y(t)$ at steady state except a slight influence on the transient response. It also can be seen from the right-hand side of the figure that the control input $u(t)$ responds to the plant variations to adjust accordingly to minimize their effect on the output $y(t)$.

Limitations of Feedback Control

Despite the overwhelmingly convincing advantages, feedback control has its limitations and it occasionally may do more harm than help if caution is not taken to address the issues of sensor accuracy, time delay, actuator saturation, and dramatic change of plant dynamics.

1. **Sensing Errors**

   For a speed tracking or position tracking control problem, the accuracy of tracking control accuracy can only be as good as that of the sensor measurement. The sensor error will directly pass to the tracking error. For example, if in an automobile cruise control system a speed of 70 miles/hour is wrongly measured as the set speed 65 miles/hours, then the feedback control system will have a 5 miles/hour tracking error without knowing it. More serious measurement mistakes like an orientation sensing error can cause a positive feedback and destabilize the system. The issues of sensing error and inaccuracy can be addressed by employing diversified redundant sensor suits and fault-tolerant filtering algorithms.

2. **Time Delay**

   For a feedback control system to work, it requires continuous repetitive cycles of operations including detection, information processing, decision, actuation, and control. Since it needs time to perform tasks in each cycle of operation, more or less there is a time latency or time delay for each control cycle. If the time delay is too long, by the time the information is received by the controller it is already out of date, not reflecting the current status of the system any more. Using out-of-date information for decision and control may lead to poor performance or even cause the system to become unstable. To alleviate the detrimental effect of time delay, the detailed dynamics model, including dynamics of the plant, actuators, sensors, and data transport delays, need to be incorporated in the control system design.

3. **Actuator Saturation**

   Actuators are designated to implement the control actions determined by the controller, but they may not be able to execute all faithfully due to physical constraints. For example, the range and capabilities of the power supplies, the engines, and the control surfaces of the airplane are all physically constrained. Normally the control-input signals are within the control-input constrained limits, but under some emergencies the controller may have to issue stronger control signals in attempting to mitigate the crisis. If the control signal exceeds the actuator limits, the actuator will saturate at its extreme value, and the actual control input delivered to the plant will be the saturated one instead of the intended one by the controller. Unless a special contingency control strategy is in place to address the actuator saturation issue, the saturation may cause a miscommunication between the plant and the controller and drive the controller output even higher that would continue keeping the input of the plant at the sustained saturation value. This wind-up phenomena and sustained actuator saturation may cause the feedback control system to depart from its intended operating equilibrium and become unstable.

4. **Dramatic Change of Plant Dynamics**

A feedback control system is usually designed based on the dynamics model representing the plant (the system to be controlled) in an operating region around a desired equilibrium. The nominal controller thus designed is supposed to work well in this particular operating region; however, it will become inadequate if the plant dynamics suffers a dramatic change due to a component failure or a violent disturbance. A remedy for this failure condition is to disengage the inadequate controller and replace it by a contingency controller specifically designed to address the failure condition.

7.2 System Representations and Properties

A system is an operator that specifies the cause/effect relationship between the input $u(t)$ and the output $y(t)$: $y(t) = \mathscr{G}[u(t)]$, as shown in Figure 7.4.

Definition 7.1 (Linear Systems)

A system or an operator $\mathscr{G}$, as shown in Figure 7.4, is said to be linear if and only if the following superposition principle is satisfied:

$$\mathscr{G}[c_1 u_1(t) + c_2 u_2(t)] = c_1 \mathscr{G}[u_1(t)] + c_2 \mathscr{G}[u_2(t)] \tag{7.8}$$

where c_1 and c_2 are arbitrary real or complex numbers. ∎

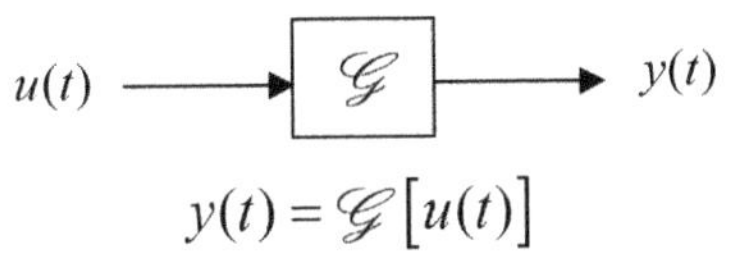

$$y(t) = \mathscr{G}[u(t)]$$

Fig. 7.4: An operator that specifies the relationship between the input $u(t)$ and the output $y(t)$.

Definition 7.2 (Time-Invariant Systems)

A system $\mathscr{G}$ is said to be time-invariant if and only if

$$\mathscr{G}[u(t-\tau)] = y(t-\tau) \tag{7.9}$$

for any $u(t)$ and any delay time τ. ∎

Definition 7.3 (Dynamic Systems)

A system $\mathscr{G}$ is said to be dynamic if its output depends on past and present values of the input.

Example 7.4 (Linear Time-Invariant Dynamic Systems)

All the systems described by differential equations are dynamic systems since the variables of the differential equation at every instant always keep their results, due to the past input, before updating to the new values. The system described by the algebraic equation,

$$y(t) = au(t) + b$$

is not a dynamic system. The system has no memory; its output $y(t)$ only depends on the current value of input $u(t)$. This algebraic equation looks simple, but it is not a linear system since the output due to an input $c_1 u(t)$ is not equal to $c_1 y(t)$ unless $b = 0$.

The dynamic system described by the differential equation

$$\frac{dy(t)}{dt} + ty(t) = u(t)$$

apparently is not time-invariant since one coefficient in the equation is function of time. However, this time-varying system is linear since

$$\begin{aligned} \frac{dy_1}{dt} + ty_1 &= u_1 \\ \frac{dy_2}{dt} + ty_2 &= u_2 \end{aligned} \quad \rightleftharpoons \quad \frac{d(c_1 y_1 + c_2 y_2)}{dt} + t(c_1 y_1 + c_2 y_2) = c_1 u_1 + c_2 u$$

For another example, the simple pendulum system described by the differential equation

$$J\ddot{\theta}(t) + B\dot{\theta}(t) + mg\ell \sin\theta(t) = \tau(t)$$

is a nonlinear system because of the $\sin\theta(t)$ term. But it can be considered a linear system if the operating range of $\theta(t)$ is small so that $\sin\theta(t)$ is approximately equal to $\theta(t)$.   ∎

A linear time-invariant system (or subsystem) can be represented by a differential equation, a transfer function, an impulse response, a state-space model, or a graphical representation like a block diagram or a signal flow graph. For some particular objective of analysis or design, we may choose one representation of the system over the others, but it is quite easy to convert from one representation to another, as described in Section 6.6.

7.2.1 Transfer Function and Differential Equation

As shown in Figure 7.5, a linear time-invariant system can be represented by a differential equation in time domain:

$$\begin{aligned} y^{(n)}(t) + a_{n-1} y^{(n-1)}(t) + \cdots + a_1 \dot{y}(t) + a_0 y(t) \\ = b_m u^{(m)}(t) + b_{m-1} u^{(m-1)}(t) + \cdots + b_1 \dot{u}(t) + b_0 u(t) \end{aligned} \tag{7.10}$$

or by a corresponding transfer function in frequency domain:

$$\frac{Y(s)}{U(s)} = G(s) = \frac{b_m s^m + b_{m-1} s^{m-1} + b_m - 2 s^{m-2} + \cdots + b_1 s + b_0}{s^n + a_{n-1} s^{n-1} + a_{n-2} s^{n-2} + \cdots + a_1 s + a_0} := \frac{N(s)}{D(s)} \tag{7.11}$$

where m and n are positive integers. The system is said to be proper or strictly proper if $m \leq n$ or $m < n$, respectively. All the practical systems to be considered are proper or strictly proper, and the controller to be designed is required to be proper or strictly proper since a non-proper controller is not implementable.

Note that the differential equation in Equation 7.10 is the time-domain description of the system, while the transfer function in Equation 7.11 is the frequency-domain description of the same system. The bridge between the differential equation and the transfer function is simply the Laplace transform. The Laplace transform of the differential equation of Equation 7.10 will lead to the transfer function in Equation 7.11. On the other hand, the inverse Laplace transform of the transfer function equation $D(s)Y(s) = N(s)U(s)$ will yield the same differential equation.

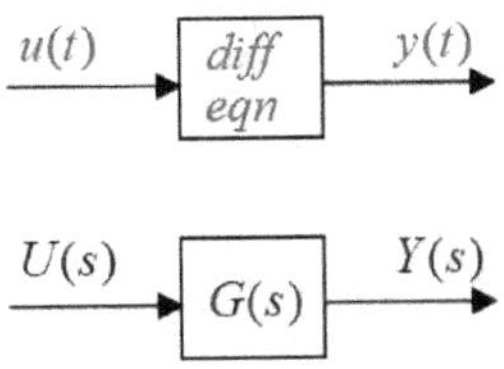

$$u(t) \rightarrow \boxed{\begin{array}{c} \textit{diff} \\ \textit{eqn} \end{array}} \rightarrow y(t) \qquad y^{(n)}(t) + a_{n-1}y^{(n-1)}(t) + \cdots + a_1\dot{y}(t) + a_0y(t)$$
$$= b_m u^{(m)}(t) + b_{m-1}u^{(m-1)}(t) + \cdots + b_1\dot{u}(t) + b_0u(t)$$

$$U(s) \rightarrow \boxed{G(s)} \rightarrow Y(s) \qquad \frac{Y(s)}{U(s)} = G(s) = \frac{b_m s^m + b_{m-1}s^{m-1} + \cdots + b_1 s + b_0}{s^n + a_{n-1}s^{n-1} + \cdots + a_1 s + a_0} := \frac{N(s)}{D(s)}$$

Fig. 7.5: Representations of linear time-invariant system: differential equation and transfer function.

Although the initial conditions should be considered in the process of solving for the output response $y(t)$, they are irrelevant to system representations, and therefore they should be ignored in the representation conversion process. To facilitate the conversion process, the variable s in the transfer function can be considered as the Laplace transform of the differentiation operator d/dt. In summary, we have the following differentiation operator conversions:

$$d/dt \rightleftarrows s, \quad d^2/dt^2 \rightleftarrows s^2, \quad \cdots \quad , \quad d^n/dt^n \rightleftarrows s^n \tag{7.12}$$

Example 7.5 (Conversion Between the Differential Equation and the Transfer Function)

Consider the system with the following differential equation,

$$\ddot{y}(t) + 3\dot{y}(t) + 2y(t) = 4\dot{u}(t) + 12u(t) \tag{7.13}$$

Let $Y(s) = \mathscr{L}[y(t)]$ and $U(s) = \mathscr{L}[u(t)]$, find the transfer function of the system.

Solution: Using the differentiation operator conversion shown in Equation 7.12, by inspection we have the conversion,

$$\ddot{y}(t) + 3\dot{y}(t) + 2y(t) = 4\dot{u}(t) + 12u(t) \quad \rightleftarrows \quad (s^2 + 3s + 2)Y(s) = (4s + 12)U(s) \tag{7.14}$$

which leads to the transfer function

$$G(s) = \frac{Y(s)}{U(s)} = \frac{4s + 12}{s^2 + 3s + 2} \tag{7.15}$$

Note that the conversion procedure is bidirectional. A differential equation can be obtained from the transfer function as easily as the other way around. ∎

7.2.2 Impulse Response and Transfer Function

As illustrated in Figure 7.6, let the input to the system $G(s)$ be a unit impulse function $\delta(t)$, then the output will be

$$Y(s) = G(s)\mathscr{L}[\delta(t)] = G(s) \quad \rightleftarrows \quad y(t) = g(t) = \mathscr{L}^{-1}[G(s)]$$

which means the impulse response $g(t)$ is the time-domain counterpart of the transfer function $G(s)$— the inverse Laplace transform of $G(s)$. Hence, the impulse response can be considered as a representation of the system, and the output $y(t)$ can be computed via the following convolution integral:

$$y(t) = \int_{-\infty}^{t} g(t - \tau)u(\tau)d\tau \tag{7.16}$$

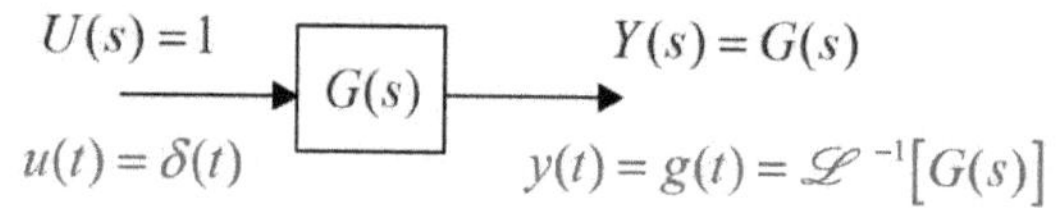

$$U(s) = 1 \qquad \boxed{G(s)} \qquad Y(s) = G(s)$$

$$u(t) = \delta(t) \qquad\qquad y(t) = g(t) = \mathcal{L}^{-1}[G(s)]$$

Fig. 7.6: Impulse response and transfer function.

Example 7.6 (Impulse Response and Convolution Integral)

Consider the system with transfer function $G(s) = b/(s+a)$, where a and b are constants. Find the impulse response of the system and compute the step response of the system using the convolution integral.

Solution: The impulse response is

$$g(t) = \mathcal{L}^{-1}[G(s)] = be^{-at}, \quad t \geq 0$$

Then the step response (i.e., the output of the system due to the unit step input, $u_s(t)$) is

$$y(t) = \int_{-\infty}^{t} g(t-\tau)u_s(\tau)d\tau = \int_{-\infty}^{t} be^{-a(t-\tau)}u_s(\tau)d\tau = \int_{0}^{t} be^{-a(t-\tau)}d\tau$$

$$= be^{-at}\int_{0}^{t} e^{a\tau}d\tau = \frac{b}{a}e^{-at}e^{a\tau}\Big|_{0}^{t} = \frac{b}{a}e^{-at}(e^{at} - e^{0}) = \frac{b}{a}(1 - e^{-at})$$

Note that the other form of the convolutional integral

$$y(t) = \int_{-\infty}^{t} g(\tau)u_s(t-\tau)d\tau$$

will yield the same result.

∎

7.2.3 State-Space Model and Transfer Function

As mentioned in previous chapters, the state-space representation or the state-space model of systems has become increasingly important due to the recent rapid advancement of computing tools and the state-space control systems theory. The state-space model usually is represented in the compact matrix form:

$$\dot{x}(t) = Ax(t) + Bu(t)$$
$$y(t) = Cx(t) + Du(t)$$

(7.17)

where the vectors $x \in R^n$, $u \in R^m$, and $y \in R^p$ are the $n \times 1$ state vector, the $m \times 1$ input vector, and the $p \times 1$ output vector, respectively. The matrices $A \in R^{n \times n}$, $B \in R^{n \times m}$, $C \in R^{p \times n}$, and $D \in R^{p \times m}$ are the $n \times n$ A matrix, the $n \times m$ B matrix, the $p \times n$ C matrix, and the $p \times m$ D matrix, respectively.

As discussed in the previous chapters, particularly in Section 6.6, the state-space model representation of a system is not unique since the state variables can be chosen arbitrarily. However, the transfer function, the characteristic equation, and the poles and zeros of all the state-space models representing the same system are invariant.

A state-space model can be obtained directly in the system modeling process, as demonstrated in Chapters 4 and 5, where the physical variables of interest, like the displacements, the velocities, the currents flowing through inductors, and the voltages across capacitors, are usually chosen as state variables. It also can be assembled from a transfer function, a differential equation, or an interconnected system, which is composed of several subsystems and components, as described in Chapter 6.

On the other hand, the transfer function of the system represented by a state-space model (A,B,C,D) can be computed using the following formula:

$$\frac{Y(s)}{U(s)} := G(s) = C(sI - A)^{-1}B + D \tag{7.18}$$

The transfer function also can be obtained by applying Mason's gain formula to a state diagram associated with the state-space model, as shown in Section 6.6.1.

7.2.4 Characteristic Equation, Poles, and Zeros

Consider the system represented by the following transfer function (Equation 7.11),

$$\frac{Y(s)}{U(s)} = G(s) = \frac{b_m s^m + b_{m-1}s^{m-1} + b_{m-2}s^{m-2} + \cdots + b_1 s + b_0}{s^n + a_{n-1}s^{n-1} + a_{n-2}s^{n-2} + \cdots + a_1 s + a_0} := \frac{N(s)}{D(s)}$$

Under the assumption that the numerical polynomial $N(s)$ and the denominator polynomial $D(s)$ have no common factor, the denominator polynomial $D(s)$ is defined as the characteristic polynomial of the system, and the equation $D(s) = 0$ is the *characteristic equation*:

$$D(s) = s^n + a_{n-1}s^{n-1} + a_{n-2}s^{n-2} + \cdots + a_1 s + a_0 = 0 \tag{7.19}$$

The *poles* of the system are defined as the roots of the characteristic equation, and the *zeros* of the system are defined as the roots of the equation $N(s) = 0$:

$$N(s) = b_m s^m + b_{m-1}s^{m-1} + b_{m-2}s^{m-2} + \cdots + b_1 s + b_0 = 0 \tag{7.20}$$

Note that the dynamic behavior of the system is mainly determined by the location of the poles of the system in the complex plane, as we learned from Sections 3.2 and 3.3. The location of the zeros also have an effect on the system response, as illustrated in the following example.

Example 7.7 (Characteristic Equation, Poles, Zeros, and Their Effect on Dynamic Behavior)

Consider the following three systems with transfer functions $G_a(s)$, $G_b(s)$, and $G_c(s)$, respectively:

$$G_a(s) = \frac{12}{s^2 + 3s + 2}, \quad G_b(s) = \frac{4s + 12}{s^2 + 3s + 2}, \quad G_c(s) = \frac{-4s + 12}{s^2 + 3s + 2} \tag{7.21}$$

The three transfer functions have exactly the same characteristic equation, $s^2 + 3s + 2 = 0$, which has two real poles at $s = -1$ and $s = -2$. Their damping ratio is $\varsigma = 3/2\sqrt{2} = 1.06$, and they are all overdamped. However, these three systems have different zero structure. $G_a(s)$ has no zero, $G_b(s)$ has a zero in the left half of complex plane at $s = -3$, but the system $G_c(s)$ has one zero in the right half of the complex plane at $s = 3$.

The step responses of these three systems are plotted on Figure 7.7. The step response of the system $G_a(s)$, which has no zero, is $y_a(t) = 6 - 12e^{-t} + 6e^{-2t}$. The derivative of $y_a(t)$ can be found as $\dot{y}_a(t) = 12e^{-t} - 12e^{-2t}$, which yields $\dot{y}_a(0) = 0$, a zero slope at $t = 0$. Hence, $y_a(t)$ rises up slowly in the beginning.

The step response of the system $G_b(s)$, which has one zero at $s = -3$, is $y_b(t) = 6 - 8e^{-t} + 2e^{-2t}$. The derivative of $y_b(t)$ can be found as $\dot{y}_b(t) = 8e^{-t} - 4e^{-2t}$, which yields $\dot{y}_b(0) = 4$, a slope of 4 at $t = 0$. Hence, $y_b(t)$ rises more quickly in the beginning and has a faster response than $y_a(t)$.

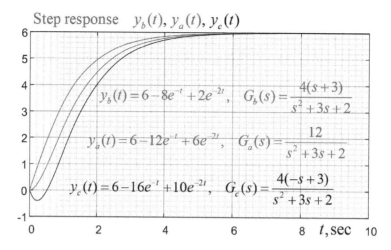

Fig. 7.7: Effect of zeros on dynamic behavior of the system.

The step response of the system $G_c(s)$, which has one zero at $s = 3$, is $y_c(t) = 6 - 16e^{-t} + 10e^{-2t}$. The derivative of $y_c(t)$ can be found as $\dot{y}_c(t) = 16e^{-t} - 20e^{-2t}$, which yields $\dot{y}_c(0) = -4$, a slope of -4 at $t = 0$. Hence, $y_c(t)$ at first was going down toward the opposite direction until $t = 0.223$s at $y_c(0.223) = -0.4$, where it reverses its course back to the correct upward direction. Hence, $y_c(t)$ has a slower response than $y_a(t)$. This initial opposite direction movement is a typical property of the systems with zeros in the right half of the complex plane. The systems with this property are called *nonminimum phase systems*.

∎

7.3 Stability of Linear Systems

Although the definition of stability has not yet been defined, we roughly grasped a little physical sense of it from the step response of the first-order system as discussed in Section 2.4.2. In Equation 2.75, the exponential term $e^{-t/\tau}$ of the step response would become unbounded if $-1/\tau > 0$, which means the characteristic equation, $\tau s + 1 = 0$, of the first-order system would have a pole $s = -1/\tau > 0$ in the right half of the complex plane. We also learned from Section 4.4.3 that the simple inverted pendulum system is unstable because some of its poles are in the right half of the complex plane. We were even more convinced by the fact that the simple inverted pendulum system was stabilized after a state feedback placed all the closed-loop system poles in the left half of the complex plane.

Basically there are two stability definitions for linear time-invariant systems. One is called **BIBO (bounded-input/bounded-output) stability**, and the other is **internal stability**. Since these two definitions are relevant to how the input and the internal initial conditions, respectively, affect the output response. Before giving the two definitions, we will review the zero-state and zero-input responses in the following subsection.

7.3.1 Zero-State Response and Zero-Input Response

The total response of a linear system can be decomposed into two parts, as shown in Figure 7.8: the zero-state response $y_U(t)$, which is the response due to the input $u(t)$ only, and the zero-input response

$y_I(t)$, which is the response due to the initial conditions only. In the following, a simple second-order linear system is employed to illustrate how the zero-state response and the zero-input response relate to the characteristic equation or the pole locations of the system.

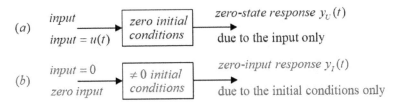

Fig. 7.8: Total response $y(t) =$ zero-state response $y_U(t)+$ zero-input response $y_I(t)$.

Example 7.8 (Effects of System Poles on Zero-State Response and Zero-Input Response)

Consider the system with the following differential equation,

$$\ddot{y}(t) + 3\dot{y}(t) + 2y(t) = 4\dot{u}(t) + 12u(t) \tag{7.22}$$

Assume $Y(s) = \mathcal{L}[y(t)]$, $U(s) = \mathcal{L}[u(t)]$, and let $y(0)$ and $\dot{y}(0)$ be the initial values of $y(t)$ and $\dot{y}(t)$, respectively, of the system. The Laplace transform of the differential equation yields the following algebraic equation:

$$s^2 Y(s) - sy(0) - \dot{y}(0) + 3\left[sY(s) - y(0)\right] + 2Y(s) = 4sU(s) + 12U(s) \tag{7.23}$$

which can be rearranged as follows,

$$Y(s) = \frac{5}{s^2+3s+2}U(s) + \frac{1}{s^2+3s+2}\dot{y}(0) + \frac{s+3}{s^2+3s+2}y(0)$$
$$:= G(s)U(s) + \left[G_1(s)\ G_0(s) \right] \begin{bmatrix} \dot{y}(0) \\ y(0) \end{bmatrix} \tag{7.24}$$

and therefore the total response of the system is the sum of the zero-state response and the zero-input response is as follows:

$$y(t) = \mathcal{L}^{-1}\left[G(s)U(s) \right] + \mathcal{L}^{-1}\left[\left[G_1(s)\ G_0(s) \right] \begin{bmatrix} \dot{y}(0) \\ y(0) \end{bmatrix} \right] := y_U(t) + y_I(t) \tag{7.25}$$

Note that the denominators of $G(s)$, $G_1(s)$, and $G_0(s)$ are all equal to the characteristic polynomial of the system. ∎

The result of Example 7.8 can be extended to a more general linear time-invariant system described by the differential equation,

$$y^{(n)}(t) + a_{n-1}y^{(n-1)}(t) + \cdots + a_1\dot{y}(t) + a_0 y(t)$$
$$= b_m u^{(m)}(t) + b_{m-1}u^{(m-1)}(t) + \cdots + b_1\dot{u}(t) + b_0 u(t) \tag{7.26}$$

and the generalized result of Equation 7.25 will be

$$y(t) = \mathcal{L}^{-1}\left[Y(s) \right] = \mathcal{L}^{-1}\left[G_U(s)U(s) \right] + \mathcal{L}^{-1}\left[G_I(s)y_0 \right] := y_U(t) + y_I(t) \tag{7.27}$$

where $y_0 = \left[y^{(n-1)}(0) \cdots \dot{y}(0)\, y(0) \right]^T$ and the denominators of $G_U(s)$ and $G_I(s)$ are equal to the characteristic polynomial of the system,

$$s^n + a_{n-1}s^{n-1} + a_{n-2}s^{n-2} + \cdots + a_1 s + a_0 \tag{7.28}$$

Remark 7.9 (Conditions for the Zero-Input Response to be Zero as $t \to \infty$ and the Zero-State Response to be Bounded)

Since the rational function $G_I(s)$ is strictly proper, it can be seen from Equation 7.27 that

$$\lim_{t \to \infty} y_I(t) = \lim_{s \to 0} sG_I(s)y_0 = 0$$

if all the roots of the characteristic equation are in the strictly left half of the complex plane. That means, **the zero-input response or the response due to the initial conditions will only decay to zero as $t \to \infty$ if the real part of the roots of the characteristic equation are strictly negative.** On the other hand, $y_U(t)$, the zero-state response, or the response due to the input only, in general may be nonzero as $t \to \infty$. However, for the system to be meaningful, $y_U(t)$ needs to be bounded if the input $u(t)$ is bounded. Since the transfer function $G_U(s)$ is proper and its poles are assumed all in the strictly left half of the complex plane, $y_U(t) = \mathscr{L}^{-1}[G_U(s)U(s)]$ will be bounded if $u(t)$ is bounded. ∎

The remark can also be recapitulated in the state-space setting. Consider a linear time-invariant system represented by the following state-space model:

$$\dot{x}(t) = Ax(t) + Bu(t)$$
$$y(t) = Cx(t) + Du(t)$$

Let $X(s)$ and $U(s)$ be the Laplace transform of $x(t)$ and $u(t)$, respectively, and x_0 represent the initial state vector $x(0)$. Then the Laplace transform of the state equation will lead to the following solution of the state equation:

$$x(t) = \mathscr{L}^{-1}\left[(sI - A)^{-1} \right] x_0 + \mathscr{L}^{-1}\left[(sI - A)^{-1} BU(s) \right] \tag{7.29}$$

Since the inverse Laplace transform of $(sI - A)^{-1}$ is the state transition matrix $\Phi(t)$,

$$\mathscr{L}^{-1}\left[(sI - A)^{-1} \right] = \Phi(t)$$

Equation 7.29 can be rewritten in terms of the state transition matrix as follows:

$$x(t) = \Phi(t)x_0 + \int_0^t \Phi(t - \tau)Bu(\tau)d\tau := x_I(t) + x_U(t) \tag{7.30}$$

Combining this state equation solution with the output equation of the state-space model, we have the following:

$$y(t) = C\Phi(t)x_0 + \left(C\int_0^t \Phi(t - \tau)Bu(\tau)d\tau + Du(t) \right) := y_I(t) + y_U(t) \tag{7.31}$$

As its counterpart, shown in Equation 7.27, the output response of the state-space model consists of two parts: One is $y_I(t)$, which is the output response due to the initial state only, and the other part is $y_U(t)$, which is the output response due to the input $u(t)$ only. It is easy to see that the response due to the initial state,

$$\lim_{t \to \infty} C\Phi(t)x_0 = 0$$

which means that $y_I(t)$ **will approach to zero as** $t \to \infty$, **if the eigenvalues of the** A **matrix (i.e., the poles of the system), are all in the strictly left half of the complex plane.** Meanwhile, with the same condition of system poles being all in the strictly left half of the complex plane, the output response due to the input only,

$$y_U(t) = C \int_0^t \Phi(t-\tau)Bu(\tau)d\tau + Du(t)$$

will be bounded for every bounded input $u(t)$. For ease of reference, the result is summarized in the following Lemma.

Lemma 7.10 (Sufficient Condition for BIBO Stability and Internal Stability)

Assume the system poles (i.e., the eigenvalues of the A matrix) are all in the strictly left of the complex plane, then we have the following:

(1) The response due to the initial state x_0, $\lim_{t \to \infty} \Phi(t)x_0 = 0$ (i.e., $x_I(t)$ will approach to zero as

   $t \to \infty$*), and*
(2) The response due to the input $u(t)$, $y_U(t) = C \int_0^t \Phi(t-\tau)Bu(\tau)d\tau + Du(t)$, is bounded for
   every bounded input $u(t)$.   ■

7.3.2 BIBO Stability and Internal Stability

From the discussion regarding how a system would respond to any initial state x_0 or any bounded input $u(t)$, it is meaningful to define system stability based on the output response of the system due to input $u(t)$ only or based on the state response due to the initial state x_0 only.

Definition 7.11 (BIBO Stability)

A system is BIBO (bounded-input/bounded-output) stable if and only if every bounded input results in a bounded output.   ■

BIBO stability is defined based on the input-output relationship. For the cart-inverted pendulum system considered in Section 4.5, the output is the angular displacement θ of the pendulum (the stick) and the objective is to keep the pendulum at or around the equilibrium, $\theta = 0$. If the system is uncompensated, the pendulum will depart from the equilibrium (i.e., θ will increase without bound) under the influence of a tiny disturbance input.

The uncompensated cart-inverted pendulum system is obviously an unstable system. But some systems may only produce unbounded output for a special kind of bounded input. For example, the notorious collapse of the Tacoma Narrows Bridge was caused by the oscillation resonance that occurs when the input frequency matches the natural frequency of the system.

Hence, the key word in the definition of BIBO stability is "every." For a system to be BIBO stable, every bounded input has to result in bounded output. But, how can it possible to examine every bounded input? A practically doable approach is using the impulse response integral as described in the following theorem.

Theorem 7.12 (Impulse Response Integral Check for BIBO Stability)

A linear time-invariant system with impulse response g(t) is BIBO stable if and only if

$$\int_0^\infty |g(t)|dt = M < \infty \tag{7.32}$$

∎

Example 7.13 (Check BIBO Stability Using the Impulse Response Integral)

Consider the system of Example 7.6, whose impulse response is $g(t) = be^{-at}$, $t \geq 0$, where a and b are constants. Since

$$\int_0^\infty be^{-at}dt = -bae^{-at}\Big|_0^\infty = \begin{cases} ba & \text{if } a > 0 \\ \infty & \text{if } a < 0 \end{cases}$$

the system is BIBO stable if and only if $a > 0$.

∎

This impulse response integral approach is doable; however, the computation of impulse response integral is tedious when the system becomes complicated. Now, we will revisit Lemma 7.10 to investigate if the sufficient condition for BIBO stability is also a necessary condition. This sufficient condition is indeed also a necessary condition since a system with a pole or poles on the imaginary axis of the complex plane is not BIBO stable.

Example 7.14 (A System That Has Poles on the Imaginary Axis Is Not BIBO Stable)

Consider a system $G(s) = 1/(s^2 + \omega_n^2)$ that has poles on the imaginary axis of the complex plane at $s = \pm j\omega_n$. The output of the system is bounded for almost all of the possible bounded inputs. However, if the input is a sinusoidal function $u(t) = cos\omega t$ or $u(t) = sin\omega t$, with its oscillation frequency ω equal to the natural frequency ω_n of the system, then the output will be an unbounded function of time t; hence, the system in not BIBO stable.

The sinusoidal function, $u(t) = cos\omega t$ and $u(t) = sin\omega t$ are the real part and the imaginary part, respectively, of the complex function $e^{j\omega t}$. For computational simplicity, $u(t) = e^{j\omega t} = cos\omega t + jcos\omega t$ is chosen as the input, then the output $y(t) = y_{Re}(t) + jy_{Im}(t)$ is also a complex function of time consisting of $y_{Re}(t)$ and $y_{Im}(t)$ as its real and imaginary parts, respectively.

With the input $U(s)$ and the system $G(s)$ given as:

$$U(s) = \mathscr{L}\left[e^{j\omega t}\right] = \frac{1}{s - j\omega} \quad \text{and} \quad G(s) = \frac{1}{s^2 + \omega^2} = \frac{1}{(s + j\omega)(s - j\omega)}$$

Then the output $Y(s)$ can be written as

$$Y(s) = G(s)U(s) = \frac{1}{(s + j\omega)(s - j\omega)^2} = \frac{c_1}{s + j\omega} + \frac{c_2}{s - j\omega} + \frac{c_3}{(s - j\omega)^2}$$

where the partial fractional expansion coefficients are

$$c_1 = \frac{-1}{4\omega^2}, \quad c_2 = -c_1 = \frac{1}{4\omega^2}, \quad c_3 = \frac{1}{2\omega}e^{-j\pi/2}$$

Recall that *the parameter a* in the following Laplace transform pairs can be a complex number:

$$\mathscr{L}^{-1}\left[\frac{1}{s+a}\right] = e^{-at}, \quad \mathscr{L}^{-1}\left[\frac{1}{(s+a)^2}\right] = te^{-at}$$

Hence, we have the output of the system $y(t)$ due to the input $u(t) = e^{j\omega t}$ in the following:

$$y(t) = c_2 \left(e^{j\omega t} - e^{-j\omega t} \right) + c_3 t e^{j\omega t} = \frac{j2 \sin \omega t}{4\omega^2} + \frac{t}{2\omega} e^{j(\omega t - \pi/2)} = j\frac{\sin \omega t}{2\omega^2} + \frac{t \left(\sin \omega t - j\cos \omega t \right)}{2\omega}$$

The equation is rearranged as

$$y(t) = \frac{t \sin \omega t}{2\omega} + j \left(\frac{\sin \omega t - \omega t \cos \omega t}{2\omega^2} \right) = y_{\text{Re}}(t) + j y_{\text{Im}}(t)$$

where $y_{\text{Re}}(t) = (1/2\omega)t \sin \omega t$ and $y_{\text{Im}}(t) = (1/2\omega^2)(\sin \omega t - \omega t \cos \omega t)$ are the output responses due to the inputs $u(t) = \cos\omega t$ and $u(t) = \sin\omega t$, respectively. **Note that both are unbounded, growing with time. Therefore, the system is not BIBO stable if it has poles on the imaginary axis.** ∎

Since the sufficient condition for BIBO stability described in Lemma 7.10 is also a necessary condition, the lemma now can be modified as the following theorem.

Theorem 7.15 (Necessary and Sufficient Condition for BIBO Stability)

A linear time-invariant system is BIBO stable if and only if all its poles are in the strictly left half of the complex plane. ∎

This theorem provides an easily verifiable necessary and sufficient condition for BIBO stability. It also makes it clear that **all the closed-loop system poles are required to be placed in the strictly left half of the complex plane** to achieve stability.

In addition to BIBO stability, which is defined based on the external input-output relationship, there is another meaningful stability definition called internal stability.

Definition 7.16 (Internal Stability)

The linear time-invariant system

$$\dot{x}(t) = Ax(t) + Bu(t)$$
$$y(t) = Cx(t) + Du(t)$$

is internally stable if the solution $x(t)$ of

$$\dot{x}(t) = Ax(t) \quad \text{with initial state } x(0) = x_0$$

tends toward zero as $t \to \infty$ for arbitrary x_0. ∎

As described in Lemma 7.10, the condition that all the eigenvalues of the A matrix are in the strictly left half of the complex plane is sufficient for the system to be internally stable. Similar to the case of BIBO stability, this condition is also a necessary condition for internal stability. If it is not, then a system with eigenvalues on the imaginary axis would be internally stable.

Example 7.17 (A System with Eigenvalues on the Imaginary Axis Is Not Internally Stable)

Consider the system

$$\dot{x}(t) = Ax(t) = \begin{bmatrix} 0 & -\omega \\ \omega & 0 \end{bmatrix} x(t) \quad \text{with initial state } x(0) = x_0 = \begin{bmatrix} x_{10} \\ x_{20} \end{bmatrix}$$

where x_{10} and x_{20} are arbitrary. Note that **the eigenvalues of the system, which are the roots of the characteristic equation $\det(\lambda I - A) = \lambda^2 + \omega^2 = 0$, are on the imaginary axis at $\pm j\omega$.** Since

$$(sI - A)^{-1}x_0 = \begin{bmatrix} s & \omega \\ -\omega & s \end{bmatrix}^{-1} \begin{bmatrix} x_{10} \\ x_{20} \end{bmatrix} = \frac{1}{s^2 + \omega^2} \begin{bmatrix} s & -\omega \\ \omega & s \end{bmatrix} \begin{bmatrix} x_{10} \\ x_{20} \end{bmatrix} = \frac{1}{s^2 + \omega^2} \begin{bmatrix} x_{10}s - x_{20}\omega \\ x_{10}\omega + x_{20}s \end{bmatrix}$$

we have the solution of the state equation as

$$x(t) = \mathscr{L}^{-1}\left[(sI - A)^{-1}x_0\right] = \begin{bmatrix} x_{10}\cos\omega t - x_{20}\sin\omega t \\ x_{10}\sin\omega t + x_{20}\cos\omega t \end{bmatrix}$$

which obviously will continue to oscillate instead of approaching to zero as $t \to \infty$. Therefore, the system is not internally stable if it has eigenvalues on the imaginary axis.   ∎

Since the sufficient condition for internal stability described in Lemma 7.10 is also a necessary condition, the lemma now is modified as the following theorem.

Theorem 7.18 (Necessary and Sufficient Condition for Internal Stability)

The linear time-invariant system

$$\dot{x}(t) = Ax(t) + Bu(t)$$
$$y(t) = Cx(t) + Du(t)$$

is internally stable if and only if the eigenvalues of the A matrix are all in the strictly left half of the complex plane.   ∎

Remark 7.19 (Internal Stability Is a Stronger Condition Than BIBO Stability)

Internal stability is a stronger stability condition than BIBO stability since BIBO stability only reflects the attributes of the system that are observable from the output and controllable from the input. There may exist an unstable hidden-mode state that leads to internal instability while the BIBO stability measure is unable to detect it. However, if all the states of the system are controllable and observable, then BIBO stability is equivalent to internal stability. Detailed discussion regarding controllability and observability will be given in Chapters 10 and 11.   ∎

Theorem 7.18 provides an easy way to check the internal stability of an existing system. It also can be employed to design a stabilizing controller to guarantee the internal stability of the closed-loop system. In the following section we will discuss how to employ this theorem and a simple state-feedback control to stabilize an originally unstable system.

7.4 Similarity Transformation in State Space

As discussed in the previous chapters, particularly in Section 6.6, the state-space model representation of a system is not unique since the state variables theoretically can be chosen arbitrarily. However, in practice the state variables are not chosen randomly. They usually are selected based on two considerations. One is to associate the state variables with the physical variables of interest, and the other is to choose state variables so that the state-space model is in a special form for the purpose of analysis or control system design. On some occasions, we may need to transform a given state-space model to a special form. This transformation is called *similarity transformation*. Under similarity transformations, the A, B, and C matrices in the state-space model may change, but the transfer function, the characteristic equation, and the poles and the zeros will remain invariant.

Assume a linear time-invariant system is described by the following state-space model:

$$\dot{x}(t) = Ax(t) + Bu(t)$$
$$y(t) = Cx(t) + Du(t)$$

(7.33)

Let $\hat{x}(t)$ be a new state vector, defined as $\hat{x}(t) = T^{-1}x(t)$, where T is a nonsingular matrix with dimension compatible with the state vector. Then we have the new transformed state-space model in the following:

$$\dot{\hat{x}}(t) = T^{-1}\dot{x}(t) = T^{-1}Ax(t) + T^{-1}Bu(t) = T^{-1}AT\hat{x}(t) + T^{-1}Bu(t)$$
$$y(t) = Cx(t) + Du(t) = CT\hat{x}(t) + Du(t)$$

(7.34)

That is, the similarity transformation $\hat{x}(t) = T^{-1}x(t)$ has transformed the original state-space model in Equation 7.33 to the new state-space model with the new state vector $\hat{x}(t)$,

$$\dot{\hat{x}}(t) = \hat{A}\hat{x}(t) + \hat{B}u(t)$$
$$y(t) = \hat{C}\hat{x}(t) + Du(t)$$

(7.35)

where

$$\hat{A} = T^{-1}AT, \quad \hat{B} = T^{-1}B, \quad \hat{C} = CT$$

(7.36)

Theorem 7.20 (Invariance Under Similarity Transformation)

The transfer function, the characteristic equation, and poles and zeros are invariant under the similarity transformation that transform the state-space model (A,B,C) to $(T^{-1}AT, T^{-1}B, CT)$.

Proof:

$$\hat{G}(s) = \hat{C}(sI - \hat{A})^{-1}\hat{B} = CT(sI - T^{-1}AT)^{-1}T^{-1}B = CT(TsI - TT^{-1}AT)^{-1}B$$
$$= C(TsIT^{-1} - TT^{-1}ATT^{-1})^{-1}B = C(sI - A)^{-1}B = G(s)$$

∎

The ability to use the similarity transformation to transform a state-space representation from one form to another is a great advantage in the analysis and design of control systems. The special forms of state-space representations include diagonal form, companion form, controller form, observability form, noncontrollable canonical form, and nonobservable canonical form. Later on in Chapters 10 and 11, the similarity transformation will be employed to achieve the Kalman decomposition, which breaks down the state space into four parts according to controllability and observability. Moreover, the similarity transformation also can be utilized to identify the stable subspace in the state space. In the following, we will introduce the diagonal form and the companion form and their advantages in control system analysis and design.

7.4.1 Diagonalization of A Matrix Using Similarity Transformation

Consider the state-space model given by Equation 7.33. Find a similarity transformation $\hat{x}(t) = T^{-1}x(t)$ that transforms the state-space model of Equation 7.33 to the new state-space model shown in Equation 7.35 so that the $\hat{A} = T^{-1}AT$ is diagonal.

$$T^{-1}AT = \Lambda = \begin{bmatrix} \lambda_1 & & & \\ & \lambda_2 & & \\ & & \ddots & \\ & & & \lambda_n \end{bmatrix} \quad \rightleftharpoons \quad AT = T\Lambda$$

(7.37)

Let e_i, $i = 1, 2, ..., n$, be column vectors of T. Then,

$$A \begin{bmatrix} e_1 & e_2 & \cdots & e_n \end{bmatrix} = \begin{bmatrix} e_1 & e_2 & \cdots & e_n \end{bmatrix} \begin{bmatrix} \lambda_1 & & & \\ & \lambda_2 & & \\ & & \ddots & \\ & & & \lambda_n \end{bmatrix} \quad \Longleftrightarrow \quad Ae_i = \lambda_i e_i \quad i = 1, 2, ..., n \quad (7.38)$$

where λ_i **must be an eigenvalue of** A **and** e_i **a corresponding eigenvector.** A nonsingular T can be found if and only if A has n linearly independent eigenvectors.

Example 7.21 (Diagonalization of a State-Space Model)

Consider the system with the following state-space model,

$$\dot{x}(t) = Ax(t) + Bu(t) = \begin{bmatrix} -2 & -2 \\ 2 & 3 \end{bmatrix} x(t) + \begin{bmatrix} -1 \\ 1 \end{bmatrix} u(t)$$

$$y(t) = Cx(t) = \begin{bmatrix} 12 & 16 \end{bmatrix} x(t) \tag{7.39}$$

To find a similarity transformation that transforms a state-space model to a diagonal form, the first step is to obtain the eigenvalues λ_1, λ_2 and their associated eigenvectors e_1, e_2.

$$\det(\lambda I - A) = \det \begin{bmatrix} \lambda + 2 & 2 \\ -2 & \lambda - 3 \end{bmatrix} = \lambda^2 - \lambda - 2 = 0 \quad \rightarrow \quad \lambda_1 = -1, \lambda_2 = 2$$

and

$$\begin{bmatrix} -1+2 & 2 \\ -2 & -1-3 \end{bmatrix} e_1 = \begin{bmatrix} 1 & 2 \\ -2 & -4 \end{bmatrix} \begin{bmatrix} -2 \\ 1 \end{bmatrix} = 0 \quad \rightarrow \quad e_1 = \begin{bmatrix} -2 \\ 1 \end{bmatrix}$$

$$\begin{bmatrix} 2+2 & 2 \\ -2 & 2-3 \end{bmatrix} e_2 = \begin{bmatrix} 4 & 2 \\ -2 & -1 \end{bmatrix} \begin{bmatrix} 1 \\ -2 \end{bmatrix} = 0 \quad \rightarrow \quad e_2 = \begin{bmatrix} 1 \\ -2 \end{bmatrix}$$

Let the similarity transformation matrix be $T = \begin{bmatrix} e_1 & e_2 \end{bmatrix}$. Then the diagonalized state-space model is obtained as follows:

$$\dot{\hat{x}}(t) = T^{-1}AT\hat{x}(t) + T^{-1}Bu(t) = \begin{bmatrix} -1 & 0 \\ 0 & 2 \end{bmatrix} \hat{x}(t) + \begin{bmatrix} 1/3 \\ -1/3 \end{bmatrix} u(t)$$

$$y(t) = CT\hat{x}(t) = \begin{bmatrix} -8 & -20 \end{bmatrix} \hat{x}(t) \tag{7.40}$$

∎

We have learned that **a given state-space model can be transformed to a diagonal form if and only if the** $n \times n$ A **matrix of the model has n linearly independent eigenvectors.** The diagonal form has several advantages. The poles of the system appear conspicuously on the diagonal line of the matrix A, and all the off-diagonal elements of the A matrix are zero. The diagonal form not only saves data storage size, it also tremendously reduces computational complexities, especially for high-order systems. **The corresponding diagonal state diagram on Figure 7.9 shows even more clearly that the system has been decomposed into two subsystems: one with its pole at** $s = -1$ **and the other with a pole at** $s = 2$.

Another important form of state-space model is the *companion form*, which will be employed to implement a pole-placement control system design later in this chapter.

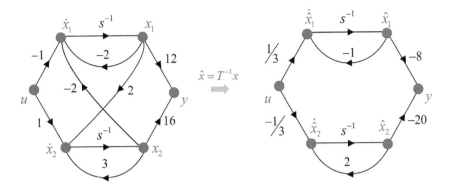

Fig. 7.9: Similarity transformation to diagonal form state diagram.

7.4.2 Obtaining a State-Space Model in Companion Form Using Similarity Transformation

To reduce the notational complexity, without loss of generality, a third-order state-space model is employed in the following to demonstrate how to transform a state-space model to a companion form. Consider the state-space model given by

$$\dot{x}(t) = Ax(t) + Bu(t) \qquad \text{where} \quad \det(\lambda I - A) = \lambda^3 + a_2\lambda^2 + a_1\lambda + a_0 \qquad (7.41)$$
$$y(t) = Cx(t)$$

The objective is to find a similarity transformation $\hat{x}(t) = T^{-1}x(t)$ that transforms the state-space model to the following companion form:

$$\dot{\hat{x}}(t) = \hat{A}\hat{x}(t) + \hat{B}u(t) \qquad \text{where} \quad \hat{A} = T^{-1}AT = \begin{bmatrix} 0 & 1 & 0 \\ 0 & 0 & 1 \\ -a_0 & -a_1 & -a_2 \end{bmatrix}, \ \hat{B} = T^{-1}B = \begin{bmatrix} 0 \\ 0 \\ 1 \end{bmatrix} \qquad (7.42)$$
$$y(t) = \hat{C}\hat{x}(t)$$

Let the similarity transformation matrix be $T = [t_3 \ t_2 \ t_1]$. Then the equations can be rearranged as follows:

$$A\begin{bmatrix} t_3 & t_2 & t_1 \end{bmatrix} = \begin{bmatrix} t_3 & t_2 & t_1 \end{bmatrix}\begin{bmatrix} 0 & 1 & 0 \\ 0 & 0 & 1 \\ -a_0 & -a_1 & -a_2 \end{bmatrix}, \quad B = \begin{bmatrix} t_3 & t_2 & t_1 \end{bmatrix}\begin{bmatrix} 0 \\ 0 \\ 1 \end{bmatrix}$$

which lead to

$$t_1 = B, \quad t_2 = At_1 + a_2t_1, \quad t_3 = At_2 + a_1t_1$$

or

$$T = \begin{bmatrix} A^2B + a_2AB + a_1B & AB + a_2B & B \end{bmatrix} \qquad (7.43)$$

Note that the similarity transformation matrix T is nonsingular if and only if the controllability matrix $\mathscr{C}(A,B) = \begin{bmatrix} B & AB & A^2B \end{bmatrix}$ is nonsingular. The definition and physical meaning of controllability and controllability matrix will be introduced later in Chapter 10. A state-space model can be transformed to a companion form if and only if the system is controllable.

The companion form similarity transformation procedure can be repeated for higher-order state-space models, and by induction a more general n-th order companion form similarity transformation formula is obtained and summarized in the following theorem.

Theorem 7.22 (Companion Form Similarity Transformation)

For the n-th order state-space model given by

$$\dot{x}(t) = Ax(t) + Bu(t)$$
$$y(t) = Cx(t)$$
where $\det(\lambda I - A) = \lambda^n + a_{n-1}\lambda^{n-1} + \cdots + a_1\lambda + a_0$ (7.44)

The similarity transformation $\hat{x}(t) = T^{-1}x(t)$ that transforms the state-space model to the following companion form,

$$\dot{\hat{x}}(t) = \hat{A}\hat{x}(t) + \hat{B}u(t)$$
$$y(t) = \hat{C}\hat{x}(t) = CT\hat{x}(t)$$
where $\hat{A} = \begin{bmatrix} 0 & 1 & & & \\ & 0 & \ddots & & \\ & & \ddots & 1 & \\ & & & 0 & 1 \\ -a_0 & -a_1 & \cdots & -a_{n-2} & -a_{n-1} \end{bmatrix}$, $\hat{B} = \begin{bmatrix} 0 \\ 0 \\ \vdots \\ 0 \\ 1 \end{bmatrix}$ (7.45)

can be obtained using the following formula:

$$T = \begin{bmatrix} t_n & t_{n-1} & \cdots & t_2 & t_1 \end{bmatrix}, \quad \text{where} \quad \begin{cases} t_n = \left(A^{n-1} + a_{n-1}A^{n-2} + \cdots + a_2 A + a_1 I \right) B \\ t_{n-1} = \left(A^{n-2} + a_{n-1}A^{n-3} + \cdots + a_3 A + a_2 I \right) B \\ \vdots \\ t_2 = \left(A + a_{n-1} I \right) B \\ t_1 = B \end{cases}$$ (7.46)

∎

Example 7.23 (Companion Form Transformation of a State-Space Model)

Consider the system with the following state-space model:

$$\dot{x}(t) = Ax(t) + Bu(t) = \begin{bmatrix} -2 & -2 \\ 2 & 3 \end{bmatrix} x(t) + \begin{bmatrix} -1 \\ 1 \end{bmatrix} u(t)$$
$$y(t) = Cx(t) = \begin{bmatrix} 12 & 16 \end{bmatrix} x(t)$$ (7.47)

The characteristic polynomial of the system is

$$\det(\lambda I - A) = \det \begin{bmatrix} \lambda + 2 & 2 \\ -2 & \lambda - 3 \end{bmatrix} = \lambda^2 - \lambda - 2 = \lambda^2 + a_1\lambda + a_0$$

The similarity transformation $\hat{x}(t) = T^{-1}x(t)$ that transforms the state-space model to the companion form:

$$\dot{\hat{x}}(t) = \hat{A}\hat{x}(t) + \hat{B}u(t) = T^{-1}AT\hat{x}(t) + T^{-1}Bu(t)$$
$$y(t) = \hat{C}\hat{x}(t) = CT\hat{x}(t)$$
where $\hat{A} = \begin{bmatrix} 0 & 1 \\ -a_0 & -a_1 \end{bmatrix}$, $\hat{B} = \begin{bmatrix} 0 \\ 1 \end{bmatrix}$

can be obtained using Equation 7.46 from Theorem 7.22 as follows:

$$T = \begin{bmatrix} t_2 & t_1 \end{bmatrix} = \begin{bmatrix} (A + a_1 I)B & B \end{bmatrix} = \begin{bmatrix} 1 & -1 \\ 0 & 1 \end{bmatrix}$$ (7.48)

Then the companion form state-space model is found as follows:

$$\dot{\hat{x}}(t) = T^{-1}AT\hat{x}(t) + T^{-1}Bu(t) = \begin{bmatrix} 0 & 1 \\ 2 & 1 \end{bmatrix}\hat{x}(t) + \begin{bmatrix} 0 \\ 1 \end{bmatrix}u(t)$$

$$y(t) = CT\hat{x}(t) = [12 \quad 14]\hat{x}(t)$$

(7.49)

■

In Example 7.21, a state-space model of Equation 7.39 was transformed to the diagonal form in Equation 7.40 using a diagonal form similarity transformation. Similarly, in Example 7.23, the same state-space model of Equation 7.39 was transformed to the companion form in Equation 7.49 using a companion form similarity transformation. The two state diagrams associated with the diagonal form and the companion form, respectively, are shown in Figure 7.9 and Figure 7.10. For ease of reference, these state-space representations are also shown in the following:

$$\dot{x}_d = \begin{bmatrix} -1 & 0 \\ 0 & 2 \end{bmatrix}x_d(t) + \begin{bmatrix} 1/3 \\ -1/3 \end{bmatrix}u(t) = A_d x_d(t) + B_d u(t)$$

$$y(t) = [-8 \quad -20]x_d(t) = C_d x_d(t)$$

(7.50)

and

$$\dot{x}_c = \begin{bmatrix} 0 & 1 \\ 2 & 1 \end{bmatrix}x_c(t) + \begin{bmatrix} 0 \\ 1 \end{bmatrix}u(t) = A_c x_c(t) + B_c u(t)$$

$$y(t) = [12 \quad 14]x_c(t) = C_c x_c(t)$$

(7.51)

These two state-space models appear quite different, and yet they actually represent the same system. There must be some mathematical relationship between them. Indeed, the following theorem provides a way to find the similarity transformation connecting them. In the following, a **minimal state-space model means that the number of state variables or the dimension of the** A **matrix is minimal. A minimal state-space model is also controllable and observable. The definition and physical meaning of controllability, observability, and minimal realization will be discussed in Chapters 10 and 11.**

Theorem 7.24 (Minimal State-Space Models Related by a Unique Similarity Transformation)

Assume (A_1, B_1, C_1) *and* (A_2, B_2, C_2) *are two minimal state-space models of a system. Then there exists a unique similarity transformation* T *so that* $A_2 = T^{-1}A_1 T$, $B_2 = T^{-1}B_1$, *and* $C_2 = C_1 T$, *and this similarity transformation matrix is*

$$T = \mathscr{C}(A_1, B_1) \cdot \mathscr{C}^{-1}(A_2, B_2) \quad \text{where} \quad \mathscr{C}(A, B) = \begin{bmatrix} B & AB & \cdots & A^{n-1}B \end{bmatrix}$$

(7.52)

where $\mathscr{C}(A, B)$ *is the controllability matrix of the state-space model* (A, B, C). ■

In the following example, the diagonal-form and the companion-form state-space models will be employed to verify that **they are connected by a similarity transformation and they share the same transfer function and characteristic equation.**

Example 7.25 (Similarity Transform Between the Diagonal and the Companion Forms)

The controllability matrices $\mathscr{C}(A_d, B_d)$ and $\mathscr{C}(A_c, B_c)$ of the diagonal and the companion state-space models, respectively, are computed in the following:

$$\mathscr{C}(A_d, B_d) = [B_d \quad A_d B_d] = \begin{bmatrix} 1/3 & -1/3 \\ -1/3 & -2/3 \end{bmatrix}, \quad \mathscr{C}(A_c, B_c) = [B_c \quad A_c B_c] = \begin{bmatrix} 0 & 1 \\ 1 & 1 \end{bmatrix}$$

(7.53)

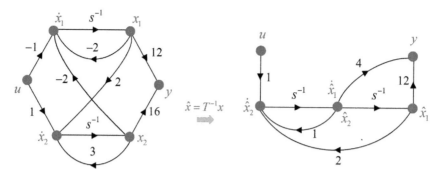

Fig. 7.10: Similarity transformation to companion form state diagram.

Hence, the similarity transformation matrix is

$$T = \mathscr{C}(A_d, B_d) \cdot \mathscr{C}^{-1}(A_c, B_c) = \begin{bmatrix} 1/3 & -1/3 \\ -1/3 & -2/3 \end{bmatrix} \begin{bmatrix} 0 & 1 \\ 1 & 1 \end{bmatrix}^{-1} = \begin{bmatrix} -2/3 & 1/3 \\ -1/3 & -1/3 \end{bmatrix} \tag{7.54}$$

which transforms the diagonal state-space model (A_d, B_d, C_d) to the companion model (A_c, B_c, C_c) as verified in the following:

$$T^{-1}A_dT = \begin{bmatrix} -2/3 & 1/3 \\ -1/3 & -1/3 \end{bmatrix}^{-1} \begin{bmatrix} -1 & 0 \\ 0 & 2 \end{bmatrix} \begin{bmatrix} -2/3 & 1/3 \\ -1/3 & -1/3 \end{bmatrix} = \begin{bmatrix} 0 & 1 \\ 2 & 1 \end{bmatrix} = A_c$$

$$T^{-1}B_d = \begin{bmatrix} -2/3 & 1/3 \\ -1/3 & -1/3 \end{bmatrix}^{-1} \begin{bmatrix} 1/3 \\ -1/3 \end{bmatrix} = \begin{bmatrix} 0 \\ 1 \end{bmatrix} = B_c$$

$$C_dT = [-8 \ \ -20] \begin{bmatrix} -2/3 & 1/3 \\ -1/3 & -1/3 \end{bmatrix} = [12 \ \ 14] = C_c$$

The transfer functions of both state-space models can be obtained using matrix computation,

$$C_d(sI - A_d)^{-1}B_d = C_c(sI - A_c)^{-1}B_c = \frac{4s + 12}{s^2 - s - 2}$$

or by applying Mason's gain formula to the state diagrams shown in Figure 7.9 and Figure 7.10, respectively. The characteristic equations of both models are also invariant under similarity transformation. They are

$$\det(\lambda I - A_d) = \det(\lambda I - A_c) = \lambda^2 - \lambda - 2 = 0$$

■

7.5 Pole Placement Control in State Space

The basic principle of pole placement control in state space is rather simple. Suppose we are given an n-th order system with a state-space model

$$\dot{x}(t) = Ax(t) + Bu(t)$$
$$y(t) = Cx(t) \tag{7.55}$$

and we have learned that the behavior of the system is mainly determined by the poles of the system, which are the roots of the characteristic equation,

$$\det(sI - A) = s^n + a_{n-1}s^{n-1} + \cdots + a_1 s + a_0$$
$$= (s - s_1)(s - s_2) \cdots (s - s_n) = 0 \tag{7.56}$$

If all the state variables in the state vector $x(t)$ are available for feedback, then the control input can be set as

$$u(t) = Fx(t) \tag{7.57}$$

so that the state equation of the closed-loop system will be

$$\det[sI - (A + BF)] = s^n + \alpha_{n-1}s^{n-1} + \cdots + \alpha_1 s + \alpha_0$$
$$= (s - \lambda_1)(s - \lambda_2) \cdots (s - \lambda_n) = 0 \tag{7.58}$$

Theorem 7.26 (Necessary and Sufficient Condition for State-Feedback Pole Placement)

For the system described by Equation 7.55, there exists a state-feedback control $u(t) = Fx(t)$ so that the roots of the closed-loop system characteristic equation $\det[sI - (A + BF)] = 0$ can be arbitrarily placed in the complex plane if and only if the controllability matrix of the system is of full rank, or

$$\text{rank} \begin{bmatrix} B & AB & \cdots & A^{n-1}B \end{bmatrix} = n \tag{7.59}$$

∎

7.5.1 State-Feedback Pole Placement: Direct Approach

There are two ways to apply the pole placement theorem. One is a *direct approach*, which is straightforward and conceptually simple, but computationally can become very complicated when the order of the system is high. The other is a *transform approach*, which requires a similarity transformation, but the computation will not become much more complicated, even when the order of the system becomes very high.

Example 7.27 (State-Feedback Pole Placement Control Using Direct Approach)

Consider the system

$$\dot{x}(t) = Ax(t) + Bu(t) = \begin{bmatrix} -2 & -2 \\ 2 & 3 \end{bmatrix} x(t) + \begin{bmatrix} -1 \\ 1 \end{bmatrix} u(t)$$

Find a state feedback $u(t) = Fx(t)$ so that the closed-loop system has damping ratio $\varsigma = 0.8$ and natural frequency $\omega_n = 5$ rad/s. That is, **the desired closed-loop system characteristic equation should be**

$$s^2 + 2\varsigma \omega_n s + \omega_n^2 = s^2 + 8s + 25 = 0 \tag{7.60}$$

or, equivalently, the desired closed-loop poles are $-4 \pm j3$. The characteristic equation of the uncompensated system is

$$|sI - A| = \begin{vmatrix} s+2 & 2 \\ -2 & s-3 \end{vmatrix} = s^2 - s - 2 = (s+1)(s-2) = 0$$

which shows that the system is unstable. It also can be seen that the controllability matrix

$$[B\ AB] = \begin{bmatrix} -1 & 0 \\ 1 & 1 \end{bmatrix}$$

is nonsingular so there exists a state-feedback controller $u(t) = Fx(t)$ so that the closed-loop system poles can be placed at any desired location of the complex plane. Let $F = [f_1\ f_2]$, then

$$A + BF = \begin{bmatrix} -2 & -2 \\ 2 & 3 \end{bmatrix} + \begin{bmatrix} -1 \\ 1 \end{bmatrix} [f_1\ f_2] = \begin{bmatrix} -2 - f_1 & -2 - f_2 \\ 2 + f_1 & 3 + f_2 \end{bmatrix}$$

and the closed-loop characteristic equation will be

$$|sI - (A + BF)| = \begin{vmatrix} s + 2 + f_1 & 2 + f_2 \\ -2 - f_1 & s - 3 - f_2 \end{vmatrix} = s^2 + (f_1 - f_2 - 1)s + (-f_1 - 2) = 0 \qquad (7.61)$$

By comparing the coefficients of the two characteristic equations, Equations 7.60 and 7.61, we have

$$\begin{aligned} f_1 - f_2 - 1 &= 8 \\ -f_1 - 2 &= 25 \end{aligned} \quad \rightarrow \quad f_1 = -27, \quad f_2 = -36$$

The state-feedback control $u(t) = Fx(t)$, where $F = [-27\ -36]$, has successfully placed the closed-loop system poles at the desired location, $s = -4 \pm j3$, in the complex plane. ∎

The direct approach works well for low-order systems, but the complexity of the computation involved will grow exponentially as the order of the system or the dimension of the A matrix increases. When the matrix dimension is more than 4, the symbolic computation of the determinant of the $sI - (A + BF)$ matrix will become very complicated, even with the help of a symbolic computing software.

Fortunately, the high-order computation issue can be resolved using similarity transformations. Since the characteristic equation and the system poles are invariant under similarity transformations, a given state-space model can be transformed to a special form like a diagonal form or a companion form, where each pole or each coefficient of the characteristic equation can be easily altered independently.

7.5.2 State-Feedback Pole Placement: Transform Approach

The state-feedback pole placement problem is briefly recited as follows: Given a system represented by the following state equation,

$$\dot{x}(t) = Ax(t) + Bu(t) \qquad (7.62)$$

with the characteristic equation

$$|sI - A| = s^n + a_{n-1}s^{n-1} + \cdots + a_1 s + a_0 = 0 \qquad (7.63)$$

the objective is to find a state-feedback control $u(t) = Fx(t)$, where

$$F = [f_1\ f_2\ \cdots\ f_n] \qquad (7.64)$$

so that the closed-loop system has the following desired characteristic equation

$$|sI - (A + BF)| = s^n + \alpha_{n-1}s^{n-1} + \cdots + \alpha_1 s + \alpha_0 = 0 \qquad (7.65)$$

With the similarity transformation, $\hat{x}(t) = T^{-1}x(t)$, the state-feedback pole placement problem can be transformed to the following. Consider the same system represented by a transformed state equation

$$\dot{x}(t) = \hat{A}\hat{x}(t) + \hat{B}u(t) = T^{-1}AT\hat{x}(t) + T^{-1}Bu(t) \tag{7.66}$$

with the same characteristic equation,

$$\left|sI - \hat{A}\right| = \left|sI - A\right| = s^n + a_{n-1}s^{n-1} + \cdots + a_1 s + a_0 = 0 \tag{7.67}$$

The objective is to find a state-feedback control $u(t) = \hat{F}\hat{x}(t)$, where

$$\hat{F} = \begin{bmatrix} \hat{f}_1 & \hat{f}_2 & \cdots & \hat{f}_n \end{bmatrix} \tag{7.68}$$

so that the closed-loop system has the following desired characteristic equation

$$\left|sI - (\hat{A} + \hat{B}\hat{F})\right| = s^n + \alpha_{n-1}s^{n-1} + \cdots + \alpha_1 s + \alpha_0 = 0 \tag{7.69}$$

Transform Approach Procedure

Step 1: Use Theorem 7.22 to find a similarity transformation $x(t) = T^{-1}\hat{x}(t)$ so that the new state equation is in companion form as follows:

$$\dot{x}(t) = \hat{A}\hat{x}(t) + \hat{B}u(t) = T^{-1}AT\hat{x}(t) + T^{-1}Bu(t) \tag{7.70}$$

where

$$\hat{A} = \begin{bmatrix} 0 & 1 & & & \\ & 0 & \ddots & & \\ & & \ddots & 1 & \\ & & & 0 & 1 \\ -a_0 & -a_1 & \cdots & -a_{n-2} & -a_{n-1} \end{bmatrix}, \quad \hat{B} = \begin{bmatrix} 0 \\ 0 \\ \vdots \\ 0 \\ 1 \end{bmatrix} \tag{7.71}$$

and the similarity transformation matrix T is

$$T = \begin{bmatrix} t_n & t_{n-1} & \cdots & t_2 & t_1 \end{bmatrix}, \quad \text{where} \quad \begin{cases} t_n = \left(A^{n-1} + a_{n-1}A^{n-2} + \cdots + a_2 A + a_1 I\right)B \\ t_{n-1} = \left(A^{n-2} + a_{n-1}A^{n-3} + \cdots + a_3 A + a_2 I\right)B \\ \vdots \\ t_2 = (A + a_{n-1}I)B \\ t_1 = B \end{cases} \tag{7.72}$$

Step 2: Let the state-feedback control be

$$u(t) = \hat{F}\hat{x}(t) = \begin{bmatrix} \hat{f}_1 & \hat{f}_2 & \cdots & \hat{f}_n \end{bmatrix}\hat{x}(t) \tag{7.73}$$

Then the closed-loop system state equation becomes

$$\dot{\hat{x}}(t) = \left(\hat{A} + \hat{B}\hat{F}\right)\hat{x}(t) \tag{7.74}$$

where

$$\hat{A} + \hat{B}\hat{F} = \begin{bmatrix} 0 & 1 & 0 & 0 & 0 \\ \vdots & 0 & \ddots & \vdots & \vdots \\ \vdots & \vdots & \ddots & 1 & 0 \\ 0 & 0 & 0 & 0 & 1 \\ -a_0 + \hat{f}_1 & -a_1 + \hat{f}_2 & \cdots\cdots\cdots & -a_{n-2} + \hat{f}_{n-1} & -a_{n-1} + \hat{f}_n \end{bmatrix} \tag{7.75}$$

Note that this companion-form state equation reveals that the closed-loop system characteristic equation is

$$s^n + \left(a_{n-1} - \hat{f}_n\right) s^{n-1} + \cdots + \left(a_1 - \hat{f}_2\right) s + \left(a_0 - \hat{f}_1\right) = 0 \qquad (7.76)$$

Step 3: For the closed-loop system to have a desired characteristic equation as Equation 7.65, the state-feedback controller parameters $f_i, i = 1, 2, ..., n$ need to be chosen so that the two characteristic equations, Equations 7.76 and 7.65, are equivalent. Hence, we have

$$
\begin{aligned}
a_0 - \hat{f}_1 &= \alpha_0 \\
a_1 - \hat{f}_2 &= \alpha_1 \\
&\vdots \\
a_{n-1} - \hat{f}_n &= \alpha_{n-1}
\end{aligned}
\qquad \rightarrow \qquad
\begin{aligned}
\hat{f}_1 &= a_0 - \alpha_0 \\
\hat{f}_2 &= a_1 - \alpha_1 \\
&\vdots \\
\hat{f}_n &= a_{n-1} - \alpha_{n-1}
\end{aligned}
\qquad (7.77)
$$

Step 4: Note that the state-feedback gain matrix $\hat{F} = \begin{bmatrix} \hat{f}_1 & \hat{f}_2 & \cdots & \hat{f}_n \end{bmatrix}$ is designed based on the transformed state equation. To find the state-feedback gain matrix F for $u(t) = Fx(t)$, recall that

$$u(t) = \hat{F}\hat{x}(t) = \hat{F}T^{-1}x(t) = Fx(t)$$

Hence,

$$F = \hat{F}T^{-1} = \begin{bmatrix} a_0 - \alpha_0 & a_1 - \alpha_1 & \cdots & a_{n-1} - \alpha_{n-1} \end{bmatrix} T^{-1} \qquad (7.78)$$

where the similarity transformation matrix T is given by Equation 7.72.   ∎

In the following example, we will employ the same system considered by Example 7.27 to demonstrate how to utilize the transformed approach to implement the state-feedback pole placement.

Example 7.28 (State-Feedback Pole Placement Control Using Transform Approach)

Consider the system

$$\dot{x}(t) = Ax(t) + Bu(t) = \begin{bmatrix} -2 & -2 \\ 2 & 3 \end{bmatrix} x(t) + \begin{bmatrix} -1 \\ 1 \end{bmatrix} u(t) \qquad (7.79)$$

Use a transform approach to design a state feedback $u(t) = Fx(t)$ so that the closed-loop system has damping ratio $\varsigma = 0.8$ and natural frequency $\omega_n = 5$rad/s. That is, **the desired closed-loop system characteristic equation should be**

$$s^2 + 2\varsigma\omega_n s + \omega_n^2 = s^2 + 8s + 25 = s^2 + \alpha_1 s + \alpha_0 = 0 \qquad (7.80)$$

or equivalently, the desired closed-loop system poles are $-4 \pm j3$.

The characteristic equation of the uncompensated system is

$$|sI - A| = \begin{vmatrix} s+2 & 2 \\ -2 & s-3 \end{vmatrix} = s^2 - s - 2 = s^2 + a_1 s + a_0 = 0 \qquad (7.81)$$

which shows that the system is unstable. It also has been shown that the controllability matrix $\begin{bmatrix} B & AB \end{bmatrix}$ is nonsingular, so there exists a state-feedback controller $u(t) = Fx(t)$ so that the closed-loop system poles can be placed at any desired location of the complex plane.

Recall that in Example 7.23 **the state-space model of Equation 7.47 was transformed to the state-space model in companion form,**

$$\dot{\hat{x}}(t)/dt = T^{-1}AT\hat{x}(t) + T^{-1}Bu(t) = \hat{A}\hat{x}(t) + \hat{B}u(t) = \begin{bmatrix} 0 & 1 \\ 2 & 1 \end{bmatrix}\hat{x}(t) + \begin{bmatrix} 0 \\ 1 \end{bmatrix}u(t)$$

via the similarity transformation $\hat{x}(t) = T^{-1}x(t)$, where the similarity transformation matrix was obtained from Equation 7.48 as

$$T = [t_2 \ \ t_1] = [(A + a_1 I)B \ \ B] = \begin{bmatrix} 1 & -1 \\ 0 & 1 \end{bmatrix}$$

Let $\hat{F} = [\hat{f}_1 \ \hat{f}_2]$, then the closed-loop system state equation becomes

$$\dot{\hat{x}}(t) = (\hat{A} + \hat{B}\hat{F})\hat{x}(t)$$

where

$$\hat{A} + \hat{B}\hat{F} = \begin{bmatrix} 0 & 1 \\ 2 & 1 \end{bmatrix} + \begin{bmatrix} 0 \\ 1 \end{bmatrix}[\hat{f}_1 \ \hat{f}_2] = \begin{bmatrix} 0 & 1 \\ 2 + \hat{f}_1 & 1 + \hat{f}_2 \end{bmatrix}$$

Note that this companion-form state equation reveals that the closed-loop system characteristic equation is

$$s^2 + (-1 - \hat{f}_2)s + (-2 - \hat{f}_1) = 0 \tag{7.82}$$

By comparing the coefficients of the two characteristic equations Equations 7.80 and 7.82, we have

$$\begin{matrix} -1 - \hat{f}_2 = 8 \\ -2 - \hat{f}_1 = 25 \end{matrix} \quad \rightarrow \quad \hat{f}_1 = -27, \quad \hat{f}_2 = -9$$

Hence, the state-feedback gain matrix is

$$F = \hat{F}T^{-1} = [-27 \ -9]\begin{bmatrix} 1 & -1 \\ 0 & 1 \end{bmatrix}^{-1} = [-27 \ -9]\begin{bmatrix} 1 & 1 \\ 0 & 1 \end{bmatrix} = [-27 \ -36]$$

The state-feedback control $u(t) = Fx(t)$**, where** $F = [-27 \ -36]$**, has successfully placed the closed-loop system poles at the desired location,** $s = -4 \pm j3$**, on the complex plane.** As expected, the result obtained here using the transform approach is the same as that obtained in Example 7.27 using the direct approach. ∎

7.6 Revisit Cart-Inverted Pendulum System

In the following, the cart-inverted pendulum system we studied in Section 4.5 will be briefly reviewed before it is employed for the design and analysis of a stabilizing control system that would convert the originally unstable equilibrium to a stable one.

Figure 7.11 shows the schematic and the nonlinear coupled equations of motion of the cart-inverted pendulum system. The physical data of the system are also shown in the figure. These data do not show the units, but they are all in MKS units, like the mass in kilograms, length in meters, and so on.

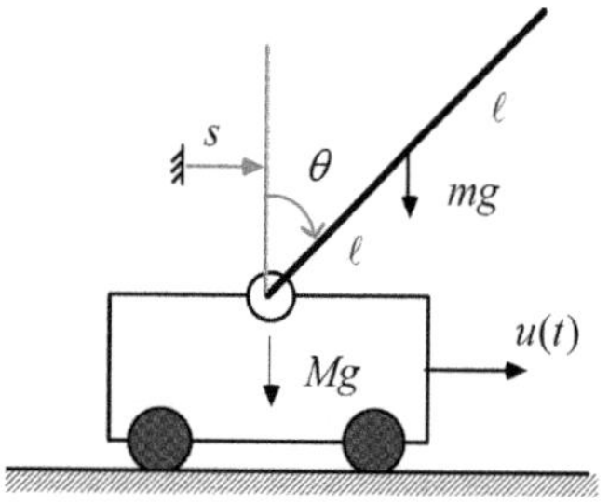

$$(4/3)m\ell^2\ddot{\theta} + B_o\dot{\theta} - mg\ell\sin\theta + m\ell\cos\theta\ddot{s} = 0$$

$$(M+m)\ddot{s} + B_s\dot{s} - m\ell\sin\theta\dot{\theta}^2 + m\ell\cos\theta\ddot{\theta} = u$$

$$M = 1.79, m = 0.104, \ell = 0.3048, g = 9.8, B_s = 0.25, B_o = 0.02$$

$$0.01288\ddot{\theta} + 0.02\dot{\theta} - 0.3107\sin\theta + 0.0317\cos\theta\ddot{s} = 0$$

$$1.894\ddot{s} + 0.25\dot{s} - 0.0317\sin\theta\dot{\theta}^2 + 0.0317\cos\theta\ddot{\theta} = u$$

Fig. 7.11: Schematic and equations of motion of a cart-inverted pendulum system.

7.6.1 State-Space Model of the Cart-Inverted Pendulum System

For ease of managing the nonlinearities of the system, the nonlinear coupled differential equations of the system are converted into a state-space model. Let the state variables be

$$x_1 = \theta, \quad x_2 = \dot{\theta}, \quad x_3 = s, \quad x_4 = \dot{s} \tag{7.83}$$

Then the equations shown in Figure 7.11 can be rewritten in the following matrix form:

$$\begin{bmatrix} 1.288 & 3.17\cos x_1 \\ 3.17\cos x_1 & 189.4 \end{bmatrix} \begin{bmatrix} \dot{x}_2 \\ \dot{x}_4 \end{bmatrix} = \begin{bmatrix} 31.07\sin x_1 - 2x_2 \\ 3.17\sin x_1 x_2^2 - 25x_4 \end{bmatrix} + \begin{bmatrix} 0 \\ 100 \end{bmatrix} u \tag{7.84}$$

Solving Equation 7.84 for $\begin{bmatrix} \dot{x}_2 & \dot{x}_4 \end{bmatrix}^T$ yields

$$\begin{bmatrix} \dot{x}_2 \\ \dot{x}_4 \end{bmatrix} = \frac{1}{\Delta} \begin{bmatrix} 5885\sin x_1 - 378.8x_2 - 10\sin x_1\cos x_1 x_2^2 + 79.25x_4\cos x_1 - 317\cos x_1 u \\ 4.083\sin x_1 x_2^2 - 32.2x_4 - 98.5\sin x_1\cos x_1 + 6.34x_2\cos x_1 + 128.8u \end{bmatrix} \tag{7.85}$$

where

$$\Delta = 244 - 10\cos^2 x_1 \tag{7.86}$$

Then we have a state-space representation for the nonlinear cart-inverted system:

$$\dot{x}(t) := \begin{bmatrix} \dot{x}_1(t) \\ \dot{x}_2(t) \\ \dot{x}_3(t) \\ \dot{x}_4(t) \end{bmatrix} = \begin{bmatrix} f_1(x,u) \\ f_2(x,u) \\ f_3(x,u) \\ f_4(x,u) \end{bmatrix} := f(x,u) \tag{7.87}$$

where

$$f_1(x,u) = x_2$$
$$f_2(x,u) = (1/\Delta)(5885\sin x_1 - 378.8x_2 - 10\sin x_1\cos x_1 x_2^2 + 79.25x_4\cos x_1 - 317\cos x_1 u)$$
$$f_3(x,u) = x_4 \tag{7.88}$$
$$f_4(x,u) = (1/\Delta)(4.083\sin x_1 x_2^2 - 32.2x_4 - 98.5\sin x_1\cos x_1 + 6.34x_2\cos x_1 + 128.8u)$$
$$\Delta = 244 - 10\cos^2 x_1$$

This state-space dynamics model can be employed to conduct analysis, design, and simulations. First, we will utilize this model to find the feasible operation points or the equilibrium points of the system.

7.6.2 Equilibriums of the Cart-Inverted Pendulum System

An equilibrium of the system is a point or a vector (x^*, u^*) that satisfies the equation $f(x^*, u^*) = 0$. Note that

$$\begin{bmatrix} f_1(x,0) \\ f_2(x,0) \\ f_3(x,0) \\ f_4(x,0) \end{bmatrix} = \begin{bmatrix} 0 \\ 0 \\ 0 \\ 0 \end{bmatrix} \quad \rightarrow \quad x_1 = 0 \text{ or } \pi, \quad x_2 = 0, \quad x_3 \text{ is arbitrary}, \quad x_4 = 0 \tag{7.89}$$

At equilibriums the angular velocity of the stick, x_2, and the velocity of the cart, x_4, should be both zero and the angular displacement of the stick should be either $2k\pi$ or $(2k+1)\pi$, where k is any integer. Hence, physically there are two groups of equilibriums: **One is the upright equilibriums,**

$$x_{up}^* = \begin{bmatrix} 0 & 0 & x_3^* & 0 \end{bmatrix}^T \tag{7.90}$$

at which the stick is at the upright position, $\theta = 0$, and the other is the downward equilibriums,

$$x_{down}^* = \begin{bmatrix} \pi & 0 & x_3^* & 0 \end{bmatrix}^T \tag{7.91}$$

at which the stick is at the downward position, $\theta = \pi$. For the stick, there are only two equilibriums: One is the up position, which is unstable, and the other is the down position, which is stable. For the cart, it can be at anywhere on the rail.

A system can only be stabilized at the equilibriums. For the upright stick position equilibrium, although it is unstable the stick can still rest on the upright position if θ can be kept at zero by feedback control or other means. On the other hand, it is impossible to stabilize the pendulum at any non-equilibrium position. For example, to keep the stick at $\theta = 10°$, the cart would have to move continuously with a constant acceleration, which is impossible to sustain.

A common practice in control system design is to first identify an operating equilibrium of interest, and find a linearized dynamics model at the equilibrium. The linearized model can then be employed in the design of control system to achieve stabilization, regulation, tracking, and so on. **For the cart-inverted pendulum system, the objective is to stabilize the pendulum at the originally unstable upright equilibrium. The two equilibriums of interest are**

$$x_U^* = \begin{bmatrix} 0 & 0 & 0 & 0 \end{bmatrix}^T \tag{7.92}$$

representing the upright equilibrium, and

$$x_D^* = \begin{bmatrix} \pi & 0 & 0 & 0 \end{bmatrix}^T \tag{7.93}$$

representing the downward equilibrium. At these two equilibriums, the cart position is assumed $x_3 = 0$, which usually is considered the center of the rail.

Example 7.29 (Phase Plane Trajectory of the Uncompensated Pendulum Subsystem)

Consider the pendulum subsystem of the cart-inverted pendulum system described by the state-space model equations in Equations 7.87 and 7.88. With the assumption that the cart is at rest ($x_4 = 0$), the dynamics equation for the pendulum subsystem will be

$$\begin{bmatrix} \dot{x}_1 \\ \dot{x}_2 \end{bmatrix} = \begin{bmatrix} x_2 \\ (5885 \sin x_1 - 378.8 x_2 - 10 \sin x_1 \cos x_1 x_2^2) / (244 - 10 \cos^2 x_1) \end{bmatrix} \tag{7.94}$$

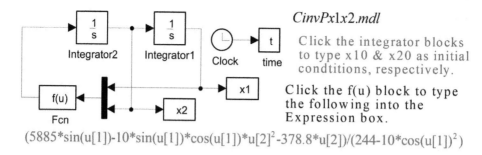

CinvPx1x2.mdl

Click the integrator blocks to type x10 & x20 as initial condtitions, respectively.

Click the f(u) block to type the following into the Expression box.

$(5885*\sin(u[1])-10*\sin(u[1])*\cos(u[1])*u[2]^2-378.8*u[2])/(244-10*\cos(u[1])^2)$

Fig. 7.12: Simulation diagram for the uncompensated nonlinear pendulum subsystem.

Based on Equation 7.94, a *Simulink* model program, `CinvPx1x2.mdl`, shown in Figure 7.12, is constructed to conduct simulations for the uncompensated nonlinear pendulum subsystem. The time responses of the two state variables, $x_1(t) = \theta(t)$ and $x_2(t) = \dot{\theta}(t)$, due to the initial condition: $x_1(0) = 0.001$ rad and $x_2(0) = 0$ rad/s are shown in the left-hand side of **Figure 7.13. The initial state is very close to the equilibrium point $[0\ 0]^T$ with the upward pendulum, but since this equilibrium is unstable the pendulum before long starts to move away toward the stable equilibrium $[\pi\ 0]^T$.**

The simulation results are obtained by running the MATLAB program: `CSD_fig7p13.m`, which will automatically call the Simulink model program `CinvPx1x2.mdl`, to conduct the simulation. The MATLAB code is listed as follows:

```
% Filename: CSD_fig7p13.m    May 6, 2020   response
% Run this CSD_fig7p13.m program to automatically call CinvPx1x2.mdl
%% Simulation
d2r = pi/180, x10=0.06*d2r, x20=0, sim_time=10,
sim_options=simset('SrcWorkspace', 'current', 'DstWorkspace', 'current');
open('CinvPx1x2'), sim('CinvPx1x2', [0, sim_time], sim_options);
%% Plot x1(t), x2(t), x2 vs x1
subplot(1,2,1), plot(t,x1,'b-',t,x2,'r-'), grid on, grid minor,
subplot(1,2,2), plot(x1,x2,'b-'), grid on, grid minor
```

During the transition, both $x_1(t)$ and $x_2(t)$ exhibit decaying oscillations before they reach a steady state at the new equilibrium point. **This decaying oscillation phenomenon is relevant to the under-damped case study of the second-order systems in Chapter 3.** The simulation results can also be seen from the phase plane trajectory shown on the right-hand side of Figure 7.13. The *phase plane trajectory* exhibits the relationship of the angular velocity $\dot{\theta}$ and the angular displacement θ, and clearly shows how the trajectory spirals from the initial state into the final state. The initial state (0.001,0) is very close to the origin (0,0), the unstable equilibrium, and the final state $(\pi,0)$ is a stable equilibrium. ∎

Example 7.30 (Phase Portrait of the Uncompensated Pendulum Subsystem)

The simulation process described can be employed to repeatedly generate phase plane trajectories of the system due to a variety of initial states on the phase plane. A collection of the phase plane trajectories like those shown on Figure 7.14 is called a *phase portrait*. This phase portrait reveals that **the origin (0,0) is a saddle point, which is an unstable equilibrium point.** If the initial state is situated exactly at (0,0) without any tiny error, ideally the perfect upward pendulum would stay without falling. But, of course, any infinitesimal deviation in reality will cause the pendulum to drift away from the unstable equilibrium. The phase portrait shows two stable equilibrium points: one on the right at $(\pi,0)$ and another on the left

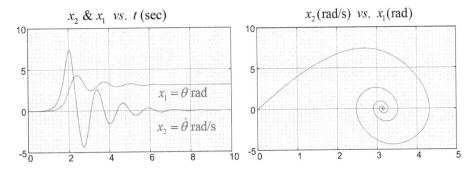

Fig. 7.13: Time responses and phase plane trajectory of the uncompensated pendulum subsystem.

at $(-\pi,0)$. The pendulum at $(0,0)$ can either fall to the right, spiraling into the stable equilibrium $(\pi,0)$, or to the left into $(-\pi,0)$. **These two equilibrium points seem different on the graph, but actually they represent the same physical angular position of the pendulum.** ■

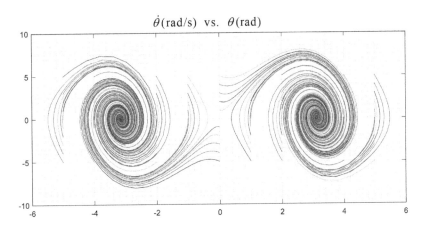

Fig. 7.14: Phase portrait of the uncompensated nonlinear pendulum system.

7.6.3 Linearized State-Space Models at the Equilibriums

The Linearized State-Space Model at the Upright Equilibrium

For the upright equilibrium at $(x_U^*, 0)$, the linearized state-space model is

$$\dot{x}(t) = A_U x(t) + B_U u(t) \tag{7.95}$$

where A_U and B_U are obtained using the following Jacobian matrices, (see Appendix C)

$$A_U = \begin{bmatrix} \frac{\delta f_1}{\delta x_1} & \frac{\delta f_1}{\delta x_2} & \frac{\delta f_1}{\delta x_3} & \frac{\delta f_1}{\delta x_4} \\ \frac{\delta f_2}{\delta x_1} & \frac{\delta f_2}{\delta x_2} & \frac{\delta f_2}{\delta x_3} & \frac{\delta f_2}{\delta x_4} \\ \frac{\delta f_3}{\delta x_1} & \frac{\delta f_3}{\delta x_2} & \frac{\delta f_3}{\delta x_3} & \frac{\delta f_3}{\delta x_4} \\ \frac{\delta f_4}{\delta x_1} & \frac{\delta f_4}{\delta x_2} & \frac{\delta f_4}{\delta x_3} & \frac{\delta f_4}{\delta x_4} \end{bmatrix}_{(x_U^*,0)} = \begin{bmatrix} 0 & 1 & 0 & 0 \\ 25.15 & -1.6188 & 0 & 0.33868 \\ 0 & 0 & 0 & 1 \\ -0.42094 & 0.027094 & 0 & -0.1376 \end{bmatrix} \tag{7.96}$$

and

$$B_U = \begin{bmatrix} \frac{\delta f_1}{\delta u} \\ \frac{\delta f_2}{\delta u} \\ \frac{\delta f_3}{\delta u} \\ \frac{\delta f_4}{\delta u} \end{bmatrix}_{(x_U^*,0)} = \begin{bmatrix} 0 \\ -1.3547 \\ 0 \\ 0.5504 \end{bmatrix} \tag{7.97}$$

The poles of the linearized state-space model at the equilibrium x_U^* are the eigenvalues of A_U:

$$\lambda [A_U] = \{0, 4.2682, -5.8926, -0.13193\} \tag{7.98}$$

which implies that the system is unstable at the upright equilibrium since there is a pole in the right half of the complex plane.

The Linearized State-Space Model at the Downward Equilibrium

For the other equilibrium $(x_D^*, 0)$, the linearized state-space model is

$$\dot{x}(t) = A_D x(t) + B_D u(t) \tag{7.99}$$

where A_D and B_D are obtained using the following Jacobian matrices,

$$A_D = \begin{bmatrix} \frac{\delta f_1}{\delta x_1} & \frac{\delta f_1}{\delta x_2} & \frac{\delta f_1}{\delta x_3} & \frac{\delta f_1}{\delta x_4} \\ \frac{\delta f_2}{\delta x_1} & \frac{\delta f_2}{\delta x_2} & \frac{\delta f_2}{\delta x_3} & \frac{\delta f_2}{\delta x_4} \\ \frac{\delta f_3}{\delta x_1} & \frac{\delta f_3}{\delta x_2} & \frac{\delta f_3}{\delta x_3} & \frac{\delta f_3}{\delta x_4} \\ \frac{\delta f_4}{\delta x_1} & \frac{\delta f_4}{\delta x_2} & \frac{\delta f_4}{\delta x_3} & \frac{\delta f_4}{\delta x_4} \end{bmatrix}_{(x_D^*,0)} = \begin{bmatrix} 0 & 1 & 0 & 0 \\ -25.15 & -1.6188 & 0 & -0.33868 \\ 0 & 0 & 0 & 1 \\ -0.42094 & -0.027094 & 0 & -0.1376 \end{bmatrix} \tag{7.100}$$

and

$$B_D = \begin{bmatrix} \frac{\delta f_1}{\delta u} \\ \frac{\delta f_2}{\delta u} \\ \frac{\delta f_3}{\delta u} \\ \frac{\delta f_4}{\delta u} \end{bmatrix}_{(x_D^*,0)} = \begin{bmatrix} 0 \\ 1.3547 \\ 0 \\ 0.5504 \end{bmatrix} \tag{7.101}$$

The poles of the linearized state-space model at the equilibrium x_D^* are the eigenvalues of A_D:

$$\lambda [A_D] = \{0, -0.13194, -0.81223 \pm j4.9487\} \tag{7.102}$$

Initial State Response Analysis and Simulation

It is clear that the upright equilibrium is unstable since the linearized state-space model at this equilibrium has a pole $s = 4.2682$ in the right half of the complex plane. The pendulum system can stay at this equilibrium only if the pendulum angular displacement, pendulum angular velocity, and the cart velocity are all perfectly kept at zero, which is practically impossible to maintain.

On the other hand, the linearized state-space model at the downward equilibrium $x_D^* = [\pi \ 0 \ 0 \ 0]^T$ has three poles: $-0.13194, -0.81223 \pm j4.9487$ in the strictly left half of the complex plane, but **there is one at the origin $s = 0$. Strictly speaking, this equilibrium is not stable since there is a pole on the imaginary axis. This $s = 0$ pole is caused by the lack of a natural mechanism to bring the cart** to the $x_3 = 0$ position. However, if x_3 is excluded in the stability consideration, the downward equilibrium can be regarded as a stable equilibrium since the other three state variables will naturally converge to the equilibrium at steady state.

A Simulink computer simulation program built based on the nonlinear state-space model shown in Equation 7.87 is employed to conduct simulations for the cart-inverted pendulum. Figure 7.15 shows the simulation results of the pendulum with initial condition

$$x(0) = [-0.524 \ 0 \ 0.5 \ 0]^T$$

The initial pendulum displacement $x(0) = -0.524$ rad $= -30°$, which is not an equilibrium, has to move toward a stable equilibrium. If there is no external intervention other than the gravity, it would choose a shortest path to reach a nearby stable equilibrium. The pendulum moves counterclockwise towards the nearby stable equilibrium $x_1^* = -\pi$, overshoots it, turns around, and then oscillates several times for about 6 seconds, it settles at the stable equilibrium $x_1^* = -\pi$.

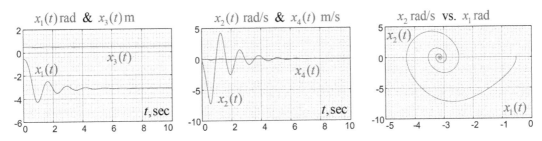

Fig. 7.15: Response due to the initial state $x_0 = [-0.524 \ 0 \ 0.5 \ 0]^T$ of the cart-inverted pendulum system.

The initial cart position is at $x_3(0) = 0.5$m. Since the gravity has no direct influence on the cart, the cart only fluctuates a tiny bit due to a very small reaction force from the swinging pendulum. Therefore, at steady state, $x_2 = 0, x_4 = 0$, and $x_1 = -\pi$, but the cart position is still at $x_3 = 0.50019$m, which is very close to its initial position. The overshoot and oscillation of $x_1(t)$ and $x_2(t)$ are mainly caused by the complex poles $-0.81223 \pm j4.9487$ whose corresponding damping ratio and natural frequency are $\varsigma = 0.162$ and $\omega_n = 5.015$rad/s, respectively.

7.6.4 Design of a Stabilizing Controller for the Upright Equilibrium

Objective of the Feedback Control Design

The objective of the cart-inverted pendulum control system design is not only to stabilize the pendulum at the upright position, $x_1 = 0$, $x_2 = 0$, and $x_4 = 0$. It will also stabilize the cart at the center of the rail position, $x_3 = 0$. Therefore, the operating equilibrium is

$$x = x_U^* = [0 \ 0 \ 0 \ 0]^T \quad \text{when} \quad u = 0 \tag{7.103}$$

Analysis of the Uncompensated System

Recall that the linearized state-space model of the cart-inverted pendulum system at the upright x_U^* equilibrium is

$$\dot{x}(t) = Ax(t) + Bu(t) = \begin{bmatrix} 0 & 1 & 0 & 0 \\ 25.15 & -1.6188 & 0 & 0.33868 \\ 0 & 0 & 0 & 1 \\ -0.42094 & 0.027094 & 0 & -0.1376 \end{bmatrix} x(t) + \begin{bmatrix} 0 \\ -1.3547 \\ 0 \\ 0.5504 \end{bmatrix} u(t) \qquad (7.104)$$

The poles of the linearized state-space model at the equilibrium x_U^* are the eigenvalues of A,

$$\lambda[A] = \{0,\ 4.2682,\ -5.8926,\ -0.13193\} \qquad (7.105)$$

The corresponding open-loop characteristic equation is

$$|sI - A| = (s-0)(s-4.2682)(s+5.8926)(s+0.13193)$$
$$= s^4 + 1.7564s^3 - 24.936s^2 - 3.3181s = s^4 + a_3 s^3 + a_2 s^2 + a_1 s + a_0 = 0 \qquad (7.106)$$

Obviously, the uncompensated system is unstable. However, the controllability matrix

$$\begin{bmatrix} B & AB & A^2B & A^3B \end{bmatrix} \qquad (7.107)$$

is nonsingular; hence, there exists a state-feedback controller

$$u(t) = Fx(t) \qquad (7.108)$$

so that the closed-loop system poles can be placed at any desired location of the complex plane.

Selection of the Desired Closed-Loop System Poles

The desired closed-loop system poles are tentatively chosen to include two real poles and a pair of complex conjugate poles as follows:

$$s_1 = -2,\ s_2 = -8,\ s_3 = -4 + j3,\ s_4 = -4 - j3$$

That is, **the desired closed-loop system characteristic equation is given as:**

$$|sI - (A + BF)| = (s+2)(s+8)(s+4-j3)(s+4+j3)$$
$$= s^4 + 18s^3 + 121s^2 + 378s + 400 = s^4 + \alpha_3 s^3 + \alpha_2 s^2 + \alpha_1 s + \alpha_0 = 0 \qquad (7.109)$$

Design of a Pole-Placement State-Feedback Controller

Although the direct approach, introduced in Section 7.5.1, for the state-feedback pole placement design is conceptually simple, the complexities involved in the computation grow exponentially as the order of the system increases. For this fourth-order system, it is still manageable using the direct approach, but **the transform approach, discussed in Section 7.5.2, is much more efficient in computation, especially if we need to repeat the design process for different sets of desired closed-loop system poles.**

In order to take advantage of the transform approach, we first need to find a similarity transformation, $\hat{x}(t) = T^{-1}x(t)$, **to transform the state-space model of the plant in Equation (7.104) to the following state-space model in companion form:**

$$\dot{\hat{x}}(t) = \hat{A}\hat{x}(t) + \hat{B}u(t) = T^{-1}AT\hat{x}(t) + T^{-1}Bu(t) \qquad (7.110)$$

where

$$\hat{A} = \begin{bmatrix} 0 & 1 & 0 & 0 \\ 0 & 0 & 1 & 0 \\ 0 & 0 & 0 & 1 \\ -a_0 & -a_1 & -a_2 & -a_3 \end{bmatrix}, \quad \hat{B} = \begin{bmatrix} 0 \\ 0 \\ 0 \\ 1 \end{bmatrix} \tag{7.111}$$

Since the controllability condition, Equation 7.107 is satisfied, the similarity transformation matrix T can be constructed using Equation 7.46 in Theorem 7.22 as follows:

$$\begin{cases} t_4 = \left(A^3 + a_3 A^2 + a_2 A + a_1 I\right) B \\ t_3 = \left(A^2 + a_3 A + a_2 I\right) B \\ t_2 = (A + a_3 I) B \\ t_1 = B \end{cases} \quad \rightarrow \quad T = \begin{bmatrix} t_4 & t_3 & t_2 & t_1 \end{bmatrix} \tag{7.112}$$

and

$$T = \begin{bmatrix} 0 & 2.752 \times 10^{-6} & -1.3547 & 0 \\ 0 & 0 & 2.752 \times 10^{-6} & -1.3547 \\ -13.272 & 0.85428 & 0.5504 & 0 \\ 0 & -13.272 & 0.85428 & 0.5504 \end{bmatrix} \tag{7.113}$$

Let

$$u(t) = \hat{F}\hat{x}(t) = \begin{bmatrix} \hat{f}_1 & \hat{f}_2 & \hat{f}_3 & \hat{f}_4 \end{bmatrix} \hat{x}(t) \tag{7.114}$$

Then the closed-loop system state equation becomes

$$\dot{\hat{x}}(t) = \left(\hat{A} + \hat{B}\hat{F}\right)\hat{x}(t) = \begin{bmatrix} 0 & 1 & 0 & 0 \\ 0 & 0 & 1 & 0 \\ 0 & 0 & 0 & 1 \\ -a_0 + \hat{f}_1 & -a_1 + \hat{f}_2 & -a_2 + \hat{f}_3 & -a_3 + \hat{f}_4 \end{bmatrix} \hat{x}(t) \tag{7.115}$$

Note that this companion-form state equation reveals that the closed-loop system characteristic equation is

$$\left|sI - \left(\hat{A} + \hat{B}\hat{F}\right)\right| = s^4 + (a_3 - \hat{f}_4)s^3 + (a_2 - \hat{f}_3)s^2 + (a_1 - \hat{f}_2)s + (a_0 - \hat{f}_1) = 0 \tag{7.116}$$

By comparing the coefficients of the two characteristic equations Equations 7.109 and 7.116, we have

$$\begin{cases} a_3 - \hat{f}_4 = \alpha_3 \\ a_2 - \hat{f}_3 = \alpha_2 \\ a_1 - \hat{f}_2 = \alpha_1 \\ a_0 - \hat{f}_1 = \alpha_0 \end{cases} \rightarrow \begin{cases} 1.7564 - \hat{f}_4 = 18 \\ -24.936 - \hat{f}_3 = 121 \\ -3.3181 - \hat{f}_2 = 378 \\ 0 - \hat{f}_1 = 400 \end{cases} \rightarrow \begin{cases} 1.7564 - 18 = \hat{f}_4 \\ -24.936 - 121 = \hat{f}_3 \\ -3.3181 - 378 = \hat{f}_2 \\ 0 - 400 = \hat{f}_1 \end{cases} \tag{7.117}$$

Hence,

$$\hat{F} = \begin{bmatrix} \hat{f}_1 & \hat{f}_2 & \hat{f}_3 & \hat{f}_4 \end{bmatrix} = \begin{bmatrix} -400 & -381.32 & -145.94 & -16.244 \end{bmatrix} \tag{7.118}$$

Since

$$u(t) = \hat{F}\hat{x}(t) = \hat{F}T^{-1}x(t) = Fx(t) \quad \rightarrow \quad F = \hat{F}T^{-1} \tag{7.119}$$

we have the state-feedback gain matrix

$$F = \hat{F}T^{-1} = \begin{bmatrix} 139.31 & 24.452 & 30.138 & 30.67 \end{bmatrix} \tag{7.120}$$

The state-feedback control $u(t) = Fx(t)$, with F given, has successfully placed the closed-loop system poles at the desired location, $s = -2, -8,$ and $-4 \pm j3$ on the complex plane.

Nonlinear Closed-Loop System Simulations

The nonlinear dynamics model shown in Equations 7.87 and 7.88 will be employed in the simulation of state-feedback stabilizing control of the cart-inverted pendulum system. In the Simulink simulation diagram shown in Figure 7.16, four integrators and four function blocks f2, f4, g2u, and g4u are employed to implement the state-space dynamics model equations given in Equations 7.87 and 7.88. The function information of $f_2(x)$, $f_4(x)$, $g_2(x)u$, and $g_4(x)u$ in Equation 7.88 need to be typed into the function blocks f2, f4, g2u, and g4u in the Simulink program, respectively. The function expressions for the function block f2 and f4 should be shown as the following:

$$(5885 * \sin(u[1]) - 10 * \sin(u[1]) * \cos(u[1]) * u[2]^2 - 378.8 * u[2] + 79.25 * u[3] * \cos(u[1]))$$
$$/ (244 - 10 * \cos(u[1])^2)$$

and

$$(4.083 * \sin(u[1]) * u[2]^2 - 32.2 * u[3] - 98.5 * \sin(u[1]) * \cos(u[1]) + 6.34 * u[2] * \cos(u[1]))$$
$$/ (244 - 10 * \cos(u[1])^2)$$

respectively. Note that u[1], u[2], and u[3] represent x_1, x_2, and x_4 respectively. There is no x_3 or u[4] in the expressions.

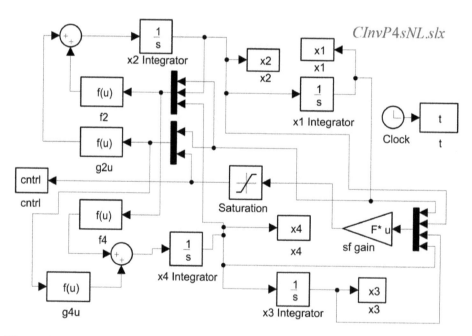

Fig. 7.16: Closed-loop simulation diagram for the cart-inverted pendulum control system.

Similarly, the function expressions for the function block g2u and g4u should be shown as the following:

$$(-317 * \cos(u[1]) * u[2]) / (244 - 10 * \cos(u[1])^2)$$

and

$$(128.8 * u[2])/(244 - 10 * \cos(u[1])^2)$$

respectively. Note that u[1] still represents x_1, but u[2] here represents the control input u instead of x_2.

The state-feedback controller is implemented by the sf gain block and the Saturation block; you can either type the following F matrix

$$F = \begin{bmatrix} 139.31 & 24.452 & 30.138 & 30.67 \end{bmatrix}$$

into the sf gain block or just type F in the block and define the matrix values elsewhere like in a MATLAB m-file or in the Command Window before running the Simulink simulation. The Saturation block is to mimic the real control-input constraint assuming the input applied force is restricted to ±80 Newtons.

In the simulation diagram, five ToWorkspace blocks: x1, x2, x3, x4, and t are there to record the simulation data in arrays of compatible dimension so that after the simulation a simple MATLAB program can be written to plot the state variables as function of t (time) or draw a phase plane trajectory of x_2 versus x_1.

Figure 7.17 shows that the pendulum with initial state $x_0 = \begin{bmatrix} -0.524 & 0 & 0.5 & 0 \end{bmatrix}$ would move towards and settle at the upright equilibrium $x_U^* = \begin{bmatrix} 0 & 0 & 0 & 0 \end{bmatrix}^T$, now is a stable equilibrium, shortly after one second without much overshoot and oscillation. This desired transient response is the direct result of the choice of the closed-loop system poles at the desired location, $s = -2, -8,$ and $-4 \pm j3$ on the complex plane. Note that the cart position x_3 is also brought to zero from its initial position $x_3(0) = 0.5$m.

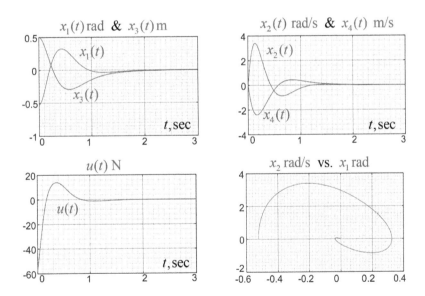

Fig. 7.17: A desired stabilizing performance of a cart-inverted pendulum system achieved by a state-feedback control.

The graph of the control input $u(t)$ is also shown in Figure 7.17. Initially the pendulum position is at $x_1 = \theta = -30°$. Apparently, the pendulum would fall to the left if no control action is taken in time. The controller has to apply a negative control-input (i.e., actuator) force to quickly move the cart to the left in order to reverse the motion of the pendulum. The pendulum did swing back moving towards the upright equilibrium. The controller, the actuator, the cart, and the pendulum and the sensor have to work together continuously to readjust the control-input force according to the control law (i.e., the *F* matrix) in order to bring the pendulum system to the desired equilibrium.

The closed-loop system simulation results shown in Figure 7.17 are obtained by running the following MATLAB program: CSDfig7p17.m, which will automatically call the Simulink model program CInvP4sNL.slx, to conduct the simulation. The plotting program, CSD_PlotCInvP.m will also be called to plot the figures. The MATLAB code is listed as follows. The open-loop system simulation results shown in Figure 7.15 can also be obtained by running the same program with Part 2B block codes replaced by Part 2A, which is the single line code F=[0 0 0 0].

```
% filename: CSDfig7p17.m
% BC Chang, Drexel University, on 5/07/2020
% Program running sequence:  MATLAB R2015a or later versions
% 1. CSDfig7p17.m % 2. CInvP4sNL.slx % 3. CSD_PlotCInvP.m
%% Part 1:  Choose initial conditions
x10_deg =-30, x10=x10_deg*pi/180, x30=0.5, u_sat=100
%% Part 2A:  For Open-loop simulation with no control F=[0 0 0 0]
% F = [0 0 0 0]
%% Part 2B: Select two real poles -r1, -r2, and one pair of complex poles
r1 = 2, r2 = 3, ze = 0.95, wn = 1
%% Desired characteristic eq: s^4+a3h*s^3+a2h*s^2+a1h*s*a0h=0
a3h=2*ze*wn+r1+r2; a2h=wn^2+(r1+r2)*2*ze*wn+r1*r2;
a1h=(r1+r2)*wn^2+r1*r2*2*ze*wn; a0h=r1*r2*wn^2;
ChEqh=[1 a3h a2h a1h a0h]; Poles_desired =roots(ChEqh),
% Linearized inverted pendulum system with frictions
A=[0 1 0 0;25.15 -1.6188 0 0.33868;0 0 0 1;-0.42094 0.027094 0 -0.1376];
B=[0; -1.3547; 0; 0.5504]; C=eye(4); D=[0 0 0 0]'; G=ss(A,B,C,D);
Ev=eig(A); a3=-(Ev(2)+Ev(3)+Ev(4)); a2=Ev(2)*Ev(3)+Ev(2)*Ev(4)+Ev(3)*Ev(4);
a1=-Ev(2)*Ev(3)*Ev(4); a0=0; ChEq=[1 a3 a2 a1 a0]; Poles_OL=roots(ChEq),
disp('checking controllability'); co=ctrb(A,B);Controllability_sv=svd(co),
% Convert A, B to companion form
t3=(A^2+a3*A+a2*eye(4))*B; t4=(A^3+a3*A^2+a2*A+a1*eye(4))*B; t1=B;
t2=(A+a3*eye(4))*B; T=[t4 t3 t2 t1]; Ah=inv(T)*A*T, Bh=inv(T)*B
% State feedback Fh
f1h=a0-a0h, f2h=a1-a1h, f3h=a2-a2h, f4h=a3-a3h, Fh=[f1h f2h f3h f4h],
Acl_h=Ah+Bh*Fh, eig(Acl_h), F=Fh*inv(T), Acl=A+B*F, eig(Acl)
%% Part 3 Simulation
% Using the following to run the simulink and plot the simulation results
sim_time=10,
sim_options=simset('SrcWorkspace', 'current', 'DstWorkspace', 'current');
open('CInvP4sNL'), sim('CInvP4sNL', [0,sim_time], sim_options);
run('CSD_PlotCInvP')
```

The stabilizing controllers for the cart-inverted pendulum system are not unique. As long as a controller is able to place all the closed-loop system poles strictly in the left half of the complex plane, the closed-loop system will be stable. However, the performance may be different from controller to controller. In common practice, a control system designer will usually consider the following factors: response time, overshoot and oscillation, steady-state response, robustness, and control-input constraint. These factors may conflict with each other; for example, a faster response may invite larger overshoot and oscillations or require more control-input power. Hence, the designer may need to consider all factors and find a best trade-off design.

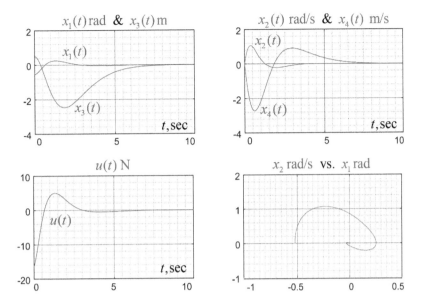

Fig. 7.18: Response of the compensated cart-inverted pendulum system with a more conservative design consuming less control resources.

Figure 7.18 shows the response graphs of the cart-inverted pendulum system with a more conservative controller design. It can be seen that the response time is slower. It takes more than seven seconds to reach the steady state, but it requires much less control-input force to complete the task. The conservative controller employed in the Figure 7.18 simulation was designed to have its closed-loop system poles to include two real poles at $s = -2$ and $s = -3$, and a pair of complex poles that associate with the damping ratio $\varsigma = 0.95$ and natural frequency $\omega_n = 1 \text{ rad/s}$. The state-feedback gain matrix of this controller is

$$F = [31.726 \quad 4.4123 \quad 0.45207 \quad 1.5148]$$

The control-input constraint or the actuator limit can be a great concern if the control-input signal issued by the controller is beyond the range of the actuator. Under this situation, the actuator will saturate. A saturation of the actuator may cause the control system to become unstable. Hence, a control system should be designed so that its control inputs are always inside the working range of the actuators.

7.7 Routh-Hurwitz Stability Criterion

The Routh-Hurwitz criterion provides an easy way to determine the number of roots of a polynomial equation in the right half of the complex plane without the need of computing the roots. Since the stability of the linear time-invariant system is determined by whether the system's characteristic equation has any root in the right half of the complex plane, the Routh-Hurwitz criterion is a perfect tool to check if a system is stable. Although the root-finding computer programs nowadays can solve for the roots of polynomial equations in a split of second, the Routh-Hurwitz criterion is still important in the design of control systems.

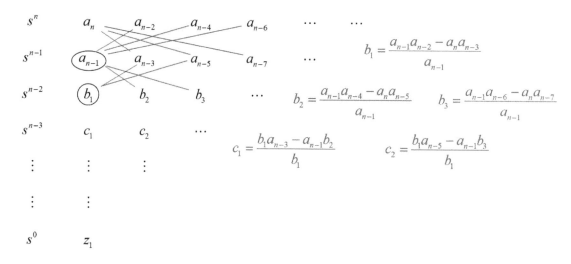

Fig. 7.19: Construction of the Routh array for a polynomial equation.

Theorem 7.31 (Necessary Condition for Stability)

Consider a system with the following characteristic equation

$$a_n s^n + a_{n-1} s^{n-1} + a_{n-2} s^{n-2} + a_{n-3} s^{n-3} + \cdots\cdots + a_1 s + a_0 = 0 \qquad (7.121)$$

Without loss of generality, the coefficient of the s^n term, a_n, is assumed to be positive. Then for the system to be stable, the characteristic equation must have no missing terms and all its coefficients are strictly positive. ∎

This theorem provides an easy-to-check necessary condition for stability. Just by inspection, we can tell if the necessary condition is satisfied. If there is a missing term or some of the coefficient is negative, then the system is unstable. On the other hand, even if the necessary conditions are all satisfied, the system can still be unstable because these conditions are not sufficient.

The Routh-Hurwitz criterion provides a necessary and sufficient condition for stability, but a Routh array, as shown in Figure 7.19 needs to be constructed before the criterion can be employed to determine the stability of the system.

To construct the *Routh array*, the first step is to build the label column on the left side of the array. The label column starts from s^n on the top, and then is followed by $s^{n-1}, s^{n-2}, s^{n-3}, \cdots\cdots$, all the way to s^0. Step 2 is to populate the first two rows directly from the coefficients of the polynomial equation in Equation 7.121: $a_n, a_{n-2}, a_{n-4}, \cdots\cdots$, on the s^n row, and $a_{n-1}, a_{n-3}, a_{n-5}, \cdots\cdots$, on the s^{n-1} row, as shown in the figure.

The elements of the third row (the s^{n-2} row) are generated by the elements of the first two rows as follows.

$$b_1 = \frac{a_{n-1}a_{n-2} - a_n a_{n-3}}{a_{n-1}}, \quad b_2 = \frac{a_{n-1}a_{n-4} - a_n a_{n-5}}{a_{n-1}}, \quad b_3 = \frac{a_{n-1}a_{n-6} - a_n a_{n-7}}{a_{n-1}}, \quad \cdots \qquad (7.122)$$

Note that the third-row elements share the same denominator, a_{n-1}, which is the first element on the left of the second-row. We circled this element, as shown in the figure, and would like to call it as a *cornerstone* element since it not only serves as the denominator of the entire row it also plays an important role in the numerator computation of the row. The numerator of b_1 is the cross-product difference $a_{n-1}a_{n-2} - a_n a_{n-3}$ of the four elements connected by the two blue lines. Similarly, the numerator of b_2 is the cross-product difference $a_{n-1}a_{n-4} - a_n a_{n-5}$ of the four elements connected by the two red lines, and the numerator of b_3 is the cross-product difference $a_{n-1}a_{n-6} - a_n a_{n-7}$ of the four elements connected by the two purple lines. It is noted that all the numerator cross product differences begin with the cornerstone element, a_{n-1}.

The fourth row (the s^{n-3} row) can be constructed in the same manner using the data of the second and the third rows and regarding the b_1 element as the cornerstone element in the construction of this row.

$$c_1 = \frac{b_1 a_{n-3} - a_{n-1}b_2}{b_1}, \quad c_2 = \frac{b_1 a_{n-5} - a_{n-1}b_3}{b_1}, \quad \ldots \ldots \tag{7.123}$$

The same process is repeated until the last row, which is the s^0 row, is completed. With the Routh array constructed as above, the Routh-Hurwitz criterion is given in the following.

Theorem 7.32 (Routh-Hurwitz Criterion: Necessary and Sufficient Condition for Stability)

For the system associated with the Routh array shown in Figure 7.19, it is stable if and only if all the elements on the first column of Routh array are strictly positive. ■

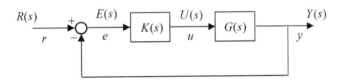

Fig. 7.20: A typical feedback control system block diagram.

The block diagram in Figure 7.20 shows a typical feedback control system structure. $G(s)$ represents the system to be controlled and $K(s)$ is the controller to be designed to achieve some desired performance. One of the important properties of the closed-loop system is stability; since the closed-loop system is not only useless, it can be harmful if it is unstable. In the following, the Routh-Hurwitz criterion will be employed to assess the stability of a control system or to determine the range of the design parameters for the closed-loop system to be stable.

Example 7.33 (Determine the Stability Range of a Proportional Control System)

Consider the feedback control system shown in Figure 7.20. Assume the plant $G(s)$, the system to be controlled, is given as

$$G(s) = \frac{1}{s(s+1)(s+2)}$$

and the controller is a proportional controller, $K(s)$, where K is a constant to be determined so that the closed-loop system has a desired performance. By the time the design is finalized, the designer may want to know the range of K in which the closed-loop system is stable.

The closed-loop system characteristic equation is

$$1 + G(s)K = 0 \quad \rightarrow \quad 1 + \frac{K}{s(s+1)(s+2)} = 0 \quad \rightarrow \quad s^3 + 3s^2 + 2s + K = 0$$

The Routh array for this characteristic equation is constructed as follows:

$$
\begin{array}{cc}
s^3 & 1 \quad 2 \\
s^2 & 3 \quad K \\
s^1 & b_1 \\
s^0 & K
\end{array}
\qquad \text{where} \quad b_1 = \frac{3 \cdot 2 - 1 \cdot K}{3} = \frac{6 - K}{3}
$$

According to the Routh-Hurwitz criterion, the system is stable if and only if the first-column elements of the Routh array are all strictly positive. Hence, the system is stable if and only if

$$K > 0 \quad \text{and} \quad 6 - K > 0$$

which is

$$0 < K < 6$$

The Routh array not only shows the stability range, $0 < K < 6$, it also provides an auxiliary equation to compute the pole locations on the imaginary axis when the value of K is on the border line. When $K = 6$, b_1 will be zero and the *auxiliary equation* **right above this zero element will be $3s^2 + 6 = 0$, which has two roots $\pm j1.414$ on the imaginary axis.** ∎

Example 7.34 (Determine a Two-Parameter Stability Region of a Control System)

Consider the feedback control system shown in Figure 7.20. Assume the plant $G(s)$, the system to be controlled, is given as

$$G(s) = \frac{s+2}{s(2s+1)}$$

and the controller is

$$K(s) = \frac{K_1}{K_2 s + 1}$$

The objective is to determine the stability region of the closed-loop system on the K_2-K_1 plane. The closed-loop system characteristic equation is

$$1 + \frac{s+2}{s(2s+1)} \frac{K_1}{K_2 s + 1} = 0 \quad \rightarrow \quad 2K_2 s^3 + (K_2 + 2)s^2 + (K_1 + 1)s + 2K_1 = 0$$

The Routh array for this characteristic equation is constructed as follows:

$$
\begin{array}{cc}
s^3 & 2K_2 \quad K_1 + 1 \\
s^2 & K_2 + 2 \quad 2K_1 \\
s^1 & b_1 \\
s^0 & 2K_1
\end{array}
\qquad \text{where} \quad b_1 = \frac{(K_2 + 2)(K_1 + 1) - 4K_1 K_2}{K_2 + 2}
$$

According to the Routh-Hurwitz criterion, the system is stable if and only if the first-column elements of the Routh array are all strictly positive. Hence, the system is stable if and only if all the following three inequalities are satisfied.

$$K_1 > 0, \quad K_2 > 0, \quad \text{and} \quad (K_2 + 2)(K_1 + 1) - 4K_1 K_2 > 0$$

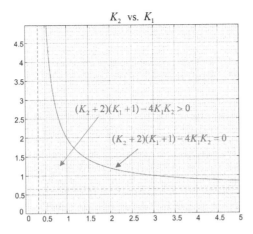

Fig. 7.21: Stability region on K_1-K_2 plane for Example 7.34.

As shown in Figure 7.21, the stability region is in the first quadrant ($K_1 > 0$ and $K_2 > 0$) under the red curve of $(K_2 + 2)(K_1 + 1) - 4K_1K_2 = 0$. The two blue dash lines, which are the asymptotes of the red curve, are inside the stable region. Any point inside the region will guarantee the stability of the closed-loop system. For instance, if $K_1 = K_2 = 1$ are chosen then $b_1 = 2/3 > 0$, and the first column elements of the Routh array are all strictly greater than zero. If $K_1 = 2$, $K_2 = 1.2$, which is a point on the border of the region, is chosen, then $b_1 = 0$ and the auxiliary equation

$$(K_2 + 2)s^2 + 2K_1 = 3.2s^2 + 4 = 0 \quad \rightarrow \quad roots = \pm j1.118$$

reveals that the closed-loop system has two poles $\pm j1.118$ on the imaginary axis. ∎

7.8 Exercise Problems

P7.1a: Consider the typical feedback control system shown in Figure 7.22. $G(s) = \frac{1}{s+1}$ represents the system to be controlled, and $K(s) = K_p + \frac{K_i}{s}$ is the PI controller to be designed to improve the performance of the system. Note that there are two external inputs: the reference input $r(t)$ and the disturbance input $d(t)$. The objective of the control system is to design a controller $K(s)$ so that the closed-loop system is stable and the output $y(t)$ will follow $r(t)$ as closely as possible despite the variation of the disturbance $d(t)$. Let the transfer function from $R(s)$ to $Y(s)$ and the transfer function from $D(s)$ to $Y(s)$ of the closed-loop system be denoted by $G_{yr}(s)$ and $G_{yd}(s)$, respectively. Then the output response $Y(s)$ will be

$$Y(s) = G_{yr}(s)R(s) + G_{yd}(s)D(s) \tag{7.124}$$

Find the transfer functions $G_{yr}(s)$ and $G_{yd}(s)$ in terms of the parameters K_p and K_i by using Mason's gain formula.

P7.1b: Let $r(t) = 10u_s(t)$ and $d(t) = u_s(t - 5)$, where $u_s(t)$ is the unit step function. Show that the steady-state tracking error is zero or the final value of $y(t)$ is 10,

$$\lim_{t \to \infty} e(t) = 0 \quad \text{or} \quad \lim_{t \to \infty} y(t) = 10$$

by using Equation 7.124 and Theorem 2.27, the final-value theorem.

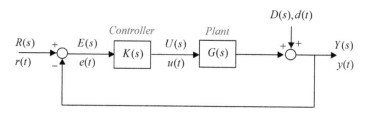

Fig. 7.22: A typical feedback control system.

P7.1c: Construct a Simulink program according to the closed-loop system block diagram shown in Figure 7.22, where $r(t) = 10u_s(t)$, $d(t) = u_s(t-5)$, $G(s) = \frac{1}{s+1}$, and $K(s) = K_p + \frac{K_i}{s}$ with K_p and K_i as free design parameters.

P7.1d: Find the closed-loop characteristic equation in terms of K_p and K_i, and use it to determine the values of K_p and K_i so that the damping ratio $\varsigma = 1$ and the natural frequency $\omega_n = 1$ rad/s. Then run the Simulink program constructed in P7.1c and plot the output $y(t)$ and the control input $u(t)$ in separate graphs versus time from $t = 0$ s to $t = 10$ s.

P7.1e: Vary the value of the damping ratio ς while keeping the natural frequency ω_n at a constant. Then run the Simulink program and plot the output response $y(t)$ and the control input $u(t)$ in separate graphs versus time from $t = 0$ s to $t = 10$ s. Observe how the damping ratio ς affects the values of K_p and K_i, the output response $y(t)$, and the control input $u(t)$.

P7.1f: Vary the value of the natural frequency ω_n while keeping the damping ratio ς at a constant. Then run the Simulink program and plot the output response $y(t)$ and the control input $u(t)$ in separate graphs versus time from $t = 0$ s to $t = 10$ s. Observe how the natural frequency ω_n affects the values of K_p and K_i, the output response $y(t)$, and the control input $u(t)$.

P7.1g: Based on the experience you gain from P7.1e and P7.1f, find a best design of K_p and K_i so that $y(t)$ has an optimal performance while satisfying the control-input constraint, $u(t) < 20$, $for\ t \geq 0$. Plot the optimal output response $y(t)$ and the control input $u(t)$ in separate graphs versus time from $t = 0$ s to $t = 10$ s.

P7.2a: Consider the dual-loop feedback control system shown in Figure 7.23. $G(s) = \frac{1}{s+1}$ is the system to be controlled, and the two parameters K_1 and K_2 in the dual-loop controller are to be designed to improve the performance of the system. Note that there are two external inputs: the reference input $r(t)$ and the disturbance input $d(t)$. The objective of the control system is to design a controller $K(s)$ so that the closed-loop system is stable and the output $y(t)$ will follow $r(t)$ as closely as possible despite the variation of the disturbance $d(t)$. Let the transfer function from $R(s)$ to $Y(s)$ and the transfer function from $D(s)$ to $Y(s)$ of the closed-loop system be denoted by $G_{yr}(s)$ and $G_{yd}(s)$, respectively. Then the output response $Y(s)$ will be

$$Y(s) = G_{yr}(s)R(s) + G_{yd}(s)D(s) \qquad (7.125)$$

Find the transfer functions $G_{yr}(s)$ and $G_{yd}(s)$ in terms of the parameters K_1 and K_2 by using Mason's gain formula.

P7.2b: Let $r(t) = 10u_s(t)$ and $d(t) = u_s(t-5)$, where $u_s(t)$ is the unit step function. Show that the steady-state tracking error is zero or the final value of $y(t)$ is 10,

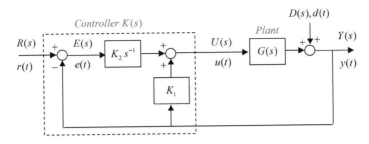

Fig. 7.23: A dual-loop feedback control system.

$$\lim_{t \to \infty} e(t) = 0 \quad \text{or} \quad \lim_{t \to \infty} y(t) = 10$$

by using Equation 7.125 and Theorem 2.27, the final-value theorem.

P7.2c: Construct a Simulink program according to the closed-loop system block diagram shown in Figure 7.22, where $r(t) = 10u_s(t)$, $d(t) = u_s(t - 5)$, $G(s) = \frac{1}{s+1}$, and the two constants K_1 and K_2 of the dual-loop controller are free design parameters.

P7.2d: Find the closed-loop characteristic equation in terms of K_1 and K_2, and use it to determine the values of K_1 and K_2 so that the damping ratio $\varsigma = 1$ and the natural frequency $\omega_n = 1$ rad/s. Then run the Simulink program constructed in P7.2c and plot the output $y(t)$ and the control input $u(t)$ in separate graphs versus time from $t = 0$ s to $t = 10$ s.

P7.2e: Vary the value of the damping ratio ς while keeping the natural frequency ω_n at a constant. Then run the Simulink program and plot the output response $y(t)$ and the control input $u(t)$ in separate graphs versus time from $t = 0$ s to $t = 10$ s. Observe how the damping ratio ς affects the values of K_1 and K_2, the output response $y(t)$, and the control input $u(t)$.

P7.2f: Vary the value of the natural frequency ω_n while keeping the damping ratio ς at a constant. Then run the Simulink program and plot the output response $y(t)$ and the control input $u(t)$ in separate graphs versus time from $t = 0$ s to $t = 10$ s. Observe how the natural frequency ω_n affects the values of K_1 and K_2, the output response $y(t)$, and the control input $u(t)$.

P7.2g: Based on the experience you gain from P7.2e and P7.2f, find a best design of K_1 and K_2 so that $y(t)$ has an optimal performance while satisfying the control-input constraint, $u(t) < 20$, $for\ t \geq 0$. Plot the optimal output response $y(t)$ and the control input $u(t)$ in separate graphs versus time from $t = 0$ s to $t = 10$ s.

P7.3: Problems P7.1 and P7.2 consider exactly the same problem with the same objective, but have different controller structures; one is the PI controller and the other is the dual-loop controller. Comment on the pros and cons of these two approaches based on the results of Problems P7.1g and P7.2g.

P7.4: Consider the following system:

$$Y(s) = G(s)U(s) = \frac{1}{s(s+1)}U(s)$$

It is easy to see that the system is not BIBO stable since there is a pole at the origin, which is on the imaginary axis, according to Theorem 7.15. But according to the definition of BIBO stability, there should exist a bounded input so that the output is unbounded. Find this bounded input and show that the output response of the system driven by this input will be unbounded.

P7.5: Explain the difference between BIBO stability and internal stability.

P7.6a: Consider the following system:

$$\dot{x}(t) = Ax(t) + Bu(t) := \begin{bmatrix} 0 & 1 & 1 \\ 4 & -3 & 0 \\ 0 & 0 & 2 \end{bmatrix} x(t) + \begin{bmatrix} 0 \\ 0 \\ 1 \end{bmatrix} u(t) \tag{7.126}$$

The objective is to find a state-feedback controller $u(t) = Fx(t)$ so that the closed-loop system poles, or the eigenvalues of $A + BF$, are placed at $s = -1,\ -2,\ -3$. Here we will employ the transform approach instead of the direct approach since the transform approach is easier in computation. The first step is to transform the state equation into a companion form. Find a similarity transformation matrix T and define a new state vector $\hat{x}(t) = T^{-1}x(t)$ so that the new state equation

$$\dot{\hat{x}}(t) = \hat{A}\hat{x}(t) + \hat{B}u(t)$$

is in companion form.

P7.6b: Design a state-feedback controller $u(t) = \hat{F}\hat{x}(t)$ so that the eigenvalues of $\hat{A} + \hat{B}\hat{F}$ are placed at $s = -1,\ -2,\ -3$.

P7.6c: Use $\hat{F}$ and T to determine the state-feedback gain matrix F for the original state equation so that the eigenvalues of $A + BF$ are the same as those of $\hat{A} + \hat{B}\hat{F}$. Verify your results.

P7.7a: Consider the typical feedback control system shown in Figure 7.22. Let $G(s) = \frac{1}{s^2 - s}$. The objective is to design a controller $K(s)$ so that the closed-loop system is stable. Can a proportional controller $K(s) = K_p$ stabilize the closed-loop system? If yes, verify your results. If not, explain why.

P7.7b: Repeat Problem P7.7a with the PI controller $K(s) = (K_p s + K_i)/s$.

P7.7c: Repeat Problem P7.7a with the following first-order controller,

$$K(s) = \frac{b_1 s + b_0}{s + a_0}$$

where a_0, b_1, b_0 are real parameters. Hint: Use Routh-Hurwitz stability criterion theorem.

8

Stability, Regulation, and Root Locus Design

I N Section 7.6.4, we witnessed that an originally unstable cart-inverted pendulum system was stabilized by a state-feedback controller that utilizes a pole placement approach to place all the closed-loop system poles at desired locations in the strictly left half of the complex plane. The controller not only keeps the pendulum at the upright position, but also moves the cart to the desired center of the rail. In Section 7.1.1, a dual-loop feedback control structure with a regulation integrator and two design parameters were employed to regulate the speed of a DC motor system. The integrator guarantees zero steady-state error in step speed tracking, and the two parameters K_1 and K_2 are chosen to achieve a desired transient response by placing the closed-loop system poles at a best possible location in the complex plane.

This chapter will provide a complete discussion of compensator design via the *root locus method* to achieve stability, regulation, and a best possible transient response implied by pole locations. It begins with a study of steady-state error and introduces the *internal model principle* and the concept of system *type*. The concept of system type and internal model principle explains how to select a feedback controller structure to achieve zero steady-state error response for certain group of references/disturbances. A cruise control example is used to provide an overview of the design process, including performance objectives, the role of feedback in achieving those goals, as well as the notion of performance robustness with respect to model uncertainty.

The root locus method is presented in some detail, including the basic construction rules, why they are useful in design, and how to do the computations using MATLAB. Simple examples illustrate key points throughout this discussion. More expansive examples are given in the last three sections. First, a DC motor *sinusoidal position tracking* controller is used to illustrate the application of the internal model principle along with root locus design.

The next section examines the *longitudinal flight path control* of the F/A–18 aircraft. In this example, manual control is simulated to illustrate the difficulty level of controlling the extremely low-damping, long-period (phugoid-mode) oscillations. A sophisticated root locus design with integral regulation and *state-feedback pole placement* is employed to achieve stability and flight path tracking. The last section illustrates how altitude regulation can be accomplished using the flight path angle tracking controller.

8.1 Type of Feedback Systems and Internal Model Principle

In the design of a feedback control system, the designer would usually consider the following: the stability of the closed-loop system, the transient response, the steady-state error, and the robust performance against plant uncertainties. In the previous chapter, we learned how the pole locations would affect the stability and the transient behavior of the system. **In this section, we will discuss how to design a controller so that the closed-loop system will have a least steady-state error.**

8.1.1 Steady-State Error

Before the discussion of a more general steady-state response issue, we will revisit the DC motor speed control problem considered in Example 5.26. The DC motor speed control system block diagram shown in Figure 8.1 is almost identical to that shown in Figure 5.22. The only difference is the controller; now the controller is a proportional controller $K(s) = K_P$ instead of an integral controller K_I/s.

Example 8.1 (Speed Control of the DC Motor System Using a Proportional Controller)

Let the Laplace transforms of $\omega_r(t)$ and $\omega_\ell(t)$ be $\Omega_r(s)$ and $\Omega_\ell(s)$, respectively. Then we have the closed-loop transfer function from $\Omega_r(s)$ to $\Omega_\ell(s)$ in the following:

$$\frac{\Omega_\ell(s)}{\Omega_r(s)} = \frac{G(s)K(s)}{1+G(s)K(s)} \tag{8.1}$$

Plugging the expressions of $K(s) = K_P$ and $G(s)$ into the closed-loop transfer function, we have

$$\frac{\Omega_\ell(s)}{\Omega_r(s)} = \frac{\frac{145.5K_P}{(s+43.14)}}{1+\frac{145.5K_P}{(s+43.14)}} = \frac{145.5K_P}{s+43.14+145.5K_P} = \frac{b}{s+a} = \frac{x_{ss}}{\tau s+1} \tag{8.2}$$

Note that this closed-loop transfer function belongs to the category of the typical first-order system we studied in Chapter 2. Recall that the dynamic behavior of the typical first-order system is characterized by the time constant τ and the steady-state step response x_{ss}. From Equation 8.2, we have the following two equations that relate the time constant τ and the steady-state response constant x_{ss} to the proportional constant K_P:

$$\tau = \frac{1}{43.14+145.5K_P}, \quad x_{ss} = \frac{145.5K_P}{43.14+145.5K_P}$$

Due to the restriction of the proportional control structure, **there is only one design parameter K_P to be determined, we only have one degree of freedom: choosing either the time constant τ or the steady-state step response constant x_{ss}.**

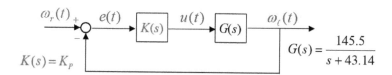

$$G(s) = \frac{145.5}{s+43.14}$$

$$K(s) = K_P$$

Fig. 8.1: A DC motor speed control system with a proportional controller.

If we choose $K_P = 0.5$ the time constant will be $\tau = 0.0086$ s, and the steady-state step response constant will be $x_{ss} = 0.628$. The time constant is faster than we need, but the steady-state step response is 37.2% away from the desired steady-state response. That means the steady-state error is 37.2%. The steady-state error can be reduced by increasing the value of K_P. If $K_P = 1$, the time constant will be $\tau = 0.0053$ s, and the steady-state step response constant will be $x_{ss} = 0.771$, which improves the steady-state error to 22.9%. Theoretically, the steady-state error could be reduced to zero if K_P increases to infinity. **However, by increasing the proportional control constant** K_P**, the control input** $u(t)$ **will increase accordingly and up to some point it may saturate the actuator.**

The simulation results are shown in Figure 8.2. On the left-hand-side graph of the figure, the red horizontal line on the top represents the desired motor speed $\omega_r(t) = 20u_s(t)$ rad/s. When $K_P = 0.5$, the step response reaches the steady state $\omega_\ell(t) = 12.56$ rad/s, shortly after $t = 0.04$ s. The rise time and settling time are fast, but the steady-state error is large. The steady-state error is 7.44 rad/s away from the desired 20 rad/s, which is $(20 - 7.44)/20 = 37.2\%$. If $K_P = 1$ is chosen, the step response will rise to the steady state $\omega_\ell(t) = 15.42$ rad/s, around $t = 0.03$ s. The rise time and settling time are faster, but the steady-state error is still large. The steady-state error is 4.58 rad/s away from the desired 20 rad/s, which is $(20 - 15.42)/20 = 22.9\%$.

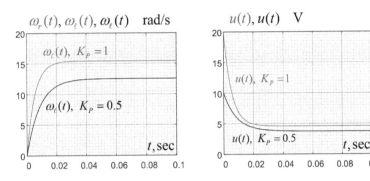

Fig. 8.2: Simulation results of the proportional feedback speed control of the DC motor system.

The control-input $u(t)$ plots are shown in the right-hand-side of Figure 8.2. It can be seen that the maximum control input occurs almost right after $t = 0$ s with $u(t) = 10$ V when $K_P = 0.5$. When K_P increases to $K_P = 1$, the required control input increases accordingly to about 20 V. Note that the control inputs always have their limitations in magnitude or in rate of change. The system needs to work within the capability of the control inputs; otherwise, the system may perform poorly or become unstable. For this particular DC motor speed control problem, the proportional control design structure is not a good one since the steady-state error is not acceptable, even when the control input is allowed to increase to 20 V. **For comparison, both the integral control design in Example 5.26 and the dual-loop control design in Example 6.1 are much better designs** since zero steady-state error is guaranteed for step responses while their transient performances are satisfactory and their control inputs are well within reasonable range. ∎

8.1.2 Type of Feedback Systems and Internal Model Principle

From the DC motor speed control example, we observe, for the same plant $G(s)$, and assume the reference input is a step function; both of the integral control design in Example 5.26 and the dual-loop control design in Example 6.1 achieve zero steady-state error response, but the proportional control design in Example 8.1 is unable to reduce the steady-state error to an acceptable level within a reasonable control-input constraint. **In the following, we will investigate what are the deciding factors for the steady-state error.**

The block diagram shown in Figure 8.3 is a typical feedback control system. The plant $G(s)$ represents a system to be controlled, which can be a transfer function or a state-space model. The objective of the feedback control system is to design a realizable controller $K(s)$, which can be also represented as a transfer function or a state-space model, so that the closed-loop system is stable, and the error $e(t)$ is as small as possible, subject to the control-input $u(t)$ constraints. In this section, we will only focus on the steady-state error, which is

$$e_{ss} = \lim_{t \to \infty} e(t) \tag{8.3}$$

If possible, we would like to design a controller so that the steady-state error e_{ss} is zero.

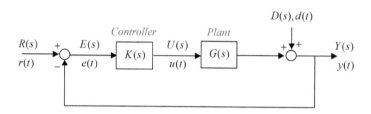

Fig. 8.3: A typical feedback control system structure.

The feedback control system shown in Figure 8.3 has two inputs: One is the disturbance input $d(t)$ and the other is the reference input $r(t)$. Since our interest is in $e(t)$ or its Laplace transform $E(s)$, we would like to know how these two inputs, $R(s)$ and $D(s)$, affect $E(s)$. The transfer function $E(s)/R(s)$ and $E(s)/D(s)$ can be obtained using Mason's gain formula or the algebraic equations approach as follows:

$$\frac{E(s)}{R(s)} = \frac{1}{1+G(s)K(s)} \quad \text{and} \quad \frac{E(s)}{D(s)} = \frac{-1}{1+G(s)K(s)}$$

Hence, $E(s)$ can be written as the sum of the two responses due to $R(s)$ and $D(s)$, respectively.

$$E(s) = \frac{1}{1+G(s)K(s)}R(s) - \frac{1}{1+G(s)K(s)}D(s) \tag{8.4}$$

According to the Laplace transform final-value theorem, if the real part of all the poles $sE(s)$ are strictly negative, then the final value of $e(t)$ can be computed in the frequency domain as follows:

$$e_{ss} := \lim_{t \to \infty} e(t) = \lim_{s \to 0} sE(s) = \lim_{s \to 0} \frac{sR(s)}{1+G(s)K(s)} + \lim_{s \to 0} \frac{-sD(s)}{1+G(s)K(s)} := e_{ssR} + e_{ssD} \tag{8.5}$$

The disturbance input $d(t)$ and the reference input $r(t)$ in general are different, but the ways they affect the steady-state error are fundamentally identical. Without loss of generality, we will just address the steady-state error e_{ssR} due to the reference input $R(s)$.

$$e_{ssR} = \lim_{s \to 0} \frac{sR(s)}{1+G(s)K(s)} \tag{8.6}$$

The reference or disturbance inputs of interest are those with poles at the origin of the complex plane and those with conjugate poles on the imaginary axis. In this subsection, we will consider the reference input described by the following m-degree polynomial time-function and its Laplace transform,

$$r(t) = R_0 + R_1 t + \frac{R_2}{2}t^2 + \cdots + \frac{R_m}{m!}t^m \quad \rightleftarrows \quad R(s) = \frac{R_0}{s} + \frac{R_1}{s^2} + \frac{R_2}{s^3} + \cdots + \frac{R_m}{s^{m+1}} \tag{8.7}$$

where m is the degree of the reference input polynomial.

In general, the *loop transfer function* $G(s)K(s)$ can be written as

$$G(s)K(s) = \frac{k(\tau_a s + 1)(\tau_b s + 1) \cdots (\tau_p s + 1)}{s^i(\tau_1 s + 1)(\tau_2 s + 1) \cdots (\tau_n s + 1)} \tag{8.8}$$

where the superscript i is an integer greater or equal to 0, and the system is called *type i system*.

Combining the above three equations, we have

$$e_{ssR} = \lim_{s \to 0} \frac{sR(s)}{1 + G(s)K(s)} = \lim_{s \to 0} \frac{R_0 + \frac{R_1}{s} + \frac{R_2}{s^2} + \cdots + \frac{R_m}{s^m}}{1 + \frac{k(\tau_a s+1)(\tau_b s+1)\cdots(\tau_p s+1)}{s^i(\tau_1 s+1)(\tau_2 s+1)\cdots(\tau_n s+1)}} \tag{8.9}$$

According to Equation 8.9, the steady-state error e_{ssR} is mainly determined by two index numbers m and i, where m is the degree of the reference input polynomial time function and i is the type of the feedback system. In the following, we will investigate the steady-state error of the typical feedback control system for each reference input case, starting from $m = 0$, the step input case, then $m = 1$, the ramp input case, and then $m = 2$, the parabolic input case, $\cdots$, etc. For each case, the type of feedback system will be determined to guarantee zero steady-state error.

Case 0: Steady-State Error Due to a Step Reference Input

Case 0: The reference input is $r(t) = R_0 u_s(t)$ with its Laplace transform $R(s) = R_0/s$, where R_0 is an arbitrary constant. Based on Equation 8.9, the steady-state error for each type of feedback system can be obtained as follows.

$$\begin{aligned} \text{Type 0 system}: & \quad e_{ssR} = \lim_{s \to 0} \frac{R_0}{1 + k/s^i} = \frac{R_0}{1 + k/s^0} = \frac{R_0}{1 + k} \\ \text{Type 1 or higher system}: & \quad e_{ssR} = \lim_{s \to 0} \frac{R_0}{1 + k/s^i} = 0 \end{aligned} \tag{8.10}$$

Example 8.2 (Case 0 Examples with Type 0 and Type 1 Systems)

The *loop transfer function* $G(s)K(s)$ of the DC motor proportional speed control system in Example 8.1 can be rewritten in the form of Equation 8.8 as

$$G(s)K(s) = \frac{145.5 K_P}{s + 43.14} = \frac{k}{s^0(\tau_1 s + 1)}$$

which is a *Type 0* system with $k = 145.5 K_P/43.14 = 3.373 K_P$. **Hence the steady-state error will be**

$$e_{ssR} = \frac{R_0}{1 + k} = \frac{R_0}{1 + 3.373 K_P}$$

If $K_P = 1$ and $R_0 = 20$ rad/s, then the steady-state error is $e_{ssR} = 20/(1 + 3.373) = 4.57$ rad/s, which is 22.9% of error.

On the other hand, the *loop transfer function* $G(s)K(s)$ of the DC motor integral speed control system in Example 5.26 is

$$G(s)K(s) = \frac{145.5 K_I}{s(s + 43.14)} = \frac{k}{s^1(\tau_1 s + 1)}$$

which is a *Type 1* system with $k = 145.5 K_I/43.14 = 3.373 K_I$. **Hence, the steady-state error is** $e_{ssR} = 0$. ∎

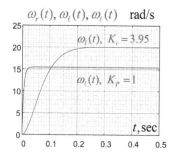
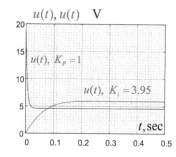

Fig. 8.4: Case 0: Comparison of Proportional and Integral Controls of DC motor speed.

This example and Equation 8.10 explain why the integral control is able to accomplish zero steady-state error for step reference input while the proportional control can't. As revealed in Figure 8.4, the proportional $K_P = 1$ controller provides fast response, but it renders a large 22.9% steady-state error even with a high control input, $u(t) = 20$ V. On the other hand, the integral $K_i = 3.95$ controller reaches the steady state shortly after 0.2s and only requires about 6V of control input. The next case to be considered is Case 1, when the reference input is a ramp function.

Case 1: Steady-State Error Due to a Ramp Reference Input

Case 1: The reference input is $r(t) = (R_0 + R_1 t) u_s(t)$ with its Laplace transform $R(s) = R_0/s + R_1/s^2$, where R_0 and R_1 are arbitrary constants. Based on Equation 8.9, the steady-state error for each type of feedback system can be obtained as follows:

$$\text{Type 0 system}: \quad e_{ssR} = \lim_{s \to 0} \frac{R_0 + R_1/s}{1 + k/s^0} = \lim_{s \to 0} \frac{R_1/s}{1 + k} = \infty$$

$$\text{Type 1 system}: \quad e_{ssR} = \lim_{s \to 0} \frac{R_0 + R_1/s}{1 + k/s^1} = \frac{R_1}{k} \tag{8.11}$$

$$\text{Type 2 or higher system}: \quad e_{ssR} = \lim_{s \to 0} \frac{R_0 + R_1/s}{1 + k/s^2} = \lim_{s \to 0} \frac{R_1/s}{k/s^2} = 0$$

Example 8.3 (Case 1 Examples with Type 1 and Type 2 Systems)

The *loop transfer function* $G(s)K(s)$ of the DC motor integral speed control system in Example 5.26 is

$$G(s)K(s) = \frac{145.5K_I}{s(s+43.14)} = \frac{k}{s^1(\tau_1 s + 1)}$$

which is a *Type 1* system with $k = 145.5K_I/43.14 = 3.373K_I$. **Hence, the steady-state error will be**

$$e_{ssR} = \frac{R_1}{k} = \frac{R_1}{3.373K_I}$$

If $K_I = 3.95$ and $R_1 = 1$ rad/s^2, then the steady-state error is $e_{ssR} = 1/(3.373)(3.95) = 0.075$ rad/s^2, which is 7.5% of error.

In contrast, a new controller $K_R(s) = (s+3)/s^2$ can be designed to achieve *Type 2* requirement for the *loop transfer function* $G(s)K_R(s)$ as follows:

$$G(s)K_R(s) = \frac{145.5(s+3)}{s^2(s+43.14)} = \frac{k(\tau_a s + 1)}{s^2(\tau_1 s + 1)}$$

which is a *Type 2* system with $k = (145.5)(3)/43.14 = 10.12$. **Hence, the steady-state error for ramp reference input will be** $e_{ssR} = 0$.

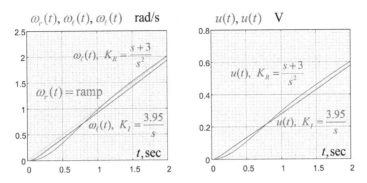

Fig. 8.5: Case 1: Comparison of integral and double integral controls of DC motor speed for ramp tracking.

The simulation results comparison of the integral control and the double integral control are shown in Figure 8.5. The integral controller $K(s) = K_i/s$ only makes the loop transfer function $G(s)K(s)$ a Type 1 system. It can be seen from the graph on the left that the vertical gap between the green and the red lines is 0.075 rad/s, which exhibits the steady-state error $e_{ssR} = 0.075$ rad/s—a 7.5% of error. **With the new double integral controller** $K_R(s) = (s+3)/s^2$, **the loop transfer function** $G(s)K_R(s)$ **is of Type 2; hence, the steady-state error is zero. It can be verified from the simulation that the green and the blue lines coincide together shortly after** $t = 1$ **s.** ■

Case 2: Steady-State Error Due to a Parabolic Reference Input

Case 2: The reference input is $r(t) = R_0 + R_1 t + \frac{R_2}{2}t^2 u_s(t)$, with its Laplace transform $R(s) = \frac{R_0}{s} + \frac{R_1}{s^2} + \frac{R_2}{s^3}$, where R_0, R_1 and R_2 are arbitrary constants. Based on Equation 8.9, the steady-state error for each type of feedback system can be obtained as follows:

$$\text{Type 0 system}: \quad e_{ssR} = \lim_{s \to 0} \frac{R_0 + R_1/s + R_2/s^2}{1 + k/s^0} = \lim_{s \to 0} \frac{R_2/s^2}{1+k} = \infty$$

$$\text{Type 1 system}: \quad e_{ssR} = \lim_{s \to 0} \frac{R_0 + R_1/s + R_2/s^2}{1 + k/s^1} = \infty$$

$$\text{Type 2 system}: \quad e_{ssR} = \lim_{s \to 0} \frac{R_0 + R_1/s + R_2/s^2}{1 + k/s^2} = \frac{R_2}{k}$$

$$\text{Type 3 or higher system}: \quad e_{ssR} = \lim_{s \to 0} \frac{R_0 + R_1/s + R_2/s^2}{1 + k/s^3} = \lim_{s \to 0} \frac{R_2/s^2}{k/s^3} = 0$$

(8.12)

$$\vdots$$

Case m: Steady-State Error Due to a Polynomial Time Function Reference Input

Case m: The reference input is

$$r(t) = R_0 + R_1 t + \frac{R_2}{2}t^2 + \cdots + \frac{R_m}{m!}t^m$$

with its Laplace transform

$$R(s) = \frac{R_0}{s} + \frac{R_1}{s^2} + \frac{R_2}{s^3} + \cdots + \frac{R_m}{s^m}$$

where R_0, R_1, R_2, $\cdots$, and R_m are arbitrary constants. Based on Equation 8.9, the steady-state error for each type of feedback system can be obtained as follows:

Type 0 system : $e_{ssR} = \lim\limits_{s \to 0} \frac{R_0 + R_1/s + \cdots + R_m/s^m}{1 + k/s^0} = \lim\limits_{s \to 0} \frac{R_m/s^m}{1+k} = \infty$

Type 1 system : $e_{ssR} = \lim\limits_{s \to 0} \frac{R_0 + R_1/s + \cdots + R_m/s^m}{1 + k/s^1} = \infty$

$\vdots$

$\vdots$ (8.13)

Type $m - 1$ system : $e_{ssR} = \lim\limits_{s \to 0} \frac{R_0 + R_1/s + \cdots + R_m/s^m}{1 + k/s^{m-1}} = \infty$

Type m system : $e_{ssR} = \lim\limits_{s \to 0} \frac{R_0 + R_1/s + \cdots + R_m/s^m}{1 + k/s^m} = \frac{R_m}{k}$

Type $m + 1$ or higher system : $e_{ssR} = \lim\limits_{s \to 0} \frac{R_0 + R_1/s + \cdots + R_m/s^m}{1 + k/s^{m+1}} = 0$

■

Remark 8.4 (Internal Model Principle)

From these discussions, it can be observed that to achieve zero steady-state error against a step reference or step disturbance inputs, whose frequency-domain representation is c/s with c an arbitrary constant, the *loop transfer function* needs to be at least *of Type 1* (i.e., $G(s)K(s)$ needs to include the *internal model 1/s* in it). Similarly, for a ramp reference or ramp disturbance inputs, whose frequency-domain representation is c/s^2 with c an arbitrary constant, the loop transfer function $G(s)K(s)$ needs to include the internal model $1/s^2$ in it in order to guarantee zero steady-state error. **This perfect steady-state tracking concept is called the** *internal model principle*, **which has been widely employed in the design of feedback control systems. The internal model principle [Francis and Wonham, 1976, Huang, 2004] also can be applied to regulate sinusoidal disturbances or to track sinusoidal reference input.**

■

Example 8.5 (Sinusoidal Tracking Using the Internal Model Principle)

Consider the same DC motor speed feedback control block diagram shown in Figure 8.1. The plant $G(s) = 145.5/(s + 43.14)$ is still the same, but the reference input has changed to the following:

$$\omega_r(t) = A\sin(\omega_0 t + \phi) \tag{8.14}$$

where the frequency is assumed to be $\omega_0 = 2$ rad/s, but the amplitude A and the phase ϕ are arbitrary. To achieve steady-state sinusoidal tracking, the *loop transfer function* $G(s)K(s)$ needs to have the *internal model* $1/(s^2 + 2^2)$ in it to match the reference sinusoidal function frequency $\omega_0 = 2$ rad/s. Therefore, the controller $K(s)$ should be of the form

$$K(s) = \frac{s+k}{s^2 + 2^2} \tag{8.15}$$

where k is the design parameter to be determined so that the closed-loop system is stable and the transient response is optimized subject to the control-input constraints.

The *loop transfer function* $G(s)K(s)$ of the DC motor sinusoidal speed control system now is

$$G(s)K(s) = \frac{145.5(s+k)}{(s+43.14)(s^2 + 2^2)}$$

which consists of the internal model function $1/(s^2 + 2^2)$ to guarantee zero tracking error at steady state. The closed-loop characteristic equation now is

$$(s + 43.14)(s^2 + 2^2) + 145.5(s + k) = 0$$

which can be rearranged into

$$1 + k\frac{145.5}{s^3 + 43.14s^2 + 149.5s + 172.56} = 0$$

and an optimal $k = 0.616$ is obtained using the *root locus design* approach, which will be introduced in the next section.

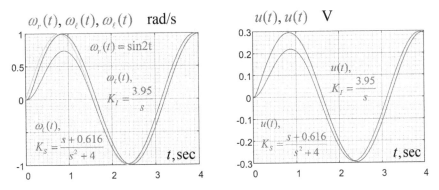

Fig. 8.6: Comparison of integral and sinusoidal controls of DC motor speed for sinusoidal tracking.

The simulation results are shown in Figure 8.6. The graph on the left shows three functions, the reference input $\omega_r(t) = \sin 2t$ in green, the output response $\omega_\ell(t)$ in blue associated with the sinusoidal controller $K_S(s) = (s + 0.616)/(s^2 + 2^2)$, and the output response $\omega_\ell(t)$ in red associated with the integral controller $K_I(s) = 3.95/s$. It can be seen that **the sinusoidal controller K_S is able to achieve perfect steady-state tracking within 2 seconds while the integral control response has a time-delay steady-state error.** The graph on the right shows that both controllers use about the same amount of control input.   ∎

8.2 An Automobile Cruise Control Example

Recall that in Section 7.1 we briefly introduced the features of feedback control that include: (1) it is a naturally perfect mechanism for automatic control; (2) it provides an easy way to modify the dynamics characteristics of the system to achieve better performance; (3) it has the ability to achieve steady-state disturbance response rejection; (4) it has the ability to achieve steady-state reference input tracking or regulation; and (5) it achieves robust stability and robust performance against plant uncertainties.

Later, in Section 8.1, we studied the steady-state error issues of feedback control systems and learned that steady-state reference input tracking and steady-state disturbance response rejection are mathematically the same. **A feedback controller can be designed to achieve zero steady-state error for certain types of reference and/or disturbance inputs, including step disturbances with arbitrary magnitude, ramp disturbances with arbitrary slope, and sinusoidal disturbances with arbitrary amplitude and phase.** This perfect steady-state design approach is based on the celebrated internal

model principle with which the loop transfer function of the closed-loop system is embedded with the dynamics model of the reference and/or disturbance inputs.

In Example 8.2, we compared the performances of the integral controller versus the proportional controller in a DC motor speed control system, and witnessed that the integral control is able to accomplish zero steady-state error for step reference input while the proportional control can't. The reason is that the loop transfer function of the closed-loop system with integral controller is

$$G(s)K(s) = \frac{145.5K_I}{s(s+43.14)} = \frac{k}{s(\tau_1 s + 1)}$$

which is equipped with the internal model $1/s$, and the reference input $r(t)$ is a step function with arbitrary magnitude R_0, whose Laplace transform is $R(s) = R_0/s$.

The basic idea of the DC motor speed control system and the internal model principle can be extended and applied to the automobile cruise control system. In the following, we consider a basic cruise control design problem based on the brief discussion in Section 1.4. The goal is to introduce the primary goals and basic methods of feedback control design in a context familiar to most readers. **The objective of basic cruise control is to regulate the vehicle speed to match a commanded speed.** In this discussion, bounce, pitch, sideslip, roll, and yaw are ignored. Our focus is on speed (i.e., velocity, v, in the body x direction). Relatively small deviations of v from the nominal speed, v^*, are of concern. The control input is the engine throttle u, whose manipulation alters the force f ultimately imposed on the vehicle by the engine through the gear train and tires. We do not consider gear shifting in view of the small deviation of speed assumption. Wind gusts are not considered, although aerodynamic drag is. Road slope, θ, is the only disturbance considered. Road slope induces a gravitational force component that contributes to vehicle acceleration.

The block diagram of Figure 1.1 illustrates the typical configuration of a basic cruise control system. Our goal is to design the control block. The cruise control system responds to a change in speed command or a disturbance (a change in road slope) by adjusting the throttle position to maintain the desired speed. The criteria for design includes the following:

1. Steady-state error: Speed error in steady state in response to command or disturbance
2. Transient response time including rise time, peak time, and settling time
3. Transient overshoot or undershoot
4. Robustness: performance tolerance to unmodeled dynamics or parameter variation

8.2.1 Assembling a Model

We begin by establishing a mathematical model for each element of the system. The vehicle dynamics is described by the following nonlinear first-order differential equation with one single state variable $v(t)$ representing the velocity of the vehicle,

$$m\frac{dv(t)}{dt} = f(t) - mg\sin\theta\,(t) - cv^2(t) \tag{8.16}$$

where m is the mass of the vehicle, f is the force generated by the engine to move the vehicle, c is the viscosity coefficient of the vehicle traveling in the air, and $\theta(t)$ is the slope angle of the road. Note that

$$\sin\theta \approx \theta \quad if \quad |\theta| \le 0.262 \text{ rad}$$

The disturbance term $mg\sin\theta$ can be replaced by $mg\theta$ if $|\theta| \le 0.262$ rad, or equivalently the slope of the road is less than 15 degrees. Thus, Equation 8.16 can be rewritten as

$$\dot{v}(t) = \frac{-c}{m}v^2(t) + \frac{1}{m}f(t) - g\theta(t) \tag{8.17}$$

Assme (v^*, f^*) is a nominal operating equilibrium of the vehicle so that

$$f^* = c(v^*)^2$$

and let $\bar{v}(t)$ and $\bar{f}(t)$, respectively, be the perturbed velocity and force variables from the equilibrium. Thus, the relationship between the real physical variables (v, f), the equilibrium (v^*, f^*), and the perturbed variables $(\bar{v}, \bar{f})$ are

$$v(t) = \bar{v}(t) + v^* \quad \text{and} \quad f(t) = \bar{f}(t) + f^* \tag{8.18}$$

Then Equation 8.17 can be linearized about the equilibrium (v^*, f^*) using the Jacobian approach shown in Equation C.5 from Appendix C as follows:

$$\dot{\bar{v}}(t) = \frac{\partial}{\partial v}\left(\frac{-c}{m}v^2 + \frac{1}{m}f\right)\Big|_{v^*,f^*} + \frac{\partial}{\partial f}\left(\frac{-c}{m}v^2 + \frac{1}{m}f\right)\Big|_{v^*,f^*} - g\theta$$

which is

$$\dot{\bar{v}}(t) = \frac{-2c}{m}v^*\bar{v}(t) + \frac{1}{m}\bar{f}(t) - g\theta(t) := -\bar{c}\bar{v}(t) + \frac{1}{m}\bar{f}(t) - g\theta(t) \tag{8.19}$$

where $\bar{c} = (2c/m)v^*$. Taking the Laplace transform of Equation 8.19 we obtain

$$s\bar{V}(s) = -\bar{c}\bar{V}(s) + \frac{1}{m}\bar{F}(s) - g\Theta(s) \tag{8.20}$$

and therefore the velocity of the vehicle is

$$\bar{V}(s) = \frac{1/m}{s+\bar{c}}\bar{F}(s) - \frac{g}{s+\bar{c}}\Theta(s) \tag{8.21}$$

Turning now to the engine dynamics, assume the engine thrust response to throttle input is very fast compared to the vehicle dynamics. Then we might ignore any dynamics and take the "ideal" engine transfer function to be $G_E(s) = 1$. We will design the controller using this assumption and then evaluate the impact of engine dynamics by testing the resultant controller with an alternative transfer function that reflects engine delay. **Thus, we will use three different engine models, all of the form**

$$G_E(s) = \left(\frac{1}{\tau s + 1}\right)^2 \tag{8.22}$$

with

1. **ideal model (used for design), $\tau = 0$**
2. **fast model, $\tau = 0.3$**
3. **slow model, $\tau = 0.6$**

This engine model is a typical second-order system with damping ratio $\varsigma = 1$ and natural frequency $\omega_n = 1/\tau$. It also can be considered as a cascade connection of two identical typical first-order system with time constant τ.

The block diagram for the control system with the component models is shown in Figure 8.7. Note that Equation 8.21 describes how the engine output force $\bar{f}(t)$ and the slope of the road $\theta(t)$ would affect the vehicle speed $\bar{v}(t)$, and Equation 8.22 is the transfer function of the engine between the throttle $\bar{u}(t)$ and the force $\bar{f}(t)$. The controller $K(s)$ is to be designed so that the closed-loop system has a desired performance.

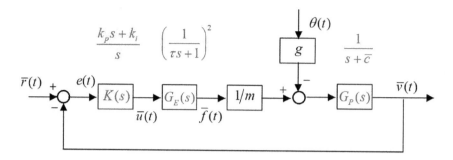

Fig. 8.7: Cruise control block diagram with component transfer functions.

Vehicle Data and a Nominal Operating Equilibrium

The vehicle considered is a typical mid-size SUV (sport utility vehicle) with mass $m = 1,929$ kg and a dimensionless drag coefficient $C_d = 0.35$. The drag force is

$$F_d = cv^2 = \frac{1}{2}\rho C_d A v^2 \tag{8.23}$$

where $\rho = 1.225$ kg/m^3 is the air density, $C_d = 0.35$ is the drag coefficient, and A is the front surface area, which is approximately computed as $A = 3$ m^2 from the height 1.67 m and the width 1.8 m. Hence, the viscosity coefficient of the vehicle is

$$c = \frac{1}{2}\rho C_d A = \frac{1}{2}(1.225)(0.35)(3) = 0.643 \text{ kg/m}$$

The nominal operating velocity is chosen to be $v^* = 30$ m/s, which is about 108 km/hr or 64.8 mile/hr, and thus the nominal operating force for v^* is

$$f^* = c(v^*)^2 = (0.643)(30^2) = 578.7 \text{ N}$$

Notice that the linearized model of the system shown in Equation 8.19 or in Figure 8.7 was obtained from linearizing the nonlinear system of Equation 8.17 at **the nominal operating equilibrium,**

$$(v^*, f^*) = (30 \text{ m/s}, 578.7 \text{ N})$$

and the linearized model is expressed in terms of the perturbed variables $\bar{v}(t)$ and $\bar{f}(t)$, whose relationship with the real physical velocity and force is given by Equation 8.18. The reference input $\bar{r}(t)$ shown in Figure 8.7 is also a perturbed velocity variable with respect to the equilibrium velocity $v^* = 30$ m/s. That is, $\bar{r}(t) = 5$ m/s means that the desired perturbed steady-state velocity is $\bar{v}(t) = 5$ m/s or the real physical velocity is $v(t) = 35$ m/s.

The parameters g, m, and $\bar{c}$ in the linearized model described by Equation 8.19 or Equation 8.21 are the gravity $g = 9.8$ m/s^2, the mass of the vehicle $m = 1,929$ kg, and **the characteristic value is** $-\bar{c} = \frac{-2c}{m}v^* = -0.02$.

It is obvious that the MKS system of units is adopted in the computation of the cruise control problem in this section. For the slope angle of the road, $\theta(t)$, although we may display it in degrees, it is imperative to adopt the unit radian in computations as commented in Remark 4.16. Recall that 1 radian is approximately 57.3 degrees. Mistakenly regarding 1 degree as 1 radian in computation will lead to a huge error!

8.2.2 Design of the Controller $K(s)$

The classical control design process is to choose a structure for the controller and then determine the controller parameters to meet the performance criteria. In this case we choose a *PI controller* (proportional plus integral controller):

$$\bar{u}(t) = k_p\left(\bar{r}(t) - \bar{v}(t)\right) + k_i \int_0^t \left(\bar{r}(\tau) - \bar{v}(\tau)\right)d\tau \tag{8.24}$$

Note that there are two terms, the first proportional to the speed error, $e(t) = \bar{r}(t) - \bar{v}(t)$, and the second proportional to the time integral of error. The design parameters are the two constants k_p and k_i. In terms of $e(t)$, Equation 8.24 is

$$\bar{u}(t) = k_p e(t) + k_i \int_0^t e(\tau)d\tau$$

Differentiating with respect to t this becomes

$$\dot{\bar{u}}(t) = k_p \dot{e}(t) + k_i e(t) \tag{8.25}$$

Taking the Laplace transform yields

$$\bar{U}(s) = \frac{k_p s + k_i}{s} E(s) := K(s)E(s) \tag{8.26}$$

Closed-Loop Transfer Functions

In the closed-loop system shown in Figure 8.7, the output variable of interest is $\bar{v}(t)$, by which the velocity of the vehicle, $v(t) = \bar{v}(t) + v^*$ can be easily obtained. Meanwhile, there are two input variables $\bar{r}(t)$ and $\theta(t)$. The former is the reference input (or called command input), and the latter is the road slope disturbance input. **The objective is to design a controller $K(s)$ so that the output $\bar{v}(t)$ will follow the reference input $\bar{r}(t)$ as closely as possible under possible influence of the road slope disturbance $\theta(t)$. Since $e(t) = \bar{r}(t) - \bar{v}(t)$, the control problem can be rephrased as to make $e(t)$ as small as possible subject to control-input constraints.**

Hence, we will need to investigate how the controller design will affect the following four closed-loop transfer functions: $G_{E\bar{R}}(s)$, $G_{E\Theta}(s)$, $G_{\bar{F}\bar{R}}(s)$, and $G_{\bar{F}\Theta}(s)$ that satisfy the following two equations:

$$E(s) = G_{E\bar{R}}(s)\bar{R}(s) + G_{E\Theta}(s)\Theta(s)$$
$$\bar{F}(s) = G_{\bar{F}\bar{R}}(s)\bar{R}(s) + G_{\bar{F}\Theta}(s)\Theta(s)$$

These transfer functions can be obtained by applying Mason's gain formula (see Section 6.2.2, or Appendix D) to the closed-loop system block diagram shown in Figure 8.7. According to Mason's gain formula, we have

$$G_{E\bar{R}}(s) = \frac{1}{\Delta}, \quad G_{E\Theta}(s) = \frac{gG_p(s)}{\Delta}, \quad G_{\bar{F}\bar{R}}(s) = \frac{K(s)}{\Delta}, \quad G_{\bar{F}\Theta}(s) = \frac{gG_p(s)K(s)}{\Delta}$$

where

$$\Delta = 1 - \ell_1 = 1 + \frac{1}{m} G_p(s)K(s) = \frac{ms^2 + (m\bar{c} + k_p)s + k_i}{ms(s + \bar{c})}$$

and therefore we have

$$
\begin{aligned}
E(s) &= G_{E\bar{R}}(s)\bar{R}(s) + G_{E\Theta}(s)\Theta(s) \\
&= \frac{ms(s+\bar{c})}{ms^2 + (m\bar{c}+k_p)s + k_i}\bar{R}(s) + \frac{mgs}{ms^2 + (m\bar{c}+k_p)s + k_i}\Theta(s)
\end{aligned}
\tag{8.27}
$$

and

$$
\begin{aligned}
\bar{F}(s) &= G_{\bar{F}\bar{R}}(s)\bar{R}(s) + G_{\bar{F}\Theta}(s)\Theta(s) \\
&= \frac{m(s+\bar{c})(k_p s + k_i)}{ms^2 + (m\bar{c}+k_p)s + k_i}\bar{R}(s) + \frac{mg(k_p s + k_i)}{ms^2 + (m\bar{c}+k_p)s + k_i}\Theta(s)
\end{aligned}
\tag{8.28}
$$

Notice that all of the four transfer functions have the same denominators (the same poles), but different numerators (different zeros). The stability, damping, and oscillation frequency are mainly determined by the poles while the steady-state response and the phase of the transient response are affected by the zeros.

Analysis of the Second-Order System for the Case With $k_i \neq 0$

It can be seen from Equations (8.27) and (8.28) that the closed-loop system is a second-order system if $k_i \neq 0$, and its characteristic equation is

$$ms^2 + (m\bar{c} + k_p)s + k_i = 0 \quad \text{or} \quad s^2 + \left(\bar{c} + \frac{k_p}{m}\right)s + \frac{k_i}{m} = 0 \tag{8.29}$$

Recall that the roots of the characteristic equation are the poles of the system. In most of the practical control system applications, the dominant poles are chosen to be a pair of complex numbers as

$$-\alpha \pm j\omega = -\varsigma\omega_n \pm j\omega_n\sqrt{1 - \varsigma^2}$$

The damping factor α and the frequency ω can be chosen to determine the decay rate and the oscillation frequency of the transient response, respectively. Alternatively, the damping ratio ς and the natural frequency ω_n can be selected to specify the maximum overshoot and the reaction time of the transient response. The relationship of the PI controller parameters (k_p, k_i) to (α, ω) or to (ς, ω_n) can be easily established via the connections of the following characteristic polynomials:

$$s^2 + 2\varsigma\omega_n s + \omega_n^2 \rightleftarrows s^2 + \left(\bar{c} + \frac{k_p}{m}\right)s + \frac{k_i}{m} \rightleftarrows s^2 + 2\alpha s + \alpha^2 + \omega^2 \tag{8.30}$$

For example, if $k_i = 100$ and $k_p = 500$ are chosen, then the damping ratio and the natural frequency for the closed-loop system will be

$$
\begin{aligned}
\omega_n^2 &= k_i/m \\
2\varsigma\omega_n &= \bar{c} + k_p/m
\end{aligned}
\rightarrow
\begin{aligned}
\omega_n &= \sqrt{k_i/m} = \sqrt{100/1929} = 0.2277\,\text{rad/s} \\
\varsigma &= (\bar{c} + k_p/m)/2\omega_n = (0.02 + 500/1929)\,0.4554 = 0.6131
\end{aligned}
$$

On the other hand, if the damping ratio $\varsigma = 0.707$ and the natural frequency $\omega_n = 1$ rad/s are chosen for the PI cruise control closed-loop system, then the PI controller parameters k_p an k_i should satisfy the following equations:

$$
\begin{aligned}
k_i/m &= \omega_n^2 \\
\bar{c} + k_p/m &= 2\varsigma\omega_n
\end{aligned}
\rightarrow
\begin{aligned}
k_i &= m\omega_n^2 = 1929 \\
k_p &= m(-\bar{c} + 2\varsigma\omega_n) = 1929(-0.02 + 1.414) = 2689.03
\end{aligned}
$$

The closed-loop system poles or their associated damping ratio and natural frequency mainly determine the stability, damping, oscillation, and transient reaction time of the closed-loop system; however, they alone do not determine the steady-state response of the closed-loop system. As discussed in Sections 8.1.1 and 8.1.2, **the steady-state tracking/regulation error is determined by the type of reference/disturbance inputs, and by the internal model embedded in the loop transfer function of the feedback systems.**

The reference input $\bar{r}(t)$ is assumed to be a step function with arbitrary magnitude. That is, $\bar{r}(t) = R_v u_s(t)$, where $u_s(t)$ is a unit step function and R_v is an arbitrary real number representing a differential change of the desired vehicle velocity from the nominal operating equilibrium velocity, $v^* = 30$ m/s. For example, if the desired vehicle speed is $v(t) = 33$ m/s, which means the desired $\bar{v}(t)$ is 3 m/s; hence, R_v should be chosen as 3 m/s. On the other hand, if the desired vehicle speed is $v(t) = 25$ m/s, which means the desired $\bar{v}(t)$ is -5 m/s; therefore, R_v should be chosen as -5 m/s.

Similarly, the road slope disturbance input $\theta(t)$ is assumed to be a step function with arbitrary magnitude. That is, $\theta(t) = \theta_d u_s(t)$, where $u_s(t)$ is a unit step function and θ_d is an arbitrary real number representing the road slope angle in radian. For example if the vehicle encounters an uphill $5°$ ramp, then θ_d should be chosen as 0.0873 rad.

Now, assume the reference input is $\bar{R}(s) = R_v/s$, and the road slope disturbance input is $\Theta(s) = \theta_d/s$, and both R_v and θ_d are arbitrary real numbers. Then the closed-loop error response $E(s)$ can be expressed as follows:

$$E(s) = \frac{1}{\Delta(s)}\left(\frac{R_v}{s} + gG_p(s)\frac{\theta_d}{s}\right) \quad \text{where} \quad \Delta(s) = 1 + \frac{1}{m}G_p(s)K(s)$$

According to the final-value theorem, if the closed-loop system is stable, we have the steady-state error,

$$e_{ss} = \lim_{t\to\infty} e(t) = \lim_{s\to 0} sE(s) = \lim_{s\to 0}\frac{1}{\Delta(s)}\left(R_v + g\theta_d G_p(0)\right)$$

Note that the loop transfer function in $\Delta(s)$ is embedded with the internal model $1/s$, which is coming from the integrator in the controller. Hence, we have

$$\lim_{s\to 0}\Delta(s) = 1 + \frac{1}{m}G_p(0)\lim_{s\to 0}K(s) = 1 + \frac{1}{m}G_p(0)\lim_{s\to 0}\frac{k_p s + k_i}{s} = \infty \quad \text{if} \quad k_i \neq 0 \qquad (8.31)$$

Therefore, the steady-state tracking/regulation error is

$$e_{ss} = \frac{1}{\lim_{s\to 0}\Delta(s)}\left(R_v + g\theta_d G_p(0)\right) = 0 \quad \text{if} \quad k_i \neq 0$$

Analysis of the First-Order System for the Case with $k_i = 0$

If $k_i = 0$ in Equation 8.26, the transfer function of the controller will become

$$K(s) = k_p$$

which is a proportional controller, and the closed-loop transfer functions in Equations 8.27 and 8.28 will reduce to the following:

$$E(s) = G_{E\bar{R}}(s)\bar{R}(s) + G_{E\Theta}(s)\Theta(s) = \frac{m(s+\bar{c})}{ms + (m\bar{c}+k_p)}\bar{R}(s) + \frac{mg}{ms + (m\bar{c}+k_p)}\Theta(s) \tag{8.32}$$

and

$$\bar{F}(s) = G_{\bar{F}\bar{R}}(s)\bar{R}(s) + G_{\bar{F}\Theta}(s)\Theta(s) = \frac{m(s+\bar{c})k_p}{ms + (m\bar{c}+k_p)}\bar{R}(s) + \frac{mgk_p}{ms + (m\bar{c}+k_p)}\Theta(s) \tag{8.33}$$

It can be seen from Equations 8.32 and 8.33 that the closed-loop system now is a first-order system, and its characteristic equation is

$$ms + (m\bar{c}+k_p) = 0 \quad \text{or} \quad \frac{m}{m\bar{c}+k_p}s + 1 = 0 \tag{8.34}$$

which is characterized by the time constant

$$\tau = \frac{m}{m\bar{c}+k_p}$$

The transient response is governed by an exponential function with time constant specified by the previous equation. **The time response is faster if the time constant is smaller or if k_p is larger.**

To investigate the steady-state response of the first-order closed-loop cruise control system with proportional controller, we will follow the same procedure we did a while ago for the system with PI controller. The reference input and the road slope disturbance input are assumed to be $\bar{r}(t) = R_v u_s(t)$ and $\theta(t) = \theta_d u_s(t)$, respectively, and both R_v and θ_d are arbitrary real numbers. Then the closed-loop error response $E(s)$ can be expressed as follows:

$$E(s) = \frac{1}{\Delta(s)}\left(\frac{R_v}{s} + gG_p(s)\frac{\theta_d}{s}\right) \quad \text{where} \quad \Delta(s) = 1 + \frac{1}{m}G_p(s)k_p$$

According to the final-value theorem, if the closed-loop system is stable, we have the steady-state error as follows:

$$e_{ss} = \lim_{t\to\infty} e(t) = \lim_{s\to 0} sE(s) = \frac{1}{\lim_{s\to 0}\Delta(s)}(R_v + gG_p(0)\theta_d) = \frac{R_v}{\Delta(0)} + \frac{gG_p(0)\theta_d}{\Delta(0)} := e_{ss\_R} + e_{ss\_\theta} \tag{8.35}$$

Since the loop transfer function $G_p(s)k_p/m$ in $\Delta(s)$ does not have the internal model $1/s$ in it, the steady-state error e_{ss} is not zero. The steady-state tracking/regulation error is contributed from two sources: e_{ss_R} due to the reference input and e_{ss_θ} due to the road slope disturbance. **For example, if $\theta_d = 0$ and $R_v = 3$ m/s, then we have the steady-state error**

$$e_{ss} = e_{ss\_R} = \frac{R_v}{\Delta(0)} = \frac{3}{1 + G_p(0)k_p/m} = \frac{3}{1 + 50k_p/1929} = \frac{3}{1 + 0.02592k_p}$$

The error can be made arbitrarily small if k_p can be made arbitrarily large. However, k_p cannot be made arbitrarily large because there is a physical constraint on the engine force f. If k_p is chosen to be $k_p = 500$, then

$$e_{ss} = e_{ss\_R} = \frac{3}{1 + 0.02592k_p} = \frac{3}{1 + (0.02592)(500)} = 0.215 \text{ m/s} \tag{8.36}$$

The reference input $\bar{r}(t) = 3u_s(t)$ means that the desired vehicle speed is $v(t) = 33$ m/s. Since the steady-state error is $e_{ss} = 0.215$ m/s, the real steady-state vehicle speed is 32.785 m/s.

For another example, assume $\theta_d = 0.0873$ rad and $R_v = 0$ m/s, then we have the steady-state error:

$$e_{ss} = e_{ss\_\theta} = \frac{gG_p(0)\theta_d}{\Delta(0)} = \frac{(9.8)(50)(0.0873)}{1 + 50k_p/1929}$$

The error can be made arbitrarily small if k_p can be made arbitrarily large. However, k_p cannot be made arbitrarily large because there is a physical constraint on the engine force f. If k_p is chosen to be $k_p = 500$, then

$$e_{ss} = e_{ss\_\theta} = \frac{(9.8)(50)(0.0873)}{1 + 50k_p/1929} = \frac{42.777}{1 + (50)(500)/1929} = 3.064 \text{ m/s} \qquad (8.37)$$

The reference input $\bar{r}(t) = 0u_s(t)$ means that the desired vehicle speed is $v(t) = 30$ m/s. Since the steady state error is $e_{ss} = 3.064$ m/s, the real steady-state vehicle speed is 26.936 m/s.

8.2.3 Simulation Results with Ideal Engine Model $G_E(s) = 1$

In Section 8.2.2, a simple PI (proportional plus integral) controller structure with two parameters k_p and k_i was introduced to achieve cruise speed control under the influence of road slope disturbances. We also discussed at great length on how the control design would affect the steady-state and the transient responses of the closed-loop system by selecting pole locations, damping ratio, and natural frequency and by utilizing the internal model theory.

In this subsection, we will present the results of four simulations in which the engine model is assumed ideal with transfer function $G_E(s) = 1$. Then in the next subsection, Section 8.2.4, two simulations are employed to show how the unmodelled engine dynamics

$$G_E(s) = \frac{1}{(\tau s + 1)^2}$$

may destabilize the system. We will also learn that a more aggressive controller for the ideal model may not be robust against unmodelled dynamics.

Furthermore, in Section 8.2.5, a feed-forward compensation is employed to reduce the disturbance response if the disturbance information is available.

The Simulink program `CruisePI.mdl` shown in Figure 8.8 will be employed to conduct simulations in this and the next subsections. This Simulink program is constructed based on the closed-loop system block diagram shown in Figure 8.7, where the transfer function of the PI controller is $K(s) = (k_p s + k_i)/s$, the engine dynamics is $G_E(s) = 1/(\tau s + 1)^2$, and the vehicle dynamics is $G_p(s) = 1/(s + \bar{c})$. For the four simulations in this section, the time constant τ is set to zero—the same assumption on which the PI controller was designed.

The step input block labeled by R represents the reference input $\bar{r}(t) = R_v u_s(t)$. The other step input block labeled by Slope serves as the road slope disturbance input, $\theta_d u_s(t)$. The output block labeled as v_a records the actual vehicle velocity $v(t) = \bar{v}(t) + v^*$, the block err labeled as er records the tracking error, $e(t)$, and the block labeled as f_a records the force $f(t) = \bar{f}(t) + f^*$. The constant blocks v_n and f_n represent the nominal operating equilibrium velocity and force, v^* and f^*, respectively.

Example 8.6 (Speed $R_v = 3$ m/s Step Tracking Responses with $k_p = 500$ and Three Values of $k_i = 0, 100, 500$)

In this simulation, the vehicle initially is assumed operating at the equilibrium, $\bar{v}(0) = 0$ m/s, or $v(0) = v^* = 30$ m/s. Let $\bar{r}(t) = R_v u_s(t)$, where $R_v = 3$ m/s, and $\theta(t)$ remains at 0 rad all the time

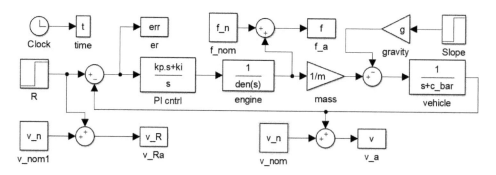

Fig. 8.8: Simulink diagram `CruisePI.mdl` for cruise control simulations.

during the simulation. There is no road slope disturbance, and the car is commanded to change speed from $\bar{v}(t) = 0$ m/s to $\bar{v}(t) = 3$ m/s, or, equivalently, from $v(t) = 30$ m/s to $v(t) = 33$ m/s.

The three speed tracking responses corresponding to the three PI controllers with $k_p = 500$ and three values of $k_i = 0, 100, 500$ are shown in Figure 8.9. The left graph is the velocity graph $v(t)$, the middle one is the error graph $e(t)$, and the one on the right is the control force graph $f(t)$. The $k_i = 0$ response is shown in pink; it rises from $v(0) = 30$ m/s exponentially with time constant τ computed based on Equation 8.34,

$$\tau = \frac{m}{m\bar{c} + k_p} = \frac{1929}{(1929)(0.02) + 500} = 3.58 \text{ s}$$

to the steady state $v(t) = 32.785$ m/s with a steady-state error, $e_{ss} = 0.215$ m/s, as calculated in Equation 8.36.

The $k_i = 100$ and $k_i = 500$ responses are shown in blue and black, respectively—they all converge to the steady state $v(t) = 33$ m/s with zero steady-state error as expected. The damping ratio and natural frequency pair (ς, ω_n) associated with the $k_i = 100$ and $k_i = 500$ designs are $(0.613, 0.228 \text{ rad/s})$ and $(0.274, 0.509 \text{ rad/s})$, respectively; hence, the $k_i = 500$ response has larger maximum overshoot and shorter oscillation period than the $k_i = 100$ response. It also can be seen that the $k_i = 500$ design requires a larger swing of control force

$$-220 \text{ N} < f(t) < 3000 \text{ N}$$

than the $k_i = 100$ design. ∎

The closed-loop system simulation results shown in Figure 8.9 are obtained by running the following MATLAB program: CSDfig8p9.m, which will automatically call the Simulink model program CruisePI.mdl, to conduct the simulation. The plotting program, Plot3C.m will also be called to plot the figures. The MATLAB code is listed as follows.

```
% CSDfig8p9.m  Cruise PI cntrl, BC Chang, Drexel University, 8/10/2019
% MATLAB R2015a or later. CSDfig8p9.m will call CruisePI.mdl to conduct
% simulation and use Plot3C.m to plot Fig8.9
% Gravity: g=9.8 m/s^2
% Vehicle Data: (A typical mid-size SUV like Lexus R350)
% Mass: m=1929 Kg
% Drag coefficient:  Cd = 0.35
% Front surface area:  A=(width)*(height)=(1.8)*(1.67)=3 m^2
% Drag force Fd = 0.5*rho*Cd*A*v^2 := c*v^2,
```

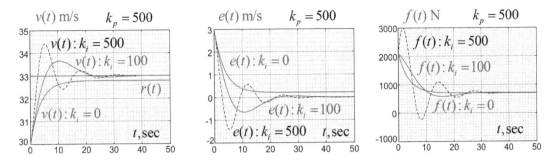

Fig. 8.9: Speed $R_v = 3$ m/s tracking responses with $k_p = 500$ and three values of $k_i = 0, 100, 500$.

```
% where v is the velocity,  c is the viscosity coefficient
% Thus,   c = 0.5*rho*Cd*A, where rho = air density = 1.225 Kg/m^3
% c = 0.5*rho*Cd*A = 0.5*1.225*0.35*3 = 0.643 Kg/m
% Choose the nominal operating equilibrium at
% v_n = 30 m/s,   which is 108 Km/Hr, or 64.8 miles/hr
% f_n = c*(v_n)^2 = 0.643*(30^2) = 578.7 N
% Hence,  c_bar =(2c/m)*v_n = 2*0.643*30/1929 = 0.02
  m = 1929, c_bar = 0.02 , g = 9.8, v_n = 30, f_n = 594.2, kp=500
%Initialization
  tau=0, R0=v_n*0.1, Slope_deg=0, Slope_rad=Slope_deg*pi/180,
%% 1st Run Simulation
  ki = 0, sim_time=50,
  sim_options=simset('SrcWorkspace', 'current','DstWorkspace', 'current');
  open('CruisePI'); sim('CruisePI', [0,sim_time], sim_options);
  run('Plot3C')
%% 2nd Run Simulation
  ki=100, sim_time=50,
  sim_options=simset('SrcWorkspace', 'current', 'DstWorkspace', 'current');
  open('CruisePI'); sim('CruisePI', [0,sim_time], sim_options);
  run('Plot3A'),
%% 3rd Run Simulation
  ki = 500, sim_time=50,
  sim_options=simset('SrcWorkspace', 'current', 'DstWorkspace', 'current');
  open('CruisePI'); sim('CruisePI', [0,sim_time], sim_options);
  run('Plot3B')
```

Example 8.7 (Road Slope $\theta_d = 0.0873$ rad Disturbance Responses with $k_p = 500$ and Three Values of $k_i = 0, 100, 500$)

The same PI controllers of Example 8.6 will be employed in the following simulation to maintain the vehicle speed at the equilibrium speed $v^* = 30$ m/s under the influence of road slope disturbance $\theta(t) = \theta_d u_s(t)$, where $\theta_d = 0.0873$ rad.

The three road slope disturbance responses corresponding to the three PI controllers with $k_p = 500$ and three values of $k_i = 0, 100, 500$ are shown in Figure 8.10. The $k_i = 0$ response is shown in pink; it drops from $v(0) = 30$ m/s exponentially, with the same time constant $\tau = 3.58$ s, as computed in Example 8.6, to the steady state $v(t) = 26.936$ m/s with a steady-state error, $e_{ss} = 3.064$ m/s, as calculated in Equation 8.37. It also can be seen from the graph that the steady-state force required to achieve this steady-state velocity is approximately 2100 N, which can be verified by the following

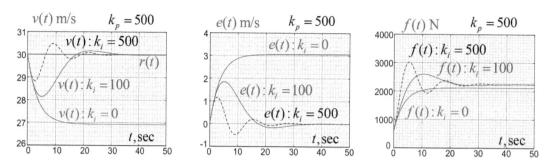

Fig. 8.10: Road slope $\theta_d = 0.0873$ rad disturbance response with $k_p = 500$ and three values of $k_i = 0, 100, 500$.

computations. From Equation 8.33 with $\bar{r}(t) = 0$ and $\theta_d = 0.0873$ rad $= 5°$, we have the force at steady state as

$$f(t) = f^* + \bar{f}(t) = f^* + \frac{mgk_p(0.0832)}{m\bar{c} + k_p} = 578.7 + \frac{(1929)(9.8)(500)(0.0832)}{(1929)(0.02) + 500} = 2111 \text{ N}$$

The $k_i = 100$ and $k_i = 500$ responses are shown in black and blue, respectively—they all converge back to steady state $v(t) = 30$ m/s with zero steady-state error as expected. The damping ratio and natural frequency pair (ς, ω_n) associated with the $k_i = 100$ and $k_i = 500$ designs are the same as those shown in Example 8.6; hence, the $k_i = 500$ response has larger maximum overshoot and shorter oscillation period than the $k_i = 100$ response. It also can be seen that the $k_i = 500$ design requires a larger swing of control force

$$578.7 \text{ N} < f(t) < 3000 \text{ N}$$

than the $k_i = 100$ design. ■

The closed-loop system simulation results shown in Figure 8.10 are obtained by running the following MATLAB program: CSDfig8p10.m, which will automatically call the Simulink model program CruisePI.mdl, to conduct the simulation. The plotting program, Plot3C.m will also be called to plot the figures. The MATLAB code is listed as follows. Note that this program is the same as CSDfig8p9.m, except the Initialization line where R0 and Slope_deg are changed to 0 and 5, respectively.

```
% CSDfig8p10.m  Cruise PI cntrl, BC Chang, Drexel University, 8/10/2019
 % MATLAB R2015a or later. CSDfig8p10.m will call CruisePI.mdl to conduct
 % simulation and use Plot3C.m to plot Fig8.10
    :
    :
%Initialization
    tau=0,  R0=v_n*0,  Slope_deg=5,  Slope_rad=Slope_deg*pi/180
    :
    :
```

Example 8.8 (Speed $R_v = 3$ m/s Step Tracking Responses with $\varsigma = 0.707$ and Three Values of $\omega_n = 0.25, 0.5, 1$ rad/s.)

The speed tracking control simulation to be considered here is the same as that conducted in Example 8.6, except that the PI controller parameters k_p and k_i are chosen based on the desired damping ratio

ς and natural frequency ω_n for the closed-loop system.

Recall that from Equation 8.30, we have the following relationship equation between (k_p, k_i) and (ς, ω_n):

$$\omega_n^2 = k_i/m \qquad\qquad k_i = m\omega_n^2$$
$$\longrightarrow \qquad (8.38)$$
$$2\varsigma\omega_n = \bar{c} + k_p/m \qquad\qquad k_p = m(2\varsigma\omega_n - \bar{c})$$

Based on Equation 8.38 and the vehicle data, $m = 1929$ kg and $\bar{c} = 0.02s^{-1}$, we obtain the three (k_p, k_i) pairs associated with the three (ς, ω_n) pairs as follows:

$$\varsigma = 0.707, \ \omega_n = 0.25 \text{ rad/s} \ \rightleftarrows \ k_p = 643.3, \ k_i = 120.6$$
$$\varsigma = 0.707, \ \omega_n = 0.5 \text{ rad/s} \ \rightleftarrows \ k_p = 1325, \ k_i = 482.3$$
$$\varsigma = 0.707, \ \omega_n = 1 \text{ rad/s} \ \rightleftarrows \ k_p = 2689, \ k_i = 1929$$

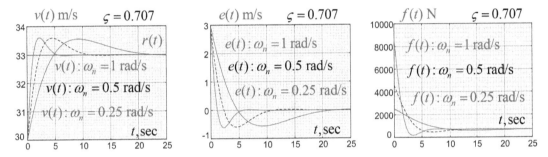

Fig. 8.11: Speed $R_v = 3$ m/s tracking responses with $\varsigma = 0.707$ and three values of $\omega_n = 0.25, 0.5, 1$ rad/s.

The three speed tracking responses corresponding to the three PI controllers associated with $\varsigma = 0.707$ and three values of $\omega_n = 0.25, 0.5, 1$ are shown in Figure 8.11. All three have perfect steady-state speed tracking with zero steady-state error. They also have the same maximum overshoots since all the three closed-loop systems have the same damping ratio. However, they differ in rise time and settling time. The system with larger ω_n will have faster transient response. The speed track response associated with $\omega_n = 1$ rad/s is shown in pink, which is the most aggressive one with quickest time response. However, the pink one requires much more control force (above 8000 N) than the other two designs (4500 N and 2500 N). ∎

The closed-loop system simulation results shown in Figure 8.11 are obtained by running the following MATLAB program: CSDfig8p11.m, which will automatically call the Simulink model program CruisePI.mdl, to conduct the simulation. The plotting program, Plot3A.m will also be called to plot the figures. The MATLAB code is listed as follows. Note that this program is the same as CSDfig8p9.m, except the six lines shown in the following list.

```
% CSDfig8p11.m  Cruise PI cntrl, BC Chang, Drexel University, 8/10/2019
 % MATLAB R2015a or later. CSDfig8p11.m will call CruisePI.mdl to conduct
 % simulation and use PlotA.m to plot Fig8.11
    :
%% 1st Run Simulation
  ze=0.707, wn=0.25, ki = m*wn^2, kp=m*(2*ze*wn-c_bar),
    :
```

```
run('Plot3A'),
%% 2nd Run Simulation
ze=0.707, wn=0.5, ki = m*wn^2, kp=m*(2*ze*wn-c_bar),
  :
run('Plot3B'),
%% 3rd Run Simulation
ze=0.707, wn=1, ki = m*wn^2, kp=m*(2*ze*wn-c_bar),
  :
run('Plot3C')
```

Example 8.9 (Road Slope $\theta_d = 0.0873$ rad Disturbance Response with $\varsigma = 0.707$ and Three Values of $\omega_n = 0.25, 0.5, 1$ rad/s)

The same PI controllers of Example 8.8, designed based on the damping ratio and natural frequency, will be employed in the following simulation to maintain the vehicle speed at the equilibrium speed $v^* = 30$ m/s under the influence of road slope disturbance $\theta(t) = \theta_d u_s(t)$, where $\theta_d = 0.0873$ rad.

The three road slope disturbance responses corresponding to the three PI controllers designed based on $\varsigma = 0.707$ and three values of $\omega_n = 0.25, 0.5, 1$ rad/s are shown in Figure 8.12. All three responses dip right after the disturbance occurs, then reverse and recover to the nominal speed with no steady-state error. However, the $\omega_n = 1$ rad/s response (in pink) recovers faster than the other two designs. All three requires the same maximum control force $f(t)$, 2,600 N, but the pink one demands $f(t)$ to act faster. ∎

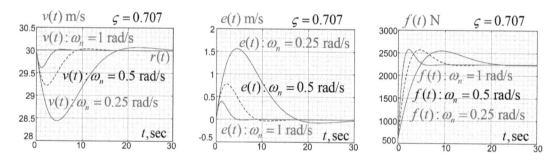

Fig. 8.12: Road slope $\theta_d = 0.0873$ rad disturbance response with $\varsigma = 0.707$ and three values of $\omega_n = 0.25, 0.5, 1$ rad/s.

8.2.4 Robustness to Model Uncertainty

In general, the dynamics model employed in the design of control system is not exactly the same as the practical system. The discrepancy may come from the unmodeled dynamics, uncertainties, and perturbations due to the change of environment. Therefore, **a well-designed control system is required to be robust against the foreseeable uncertainties and perturbations in the plant dynamics.**

Recall that in the cruise control system design subsection, Section 8.2.2, we employed $G_E(s) = 1$ as the ideal dynamics model of the engine, which is a good approximation of the second-order engine dynamics model,

$$G_E(s) = \frac{1}{(\tau s + 1)^2} \tag{8.39}$$

if the time constant τ is close to zero. However, the time constant will not be zero in reality, and so it is important to know how robust the system will be against the variation of τ. **In the following two examples, we will evaluate the robustness of two PI controller designs considered in Section 8.2.3.**

Example 8.10 (Robustness Evaluation of the PI Controller Design Based on $\varsigma = 0.707$ and $\omega_n = 1$ rad/s.)

In this example, we will conduct simulations to evaluate the robustness of the more aggressive controller design considered in Example 8.8, which is the PI controller designed based on damping ratio $\varsigma = 0.707$ and natural frequency $\omega_n = 1$ rad/s.

The simulations are similar to those conducted in Example 8.8, except that **the unmodeled engine dynamics shown in Equation 8.39 is employed to evaluate how the variation of the time constant τ in Equation 8.39 will affect the closed-loop system performance. The simulation results are shown in Figure 8.13.** There are three speed tracking responses shown in the figure. The response curve in blue color with $\tau = 0$ is exactly the same as the pink response in Figure 8.11 where the engine dynamics model was assumed ideal, $G_E(s) = 1$. The $\tau = 0.3$ s response shown in black color is apparently worse than the blue one. It has larger overshoot and more oscillations. If the time constant is increased to $\tau = 0.6$ s, the response will deteriorate to the response curve in pink whose oscillation amplitude is growing with time; that is, the system becomes unstable!   ∎

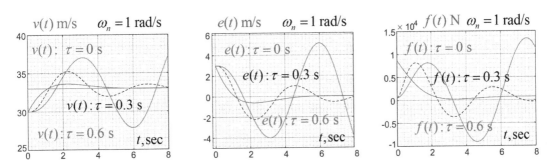

Fig. 8.13: Robustness evaluation of the cruise control system with the PI controller designed based on $\varsigma = 0.707$ and $\omega_n = 1$ rad/s.

The closed-loop system simulation results shown in Figure 8.13 are obtained by running the following MATLAB program: CSDfig8p13.m, which will automatically call the Simulink model program CruisePI.mdl, to conduct the simulation. The plotting program, Plot3A.m will also be called to plot the figures. The MATLAB code is listed as follows. Note that this program is the same as CSDfig8p11.m, except the six lines shown in the following list.

```
% CSDfig8p13.m  Cruise PI cntrl, BC Chang, Drexel University, 8/10/2019
 % MATLAB R2015a or later. CSDfig8p13.m will call CruisePI.mdl to conduct
 % simulation and use Plot3A.m to plot Fig8.13
     :
%% 1st Run Simulation
 tau=0, ze=0.707, wn=1, ki = m*wn^2, kp=m*(2*ze*wn-c_bar),
 % Simulation
 sim_time=8,
     :
```

```
%% 2nd Run Simulation
  tau=0.3, ze=0.707, wn=1, ki = m*wn^2, kp=m*(2*ze*wn-c_bar),
% Simulation
  sim_time=8,
     :
%% 3rd Run Simulation
  tau=0.6, ze=0.707, wn=1, ki = m*wn^2, kp=m*(2*ze*wn-c_bar),
% Simulation
  sim_time=8
     :
```

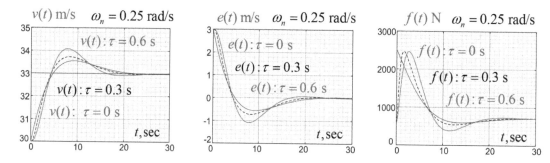

Fig. 8.14: Robustness evaluation of the cruise control system with the PI controller designed based on $\varsigma = 0.707$ and $\omega_n = 0.25$ rad/s.

In the next example, we will evaluate the robustness of the cruise control system with a less aggressive PI controller. Usually a less aggressive controller has a better robustness although it may not have an optimal performance for the nominal system.

Example 8.11 (Robustness Evaluation of the PI Controller Design Based on $\varsigma = 0.707$ and $\omega_n = 0.25$ rad/s.)

In this example, we will conduct simulations to evaluate the robustness of the less aggressive controller design considered in Example 8.8, which is the PI controller designed based on damping ratio $\varsigma = 0.707$ and natural frequency $\omega_n = 0.25$ rad/s. **Note that the natural frequency chosen in this example is only 25% of that chosen by the aggressive controller in Example 8.10.**

The simulations are similar to those conducted in Example 8.10, except that the PI controller is designed based on damping ratio $\varsigma = 0.707$ and natural frequency $\omega_n = 0.25$ rad/s. The simulation results are shown in Figure 8.14. There are three speed tracking responses shown in the figure. The response curve in blue color with $\tau = 0$ is exactly the same as the blue response in Figure 8.11 where the engine dynamics model was assumed ideal, $G_E(s) = 1$. The $\tau = 0.3$s and $\tau = 0.6$s responses in Figure 8.14 are in black and pink, respectively. Both are worse than the blue one. However, they remain stable. **This less aggressive (or more conservative) controller design has better robustness against unmodeled dynamics than the aggressive one.** ∎

Remark 8.12 (Trade-Off Between Performance and Robustness)

The essential lesson learned from Examples 8.10 and 8.11 is that pushing for high performance often leads to a non-robust result. If we choose to go with the robust design, that is the least aggressive controller, we have relatively poor performance, as can be seen in Figures 8.11 and 8.12. However, the controller is more robust. Performance degrades with the perturbed engine dynamics, but still workable. **In general, the trade-off between performance and robustness needs to be evaluated in the overall context of the controller design. If high performance is desired, then accurate models are required. If system parameters will change with environment or age, then robustness becomes essential.** ■

8.2.5 Disturbance Feed-Forward Compensation

One approach to performance enhancement is to add *disturbance feedforward* while using the robust control. Disturbance feed-forward is based on the notion of sensing the disturbance, in this case road slope, and taking action immediately rather than waiting to respond to error. The sensed signal is used to provide a control command that is added directly to the control input. Such a configuration is shown in Figure 8.15. Including the engine dynamics (G_E) and the feed-forward compensator (G_f), the system error response is given by

$$E(s) = \frac{1}{1 + (1/m)K(s)G_E(s)G_p(s)}\bar{V}(s) + \frac{((1/m)G_f(s)G_E(s) - g)G_p(s)}{1 + (1/m)K(s)G_E(s)G_p(s)}\Theta(s) \tag{8.40}$$

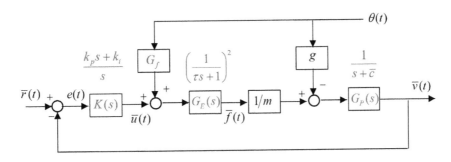

Fig. 8.15: Cruise control block diagram with disturbance feed-forward compensation.

Note that the feed-forward transfer function G_f can include control enhancement and/or filter elements as well as sensor dynamics. **G_f will alter the zeros of the disturbance to error transfer function but will not affect the poles. Consequently, it has no effect on system stability.** Figure 8.16 illustrates the effect of feed-forward.

The error response due to a road slope step disturbance is illustrated using the less aggressive ($\varsigma = 0.707, \omega_n = 0.25$ rad/s) controller with slow ($\tau = 0.6$ s) engine dynamics with feed-forward compensation $G_f = 0.5mg$ (the purple response, note that m and g are the mass and the gravity, respectively) and without feed-forward $G_f = 0$ (the black response). The blue color response, which assumes ideal engine ($\tau = 0$) and no feed-forward compensation $G_f = 0$, is included to show that the response will deteriorate, as shown in black for the slow engine $\tau = 0.6$ s. Whereas feedback allows the control designer to alter the system poles that determine the damping ratio and natural frequency, feed-forward does not. However, feed-forward does alter the zeros of the transfer function $G_{E\Theta}(s)$ from disturbance to error. The effect of that, in this case, is to reduce the effect on peak overshoot and undershoot.

If G_f is chosen as $G_f = mg$, the disturbance response would have perfect cancellation for the case of ideal ($\tau = 0$ s) engine. However, it would cause more oscillation in disturbance response for the case of a slow engine with $\tau = 0.6$ s. For this reason, a compromise choice $G_f = 0.5mg$ was adopted in the simulation of Figure 8.16.

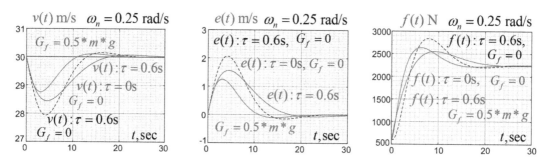

Fig. 8.16: Comparison of the three step responses due to a road slope disturbance.

8.3 Root Locus Preliminaries

The classical approach to feedback controller design involves two basic steps. First, choose a compensator of a particular structure, (i.e., select a compensator transfer function). There are a number of commonly used compensator transfer functions, four of which we have already seen: the integral compensator in Example 5.26, the proportional compensator in Example 8.1, the dual-loop feedback controller in Example 6.1, and the PI controller in Section 8.2. **Each compensator or controller has a number of free design parameters that need to be determined to meet the demands of the system performance goals. The root locus method is an approach to selecting those parameters to achieve desired transient performance of the closed-loop system.**

The root locus approach usually begins with a typical feedback control system structure, as shown in Figure 8.17, where $G(s)$ is a fixed dynamics model consisting of both the plant and the controller dynamics, and K is a design parameter to be determined to locate a desired feasible pole locations in the complex plane. **The root locus approach shows a portrait of how the closed-loop system poles move through the complex plane as the parameter K varies from 0 to ∞.** The closed-loop characteristic equation of the following form is called a *typical root locus equation*.

$$1 + KG(s) = 1 + K\frac{N(s)}{D(s)} = 0 \tag{8.41a}$$

where

$$\frac{N(s)}{D(s)} = \frac{s^m + b_{m-1}s^{m-1} + \cdots + b_1 s + b_0}{s^n + a_{n-1}s^{n-1} + \cdots + a_1 s + a_0} = \frac{(s-z_1)(s-z_2)\cdots(s-z_m)}{(s-p_1)(s-p_2)\cdots(s-p_m)} \tag{8.41b}$$

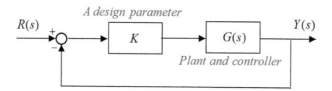

Fig. 8.17: A typical feedback control system block diagram for root locus analysis and design.

Note that the **design parameter** K in Equation 8.41 is a scalar parameter instead of $K(s)$, which usually represents the transfer function of a controller. In some applications, the control system structure may not match the structure shown in Figure 8.17 and the closed-loop characteristic equation is not in the form of typical root locus equation. **In this case, if the closed-loop characteristic polynomial is a linear function of the parameter K, then the closed-loop characteristic equation can be converted into the form of typical root locus equation as shown in Example 8.13.**

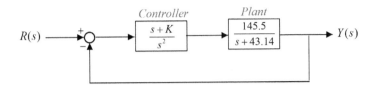

Fig. 8.18: A controller design candidate suitable for the root locus approach.

Example 8.13 (Convert a Closed-Loop Characteristic Equation Into the Form of the Typical Root Locus Equation)

Consider the feedback control system shown in Figure 8.18. Recall that this problem originating from the ramp input tracking control problem of Example 8.3. In order to achieve steady-state ramp function tracking, the loop transfer function needs to include the internal model $1/s^2$. But just setting the controller to $K(s) = 1/s^2$ is not good enough since the closed-loop system will not be stable. Hence, the controller is chosen to be $K(s) = (s+K)/s^2$, as shown in Figure 8.18, where K is a free design parameter to be determined so that closed-loop system is stable and the transient response is optimized, subject to control-input constraints.

The closed-loop characteristic equation is

$$1 + \frac{(s+K)}{s^2} \frac{145.5}{s+43.14} = 0$$

which is not a typical root locus equation. But the characteristic polynomial equation

$$s^3 + 43.14s^2 + 145.5s + 145.5K = 0$$

can be rearranged into

$$1 + K\frac{145.5}{s^3 + 43.14s^2 + 145.5s} = 1 + KG(s) = 0 \tag{8.42}$$

which now is a typical root locus equation.   ∎

Note that the closed-loop system in Figure 8.18 and the closed-loop system in Figure 8.17 with $G(s)$ defined by Equation 8.42 are not identical, but they share the same closed-loop system poles. Hence, Equation 8.42 can be employed to place the closed-loop system poles for the system of Figure 8.18.

Definition 8.14 (Loop Transfer Function and LTF Poles and Zeros)

In the root locus equation, Equation 8.41, $1 + KG(s) = 0$, $KG(s)$ is referred as the loop transfer function (LTF), and the poles and zeros of $KG(s)$ as LTF poles and LTF zeros, respectively.

Remark 8.15 (Loop Transfer Function and LTF Poles and Zeros)

The $KG(s)$ of the root locus equation, Equation 8.41, $1 + KG(s) = 0$, is also referred as the open-loop transfer function, and consequently, the poles and zeros of $KG(s)$ are regarded as the open-loop poles and zeros in the literature. These terminologies make sense for simple cases like the one shown in Figure 8.17. But for more general cases like the one in Figure 8.18, and another one in Figure 8.38, which will be introduced later in this chapter, these terminologies will become misleading and confusing since **the open-loop poles and zeros in general are not the same as the LTF poles and zeros of** $KG(s)$. ■

A Trivial Root Locus Analysis and Design Problem

Before we start to learn how to draw root loci diagrams using the root loci construction rules, we will consider a trivial second-order system by which its root loci diagram can be easily constructed and then be employed to demonstrate the basic concept of root locus analysis and design. Furthermore, this simple system can also serve as the first example to verify the root loci construction rules, which will be introduced shortly.

Consider the feedback control system in Figure 8.17 with $G(s) = 1/(s^2 + 4s + 3)$. The characteristic equation is

$$1 + K \frac{1}{s^2 + 4s + 3} = 0 \quad \rightleftarrows \quad s^2 + 4s + 3 + K = 0$$

whose two roots are

$$\begin{matrix} s_1 \\ s_2 \end{matrix} = \frac{1}{2}\left(-4 \pm \sqrt{4^2 - 4(3+K)}\right) = -2 \pm \sqrt{1-K} \tag{8.43}$$

Table 8.1: The roots of the characteristic equation $s^2 + 4s + 3 + K = 0$ as K varies from 0 to ∞.

K	$K=0$	$K=0.75$	$K=1$	$K=1.25$	$K=5$	$K \to \infty$
s_1	-1	-1.5	-2	$-2+j0.5$	$-2+j2$	$-2+j\infty$
s_2	-3	-3.5	-2	$-2-j0.5$	$-2-j2$	$-2-j\infty$

The trajectories of the roots for $0 \le K < \infty$ are called the root loci of the system. Based on Equation 8.43 we can construct Table 8.1 that lists how the values of the two roots vary as K changes from 0 to ∞, which in turn can be used to draw the root loci of the system, as shown in Figure 8.19.

From either the root loci or the table, it can be seen that when $K = 0$ the two roots are $s = -1$ and $s = -3$, which are the two poles of $G(s) = 1/(s+1)(s+3)$. As K increases, the two roots move on the real axis towards each other until they meet at $s = -2$ when $K = 1$. When K is changing from $K = 1$ to $K > 1$, the double roots split into two complex conjugate roots $-2 \pm j\omega$. The point $s = -1$ is called a break-out point, and after the roots break away from the real axis, the two roots will continue to stay on the two vertical straight lines, one going up and the other down all the way to infinity when $K \to \infty$.

This simple root loci diagram can be employed to place the closed-loop system poles at desired feasible locations. For example, if we would like the closed-loop system to have a damping ratio $\varsigma = 0.707$, we can draw a $\varsigma = \cos 45°$ blue dash line, as shown in Figure 8.19. Then the intersection point will give the closed-loop system pole locations at $s = -2 \pm j2$, and reveal the damping ratio, natural frequency, and the value of K.

8.3.1 Root Loci Construction Rules

For the previous example, which is a second-order system with a design parameter K, it is easy to solve for the two roots as functions of K and then the trajectories of the roots (i.e., the root loci) can be drawn

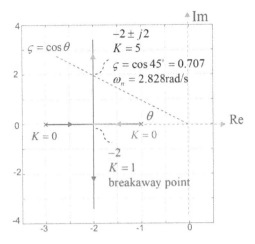

Fig. 8.19: Root loci of the simple system.

accordingly on the complex plane. But this trivial approach is not viable for high-order systems. The root locus approach is one of the main classical control tools in the analysis and design of control systems. It provides a set of root loci construction rules that make the sketch of root loci possible for high order systems without computing the roots. **More importantly, it sheds light on how the pole-zero pattern of $G(s)$ affects the root loci of $1 + KG(s) = 0$, which is very helpful in determining the structure of the controller.** In this subsection we will demonstrate how to apply the root loci construction rules without explaining the detailed theory.

Consider the feedback control system as shown in Figure 8.20. The *loop transfer function* of the system is

$$K \frac{s+3}{s(s+1)(s+2)(s+4)}$$

which is the product of the transfer functions of the plant, the controller, and the sensor. Note that the design parameter K is a part of the controller. Hence, the *characteristic equation* of the closed-loop system is

$$1 + K\frac{s+3}{s(s+1)(s+2)(s+4)} = 1 + KG(s) = 0 \qquad (8.44)$$

which is equivalent to the following characteristic equation in polynomial form,

$$s(s+1)(s+2)(s+4) + K(s+3) = 0 \qquad (8.45)$$

The objective is to find out how the closed-loop system poles vary on the complex plane as K increases from $K = 0$ to $K = \infty$. Note that the closed-loop system poles are the roots of the closed-loop characteristic equation shown in Equations 8.44 and 8.45. They are NOT the poles of the loop transfer function $KG(s)$ unless $K = 0$.

From Equation 8.45, it can be seen that at $K = 0$ the closed-loop system poles are the poles of the loop transfer function, $s = 0, -1, -2, -4$. Notice that in Figure 8.21 each loop transfer function pole is indicated by a cross $\times$ and the single zero of the loop transfer function is represented by a circle $\circ$ at $s = -3$.

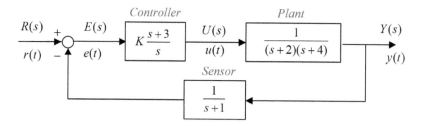

Fig. 8.20: An introductory root loci construction example.

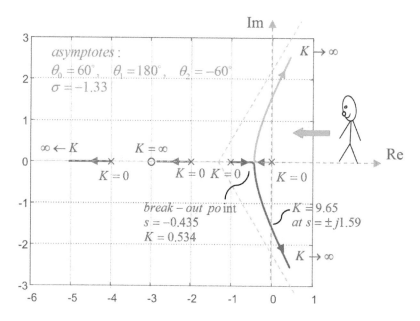

Fig. 8.21: Root loci sketch of the introductory example.

Now, we will sketch the root loci of the system of Equation 8.44 following the basic root loci construction rules. The detailed explanation and theorem related to these rules will be given later in the chapter.

Root Loci Construction Rules

Rule 1: *Number of Branches.* The number of branches of the root loci is **equal to the number of the loop transfer function poles.**

For the introductory example, there are four branches since the loop transfer function has four poles.

Rule 2: *Symmetry.* The root loci **are symmetric about the real axis.**

The root loci are symmetrical with respect to the real axis since the roots are either real numbers or conjugate complex numbers.

Rule 3: *Starting and Ending Points.* **Each branch begins** $(K = 0)$ **at an LTF pole and ends** $(K \to \infty)$ **at an LTF zero or at infinity.** Here, the LTF poles stand for the poles of the loop transfer function $KG(s)$ in the root locus equation $1 + KG(s)$. The LTF zeros are defined similarly.

The start point $K = 0$ points are at the LTF poles $s = 0, -1, -2, -4$. One of the $K = \infty$ end point is at the LTF zero $s = -3$, and the other three $K = \infty$ end points will be at the infinity, defined by the asymptotes given by Rule 5.

Rule 4: *Real Axis Segments.* **For $K > 0$, if the total number of real poles and zeros to the right of a point on the real axis is odd, this point lies on the root loci.**

As seen from Figure 8.21, assume a man is walking on the real axis line toward the left from a very right end with no pole or zero behind him. There would be no root loci until he encounters the first pole or zero to begin with the first root loci segment on the real axis. The first segment will end when the person meets the second pole or zero. Hence, the root loci will alternate on and off successively until the negative infinity end of the real axis. For this example, there are three real axis segments: between $s = 0$ and $s = -1$, between $s = -2$ and $s = -3$, and from $s = -4$ all the way to $s = -\infty$.

Rule 5: *Behavior at Infinity.* **The root loci branches that tend to infinity do so along asymptotes with angles θ, and these asymptotes all intersect at a common point σ, on the real axis as defined by:**

$$\theta_\ell = \frac{(2\ell + 1)\pi}{n - m}, \quad \ell = 0, 1, 2, \cdots, n - m - 1; \qquad \sigma = \frac{b_{m-1} - a_{n-1}}{n - m} = \frac{\sum_j p_j - \sum_i z_i}{n - m}$$

For this introductory example, there will be three asymptotes. The angles of these three asymptotes and the intersection of these asymptotes with the real axis are

$$\theta_0 = \tfrac{\pi}{4-1} = \tfrac{\pi}{3} = 60°, \quad \theta_1 = \tfrac{3\pi}{4-1} = \pi = 180°, \quad \theta_2 = \tfrac{5\pi}{4-1} = \tfrac{5\pi}{3} = -60°$$

$$\sigma = \tfrac{0 + (-1) + (-2) + (-4) - (-3)}{4 - 1} = \tfrac{-4}{3} = -1.33$$

The three asymptotes are shown in dashed yellow lines in the graph.

Rule 6: *Real Axis BreakOut and BreakIn Points.* **The root locus breaks out from the real axis where the gain K is a (local) maximum on the real axis, and breaks in to the real axis where K is a (local) minimum.**

To locate candidate break points simply solve

$$\frac{d}{ds}\left(\frac{1}{G(s)}\right) = 0 \quad or \quad N(s)\frac{dD(s)}{ds} - \frac{dN(s)}{ds}D(s) = 0$$

where $G(s) = N(s)/D(s)$, and then find the value of K at the break point by

$$K = \frac{1}{|G(s)|}$$

In Figure 8.21, the root loci on the second and the third real axis segments will stay on their respective segments for all values of K. The only break-out point will occur at the first real axis segment between $s = 0$ and $s = -1$. Since $N(s) = s + 3$ and $D(s) = s^4 + 7s^3 + 14s^2 + 8s$, we have

$$N(s)\frac{dD(s)}{ds} - \frac{dN(s)}{ds}D(s) = 0 \quad \to \quad 3s^4 + 26s^3 + 77s^2 + 84s + 24 = 0$$

and its roots at $-3.311 \pm j0.68124$, -1.6097, and -0.43492. Hence, the break-out point occurs at

$$s = -0.43492.$$

The value of K at the break-out point can be computed from the following.

$$K = \left| \frac{1}{G(-0.43492)} \right| = 0.53459$$

Rule 7: *Imaginary Axis Crossings.* **Use the Routh stability test to determine values of K for which loci cross the imaginary axis.**

The characteristic equation of Equation 8.45 can be rewritten as the following polynomial equation:

$$s^4 + 7s^3 + 14s^2 + (8+K)s + 3K = 0 \qquad (8.46)$$

The Routh array for this characteristic equation is constructed as follows:

$$
\begin{array}{ll}
s^4 & 1 \quad\quad 14 \quad\quad 3K \\
s^3 & 7 \quad\quad 8+K \\
s^2 & b_1 \quad\quad 3K \\
s^1 & c_1 \\
s^0 & 3K
\end{array}
\qquad \text{where} \qquad
\begin{cases}
b_1 = \frac{1}{7}(90 - K) \\
c_1 = \frac{-1}{90-K}\left(K^2 + 65K - 720\right)
\end{cases}
$$

According to the Routh-Hurwitz criterion, the system is stable if and only if the first-column elements of the Routh array are all strictly positive. Hence, the system is stable if and only if all the following three inequalities are satisfied:

$$K > 0, \quad 90 - K > 0, \quad \text{and} \quad K^2 + 65K - 720 < 0$$

which is equivalent to

$$0 < K < 9.6456$$

Hence, when $K = 9.6456$, two of the root loci branches cross the imaginary axis. The intersection points can be computed from the auxiliary equation,

$$b_1 s^2 + 3K = 11.4792 s^2 + 28.9368 = 0 \quad \rightarrow \quad s = \pm j1.588$$

Therefore, when $K = 9.6456$ the root loci intersect the imaginary axis at $s = \pm j1.588$. Up to now, with the information obtained from Rule 1 to Rule 7, we are able to complete the root loci diagram sketch in Figure 8.21 for the introductory root loci example without the need of Rule 8.

Rule 8: *Angle of Departure from Poles or Angle of Arrival to Zeros.* **Assume $\bar{s}$ is at the vicinity of any LTF pole or zero, pz, then the angle of departure from or the angle of arrival to pz, $\angle(\bar{s} - pz)$, can be computed from the following equation:**

$$G(\bar{s}) = \sum_{i=1}^{m} \angle(\bar{s} - z_i) - \sum_{j=1}^{n} \angle(\bar{s} - p_j) = (2\ell + 1)\pi \qquad 0 \leq K < \infty$$

Example 8.16 (Angle of Departure from a Complex Pole on a Root Loci)

Assume the LTF poles and zero shown on the root loci diagram of Figure 8.22 are $p_1 = 0$, $p_2 = j1$, $p_3 = -j1$, $p_4 = -3$, and $z_1 = -1$, and a complex number $\bar{s}$ is at the vicinity of p_2. Then the angle of departure from p_2, $\angle(\bar{s} - p_2)$ can be computed from

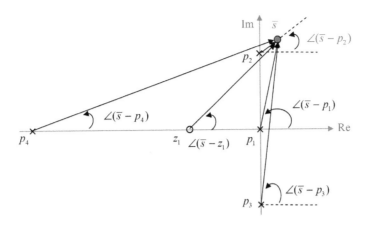

Fig. 8.22: An example demonstrating angle of departure.

$$\angle(\bar{s}-z_1)-\angle(\bar{s}-p_1)-\angle(\bar{s}-p_2)-\angle(\bar{s}-p_3)-\angle(\bar{s}-p_4)=(2\ell+1)\pi$$

which can be rewritten as follows:

$$\angle(\bar{s}-p_2)=\angle(p_2-z_1)-\angle(p_2-p_1)-\angle(p_2-p_3)-\angle(p_2-p_4)-(2\ell+1)\pi$$

Notice that the $\bar{s}$ on the right-hand side of the equation has been replaced by p_2 since $\bar{s}$ and p_2 are virtually the same point observed from far away. Therefore, the angle of departure from p_2 is

$$\angle(\bar{s}-p_2)=45°-90°-90°-18.4°+180°=26.6°$$

With this LTF pole-zero pattern, there are four root loci branches. One started from $p_1=0$ moving to the left and ended at the zero $z_1=-1$. The second branch begins at $p_4=-3$, heading to the left on the negative real axis all the way to the $180°$ asymptote. The other two of the four branches will depart from poles $p_2=j1$ and $p_3=-j1$ with the angles of departure, $26.6°$ and $-26.6°$, respectively, into the right half plane. Since the other two of the three asymptotes are heading into the right half of the complex plane with $\pm60°$ angles, the two branches leaving from $p_2=j1$ and $p_3=-j1$ will merge to the two asymptotes, and have no chance to turn around going back to the left half of the complex plane. **Hence, there exists no value of $K>0$ so that the closed-loop system can be stable. We will address this issue later in Section 8.5 regarding a sinusoidal position tracking problem. One remedy is to add LTF zeros on the negative real axis to change the departure angle and the asymptotes.** ∎

For the introductory example, all the LTF poles and zero are on the three real axis segments. It is easy to see on the first segment the angle of departure from the pole at $s=0$ will be $180°$ since the root trajectory of this branch has to go to the left to cover this part of root loci according to Rule 4. For the same reason, the angle of departure for the pole at $s=-1$ will be $0°$. In the following example, we will verify the departure angles of these two poles.

Example 8.17 (Angle of Departure from the Real Poles on the Introductory Root Loci)

The LTF pole-zero pattern of the introductory root loci example is shown again in Figure 8.23, where $p_1=0$, $p_2=-1$, $p_3=-2$, $p_4=-4$, and $z_1=-3$, and a complex number $\bar{s}$ is at the vicinity of p_2. Then the angle of departure from p_2, $\angle(\bar{s}-p_2)$ can be computed from the following equation,

$$\angle(\bar{s}-z_1)-\angle(\bar{s}-p_1)-\angle(\bar{s}-p_2)-\angle(\bar{s}-p_3)-\angle(\bar{s}-p_4)=(2\ell+1)\pi$$

which can be rewritten as follows,

$$\angle(\bar{s}-p_2)=\angle(p_2-z_1)-\angle(p_2-p_1)-\angle(p_2-p_3)-\angle(p_2-p_4)-(2\ell+1)\pi$$

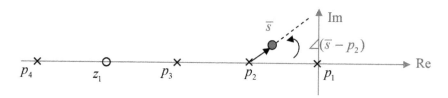

Fig. 8.23: Angle of departure for the introductory example.

Notice that the $\bar{s}$ on the right-hand side of the equation has been replaced by p_2 since $\bar{s}$ and p_2 are virtually the same point seen from far away. Therefore the angle of departure from p_2 is

$$\angle(\bar{s}-p_2)=0-\pi-0-0+\pi=0$$

which means the root loci departs from the pole p_2 to the right.

If $\bar{s}$ is chosen to be at the vicinity of z_1, then the angle of arrival to z_1 will be

$$\angle(\bar{s}-z_1)=\angle(z_1-p_1)+\angle(z_1-p_2)+\angle(z_1-p_3)+\angle(z_1-p_4)-(2\ell+1)\pi$$

and

$$\angle(\bar{s}-z_1)=\pi+\pi+\pi+0-3\pi=0$$

Hence, the angle of arrival to the zero z_1 is $0°$, which means the root loci comes from the right to arrive at z_1.   ∎

8.3.2 Root Loci Construction Using MATLAB

In applications, the root locus plot can be generated by computation using established functions like MATLAB's `rlocus`.

The two graphs in Figure 8.24 show the same root locus plot generated using the following MATLAB code:

```
% CSD Fig8.24 Use rlocus(G,K) for the intro example
s=tf('s');
G=(s+3)/((s)*(s+1)*(s+2)*(s+4));
figure(7)
K=logspace(-3,2,1000);
rlocus(G,K)
```

The graph on the left shows the root loci with the grid on. The grid can be turned on by executing the sgrid command on the Command Window or simply by a right click of the mouse over the root loci graph to pop up a small window manual where the grid can be turned on or off. **The grid shows the constant damping ratio (ς) lines and the constant natural frequency (ω_n) circles. The black square**

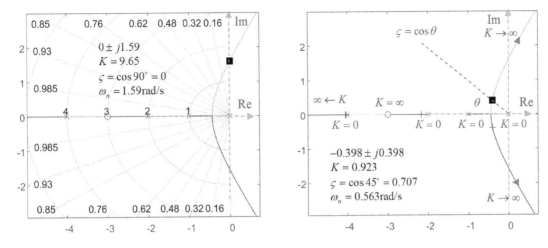

Fig. 8.24: The root loci of the introductory example plotted using MATLAB rlocus.

cursor that appeared on the root loci was obtained by a left click on the root loci. The black square cursor can be further dragged along the root loci to a position of interest. While the black cursor is moving, a small display panel also moves with it, showing the associated pole location, value of K, damping ratio, and natural frequency. On the left graph, the black cursor is positioned at the intersection of the root loci and the imaginary axis, at which the complex conjugate poles are $\pm j1.59$ and the gain $K = 9.65$, and the damping ratio and the natural frequency are $\varsigma = 0$ and $\omega_n = 1.59$ rad/s, respectively. If the black cursor is moved to the break-out point, the display panel will show that the double poles at $s = -0.435$, the gain $K = 0.534$, the damping ratio $\varsigma = 1$, and the natural frequency $\omega_n = 0.435$ rad/s.

The graph on the right shows the same root loci but with the grid off. The black cursor is moved to the position where the complex conjugate poles are at $-0.398 \pm j0.398$, and the gain $K = 0.923$. At these pole locations, the corresponding damping ratio and the natural frequency are $\varsigma = 0.707$ and $\omega_n = 0.563$ rad/s.

By executing the MATLAB's command [K,Poles]=rlofind(G), a new cursor consisting of a long horizontal line and a long vertical line appears to hover over the entire Root Locus window. By positioning the cursor, the intersection of these two long lines, at the point $-0.398 + j0.398$ on the loci marked by the previous black square cursor, the value of the gain K and all associated closed-loop poles are identified, as shown in the following:

```
% CSD Fig8.24 Use rlofind to locate all poles
>> [K,Poles]=rlocfind(G) Select a
   point in the graphics window selected_point =
   -3.9777e-01 + 3.9790e-01i
   K =
      9.2300e-01
   Poles =
      -4.0383e+00 + 0.0000e+00i
      -2.1661e+00 + 0.0000e+00i
      -3.9777e-01 + 3.9790e-01i
      -3.9777e-01 - 3.9790e-01i
```

It also can be seen that a red cross appears on each branch of the loci at all of the identified poles. **If the value of $K = 0.923$ is chosen in the controller design, the two poles $-0.398 \pm j0.398$ will be the dominant ones to determine the behavior of the closed-loop system, and the associated damping ratio and natural frequency will be $\varsigma = 0.707$ and $\omega_n = 0.563$ rad/s, respectively.**

A Simulink simulation program is built based on the block diagram of the feedback control system shown in Figure 8.20. The step response simulation results with $K = 0.923$ and $K = 0.534$ are shown in Figure 8.25. When K is chosen to be $K = 0.923$, the step response is underdamped with about 5% maximum overshoot, which occurs at $t = 6.5$ s. Comparing with the step response of the typical second-order system with the same damping ratio and natural frequency, the step response of this fourth-order feedback control system has only about 1% higher in maximum overshoot and is only about 1.5 seconds faster in the peak time. On the other hand, when K is chosen to be $K = 0.534$, the step response will be critically damped. If K is chosen between these two values, the step response will be between these two step response waveforms. If K is chosen to be $K = 9.65$, the step response will be undamped sinusoidal function with oscillation frequency equal to $\omega_n = 1.59$ rad/s.

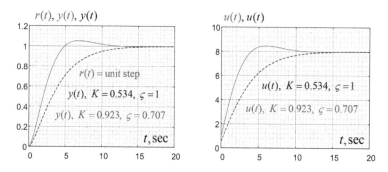

Fig. 8.25: The step response simulation results with $K = 0.923$ and $K = 0.534$.

The two step response graphs in Figure 8.25 are obtained from running the generated using the following MATLAB program:

```
% CSDfig8p25.m  5/08/2020 Intro Root Loci Example
% Design A: K=0.923, damping ratio 0.707
% Design B: K=0.534, damping ratio 1, critically damped
%% System
s=tf('s'); G1=(s+3)/s; G2=1/((s+2)*(s+4)); G3=1/(s+1);
%% Design A   step response
K=0.923, t=linspace(0,20,201); GR=(K*G1*G2)/(1+K*G1*G2*G3);
GU=(K*G1)/(1+K*G1*G2*G3); R=tf(1,1); [r,t]=step(R,t);
[y,t]=step(GR,t); [u,t]=step(GU,t); run('plot2a')
%% Design B   step response
K=0.534, t=linspace(0,20,201); GR=(K*G1*G2)/(1+K*G1*G2*G3);
GU=(K*G1)/(1+K*G1*G2*G3); R=tf(1,1); [r,t]=step(R,t);
[y,t]=step(GR,t); [u,t]=step(GU,t); run('plot2b')
```

where `plot2a.m` is given in the following, and `plot2b.m` is the same except replacing b- by k--.

```
% plot2a.m
figure(5), subplot(1,2,1), plot(t,r,'r-', t,y,'b-'), grid on,
grid minor, title('r & y'), hold on, subplot(1,2,2),
plot(t,u,'b-'), grid on, grid minor, title('u'), hold on
```

8.4 Root Locus Analysis and Design

Notwithstanding the ease of creating a root locus plot using a computer, intelligent use of root locus as a design tool requires understanding the underlying nature of the root loci behavior. Only with this understanding can we manipulate the loci by selecting the right compensator and adjusting its parameters. Recall, in the example of the previous section, we considered a system with a PI compensator and examined the root loci with respect to the gain parameter K. In fact, the PI compensator has two parameters, the gain and the zero location. The root locus is defined in terms of a single parameter. It is true that we could choose the zero location rather than the gain. Or we could develop two separate plots, one for each parameter. But then we would have to sort out the coupling between the two. It is generally best to focus on the gain K as the root locus parameter and use our underlying knowledge of root locus behavior to choose the correct compensator and manipulate its other parameters according to our knowledge of how it would affect the loci. To this end, in this section we explore the basic theory of the root locus process.

Our ultimate goal is to use the root locus method as a way to achieve acceptable closed-loop pole locations. So, what are acceptable pole locations? With the root locus method we do not specify specific desired pole locations. Instead we identify an acceptable region in the complex plane within which, with some exceptions, we wish all poles to reside. Figure 8.26 shows one simple and effective way such a region may be specified. Note that any pole residing within the shaded region will have a better damping ratio ς and damping factor α.

Consider the feedback loop of Figure 8.27, where the loop transfer function is

$$KG\left(s\right) = K\frac{N\left(s\right)}{D\left(s\right)} = K\frac{s^{m} + b_{m-1}s^{m-1} + \cdots + b_{0}}{s^{n} + a_{n-1}s^{n-1} + \cdots + a_{0}} = K\frac{\left(s - z_{1}\right)\cdots\left(s - z_{m}\right)}{\left(s - p_{1}\right)\cdots\left(s - p_{n}\right)} \qquad (8.47)$$

Here, we assume that $N\left(s\right)$ and $D\left(s\right)$ are completely known but K is a parameter we can adjust. Thus, we know the poles and zeros of the loop transfer function. Our intent is to determine how the closed-loop poles vary as we manipulate K. For this purpose, we define the root locus problem as follows.

Definition 8.18 (The Root Locus Problem)

Generate a sketch in the complex plane of the closed-loop pole trajectories as a function of the gain parameter K. These trajectories are referred to as the root loci.

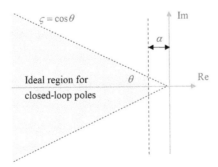

Fig. 8.26: The goal is to design a compensator such that the closed-loop system poles lie in the shaded region. Note that the region is characterized by two parameters: the damping ratio ς (or θ) and the damping factor α.

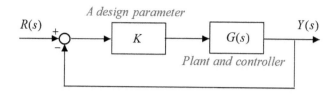

Fig. 8.27: A typical feedback control system block diagram for root locus analysis and design.

8.4.1 The Root Locus Method

The closed-loop system poles are the roots (or zeros) of

$$1 + KG(s) = 0 \tag{8.48}$$

Equation 8.48 can be expressed as

$$D(s) + KN(s) = 0 \tag{8.49}$$

or

$$KG(s) = K\frac{N(s)}{D(s)} = -1 \tag{8.50}$$

Moreover, $-1 = e^{j(2\ell+1)\pi}$ for all integers ℓ. This establishes the following result.

Theorem 8.19 (Magnitude and Angle Equations)

Due to Equation 8.50 and $-1 = e^{j(2\ell+1)\pi}$, for all integers ℓ, the closed-loop poles satisfy

$$KG(s) = K\frac{N(s)}{D(s)} = e^{j(2\ell+1)\pi}, \quad \ell = 0, \pm 1, \pm 2, \cdots \tag{8.51}$$

which can be decomposed into two equations: **the magnitude equation,**

$$|G(s)| = \frac{1}{K} \quad \rightleftarrows \quad \frac{\prod_{i=1}^{m} |s - z_i|}{\prod_{j=1}^{n} |s - p_j|} = \frac{1}{K}, \quad 0 \leq K < \infty \tag{8.52}$$

and **the angle equation,**

$$\angle G(s) = (2\ell+1)\pi \quad \rightleftarrows \quad \sum_{i=1}^{m} \angle(s - z_i) - \sum_{j=1}^{n} \angle(s - p_j) = (2\ell+1)\pi, \quad 0 \leq K < \infty \tag{8.53}$$

∎

According to Theorem 8.19, if a point $\bar{s}$ is on the root loci it has to satisfy the angle equation, Equation 8.53 and its associated gain K should satisfy the magnitude equation, Equation 8.52.

Example 8.20 (Application of the Angle Formula)

The introductory root loci example discussed in Section 8.3.1 is employed here to illustrate the angle formula of Theorem 8.19. Recall that the loop transfer function of the system is

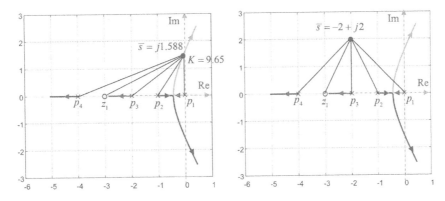

Fig. 8.28: A graphical view of the application of the angle formula.

$$KG(s) = K\frac{s+3}{s(s+1)(s+2)(s+4)}$$

and its associated root loci diagram was given in Figure 8.24.

The graph on the left of Figure 8.28 illustrates **the test point $\bar{s} = j1.588$ satisfies the angle equation and therefore is on the root loci. The magnitude equation will also be used to compute the associated gain K, which is supposed to be $K = 9.65$.** For the graph on the right, the test point is $\bar{s} = -2+j2$, which is not on the root loci, should not satisfy the angle equation.

For $\bar{s} = j1.588$, the algebraic sum of the angles is

$$\angle(\bar{s}-z_1) - (\angle(\bar{s}-p_1) + \angle(\bar{s}-p_2) + \angle(\bar{s}-p_3) + \angle(\bar{s}-p_4))$$
$$= \tan^{-1}(1.588/3) - (\tan^{-1}(1.588/0) + \tan^{-1}(1.588/1) + \tan^{-1}(1.588/2) + \tan^{-1}(1.588/4))$$
$$= 27.894° - (90° + 57.800° + 38.450° + 21.653°) = 27.894° - 207.903° = 180.009°$$

which satisfies the angle equation, Equation 8.53. Therefore, **the point $\bar{s} = j1.588$ indeed is on the root loci.** Furthermore, from the magnitude equation, Equation 8.52, we have

$$K = \frac{|\bar{s}|\cdot|\bar{s}+1|\cdot|\bar{s}+2|\cdot|\bar{s}+4|}{|\bar{s}+3|} = \frac{|j1.588|\cdot|j1.588+1|\cdot|j1.588+2|\cdot|j1.588+4|}{|j1.588+3|}$$
$$= \frac{(1.588)(1.8766)(2.5538)(4.3037)}{3.3944} = 9.649$$

which matches the gain value $K = 9.65$ obtained in Section 8.3.1.

For $\bar{s} = -2+j2$, the algebraic sum of the angles is

$$\angle(\bar{s}-z_1) - (\angle(\bar{s}-p_1) + \angle(\bar{s}-p_2) + \angle(\bar{s}-p_3) + \angle(\bar{s}-p_4))$$
$$= \tan^{-1}(2/1) - (\tan^{-1}(2/-2) + \tan^{-1}(2/-1) + \tan^{-1}(2/0) + \tan^{-1}(2/2))$$
$$= 63.435° - (135° + 116.565° + 90° + 45°) = -323.13° = 36.87° \neq (2\ell+1)\cdot 180°$$

which does not satisfy the angle equation Equation 8.53, and therefore **this point $\bar{s} = -2+j2$ is not on the root loci.** ∎

8.4.2 Explaining the Root Loci Construction Rules

In Section 8.3.1, we listed the root loci construction rules and employed them to construct the root loci of a system with four poles and one zero in Figure 8.21. In the following, we will investigate the reasoning behind these rules.

Rule 1: *Number of Branches.* The number of branches of the root locus is n, which is the number of LTF poles (the poles of the loop transfer function $KG(s)$). This follows from the fact that the order of the polynomial $N(s) + KD(s)$ is the order of $D(s)$.

Rule 2: *Symmetry.* The root locus is symmetric about the real axis. This follows from the fact that complex poles occur in conjugate pairs.

Rule 3: *Starting and Ending Points.* Each loci begins ($K = 0$) at an LTF pole and ends ($K \to \infty$) at an LTF zero or at infinity. This is easily established by noting the following two facts:

$$D(s) + KN(s) = 0 \quad \to \quad D(s) = 0 \quad \text{as} \quad K \to 0$$

$$\tfrac{1}{K}D(s) + N(s) = 0 \quad \to \quad N(s) = 0 \quad \text{as} \quad K \to \infty \quad \text{if } s \text{ is bounded}$$

Rule 4: *Real Axis Segments.* For $K > 0$, real axis segments to the *left of an odd number* of poles and zeros are part of the root locus.

Proof: According to the angle equation, Equation 8.53, assume $\bar{s}$ is a point on the real axis; then the angles $\angle(\bar{s} - z_i)$ or $\angle(\bar{s} - p_j)$ from the conjugate poles or zeros will cancel each other out and the angles from the poles or zeros on the left of $\bar{s}$ will be zero. Hence, only the real poles and zeros on the right-hand side of $\bar{s}$ need to be counted in using the angle equation. **If the number of the poles and zeros on the right-hand side of $\bar{s}$ is odd, then the algebraic sum of the angles is $(2\ell + 1)\pi$, and therefore the point $\bar{s}$ is part of the root loci.** Otherwise, it is not on the root loci.

Rule 5: *Behavior at Infinity.* The root locus branches that tend to infinity do so along asymptotes with angles θ, and these asymptotes all intersect at a common point σ on the real axis as defined by

$$\theta_\ell = \frac{(2\ell + 1)\pi}{n - m}, \quad \ell = 0, 1, 2, \cdots, n - m - 1; \qquad \sigma = \frac{b_{m-1} - a_{n-1}}{n - m} = \frac{-\sum_i z_i + \sum_j p_j}{n - m} \tag{8.54}$$

where $b_{m-1}, a_{n-1}, n, m, z_i,$ and p_j are given in Equation 8.47.

Proof: Recall the closed-loop characteristic equation:

$$D(s) + KN(s) = 0 \quad \rightleftharpoons \quad \frac{D(s)}{N(s)} = -K$$

We are interested in the situation where s is a very large complex number. It is easier to consider the very small complex number $\varepsilon = 1/s$, so rewriting in terms of ε, we obtain the approximations

$$D(s) = s^n + a_{n-1}s^{n-1} + \cdots + a_0 = \frac{1}{\varepsilon^n}\left(1 + a_{n-1}\varepsilon + \cdots + a_0\varepsilon^n\right) = \frac{1}{\varepsilon^n}\left(1 + a_{n-1}\varepsilon + O(\varepsilon^2)\right)$$

where

$$a_{n-1} = -(p_1 + \cdots + p_n)$$

Similarly

$$N(s) = \frac{1}{\varepsilon^m}\left(1 + b_{m-1}\varepsilon + O(\varepsilon^2)\right)$$

where

$$b_{m-1} = -(z_1 + \cdots + z_m)$$

Now, transforming back to s,

$$\frac{D(s)}{N(s)} \approx s^{n-m}\frac{a_{n-1} + s}{b_{m-1} + s} = -K$$

so we can write

$$s\left[1 + \frac{b_{m-1} - a_{n-1}}{(m-n)s} + O\left(\frac{1}{s^2}\right)\right] = (-K)^{1/(n-m)}$$

or

$$s + \frac{b_{m-1} - a_{n-1}}{(m-n)} = (-K)^{1/(n-m)}$$

Now, write s as $s \to \sigma + \rho e^{j\theta}$ and substitute

$$\sigma + \rho e^{j\theta} + \frac{b_{m-1} - a_{n-1}}{(m-n)} = K^{1/(n-m)} e^{j(\pi + \ell 2\pi)/(n-m)}$$

which leads to

$$\sigma = \frac{b_{m-1} - a_{n-1}}{(n-m)}, \quad \rho = K^{1/(n-m)} \quad \theta_\ell = (2\ell+1)\pi/(n-m)$$

This means that each asymptote is a straight line, which may be viewed as a linear function of the parameter ρ. As ρ varies from 0 to ∞, each asymptote evolves from the point σ along a line at one of the possible angles θ_ℓ. ∎

Rule 6: *Real Axis Break-Out and Break-In Points.* The root locus breaks out from the real axis where the gain K is a (local) maximum on the real axis and breaks in to the real axis where K is a (local) minimum.

To locate candidate break points simply solve

$$\frac{d}{ds}\left(\frac{1}{G(s)}\right) = 0 \quad or \quad N(s)\frac{dD(s)}{ds} - \frac{dN(s)}{ds}D(s) = 0 \tag{8.55}$$

where $G(s) = N(s)/D(s)$, and then find the value of K at the break point by

$$K = \frac{1}{|G(s)|}$$

Rule 7: *Imaginary-Axis Crossings.* Use the Routh stability test to determine values of K for which loci cross the imaginary axis.

Rule 8: *Angle of Departure from Poles or Angle of Arrival to Zeros.* Assume $\bar{s}$ is at the vicinity of any LTF pole or zero, pz; then the angle of departure from or the angle of arrival to pz, $\angle(\bar{s} - pz)$, can be computed from the following equation:

$$G(\bar{s}) = \sum_{i=1}^{m} \angle(\bar{s} - z_i) - \sum_{j=1}^{n} \angle(\bar{s} - p_j) = (2\ell+1)\pi \qquad 0 \leq K < \infty \tag{8.56}$$

∎

Remark 8.21 (Angle of Departure and Arrival)

The equation, Equation 8.56, employed to compute the angle of departure or arrival from the poles or to the zeros, is basically the same as the angle equation of Equation 8.53. In fact, the computation of the angle of departure (or arrival) in root locus analysis and design is one of the two important applications of the angle equation. **The test point $\bar{s}$ is assumed in the vicinity of pz, which is a pole or zero of interest, but its orientation $\angle(\bar{s} - pz)$ is unknown. Since $\bar{s}$ and pz is so close, they can be considered**

virtually the same point, as observed from the rest of the poles and zeros. Therefore in Equation 8.56, every $\bar{s}$ except the one in $\angle(\bar{s} - pz)$ will be replaced by pz to simplify the computation. A couple of angle of departure (arrival) computations were illustrated in Example 8.16 and Example 8.17. Another important application of the angle equation was demonstrated in Example 8.20 to determine whether a given test point $\bar{s}$ is on the root loci.   ∎

8.5 A Sinusoidal Position Tracking Control System

In this section, **a feedback controller will be designed for a DC motor system to achieve a perfect steady-state sinusoidal position tracking and a desired transient response.** The dynamics model of the plant, which is a DC motor system with gear train and load, is given by

$$\frac{\Theta(s)}{U(s)} = \frac{145.5}{s(s+43.14)} \tag{8.57}$$

from Equation 5.68 in Chapter 5. **The reference input is**

$$\theta_R(t) = A\sin(\omega_0 t + \phi) \tag{8.58}$$

where the frequency is $\omega_0 = 10$ rad/s, but the amplitude A and the phase ϕ are arbitrary. The objective is to design a controller so that the closed-loop system is stable and the plant output $\theta(t)$, the angular displacement, will follow the sinusoidal reference input $\theta_R(t)$ as closely as possible.

According to the internal model principle (Remark 8.4), the loop transfer function needs to have the internal model $1/(s^2 + 10^2)$ in it to match the reference sinusoidal function frequency $\omega_0 = 10$ rad/s. Thus, the structure of the controller is chosen to be of the form,

$$K\frac{(s+c_1)(s+c_2)}{s^2 + 10^2} \tag{8.59}$$

Notice that two zeros, $s = -c_1$ and $s = -c_2$, are added to the controller in Figure 8.29, where c_1 and c_2 are positive real numbers to be determined in the design process. There is a practical reason for adding these two zeros to the loop transfer function. It can be explained from the root locus diagrams in Figure 8.30.

Without adding the two zeros, the loop transfer function of the system would be

$$KG(s) = K\frac{145.5}{s(s+43.14)(s^2 + 10^2)}$$

which gives four poles at $p_1 = 0$, $p_2 = j10$, $p_3 = -j10$, and $p_4 = -43.14$, but no zeros. The root loci of the closed-loop characteristic equation $1 + KG(s) = 0$ are shown on the left graph of Figure 8.30. The four branches of root loci begin at the four pole locations when $K = 0$, and eventually, as $K \to \infty$, they will approach the infinity locations defined by the four asymptotes, respectively. The angles of the four asymptotes and their common intersection point are

$$\theta_0 = \frac{\pi}{4}, \quad \theta_1 = \frac{3\pi}{4}, \quad \theta_2 = \frac{5\pi}{4} = \frac{-3\pi}{4}, \quad \theta_3 = \frac{7\pi}{4} = \frac{-\pi}{4}$$

$$\sigma = \frac{0 + (j10) + (-j10) + (-43.14)}{4} = -10.79$$

There is only one real root loci segment, which is between the two LTF poles $p_1 = 0$ and $p_4 = -43.14$. The two branches starting from $p_1 = 0$ and $p_4 = -43.14$ will move toward each other and meet at the break-out point $s = -31.85$, which is one of the roots of the equation, Equation 8.55,

$$dD(s)/ds = 4s^3 + 129.42s^2 + 200s + 4314 = 0$$

After breakout, the two branches will become complex and move towards the two asymptotes with angles $135°$ and $-135°$.

The other two root loci branches will start at the two LTF poles on the imaginary axis, $p_2 = j10$, $p_3 = -j10$, when $K = 0$. As K increases, the root loci will depart from these two poles. The angle of departure computed based on Rule 8 or Equation 8.56 will reveal which direction the root loci would move. The angle of departure from the pole p_2 can be obtained from the following equation:

$$-(\angle(\bar{s}-p_1) + \angle(\bar{s}-p_2) + \angle(\bar{s}-p_3) + \angle(\bar{s}-p_4)) = (2\ell+1)\pi$$
$$\rightarrow \quad -(\angle(p_2-p_1) + \angle(\bar{s}-p_2) + \angle(p_2-p_3) + \angle(p_2-p_4)) = (2\ell+1)\pi$$
$$\rightarrow \quad -((\pi/2) + \angle(\bar{s}-p_2) + (\pi/2) + \tan^{-1}(10/43.14)) = (2\ell+1)\pi$$
$$\rightarrow \quad -(\angle(\bar{s}-p_2) + 13°) = 0° \quad \rightarrow \quad \angle(\bar{s}-p_2) = -13°$$

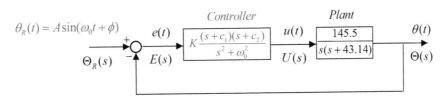

Fig. 8.29: A sinusoidal position tracking control system.

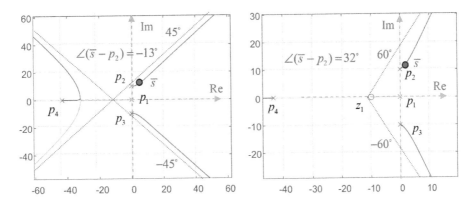

Fig. 8.30: Root locus diagrams explaining why the two zeros are added to the controller structure.

Hence, the root loci will depart from p_2 into the right half of the complex plane with the departure angle $\angle(\bar{s}-p_2) = -13°$. Then this branch of root loci will continue to move in the right half plane towards the asymptote with angle $\theta_0 = 45°$. The branch originating from p_3 will also move into the right half plane with departure angle $\angle(\bar{s}-p_3) = 13°$ and then approach the asymptote with angle $\theta_3 = -45°$.

These two branches will never come to the left half of the complex plane by changing the $K > 0$ gain value. **Therefore, the controller structure**

$$K\frac{1}{s^2 + 10^2}$$

does not work since the closed-loop system is not stable for any value of $K > 0$.

Next, we will investigate if adding a zero $s = -10$ to the controller would help. **By adding this zero, the loop transfer function will become**

$$KG(s) = K\frac{145.5(s + 10)}{s(s + 43.14)(s^2 + 10^2)}$$

which still keeps the same four poles at $p_1 = 0$, $p_2 = j10$, $p_3 = -j10$, $p_4 = -43.14$. The root loci of the closed-loop characteristic equation $1 + KG(s) = 0$ are shown on the right graph of Figure 8.30. The four branches of root loci begin at the four LTF pole locations when $K = 0$, and as $K \to \infty$, the branch originating from $p_1 = 0$ will arrive at the LTF zero, $z_1 = -10$, while the other three branches will move towards the infinity locations defined by the three asymptotes, respectively. The angles of the three asymptotes and their common intersection point are

$$\theta_0 = \tfrac{\pi}{3}, \quad \theta_1 = \pi, \quad \theta_2 = \tfrac{5\pi}{3} = \tfrac{-\pi}{3}$$

$$\sigma = \frac{-(-10) + 0 + (j10) + (-j10) + (-43.14)}{3} = -11.05$$

There are two real root loci segments; one starts from $p_1 = 0$ moving toward the left and ends up at $z_1 = -10$ when $K = \infty$, and the other starts from $p_4 = -43.14$ moving to the left on the negative real axis, which is the asymptote with angle $\theta_1 = \pi$.

The other two root loci branches will start at the two LTF poles on the imaginary axis, $p_2 = j10$, $p_3 = -j10$, when $K = 0$. As K increases, the root loci will depart from these two poles. The angle of departure computed based on Rule 8 or Equation 8.56 will reveal which direction the root loci would move. The angle of departure from the pole p_2 can be obtained from the following equation:

$$\angle(\bar{s} - z_1) - (\angle(\bar{s} - p_1) + \angle(\bar{s} - p_2) + \angle(\bar{s} - p_3) + \angle(\bar{s} - p_4)) = (2\ell + 1)\pi$$

$$\rightarrow \quad \angle(p_2 - z_1) - (\angle(p_2 - p_1) + \angle(\bar{s} - p_2) + \angle(p_2 - p_3) + \angle(p_2 - p_4)) = (2\ell + 1)\pi$$

$$\rightarrow \quad (\pi/4) - ((\pi/2) + \angle(\bar{s} - p_2) + (\pi/2) + \tan^{-1}(10/43.14)) = (2\ell + 1)\pi$$

$$\rightarrow \quad 45° - (\angle(\bar{s} - p_2) + 13°) = 0° \quad \rightarrow \quad \angle(\bar{s} - p_2) = 32°$$

Hence, the root loci will depart from p_2 into the right half of the complex plane with the departure angle $\angle(\bar{s} - p_2) = 32°$. Then this branch of root loci will continue to move in the right half plane towards the asymptote with angle $\theta_0 = 60°$. The branch originating from p_3 will also move into the right half plane with departure angle $\angle(\bar{s} - p_3) = -32°$ and then approach the asymptote with angle $\theta_2 = -60°$. These two branches will never come to the left half of the complex plane by changing the $K > 0$ gain value or by moving the added zero z_1 to anywhere on the real axis.

Therefore, the controller structure

$$K\frac{s + c}{s^2 + 10^2}$$

still does not work since the closed-loop system is not stable for any value of $K > 0$ and any value of c. Nevertheless, by adding the two zeros, $s = -c_1$ and $s = -c_2$, to the controller, as shown in **Equation 8.59, and with the zero locations carefully selected, the angles of departure from the**

poles on the imaginary axis can be managed so that the root loci will depart into the left half of the complex plane. Furthermore, the asymptotes can also be confined in the left half plane. With the basic root locus consideration and the sinusoidal tracking objective in mind, the controller structure is selected so that the loop transfer function is

$$KG(s) = K\frac{145.5(s+1)(s+2)}{s(s+43.14)(s^2+10^2)} \tag{8.60}$$

which still has four LTF poles at $p_1 = 0$, $p_2 = j10$, $p_3 = -j10$, and $p_4 = -43.14$, but **with two added LTF zeros at $z_1 = -1$ and $z_1 = -2$. The root loci of the closed-loop characteristic equation $1 + KG(s) = 0$ are shown on Figure 8.31.** The graph on the left of the figure shows the entire root loci diagram, but around the origin area two zeros and one pole are crowded together. The graph on the right provides an expansion view of the area close to the imaginary axis and the origin.

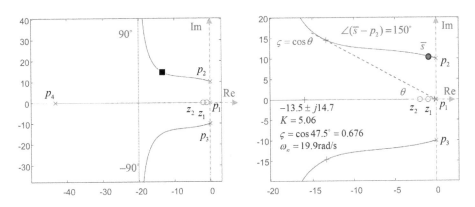

Fig. 8.31: Root locus design for sinusoidal position tracking control system.

There are two real root loci segments on the real axis. One starts from $p_1 = 0$, moving to the left, and ends at $z_1 = -1$, and another starts from $p_4 = -43.14$, moving toward the right, and terminates at $z_2 = -2$. The other two branches of root loci begin at the imaginary pole locations $p_2 = j10$ and $p_3 = -j10$ when $K = 0$, and as $K \to \infty$, they will approach the infinity locations defined by the two asymptotes, respectively. The angles of the two asymptotes and their common intersection point are

$$\theta_0 = \frac{\pi}{2}, \quad \theta_1 = \frac{-\pi}{2}$$
$$\sigma = \frac{-[(-1)+(-2)]+[0+(j10)+(-j10)+(-43.14)]}{4-2} = -20.07 \tag{8.61}$$

Notice that the two asymptotes completely reside in the left half of the complex plane. It is mainly the result of adding the two LTF zeros, $z = -1$ and $z = -2$, to the controller structure. The addition of the two zeros also affects the angle of departure in a big way from the following computation of the angle of departure from $p_2 = j10$:

$$\angle(\bar{s}-z_1) + \angle(\bar{s}-z_2) - (\angle(\bar{s}-p_1) + \angle(\bar{s}-p_2) + \angle(\bar{s}-p_3) + \angle(\bar{s}-p_4)) = (2\ell+1)\pi$$
$$\to \quad \angle(p_2-z_1) + \angle(p_2-z_2) - (\angle(p_2-p_1) + \angle(\bar{s}-p_2) + \angle(p_2-p_3) + \angle(p_2-p_4)) = (2\ell+1)\pi$$
$$\to \quad \tan^{-1}(10/1) + \tan^{-1}(10/2) - ((\pi/2) + \angle(\bar{s}-p_2) + (\pi/2) + \tan^{-1}(10/43.14)) = (2\ell+1)\pi$$
$$\to \quad 84.29° + 78.69° - (\angle(\bar{s}-p_2) + 13°) = 0° \quad \to \quad \angle(\bar{s}-p_2) = 150°$$
$$\tag{8.62}$$

Hence, the root loci will depart from p_2 into the left half of the complex plane with the departure angle $\angle(\bar{s} - p_2) = 150°$. This branch of root loci will continue to move in the left half plane toward the asymptote with angle $\theta_0 = 90°$. Similarly, the branch originating from p_3 will also move into the left half plane with departure angle $\angle(\bar{s} - p_3) = -150°$ and then approach to the asymptote with angle $\theta_1 = -90°$.

Notice that from Equation 8.62, adding the two zeros, $s = -1$ and $s = -2$, to the loop transfer function has changed the angle of departure $\angle(\bar{s} - p_2)$ from $-13°$ to $150°$ due to their respective 84.29° and 78.69° angle shift contributions.

The two graphs in Figure 8.31 are obtained from the same root locus plot generated using the following MATLAB code:

```
% CSD Fig8.31 Use rlocus(G,K) for sinusoidal tracking control
 s=tf('s');  Gp=145.5/(s*(s+43.14)); Gr=(s+1)*(s+2)/(s^2+100),
 G=Gp*Gr, figure (6), K=logspace(-3,1.5,500); rlocus(G,K)
```

On the root loci diagram, the black square cursor is moved to the position where the complex conjugate poles are at $-13.5 \pm j14.7$ with the gain $K = 5.06$. At these pole locations, the corresponding damping ratio and the natural frequency are $\varsigma = 0.676$ and $\omega_n = 19.9$ rad/s.

By executing the MATLAB's command `[K,Poles]=rlofind(G)`, a new cursor consisting of a long horizontal line and a long vertical line appear to hover over the entire Root Locus window. By positioning the cursor, the intersection of these two long lines, at the point $-13.5 + j14.7$ on the loci marked by the previous black square cursor, the value of the gain K and all associated closed-loop poles are identified, as shown in the following:

```
% CSD Fig8.31 Use rlocfind to locate all poles
>> [K,Poles]=rlocfind(G)
   Select a point in the graphics window
   selected_point =  -1.3438e+01 + 1.4709e+01i
   K =   5.0642e+00
   Poles =
      -1.3475e+01 + 1.4671e+01i
      -1.3475e+01 - 1.4671e+01i
      -1.5958e+01 + 0.0000e+00i
      -2.3273e-01 + 0.0000e+00i
```

It also can be seen that a red cross sign appears on each branch of the loci at the identified pole location.

The MATLAB simulation program, CSDfig8p32sinu.m, is built based on the block diagram of the feedback control system shown in Figure 8.29. This simulation demonstrates the effectiveness of the the sinusoidal position tracking controller

$$\frac{5.06(s+1)(s+2)}{s^2 + 10^2}$$

as shown in Figure 8.32. The MATLAB program is shown in the following.

```
% CSDfig8p32sinu.m  5/08/2020 Sinu Tracking Example
  Gm=145.5/(s*(s+43.14))
% Design A: Gk=5.06*(s+1)*(s+2)/(s^2+100)
% Design B: Gk=3.95*tf(1,1)
%% System
  s=tf('s'); Gm = 145.5/(s*(s+43.14)); t=linspace(0,2,201);
  r=sin(10*t),
```

```
%% Design A  step response
  Gk=5.06*(s+1)*(s+2)/(s^2+100); GY=(Gk*Gm)/(1+Gk*Gm);
  GU=Gk/(1+Gk*Gm); [y,t]=lsim(GY,r,t); [u,t]=lsim(GU,r,t);
  run('plot2a')
%% Design B  step response
  Gk=3.95*tf(1,1); GY=(Gk*Gm)/(1+Gk*Gm); GU=Gk/(1+Gk*Gm);
  [y,t]=lsim(GY,r,t); [u,t]=lsim(GU,r,t); run('plot2b')
```

where the plotting programs `plot2a.m` and `plot2b.m` are the same as those given at the end of Section 8.3.2.

It can be seen that the blue $\theta(t)$ **catches up and coincides with the sinusoidal reference input, the green** $\theta_R(t)$**, within 0.25 seconds.** In contrast, the proportional controller with gain $K = 3.95$ is unable to track the sinusoidal reference input, although it is a Type 1 controller capable of perfect step reference tracking. The red $\theta(t)$ continues to lag behind at steady state.

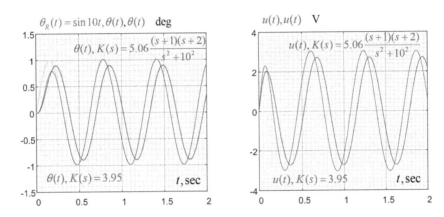

Fig. 8.32: Simulation results of the sinusoidal position tracking control system.

8.6 Controller Design for F/A–18 Flight Path Control

The F/A–18 aircraft flight dynamics model [Buttrill et al., 1992, Chakraborty et al., 2011, Chang et al., 2016] will be employed as a test bed in the following flight path control system designs. The lateral subsystem is set to fly straight without any roll or yaw motion; hence, we will only focus on the control of the longitudinal subsystem. The longitudinal state vector is $x = \begin{bmatrix} V & \alpha & q & \theta \end{bmatrix}^T$, where $V, \alpha, q,$ and θ are the air speed, the angle of attack, the pitch rate, and the pitch angle, respectively. The longitudinal control-input vector is $u = \begin{bmatrix} \delta_e & \delta_T \end{bmatrix}^T$, where δ_e and δ_T are the elevator control and thrust control, respectively.

Assume the nominal flight trim; here, a trim is a desired equilibrium, chosen to be

$$x^* = [436 \text{ ft/s} \quad 10° \quad 0°/s \quad 10°]^T, \quad u^* = [-1.26° \quad 5470.5 \text{ lbf}]^T \tag{8.63}$$

which is a level flight with $10°$ angle of attack. At this trim, a local linearized model [Chan et al., Dec. 2019] can be obtained as follows:

$$\dot{x}(t) = A\bar{x}(t) + B\bar{u}(t), \quad \text{where}$$

$$A = \begin{bmatrix} -0.02389 & -28.32 & 0 & -32.2 \\ -0.00033 & -0.362 & 1 & 0 \\ 0 & -2.212 & -0.2532 & 0 \\ 0 & 0 & 1 & 0 \end{bmatrix}, \quad B = \begin{bmatrix} -3.8114 & 0.000952 \\ -0.05145 & 0 \\ -2.8791 & 0 \\ 0 & 0 \end{bmatrix} \qquad (8.64)$$

Note that $x = \bar{x} + x^*$ and $u = \bar{u} + u^*$ since $(\bar{x}, \bar{u})$ are the differential values, or the perturbed values of (x, u) from the trim (x^*, u^*). In other words, the origin of the $(\bar{x}, \bar{u})$ coordinate is (x^*, u^*) while the origin of the (x, u) coordinate is $(0, 0)$. For example, the differential air speed $\bar{V} = 44$ ft/s means that the real air speed is $V = \bar{V} + 436\text{ft/s} = 480\text{ft/s}$.

For the flight path control problem to be considered in this section, the variable to be regulated is the flight path angle $\gamma = \theta - \alpha$ and the control input is δ_e, while the thrust δ_T is fixed at the trimmed value 5,470.5 lbf all the time. Therefore, the local linear state-space model with input $\bar{\delta}_e$ and output $\bar{\gamma}$ will be

$$\dot{x}(t) = A\bar{x}(t) + B_e\bar{\delta}_e(t) = A\bar{x}(t) + [-3.8114 \quad -0.05145 \quad -2.8791 \quad 0]^T \bar{\delta}_e(t)$$
$$\bar{\gamma}(t) = C\bar{x}(t) = [0 \quad -1 \quad 0 \quad 1]\bar{x}(t) \qquad (8.65)$$

where the A matrix remains the same as that in Equation 8.64, B_e is the first column vector of the matrix B in Equation 8.64, and $C = [0 \ -1 \ 0 \ 1]$. It also can be seen that $\bar{\delta}_e = \delta_e + 1.26°$ and $\bar{\gamma} = \gamma$ since at the trim given by Equation 8.63, $\delta_e^* = -1.26°$ and γ^* is zero. The plant transfer function from the elevator control input $\bar{\delta}_e$ to the flight path angle output $\bar{\gamma}$ of the F/A–18 aircraft at the nominal trim, given by Equation 8.63 is

$$G_p(s) = \frac{\bar{\Gamma}(s)}{\bar{\Delta}_e(s)} = \frac{0.051453(s + 4.3935)(s - 4.1059)(s - 0.03491)}{(s^2 + 0.6189s + 2.286)(s^2 + 0.02027s + 0.01026)} \qquad (8.66)$$

The plant has two pairs of complex conjugate poles,

$$\begin{array}{l} p_1 \\ p_2 \end{array} = -0.010133 \pm j0.10077 := -\alpha_L \pm j\omega_L \quad \text{and} \quad \begin{array}{l} p_3 \\ p_4 \end{array} = -0.30945 \pm j1.4799 := -\alpha_S \pm j\omega_S$$
$$(8.67)$$

Notice that the first pair of poles, p_1 and p_2, has a small damping factor $\alpha_L = 0.010133$ and a low frequency $\omega_L = 0.10077$ rad/s, and the other p_3 and p_4 pair has a relatively larger damping factor, 0.3095, and a higher frequency, $\omega_S = 1.48$ rad/s. In traditional aircraft parlance, this lower frequency behavior is referred to as the *long-period mode* or *phugoid mode*, since the period is $T_L = 2\pi/\omega_L = 2\pi/0.1008 = 62.4$ s. On the other hand, the higher frequency behavior is referred to as the *short-period mode* since the short period is $T_S = 2\pi/\omega_S = 2\pi/1.48 = 4.25$ s. The subscripts L and S stand for long period and short period, respectively. The damping ratio ς and the natural frequency ω_n, associated with the long-period and short-period modes, can be obtained using Equation 3.60, respectively as follows:

$$\begin{array}{ll} \text{long-period mode:} & \varsigma = 0.1, \quad \omega_n = 0.101 \text{ rad/s} \\ \text{short-period mode:} & \varsigma = 0.205, \quad \omega_n = 1.51 \text{ rad/s} \end{array} \qquad (8.68)$$

The performance of the uncompensated system is very poor since the damping ratio $\varsigma = 0.1$ and the natural frequency $\omega_n = 0.101$ rad/s of the dominant Phugoid mode are so small that it would cause unacceptably long and large up and down oscillations in longitudinal motion.

The plant also has three real zeros, and two of them are in the right half of the s-plane,

$$z_1 = -4.3935, \quad z_2 = 0.034907, \quad \text{and} \quad z_3 = 4.1059 \qquad (8.69)$$

so the system is a *nonminimum phase system*.

The computational results relevant to the F/A–18 subsystem from the elevator control input δ_e to the flight path angle output $\gamma = \alpha - \theta$ are obtained by running the following MATLAB program:

```
% CSD_eq8p66 F/A-18 Ele to Gamma ss model tf Poles Zeros
A =[ -2.3893e-02   -2.8317e+01           0  -3.2200e+01;
     -3.2923e-04   -3.6208e-01   1.0000e+00           0;
      4.0491e-11   -2.2115e+00  -2.5319e-01           0;
               0            0   1.0000e+00           0];
B =[ -3.8114e+00    9.5196e-04;
     -5.1453e-02   -3.8506e-07;
     -2.8791e+00            0;
               0            0];
b = B(:,1); c = [0 -1  0  1]; d = 0; eig(A), damp(A)
G_ge = ss(A,b,c,d), zpk(G_ge), [Z,Kz]=zero(G_ge),  P=pole(G_ge)
```

In the following, **two controller structures will be considered to work together with the root locus design approach in designing a feedback controller** to achieve closed-loop stability, steady-state tracking, and desired transient performance for the F/A–18 aircraft flight path control problem. The two feedback controller structures are the PI (proportional and integral controller, and the state-feedback controller with integrator.

Before getting into the controller design, we will first analyze the open-loop system and observe how the elevator control input δ_e will affect the longitudinal state variables V, α, θ, and the flight path angle $\gamma = \theta - \alpha$.

8.6.1 Open-Loop Manual Longitudinal Flight Control of F/A–18 by δ_e

As described in Equations 8.67 and 8.68, the longitudinal flight dynamics have two pair of complex conjugate poles—one associated with the long-period (phugoid) mode and the other with the short-period mode. **The damping ratios and damping factors of both modes are poor, which implies large overshoot and long oscillation periods,** especially for the long-period mode dynamics. Furthermore, the nonminimum-phase zeros—the zeros in the RHP, as shown in Equation 8.69—are not helpful since they will cause the system response to go to the opposite direction, initially, before reversing back to the intended direction. The analysis and simulation to be conducted in the following will reveal that manually controlling an uncompensated aircraft flight system is quite a challenging job.

An open-loop manual control simulation can be implemented based on the block diagram shown in Figure 8.33. The relationship among the real control input u, the control input trim u^*, and the differential control input $\bar{u}$ is described by the following:

$$\bar{u} = u - u^*, \quad \text{where} \quad \bar{u} = \begin{bmatrix} \bar{\delta}_e \\ \bar{\delta}_T \end{bmatrix}, \quad u^* = \begin{bmatrix} \delta_e^* \\ \delta_T^* \end{bmatrix}, \quad u = \begin{bmatrix} \delta_e \\ \delta_T \end{bmatrix} \tag{8.70}$$

Similarly, the real state vector x, the state vector trim x^*, and the differential state vector $\bar{x}$ are related by the following equation,

$$x = \bar{x} + x^*, \quad \text{where} \quad x = \begin{bmatrix} V \\ \alpha \\ q \\ \theta \end{bmatrix}, \quad \bar{x} = \begin{bmatrix} \bar{V} \\ \bar{\alpha} \\ \bar{q} \\ \bar{\theta} \end{bmatrix}, \quad x^* = \begin{bmatrix} V^* \\ \alpha^* \\ q^* \\ \theta^* \end{bmatrix} \tag{8.71}$$

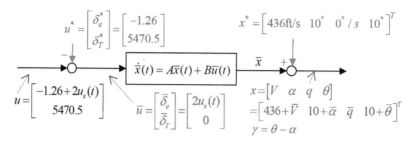

Fig. 8.33: Open-loop longitudinal manual control block diagram for F/A–18.

In this simulation, the initial condition is at the trim

$$x(0) = x^* = [436 \text{ ft/s}\ \ 10°\ \ 0°/s\ \ 10°]^T, \quad u(0) = u^* = [-1.26°\ \ 5470.5 \text{ lbf}]^T$$

and the elevator input $\delta_e(t)$ is assumed to have a $2°$ jump from $-1.26°$ to $0.74°$ at $t = 0$ (i.e., $\delta_e(t) = 2° u_s(t) - 1.26°$) or equivalently $\bar{\delta}_e(t) = 2° u_s(t)$, while the thrust input continues to stay at $\delta_T(t) = 5470.5$ lbf throughout the simulation.

The main objective of the $2°$ jump of the elevator input is to increase the flight path angle $\gamma = \theta - \alpha$ **via the changes of the pitch angle** θ **and the angle of attack** α. However, the action of the elevator will affect all the longitudinal state variables including the air speed V. In addition to the transfer function from the elevator $\bar{\Delta}_e(s)$ to the flight path angle $\bar{\Gamma}(s)$, which has been given in Equation 8.66, the transfer functions from the elevator $\bar{\Delta}_e(s)$ to the pitch angle $\bar{\Theta}(s)$, the angle of attack $\bar{A}(s)$, and the air speed $\bar{V}(s)$, respectively, can also be derived from the state-space model of Equations 8.64 and 8.65 as follows.

$$\frac{\bar{\Theta}(s)}{\bar{\Delta}_e(s)} = \frac{-2.8791(s - 0.001872)(s + 0.34832)}{(s^2 + 0.6189s + 2.286)(s^2 + 0.02027s + 0.01026)} \tag{8.72a}$$

$$\frac{\bar{A}(s)}{\bar{\Delta}_e(s)} = \frac{-0.051453(s + 56.185)(s^2 + 0.02361s + 0.01056)}{(s^2 + 0.6189s + 2.286)(s^2 + 0.02027s + 0.01026)} \tag{8.72b}$$

$$\frac{\bar{V}(s)}{\bar{\Delta}_e(s)} = \frac{-3.8114(s + 6.6232)(s + 0.18029)(s - 6.5705)}{(s^2 + 0.6189s + 2.286)(s^2 + 0.02027s + 0.01026)} \tag{8.72c}$$

The poles of the four transfer functions in Equations 8.72a, 8.72b, 8.72c, and 8.66 are identical. They are the two pairs of complex conjugate poles shown in Equation 8.67—one pair associates with the long-period dynamics mode and the other with the short-period mode. However, the zeros of these four transfer functions are quite different. We will see that the time-domain responses of the longitudinal flight dynamics systems are mainly determined by the poles and zeros of these transfer functions.

The open-loop manual elevator control step response simulation results are shown in Figure 8.34. The upper-right graph shows that the real elevator control input applied to the aircraft is $\delta_e(t) = -1.26° + 2° u_s(t)$, which is equivalent to applying $\bar{\delta}_e(t) = 2° u_s(t)$ to the input of the linearized state-space model shown in Figure 8.33. The output of the linearized model is

$$\bar{x}(t) = \begin{bmatrix} \bar{V}(t) & \bar{\alpha}(t) & \bar{q}(t) & \bar{\theta}(t) \end{bmatrix}^T$$

Note that the real angle of attack response, $\alpha(t) = \bar{\alpha}(t) + 10°$, and the real pitch angle response, $\theta(t) = \bar{\theta}(t) + 10°$, respectively, are recorded on the upper-right and the bottom-left graphs. The upper-left graph shows the step response of the flight path angle $\gamma(t) = \theta(t) - \alpha(t) = \bar{\theta}(t) - \bar{\alpha}(t)$, while the real air speed $V(t) = \bar{V}(t) + 436$ ft/s is recorded on the bottom right graph.

Steady-State Response Analysis

The simulation shows that the values of V, $\bar{\alpha}$, $\bar{\theta}$, and γ at $t = 1000$ s are

$$V(1000) = 480.5 \text{ ft/s}, \quad \bar{\alpha}(1000) = -2.60°, \quad \bar{\theta}(1000) = 0.16°, \quad \gamma(1000) = 2.76° \qquad (8.73)$$

At the end of the 1,000-second simulation, all the state variable values seem to have reached their steady state. The steady-state values or the final values can also be obtained in frequency domain using the final-value theorem (Theorem 2.27). The theorem and the transfer functions in Equations 8.72a, 8.72b, 8.72c, and 8.66 are employed to obtain the steady-state values of $\bar{V}$, $\bar{\alpha}$, $\bar{\theta}$, and $\bar{\gamma}$ in the following.

$$\bar{V}(\infty) = \lim_{s \to 0} s\bar{V}(s) = \lim_{s \to 0} \frac{-3.8114(s+6.6232)(s+0.18029)(s-6.5705)}{(s^2+0.619s+2.286)(s^2+0.02027s+0.01026)} \frac{2°}{s} \frac{\pi}{180°} = 44.5 \text{ ft/s}$$
$$\qquad (8.74a)$$

$$\bar{\alpha}(\infty) = \lim_{s \to 0} s\bar{A}(s) = \lim_{s \to 0} \frac{-0.051453(s+56.19)(s^2+0.02361s+0.01056)}{(s^2+0.619s+2.286)(s^2+0.02027s+0.01026)} \frac{2°}{s} = -2.60° \qquad (8.74b)$$

$$\bar{\theta}(\infty) = \lim_{s \to 0} s\bar{\Theta}(s) = \lim_{s \to 0} \frac{-2.8791(s-0.001872)(s+0.34832)}{(s^2+0.619s+2.286)(s^2+0.02027s+0.01026)} \frac{2°}{s} = 0.16° \qquad (8.74c)$$

$$\bar{\gamma}(\infty) = \lim_{s \to 0} s\bar{\Gamma}(s) = \lim_{s \to 0} \frac{0.051453(s+4.3935)(s-4.1059)(s-0.03491)}{(s^2+0.619s+2.286)(s^2+0.02027s+0.01026)} \frac{2°}{s} = 2.76° \qquad (8.74d)$$

Note that the steady-state real air speed is

$$V(\infty) = \bar{V}(\infty) + 436 \text{ ft/s} = (44.5 + 436) \text{ ft/s} = 480.5 \text{ ft/s}$$

Hence, the simulation steady-state responses shown in Equation 8.73 match perfectly with the final values in Equation 8.74 obtained by final-value theorem.

Remark 8.22 (Control of the Flight Path Angle)

The control of the flight path angle γ is achieved via the changes of the pitch angle θ and the angle of attack α. From the simulation results in Figure 8.34, it is observed that a $2°$ increase of the elevator control input δ_e has caused the angle of attack to go down from $\bar{\alpha} = 0°$ to $\bar{\alpha} = -2.60°$ at steady state, but it has very little effect on the steady-state response of the pitch angle with final value, which slightly moves up from $\bar{\theta} = 0°$ to $\bar{\theta} = 0.16°$. Thus, the flight path angle will go up to $\gamma = \bar{\theta} - \bar{\alpha} = 0.16° - (2.60°) = 2.76°$. On the other hand, you can conduct a similar simulation using the thrust control δ_T as the input and you will observe that the increase of the thrust will cause the pitch angle $\bar{\theta}$ and the flight path angle γ to go up at steady state without much effect on the steady-state value of the angle of attack. ∎

Transient Response Analysis

Recall that longitudinal dynamics has two pairs of complex conjugate poles as shown in Equation 8.67. The pair $-\alpha_L \pm j\omega_L$ is associated with the long-period dynamics mode, and the other, $-\alpha_S \pm j\omega_S$, with the short-period mode. Since the damping factor α_S is about 30 times large than α_L, the short-period mode will decay much faster than the long-period mode. Therefore, under normal circumstances the long-period mode will be the dominant one. As shown in Figure 8.34, **the step responses of $\gamma(t)$, $\bar{\theta}(t)$, and $V(t)$ oscillate with the same long period** $T_L = 2\pi/\omega_L = 62.4$ s. The oscillation period of $\gamma(t)$ can be measured from the duration between the first and the second peaks as $T_\gamma = 105 - 42 = 63$ s, which agrees with T_L. The amplitude of oscillation is large due to the small damping ratio $\varsigma = 0.1$. These long-period step responses take more than 500 seconds to converge to their steady-state values.

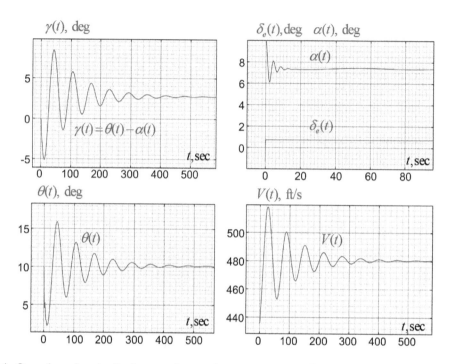

Fig. 8.34: Open-loop longitudinal manual control step responses of F/A–18 due to the elevator input $\delta_e(t) = -1.26° + 2°u_s(t)$.

The open-loop longitudinal manual control step responses of F/A–18 due to the elevator input $\delta_e(t) = -1.26° + 2°u_s(t)$ are obtained by running the following MATLAB program:

```
%% CSDfig8p34.m  5/09/2020 Intro Root Loci Example
d2r=pi/180; r2d=180/pi;
A =[ -2.3893e-02   -2.8317e+01            0  -3.2200e+01;
     -3.2923e-04   -3.6208e-01   1.0000e+00           0;
      4.0491e-11   -2.2115e+00  -2.5319e-01           0;
               0             0   1.0000e+00           0];
B =[ -3.8114e+00    9.5196e-04;
     -5.1453e-02   -3.8506e-07;
     -2.8791e+00            0;
               0            0];
b=B(:,1); c=[0 -1  0  1]; d=0; G_ge=ss(A,b,c,d); c_theta=[0 0 0 1];
G_te=ss(A,b,c_theta,d); c_alpha=[0 1 0 0]; G_ae=ss(A,b,c_alpha,d);
c_V = [1 0 0 0]; G_Ve = ss(A,b,c_V,d);
display('G_ge'), zpk(G_ge),  display('G_te'), zpk(G_te),
```

```
display('G_ae'), zpk(G_ae),  display('G_Ve'), zpk(G_Ve),
%% Step responses
 t=linspace(0,500,5001); [gamma,t]=step(G_ge,t);
 [theta,t]=step(G_te,t); [alpha,t]=step(G_ae,t);
 [v,t]=step(G_Ve,t); [u,t]=step(tf(1,1),t); Gamma=gamma*2;
 Alpha=alpha*2+10; Ele=u*2-1.26; V=v*2*d2r+436; Theta=theta*2+10;
 run('plot22A')
```

where `plot22A.m` is given in the following:

```
%filename: plot22A.m
 ts=t(1:501); figure(4), subplot(2,2,1), plot(t,Gamma,'b-'), grid on,
 grid minor, title('Gamma'), subplot(2,2,2),
 plot(ts,Ele(1:501),'r-',ts,Alpha(1:501),'b-'), grid on, grid minor,
 title('Elevator,AoA'), subplot(2,2,3), plot(t,Theta,'b-'), grid on,
 grid minor, title('Pitch') subplot(2,2,4), plot(t,V,'b-'), grid on,
 grid minor, title('Speed V')
```

One may wonder why the angle of attack step response $\bar{\alpha}(t)$ is not dominated by the long-period mode. It is because the angle of attack transfer function $\bar{A}(s)/\bar{\Delta}_e(s)$ has one pair of complex conjugate zeros that are almost identical to the long-period poles. The effect of the long-period mode poles is greatly reduced by these nearby zeros. Hence, the $\bar{\alpha}(t)$ step response is dominated by the short-period mode, with much higher oscillation frequency. The oscillation period of $\bar{\alpha}(t)$ can be roughly measured by the time duration between the second and the third peaks as $T_\alpha = 4.5$ s, which agrees with the oscillation period computed based on ω_S, $T_S = 2\pi/\omega_S = 4.25$ s.

It is also observed that the initial movements of $\gamma(t)$ and $\bar{\theta}(t)$ were in the opposite direction of the intended motion. Both $\gamma(t)$ and $\bar{\theta}(t)$ move down in the first 10 seconds before reversing up to slowly converge toward the steady-state values. These phenomena are caused by the RHP zeros of their respective transfer functions $\bar{\Gamma}(s)/\bar{\Delta}_e(s)$ and $\bar{\Theta}(s)/\bar{\Delta}_e(s)$.

The angle of attack transfer function $\bar{A}(s)/\bar{\Delta}_e(s)$ has no RHP zeros; hence, it does not have the initial opposite movement issue. However, not all RHP zero, will lead to an initial opposite movement. The air speed transfer function $\bar{V}(s)/\bar{\Delta}_e(s)$ has a RHP zero at $s = 6.5705$, but its initial movement is in the intended up direction; apparently it has no initial opposite movement. This RHP zero does not cause any initial opposite movement issue due to its large distance from the imaginary axis.

Remark 8.23 (Poor Transient Performance of the Uncompensated Longitudinal Dynamics)

The uncompensated longitudinal dynamics is sensitive and susceptible to disturbances and control actions. Due to the extremely small damping factor, poor damping ratio, long oscillation period, and the initial opposite movement caused by the RHP zeros that are close to the imaginary axis, it is very difficult, if not impossible, to manually control the aircraft without a feedback compensator.

∎

8.6.2 PI Controller Design for F/A–18 Flight Path Control

The block diagram of the feedback PI control system is shown in Figure 8.35, where the state-space model (A, B_e, C) was given in Equations 8.64 and 8.65, and the transfer function from $\bar{\delta}_e$ to γ,

$$G_p(s) = \Gamma(s)/\bar{\Delta}_e(s) = C(sI - A)^{-1}B_e$$

was given in Equation 8.66.

The loop transfer function of the PI feedback control system shown in Figure 8.35 is

$$KG(s) = K\frac{0.051453\,(s+4.3935)\,(s-4.1059)\,(s-0.03491)\,(s+1)}{s(s^2+0.6189s+2.286)(s^2+0.02027s+0.01026)} \tag{8.75}$$

Note that the PI controller has added one pole, $p_5 = 0$, and one zero, $z_4 = -1$, to the loop transfer function $KG(s)$. Hence, the closed-loop characteristic equation is

$$1 + KG(s) = 0$$

and the root loci diagram of the closed-loop system is shown in Figure 8.36. The upper-left graph of the figure shows a more complete root loci diagram, but the part of root loci involving p_1, p_2, p_5, and z_2 are crowded together around the origin area and only can be seen in the upper-right graph with expanded view.

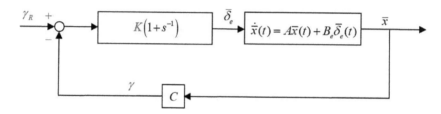

Fig. 8.35: PI controller for F/A–18 flight path angle control problem.

The objective is to find a best gain value of K to achieve closed-loop system stability, zero or small steady-state error, and an optimal transient response subject to the control-input constraints. When $K = 0$, all the roots (poles) are at p_1, p_2, p_3, p_4, and p_5. As K increases from $K = 0$, the root loci branch originating from $p_5 = 0$ will move on the real axis toward the left and reach at $z_4 = -1$ when $K \to \infty$. Meanwhile, the two branches originating from the short-period poles $p_3 = -0.3095 + j1.48$ and $p_4 = -0.3095 - j1.48$ will move to the left and bend toward the real axis and meet at the break-in point $s = -8.08$ when $K = 251$, then split into two branches, both on the real axis—one toward the right to the zero $z_1 = -4.3935$ and the other toward the infinity on the negative real axis, which is the only one asymptote of this root loci diagram.

The last two branches start from the long-period poles $p_1 = -0.010133 + j0.10077$ and $p_2 = -0.010133 - j0.10077$. As K increases, the two branches will move to the right and intersect the imaginary axis at $\pm j0.0828$, when $K = 0.00856$. After crossing to the right half plane, the two branches will continue to bend toward the real axis and meet at $s = 0.0811$ when $K = 0.0758$. Then, as K continues to increase, the two branches now are both on the real axis—one moving toward the right to the zero $z_3 = 4.1059$, and another toward the left to the zero $z_2 = 0.034907$.

The four graphs on Figure 8.36 are obtained from the same root locus plot generated using the following MATLAB code:

```
% CSDfig8p36 Use rlocus(G,K) for F/A-18 PI control
 Ki=1, s=tf('s'); Np=0.051453*(s+4.3935)*(s-4.1059)*(s-0.03491);
 Dp=(s^2+0.6189*s+2.286)*(s^2+0.02027*s+0.01026);
 Gp=Np/Dp; Gc=(s+Ki)/s; G=Gc*Gp;
 figure(10), K=logspace(-3,3,1000); rlocus(G,K)
```

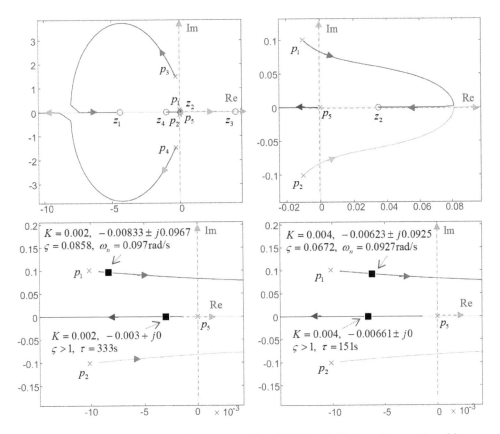

Fig. 8.36: Root locus design of the PI controller for F/A–18 flight path control problem.

From the root loci diagram, we can observe how the gain K will affect the root locations on the five branches, and the closed-loop system behavior will be determined mainly by these five root locations. We will see some of the root locations are more dominant than the others. In general, the closed-loop system poles that are closer to the imaginary axis are the dominant ones. To choose the right value of the gain K, the first step is to find the range of K that will guarantee the stability of the closed-loop system. **The stability range of K is $0 < K < 0.00856$** since the two branches originating from p_1 and p_2 will cross the imaginary axis entering into the right half s-plane if $K > 0.00856$ and the root before entering the real branch between p_5 and z_4 was in the right half of s-plane when $K < 0$.

In the following, we will choose two K values, $K = 0.002$ as shown in the lower-left graph, and $K = 0.004$ in the lower-right graph of Figure 8.36, and compare their corresponding closed-loop system pole locations and time-domain performances.

Root Locus Design with $K = 0.002$

If K is selected as $K = 0.002$, the five closed-loop system poles are

$$s_5 = -0.003 = -\alpha_5, \quad \begin{matrix} s_1 \\ s_2 \end{matrix} = -0.00833 \pm j0.0967 := -\alpha_1 \pm j\omega_1, \quad \begin{matrix} s_3 \\ s_4 \end{matrix} = -0.31 \pm j1.48 := -\alpha_3 \pm j\omega_3$$

$$(8.76)$$

and their associated time constant and damping ratio, natural frequency are obtained as follows:

$$s_5: \quad \tau_5 = 1/\alpha_5 = 333s$$

$$s_1, s_2: \quad \tau_1 = 1/\alpha_1 = 120s, \quad \varsigma = 0.086, \quad \omega_n = 0.097 \text{ad/s}, \quad o.s. = 76.3\%$$

$$s_3, s_4: \quad \tau_3 = 1/\alpha_3 = 3.23s, \quad \varsigma = 0.205, \quad \omega_n = 1.51 \text{ rad/s}, \quad o.s. = 51.8\%$$

Note that the damping factor α_3 is 103 times and 37 times, respectively, larger than α_5 and α_1; therefore, the effect of the poles at s_3 and s_4 will decay much earlier and become irrelevant. Comparably, since the damping factor α_1 is only **2.8 times larger than** α_5, **it has slight influence at the early time to cause some oscillations that will die out exponentially with time constant 120 s. From then on, the dominant pole s_5 will be the only one left to dictate the time response. The dominant pole** $s_5 = -0.003$ **is real, with large time constant 333 s; hence, it causes slow response but contributes no oscillations,** as shown in the graphs of Figure 8.37.

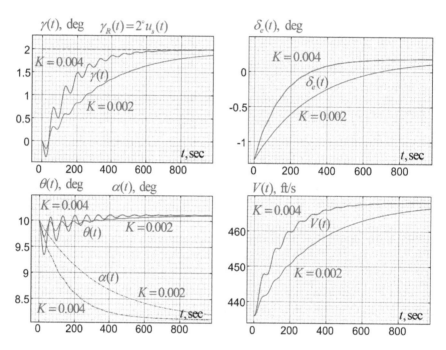

Fig. 8.37: Simulation results of F/A–18 aircraft using PI controller and root locus design.

A MATLAB simulation program is created based on the PI feedback control system shown in Figure 8.35, and the flight path angle command is assumed to be a 2° step function. The graphs of Figure 8.37 show two simulation results: one with $K = 0.002$ in blue, and the other with $K = 0.004$ in red. The graph on the upper left shows the two flight path angle responses $\gamma(t)$ due to the reference input $\gamma_R(t) = 2°u_s(t)$ for both $K = 0.002$ and $K = 0.004$, respectively. The upper-right graph reveals the control-input efforts $\delta_e(t)$ dictated by the feedback controller. The angle of attack responses $\alpha(t)$ are also shown in this graph. The pitch angle $\theta(t)$ and the air speed $V(t)$ responses are shown in the lower-left and the lower-right graphs, respectively.

From the blue step responses $\gamma(t)$ and $\theta(t)$, shown on the upper-left and lower-left graphs of Figure 8.37, it is observed that the step response rises extremely slowly as an exponential-like curve with time constant close to $\tau_5 = 333$ s. It also can be seen that the small oscillations in the first 300 s are contributed by the pair of complex conjugate poles at s_1 and s_2. The period of the oscillations can be approximately measured from the peak-to-peak time of the $\theta(t)$ plot as $T_{pp} = 192s - 127s = 65s$, which closely matches the period computed based on the frequency $\omega_1 = 0.0967$ rad/s: $T_1 = 2\pi/0.0967 = 65$ s. **The pair of complex conjugate poles at s_3 and s_4 virtually have no visible effect on the step response.**

The design with the PI feedback control with $K = 0.002$ has shown great improvement over the open-loop manual control. However, the flight path angle rises very slowly, and only reaches 95% of its target value $2°$ after 1000s of time. **The response time can be improved if the pole s_5 on the lower-left graph of Figure 8.36 can be moved to the left. However, as we increase K to move the pole s_5 to the left, the poles s_1 and s_2 will move to the right at the same time. Hence, the pole s_5 should not be moved too much to the left to prevent s_1 and s_2 from becoming dominant poles.** If s_1 and s_2 become dominant poles, the associated time response will be oscillatory.

The four graphs of the simulation results of the PI flight path angle control of F/A–18 ahown on Figure 8.37 are obtained from using the following MATLAB program:

```
%% CSDfig8p37Step.m  5/09/2020 Intro Root Loci Example
d2r=pi/180; r2d=180/pi;
A =[ -2.3893e-02  -2.8317e+01           0  -3.2200e+01;
     -3.2923e-04  -3.6208e-01  1.0000e+00           0;
      4.0491e-11  -2.2115e+00  -2.5319e-01           0;
               0            0  1.0000e+00           0];
B =[ -3.8114e+00   9.5196e-04;
     -5.1453e-02  -3.8506e-07;
     -2.8791e+00            0;
               0            0];
b=B(:,1); c=[0 -1  0  1]; d=0; G_ge=ss(A,b,c,d); c_theta=[0 0 0 1];
G_te=ss(A,b,c_theta,d); c_alpha=[0 1 0 0]; G_ae=ss(A,b,c_alpha,d);
c_V = [1 0 0 0]; G_Ve = ss(A,b,c_V,d); Gc=tf([1 1],[1 0]);
%% Design A  with K=0.002
K=0.002, Del=1+K*Gc*(G_ge); G_gR=K*Gc*G_ge/Del; G_eR=K*Gc/Del;
G_tR=K*Gc*G_te/Del; G_VR=K*Gc*G_Ve/Del; G_aR=K*Gc*G_ae/Del
display('G_gR'), zpk(G_gR),  display('G_tR'), zpk(G_tR),
display('G_aR'), zpk(G_aR),  display('G_VR'), zpk(G_VR),
display('G_eR'), zpk(G_eR),
% Step responses
t=linspace(0,1000,10001); [gamma,t]=step(G_gR,t);
[theta,t]=step(G_tR,t); [alpha,t]=step(G_aR,t); [v,t]=step(G_VR,t);
[u,t]=step(G_eR,t); Gamma=gamma*2; Alpha=alpha*2+10; Ele=u*2-1.26;
V=v*2*d2r+436; Theta=theta*2+10; run('plot22a')
%% Design B  with K=0.004
K=0.004, Del=1+K*Gc*(G_ge); G_gR=K*Gc*G_ge/Del; G_eR=K*Gc/Del;
G_tR=K*Gc*G_te/Del; G_VR=K*Gc*G_Ve/Del; G_aR=K*Gc*G_ae/Del
display('G_gR'), zpk(G_gR),  display('G_tR'), zpk(G_tR),
display('G_aR'), zpk(G_aR),  display('G_VR'), zpk(G_VR),
display('G_eR'), zpk(G_eR),
% Step responses
t=linspace(0,1000,10001); [gamma,t]=step(G_gR,t);
[theta,t]=step(G_tR,t); [alpha,t]=step(G_aR,t); [v,t]=step(G_VR,t);
[u,t]=step(G_eR,t); Gamma=gamma*2; Alpha=alpha*2+10; Ele=u*2-1.26;
V=v*2*d2r+436; Theta=theta*2+10; run('plot22b')
```

where plot22a.m is given below, and plot22b.m is a copy of it with b replaced by r.

```
%filename: plot22a.m
 figure(4), subplot(2,2,1), plot(t,Gamma,'b-'), grid on, title('Gamma'),
```

```
hold on, subplot(2,2,2), plot(t,Ele,'b-'), grid on, title('Elevator,AoA'),
hold on, subplot(2,2,3), plot(t,Theta,'b-',t,Alpha,'b--'), grid on,
title('Pitch,AoA'), hold on, subplot(2,2,4), plot(t,V,'b-'), grid on,
title('Speed V'), hold on
```

Root Locus Design with $K = 0.004$

If K is selected to be $K = 0.004$, the five closed-loop system poles are

$$s_5 = -0.00661 = -\alpha_5, \quad \begin{matrix} s_1 \\ s_2 \end{matrix} = -0.00623 \pm j0.0925 := -\alpha_1 \pm j\omega_1, \quad \begin{matrix} s_3 \\ s_4 \end{matrix} = -0.31 \pm j1.48 := -\alpha_3 \pm j\omega_3$$

(8.77)

and their associated time constant and damping ratio, natural frequency are obtained as follows:

$$s_5: \quad \tau_5 = 1/\alpha_5 = 151s$$
$$s_1, s_2: \quad \tau_1 = 1/\alpha_1 = 160s, \quad \varsigma = 0.0672, \quad \omega_n = 0.0927 \text{ rad}/s, \quad o.s. = 80.9\%$$
$$s_3, s_4: \quad \tau_3 = 1/\alpha_3 = 3.23s, \quad \varsigma = 0.205, \quad \omega_n = 1.51 \text{ rad}/s, \quad o.s. = 51.8\%$$

By increasing K from 0.002 to 0.004, the real branch pole s_5 has slightly moved to the left to change the damping factor α_5 from 0.003 to 0.00661, which leads to the reduction of the time constant τ from 333 s to 151 s. Meanwhile, the complex poles s_1 and s_2 have moved closer to the imaginary axis to change the damping factor α_1 from 0.00833 to 0.00623, or equivalently, to reduce the damping ratio ς from 0.086 to 0.0672. **The real pole s_5 and the complex poles s_1 and s_2 are both dominant.**

On the upper-left and lower-left graphs of Figure 8.37, **the red step response waveform shows its faster rise than the blue one, but at the expense of more oscillations due to the complex poles s_1 and s_2.** The period of the oscillations can be approximately measured from the peak-to-peak time of the $\bar{\theta}(t)$ plot as $T_{pp} = (200 - 132)$ s = 68 s, which closely matches the period computed based on the frequency $\omega_1 = 0.0925$ rad/s: $T_1 = 2\pi/0.0925 = 68$ s. The pair of complex conjugate poles at s_3 and s_4 do not have perceivable effect on the step response. A close-up view of these two graphs at the first 20 seconds, both red and blue step responses all went to the opposite direction before reversing back to the intended positive direction, which is the nonminimum-phase effect caused by the right-half plane zeros.

Remark 8.24 (PI Controller Design for F/A–18 Flight Path Control)

From the root locus analysis of the PI flight path control for the F/A–18 aircraft, it is clear that there are three groups of root loci branches. The two branches originating from p_3 and p_4 can only move to the left to increase their already large damping factor $\alpha_3 = \alpha_5 = 0.309$; hence, the poles s_3 and s_4 on these two branches will not have much noticeable effect on the closed-loop response except in the first 3 seconds no matter what value of K is chosen. Meanwhile, the real pole s_5 is leaving from p_5 at the origin toward the left for $z_4 = -1$ and the two complex poles s_1 and s_2 originating from p_1 and p_2 are heading to the right toward the imaginary axis. These two groups are moving in opposite directions. When K is very small (e.g. $K = 0.002$) s_5 is the dominant pole that leads to a terribly slow response.

On the other hand, s_1 and s_2 will increase their influence or even become dominant, which leads to large up and down oscillations when K increases. **Apparently there is no acceptable compromise; the response at $K = 0.004$, which is approximately a better compromise, is still slow and oscillatory. This issue still remains even the zero z_4 is placed elsewhere.**

Adding zeros and/or poles to the PI controller, as we did in Section 8.5, or augmenting an inner feedback loop to the controller structure may be helpful in providing a more friendly pole-zero pattern in the root locus diagram; however, the procedure is tedious and it still employs only the flight path angle information, instead of utilizing the full available information, in the feedback control system design.

∎

8.6.3 State-Space Pole Placement and Root Locus Design for F/A–18 Flight Path Control

The root locus design approach with the PI controller structure discussed in the previous subsection, Section 8.6.2, does not provide an acceptable solution for the F/A–18 flight path tracking control problem. The response is either too slow or too oscillatory. In this subsection, we will employ the state feedback structure with tracking integrator, shown in Figure 8.38, in the root locus design to improve the flight path tracking control performance.

In the block diagram shown in Figure 8.38, the state-space model (A, B_e, C) was given in Equations 8.64 and 8.65. The state-feedback gain matrix F is chosen to place the closed-loop system poles at some favorable pole locations for the loop transfer function in root locus design. The integrator s^{-1} is employed to serve as the internal model to achieve zero-error step response at steady state, and the integral parameter K is to be determined using the root locus design approach so that the closed-loop system poles are at desired locations to provide desired transient response.

The state-space pole placement approach discussed in Section 7.5 can be employed to find the state-feedback gain matrix

$$F = \begin{bmatrix} -0.19318 & 0.9557 & 3.2363 & 6.2859 \end{bmatrix} \tag{8.78}$$

so that the eigenvalues of $A + B_e F$ are at -0.17, -5.9, and $-1.6 \pm j1.8$.

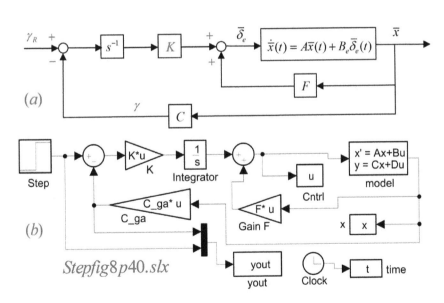

Fig. 8.38: The state-feedback controller with integrator tracking for F/A–18 flight path control.

Recall that the root locus diagram is constructed based on the root locus equation $1 + KG(s) = 0$ as defined in Equation 8.41, in which $KG(s)$ is called the loop transfer function of the closed-loop system shown in Figure 8.17. Hence, the loop transfer function of the closed-loop system in Figure 8.38 is

$KG(s)$, where $-G(s)$ is the transfer function from u_K to x_i assuming the block K is removed from the loop. This $G(s)$ can be found as a rational function in s,

$$G(s) = s^{-1}C(sI-(A+B_eF))^{-1}B_e = \frac{0.051453\,(s+4.3935)\,(s-4.1059)\,(s-0.034907)}{s(s+0.17)\,(s+5.9)\left((s+1.6)^2+1.8^2\right)} \quad (8.79)$$

or in the form of a state-space model,

$$G(s): \quad \begin{bmatrix} \dot{\bar{x}} \\ \dot{x}_i \end{bmatrix} = \begin{bmatrix} A+B_eF & 0 \\ C & 0 \end{bmatrix}\begin{bmatrix} \bar{x} \\ x_i \end{bmatrix} + \begin{bmatrix} B_e \\ 0 \end{bmatrix}u_k := A_G\begin{bmatrix} \bar{x} \\ x_i \end{bmatrix} + B_Gu_k$$

$$x_i = \begin{bmatrix} 0 & 1 \end{bmatrix}\begin{bmatrix} x \\ x_i \end{bmatrix} := C_G\begin{bmatrix} x \\ x_i \end{bmatrix} \quad (8.80)$$

Note that these two expressions represent exactly the same system: the former in frequency domain and the latter in time domain. It also can be seen that **the numerator polynomial of $G(s)$ in Equation 8.79 is the same as that of the plant transfer function from the elevator control input $\bar{\delta}_e$ to the flight path angle output $\bar{\gamma}$, $G_p(s) = \bar{\Gamma}(s)/\bar{\Delta}_e(s)$, in Equation 8.66. But the poles of $G(s)$ are now the eigenvalues of $A+B_eF$** instead of the poles of $G_p(s)$ in Equation 8.66. These two facts verify that the state-feedback control may alter the pole locations, but it is unable to move the zeros.

Now we are ready to draw the root locus diagram using the following MATLAB code according to the state-feedback matrix F of Equation 8.78 and the $G(s)$ state-space model of Equation 8.80.

```
% CSD Fig8.39 State-feedback rlocus(G,K) for F/A-18 \gamma-tracking
% Draw the root locus diagram according to G(s) in Eq. (8.64)
 A_x =[ -2.3893e-02  -2.8317e+01           0  -3.2200e+01;
        -3.2923e-04  -3.6208e-01  1.0000e+00           0;
         4.0491e-11  -2.2115e+00  -2.5319e-01           0;
                  0            0  1.0000e+00           0];
 B_x =[ -3.8114e+00   9.5196e-04;
        -5.1453e-02  -3.8506e-07;
        -2.8791e+00           0;
                  0           0];
 A=A_x; Be=B_x(:,1);
% Find a state feedback so that the eigenvalues of A+BF are
% at -0.17, -5.9, -1.6+j1.8, and -1.6-j1.8
 P=[-0.17 -5.9 -1.6+1.8i -1.6-1.8i]; F=place(A,Be,P); F=-F;
 damp(A+Be*F); C=[0 -1 0 1];    % track flight path angle;
 A_G=[A+Be*F zeros(4,1); C 0]; B_G=[Be; 0]; C_G=[zeros(1,4) 1];
 D_G=0; G=ss(A_G,B_G,C_G,D_G); pole_G = pole(G); zpk(G),
 [zero_G,gain_G]=zero(G); figure(12); K=logspace(-1,6,1000);
 rlocus(G,K)
```

The root locus diagram associated with the closed-loop system in Figure 8.38 with the state-feedback gain matrix F of Equation 8.78 is shown in Figure 8.39. The left graph of Figure 8.39 shows a more complete overview of the root loci diagram, but the root loci around the origin area is too small to show the details. The enlarged one on the right graph gives a better view of the root loci near the imaginary axis.

The poles of the $G(s)$ in Equation 8.79 or Equation 8.80 include the eigenvalues of $A+B_eF$ together with the integrator pole at the origin:

$$p_1 = -0.17, \quad p_2 = 0, \quad \begin{matrix} p_3 \\ p_4 \end{matrix} = -1.6 \pm j1.8, \quad p_5 = -5.9$$

and the zeros of $G(s)$ are the same as those of $G_p(s)$ in Equation 8.66:

$$z_1 = -4.3935, \quad z_2 = 0.034907, \quad z_3 = 4.1059$$

When $K = 0$, all the roots (closed-loop system poles) are at p_1, p_2, p_3, p_4, and p_5. As $K \to \infty$, the roots will either move to the three zeros, z_1, z_2, and z_3, or approach to the two asymptote straight lines intersecting the real axis at

$$\sigma = \frac{-(z_1 + z_2 + z_3) + (p_1 + p_2 + p_3 + p_4 + p_5)}{5 - 3} = -4.5087$$

with angles $\theta_0 = \pi/2$ and $\theta_1 = -\pi/2$, respectively.

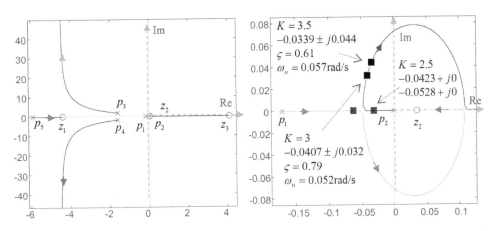

Fig. 8.39: Root locus design of the integral tracking controller with state-feedback compensation for the F/A–18 flight path control problem.

When K is increased from $K = 0$, the root loci branch originating from $p_5 = -5.9$ will move on the real axis toward the right and arrive at $z_1 = -4.3935$ as $K \to \infty$. The two root loci branches started from p_3 and p_4, $-1.6 \pm j1.8$, will move to the left bending up and down, respectively, and approach to the two asymptotes as $K \to \infty$. **The other two branches originating from $p_1 = -0.17$ and $p_2 = 0$ will move toward each other on the negative real axis. When $K = 2.52$, they meet at the break-out point $s = -0.0475$ and split into two branches—one up, and the other down—following the circular trajectory with radius approximately equal to 0.07825. When $K = 6.12$ the two branches will** intersect the imaginary axis at $\pm j0.718$ and move into the RHP. As K increases to $K = 16.4$, the two branches will meet the positive real axis at the break-in point $s = 0.109$ and split into two on the positive real axis—one moves to the left toward $z_2 = 0.034907$ and the other to the right toward $z_3 = 4.1059$.

From the root loci branches shown in Figure 8.39, it is obvious that the roots on the two branches originating from p_1 and p_2 are the dominant poles since the other three branches are much further away from the imaginary axis. We will choose three values of K: $K = 3$, $K = 3.5$, and $K = 2.5$ as shown on the right graph of Figure 8.39, and compare their corresponding closed-loop system pole locations and time-domain performances.

Root Locus Design with $K = 3$

If K is selected to be $K = 3$, the five closed-loop system poles are

$$\begin{matrix} s_1 \\ s_2 \end{matrix} = -0.0407 \pm j0.032 := -\alpha_1 \pm j\omega_1, \quad \begin{matrix} s_3 \\ s_4 \end{matrix} = -1.65 \pm j1.86 := -\alpha_3 \pm j\omega_3, \quad s_5 = -5.88 = -\alpha_5$$

and their associated time constant and damping ratio, natural frequency are obtained as follows.

$$s_1, s_2: \quad \tau_1 = 1/\alpha_1 = 24.6\text{s}, \quad \varsigma = 0.79, \quad \omega_n = 0.052 \text{ rad/s}, \quad o.s. = 1.76\%$$

$$s_3, s_4: \quad \tau_3 = 1/\alpha_3 = 0.61\text{s}, \quad \varsigma = 0.665, \quad \omega_n = 2.49 \text{ rad/s}, \quad o.s. = 6.09\%$$

$$s_5: \quad \tau_5 = 1/\alpha_5 = 0.17\text{s}$$

Note that the damping factor α_1 is 41 times and 144 times, respectively, smaller than α_3 and α_5; therefore, the effect of the poles at s_3, s_4, and s_5 will decay much earlier and become irrelevant.

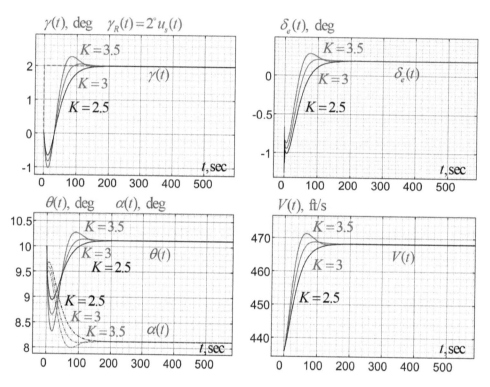

Fig. 8.40: Simulation results of F/A–18 aircraft using integral tracking controller with state-feedback compensation and root locus design.

The Simulink simulation program, Stepfig8p40.slx, shown on Figure 8.38(b), is created based on the state feedback and integral tracking control block diagram shown in Figure 8.38(a). The flight path angle command is assumed to be a $2°$ step function. The graphs of Figure 8.40 show three simulation results: $K = 3$ in blue, $K = 3.5$ in red, and $K = 2.5$ in black. The graph on the upper left shows the three flight path angle responses $\gamma(t)$ due to the reference input $\gamma_R(t) = 2°u_s(t)$ for $K = 3$, $K = 3.5$, and $K = 2.5$, respectively. The upper-right graph reveals the control-input efforts $\delta_e(t)$ dictated by the feedback controller. The angle of attack responses $\alpha(t)$ and the pitch angle response $\theta(t)$ are shown in the lower-left graph. The air speed $V(t)$ responses are shown in the lower-right graph.

From the blue step response $\gamma(t)$ shown on the upper-left graph of Figure 8.40, it is observed that the step response initially goes down in the opposite direction from $0°$ to $-0.8°$ at $t = 13$ s to reverse the moving direction to rise to 90% of the desired value at $t = 73$ s, and continue to reach the peak at $t = 113$ s with less than 2% of overshoot. The initial wrong direction motion was caused by the nonminimum-phase effect due to the RHP zero at $s = 0.034907$. However, this half-period swing is the only visible oscillation and the step response reaches the steady state shortly after $t = 113$ s.

It also can be seen that the half period of the half-period swing can be measured from the valley to peak times in the $\gamma(t)$ plot: $T_{vp} = 113 - 13 = 100$ s, which matches the half period computed based on the frequency $\omega_1 = 0.032$ rad/s (i.e., $T_{vp} = \pi/0.032 = 98.2$ s).

Root Locus Design with $K = 3.5$

If the integral parameter K is slightly changed from $K = 3$ to $K = 3.5$, the s_1 and s_2 closed-loop system poles will move from $-0.0407 \pm j0.032$ to $-0.0339 \pm j0.044$, as shown in the right graph of Figure 8.39. This slight change of K has increased the oscillation frequency ω_1 from 0.032 rad/s to 0.044 rad/s, which would decrease the half-period of the half-period swing from 98.2 s to $\pi/0.044 = 71.4$ s, so that the step response will rise more quickly. However, the damping ratio will reduce from 0.79 to 0.61, and the maximum overshoot will increase from 1.7% to 8.9%.

Root Locus Design with $K = 2.5$

On the other hand, if the integral parameter K is slightly changed from $K = 3$ to $K = 2.5$, the two dominant closed-loop system poles s_1 and s_2 will move from $-0.0407 \pm j0.032$ back to the negative real axis so that the two poles are -0.0423 and -0.0528. Hence, the response will be overdamped, which has no overshoot but is slower than the $K = 3.0$ response.

The four graphs of the simulation results of the PI flight path angle control of F/A–18 ahown on Figure 8.37 are obtained from using the following MATLAB program:

```
% CSDfig8p40.m 5/09/2020  F/A-18 SF rLocus Intgrl Tracking
% Run CSDfig8p39.m before running this program
% call simulink file: Stepfig8p40.slx, plot_regA.m ...
% Run CSDfig8p39.m to obtain A_x, B_x, and F
 A=A_x; B=B_x(:,1); C=eye(4); D=[0 0 0 0]', C_ga=[0 -1 0 1]
 d2r-pi/180; r2d=1/d2r; R_gamma=2*d2r
% Design A: K=3,  % Design B: K=3.5,  % Design C: K=2.5
%% Design A Simulation
 K=3, sim_time=500,
 sim_options=simset('SrcWorkspace', 'current', 'DstWorkspace', 'current');
 open('Stepfig8p40'), sim('Stepfig8p40', [0, sim_time], sim_options);
%% Plot
 Ele=-1.26+u*r2d; V=x(:,1)+436; Alpha=x(:,2)*r2d+10; Theta=x(:,4)*r2d+10;
 Gamma=yout(:,1)*r2d; R=yout(:,2)*r2d; run('plot2x2a');
%% Design B Simulation
 K=3.5, sim_time=500,
 sim_options=simset('SrcWorkspace', 'current', 'DstWorkspace', 'current');
 open('Stepfig8p40'), sim('Stepfig8p40', [0, sim_time], sim_options);
 Ele=-1.26+u*r2d; V=x(:,1)+436; Alpha=x(:,2)*r2d+10; Theta=x(:,4)*r2d+10;
 Gamma=yout(:,1)*r2d; R=yout(:,2)*r2d; run('plot2x2b');
%% Design C Simulation
 K=2.5, sim_time=500,
```

```
sim_options=simset('SrcWorkspace', 'current', 'DstWorkspace', 'current');
open('Stepfig8p40'), sim('Stepfig8p40', [0, sim_time], sim_options);
Ele=-1.26+u*r2d; V=x(:,1)+436; Alpha=x(:,2)*r2d+10; Theta=x(:,4)*r2d+10;
Gamma=yout(:,1)*r2d; R=yout(:,2)*r2d; run('plot2x2c');
```

where `plot2x2a.m` is given below. The other two copies, `plot2x2b.m` and `plot2x2c.m`, will print in red and black colors, respectively.

```
%filename: plot2x2a.m
figure(4), subplot(2,2,1), plot(t,Gamma,'b-'), grid on, title('Gamma'),
hold on, subplot(2,2,2), plot(t,Ele,'b-'), grid on, title('Elevator,AoA'),
hold on, subplot(2,2,3), plot(t,Theta,'b-',t,Alpha,'b--'), grid on,
title('Pitch,AoA'), hold on, subplot(2,2,4), plot(t,V,'b-'), grid on,
title('Speed V'), hold on
```

8.6.4 Comparison of the PI Controller and the Integral Controller with State-Feedback Compensation

It seems to be an unfair comparison since in the state-feedback compensation all the four state variables of the longitudinal dynamics system are assumed available for feedback, while in the PI controller only the flight path angle is utilized in the design. However, these state variables are usually available—either by direct measurement or state reconstruction using the observer and estimation theory, which will be covered in Chapter 11. More information utilized in the controller design will certainly make the control system perform better.

By comparing the root locus diagrams in Figures 8.36 and 8.39, it can be seen that the state-feedback has replaced the LTF poles and greatly changed the shape of the root loci graph so that a more favorable set of closed-loop system poles can be obtained.

In Figure 8.36, the best possible range of the K values is between $K = 0.002$ and 0.004. With $K = 0.002$, the damping factor of the dominant pole $s_5 = -0.003$ is 0.003, which implies a 333 s time constant and more than 1,000 seconds of settling time in step response. It is an unacceptable slow step response. Furthermore, the nearby complex conjugate poles s_1 and s_2 at $-0.00833 \pm j0.0967$ will add some long-period lightly damped oscillation to the response. By increasing K, the s_5 pole will move to the left to decrease the time constant and make the response a little bit faster. But doing so will at the same time move the complex conjugate poles s_1 and s_2 to the right to make the response more oscillatory. At $K = 0.004$, the pair of complex poles s_1 and s_2 are at $-0.00623 \pm j0.0925$, which are as dominant as the real $s_5 = -0.00661$. It is much more oscillatory and it is still slow. There is no good choice available out of this root locus diagram.

On the other hand, the root locus diagram in Figure 8.39 provides much better options to find a set of closed-loop system poles for an acceptable closed-loop system performance. In Figure 8.39, only the root loci branches originating from $p_1 = -0.17$ and $p_2 = 0$ are relevant since the damping factors associated with the other three root loci branches are much larger and their associated response will decay much earlier. With the choices of $K = 3.0$, $K = 3.5$, and $K = 2.5$, and their corresponding root locations on the right graph of the figure, the damping factors are about 10 times larger than those of the dominant poles in Figure 8.36. The damping ratios are also about 10 times larger than those of the PI control design. Therefore, the performance of the closed-loop system performance designed by the state feedback, together with the integral tracking, is about 10 times faster in step response with much less oscillation.

The time-domain responses foretold by these observations of the root-locus diagrams are verified by the simulation results shown in Figures 8.37, 8.40, and 8.41, and in Table 8.2.

Table 8.2: Performance comparison of the four closed-loop systems with their respective controllers $K = 3.0$, $K = 3.5$, $K = 2.5$ in the state-feedback with integral tracking structure and $K = 0.002$, $K = 0.004$ in PI controller structure.

K	**SfI** $K = 3.0$	**SfI** $K = 3.5$	**SfI** $K = 2.5$	**PI** $K = 0.002$	**PI** $K = 0.004$
Rise time	$74s$	$58s$	$100s$	$790s$	$380s$
Settle time	$80s$	$110s$	$110s$	$1000s$	$460s$
Max overshoot	2%	14%	0%	0%	0%
Initial NMP dip	40%	50%	30%	9%	$17s$
Osc amplitude	0%	0%	0%	18%	$35s$
Osc period	N.A.	N.A.	N.A.	$65s$	$68s$
S.S. tracking error	0	0	0	0	0
δ_e deflection	$(-1.26°, 0.2°)$	$(-1.26°, 0.2°)$	$(-1.26°, 0.2°)$	$(-1.26°, 0.29°)$	$(-1.26°, 0.2°)$

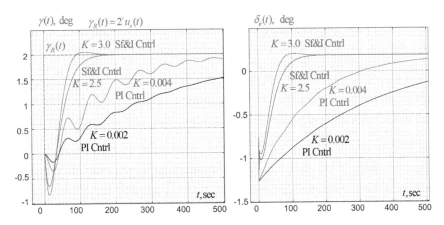

Fig. 8.41: Comparison of F/A–18 aircraft flight path tracking responses using the PI controller and the integral tracking controller with state-feedback compensation.

8.7 Aircraft Altitude Regulation via Flight Path Angle Tracking Control

In the previous section, Section 8.6, we discussed how to design a feedback control system so that the flight path angle of the aircraft can follow the flight path angle command. In practice, the flight path angle tracking control is often employed to regulate the flight altitude of aircraft.

Although a six degree-of-freedom aircraft dynamics has 12 state variables, total air speed V, angle of attack α, side slip β, roll rate p, pitch rate q, yaw rate r, roll angle ϕ, pitch angle θ, yaw angle ψ, latitude position pN, longitude position pE, and the altitude h, only eight of them, V, α, β, p, q, r, ϕ, and θ, are directly controlled by the four control inputs: aileron δ_a, rudder δ_r, elevator δ_e, and thrust δ_T. The other four state variables, including pN, pE, h, and ψ, are functions of the 8 trim (directly controlled) state variables. The relationship between the derivative of the altitude $\dot{h}$ and the trim state variables is described by

$$\dot{h}(t) = V \sin\theta \cos\alpha \cos\beta - V \sin\phi \cos\theta \sin\beta - V \cos\phi \cos\theta \cos\beta \sin\alpha \qquad (8.81)$$

If the lateral system is controlled to keep the aircraft fly straight (i.e., $\phi = 0$ and $\beta = 0$), then the altitude equation can be simplified to the following,

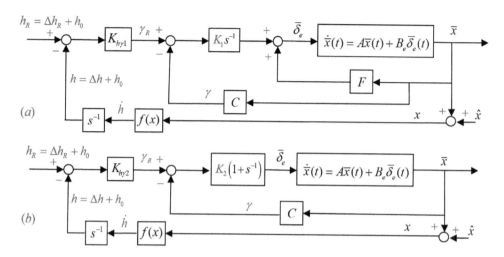

Fig. 8.42: Flight path angle tracking control is employed to achieve F/A–18 altitude regulation.

$$\dot{h}(t) = V \sin \theta \cos \alpha - V \cos \theta \sin := f(x) \tag{8.82}$$

The altitude regulation via the flight path angle tracking control can be achieved based on either one of the two schematic block diagrams shown in Figure 8.42. These two block diagrams are similar. The only difference is in the flight path angle tracking controller. **Figure 8.42(a) employs the state feedback with integral tracking control structure, as shown in Figure 8.38 while Figure 8.42(b) adopts the PI controller, as in Figure 8.35.**

Note that in the altitude equation of Equation 8.82, the derivative of the altitude $\dot{h}$ is a function of the actual-value state variables $x(t)$ instead of the perturbed-value state variables $\bar{x}(t)$ in the linearized state-space model. Since the nominal flight trim is chosen to be the straight-level flight with 10° angle attack, as shown in Equation 8.63, the relationship between $x(t)$ and $\bar{x}(t)$ is shown as

$$
\begin{aligned}
x(t) &= [V(t) \ \alpha(t) \ q(t) \ \theta(t)]^T = \bar{x}(t) + x^* \\
&= [\bar{V}(t) \ \bar{\alpha}(t) \ \bar{q}(t) \ \bar{\theta}(t)]^T + [436 \ 10\pi/180 \ 0 \ 10\pi/180]^T
\end{aligned}
\tag{8.83}
$$

where 10° and 0°/s are replaced by $10\pi/180$ rad and 0 rad/s, respectively, because in computations we should only use radians instead of degrees as the unit of angles.

The integration of $\dot{h}$ is $h = \Delta h + h_0$, where h_0 is the initial value of h. The altitude reference input is $h_R = \Delta h_R + h_0$, where Δh_R is the desired increment of altitude. The objective of the outer-loop control is to continuously adjust the desired flight path γ_R according to the difference $\Delta h_R - \Delta h$ until the difference reaches zero. The inner-loop flight path integral gains K_1 and K_2 were obtained in the previous section using the root locus diagram as $K_1 = 3.5$ and $K_2 = 0.004$, respectively, for the state-feedback with integral tracking and the PI control design approaches. The outer loop $h - \gamma$ gain $K_{h\gamma1}$ and $K_{h\gamma2}$ can also be chosen using root locus design or simply by a few iterative simulations. These $h - \gamma$ gains are chosen as $K_{h\gamma1} = 2 \times 10^{-5}$ and $K_{h\gamma2} = 6 \times 10^{-6}$ in the altitude tracking control simulations results shown in Figure 8.43.

Note that in these flight path and altitude control examples, only the elevator is employed to control the flight path with the thrust fixed at the trim. If both the elevator and the thrust are utilized, the performance would have been better.

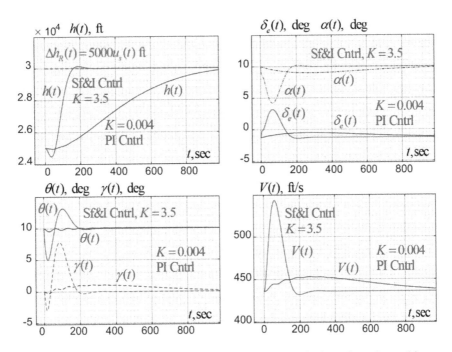

Fig. 8.43: Simulations of altitude regulation of F/A–18 using flight path angle tracking control.

8.8 Exercise Problems

P8.1a: Consider the typical feedback control system shown in Figure 8.44. Let the plant be $G(s) = \frac{1}{s+1}$, and the controller be a proportional controller $K(s) = K_p$. Note that there are two external inputs: the reference input $r(t)$ and the disturbance input $d(t)$. Let the transfer function from $R(s)$ to $E(s)$ and the transfer function from $D(s)$ to $E(s)$ of the closed-loop system be denoted by $G_{er}(s)$ and $G_{ed}(s)$, respectively. Then the error response $E(s)$ will be

$$E(s) = G_{er}(s)R(s) + G_{ed}(s)D(s) \tag{8.84}$$

Find the transfer functions $G_{er}(s)$ and $G_{ed}(s)$ in terms of the parameter K_p.

P8.1b: Let $r(t) = 10u_s(t)$ and $d(t) = -2u_s(t)$, where $u_s(t)$ is the unit step function. Find the steady-state tracking error

$$\lim_{t \to \infty} e(t) = \lim_{s \to 0} sE(s)$$

in terms of the parameter K_p by using Equation 8.84 and Theorem 2.27, the final-value theorem.

P8.1c: Repeat Problem P8.1a with the controller replaced by the PI controller $K(s) = K_p + \frac{K_i}{s}$. Find the transfer functions $G_{er}(s)$ and $G_{ed}(s)$ in terms of the parameters K_p and K_i.

P8.1d: Repeat Problem P8.1b with the controller replaced by the PI controller $K(s) = K_p + \frac{K_i}{s}$. Find the steady-state tracking error

$$\lim_{t \to \infty} e(t) = \lim_{s \to 0} sE(s)$$

in terms of the parameters K_p and K_i by using Equation 8.84 and Theorem 2.27, the final-value theorem.

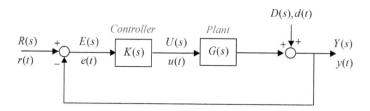

Fig. 8.44: A typical feedback control system structure.

P8.1e: Comment on the steady-state tracking error results of Problems P8.1b and P8.1d, and explain what causes the difference.

P8.2a: Consider a simplified version of Equation 8.16 as

$$\dot{x}(t) = \frac{-c}{M}x^2(t) + \frac{1}{M}u(t) := f(x(t), u(t)) \tag{8.85}$$

where the single state variable $x(t)$ represents the velocity of the vehicle, $u(t)$ is the force generated by the engine to move the vehicle, $M = 1,929$ kg is the mass of the vehicle, $c = 0.643$ kg/m is the viscosity coefficient of the vehicle traveling in the air. The nonlinear function $f(x(t), u(t))$ is included for notational consistency with the Jacobian linearization process of Appendix C. The equilibriums can be obtained by setting $\dot{x}(t) = 0$, or by setting the right-hand side of Equation 8.85 to be zero,

$$-c(x^*)^2 + u^* = 0 \quad \rightarrow \quad u^* = 0.643(x^*)^2 \tag{8.86}$$

This equilibrium equation specifies the relationship between the velocity x^* and the input force u^*. Unlike the simple inverted pendulum example in Section 4.4.2, which has only two equilibrium points, there are infinite many equilibrium points on the equilibrium curve line specified by Equation 8.86. Recall that in Section 8.2.1, we selected $x^* = 30$ m/s, which leads to $u^* = 0.643(30)^2 = 578.7$ N, and the linearized state-space model at this equilibrium $(x^*, u^*) = (30$ m/s, 578.7 N) was found as Equation 8.19. Now, assume we want to investigate the system behavior when the vehicle velocity is around 20 m/s, what equilibrium point (x^*, u^*) shall we select?

P8.2b: At the equilibrium point $(x^*, u^*) = (20$ m/s, $u^*)$, which you have just chosen at the end of Problem P8.2a, find the linearized state equation of the vehicle $\dot{\bar{x}}(t) = A\bar{x}(t) + B\bar{u}(t)$ according to Equation C.5 of Appendix C.

P8.3a: Consider the proportional feedback control system on Figure 8.45. The objective is to draw the root loci diagram for the system according to the root loci construction rules in Section 8.3.1 and then

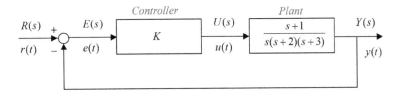

Fig. 8.45: Review the root loci construction rules.

determine a value of K based on the diagram so that the closed-loop system poles are at optimal locations to deliver a desired performance. The first step is to follow Rules 1, 2, and 3 to identify the loop transfer function (LTF) of the system, the number of LTF poles as n, the number of LTF zeros as m, and then mark the n LTF poles and m LTF zeros on the complex plane as $\times$ and $\circ$, respectively.

P8.3b: The second step is to draw the root loci segments on the real axis of the complex plane according to Rule 4. Although this step is quite straightforward, it is the most important step in the root loci construction. Note that all root loci are originating from LTF pole locations and terminated either at LTF zero locations or at infinity on the asymptotes, which will be given by Rule 5.

P8.3c: Follow Rule 5 or Equation 8.54 to compute the angles and the intersection of the asymptotes with the real axis. Then draw these $n - m$ asymptotes on the complex plane in dashed lines.

P8.3d: On each root loci segment on the real axis, if both ends of the segment are poles, then there will be a break-out point on this segment. If both ends are zeros, then there will be a break-in point on the segment. The break-out or break-in points can be obtained by Rule 6 or Equation 8.55 in Section 8.4.2.

P8.3e: Rule 7 is about the imaginary axis crossing. The root loci of the system only intersects with the imaginary at the origin when $K = 0$. Rule 8 provides a formula to compute the angle of departure or arrival. Since all the LTF poles and zeros of the system are on the real axis, the angles of departure or arrival are trivial—either 0 or 180 degree. Now, based on the information above, a sketch of the root loci diagram can be roughly drawn. Meanwhile, a more precise root loci diagram can be obtained using the MATLAB command `rlocus` as demonstrated in Section 8.3.2. Compare your root loci diagram sketch with the graph generated by the MATLAB program, and find a best choice of K based on the closed-loop pole locations and their corresponding damping ratios, natural frequencies, and time constants.

P8.3f: Build a Simulink or MATLAB simulation program according to the feedback control system block diagram in Figure 8.45. Then conduct simulations by applying a step input to $r(t)$, and observe the steady-state and transient step responses at $y(t)$ and $u(t)$. You may need to determine a trade-off between the performance on $y(t)$ and the control effort constraint on $u(t)$ by iterating the value of K several times. Finally, comment on your design and the simulation results.

P8.4a: Consider another proportional feedback control system similar to that shown in Figure 8.45 but with the plant transfer function replaced by the following:

$$G(s) = \frac{s+6}{s(s+2)^2}$$

Find the angles of the asymptotes and the intersection of the asymptotes with the real axis.

P8.4b: Compute the break-out/break-in point (or points) on the root loci, and compute the value of K at these points using the magnitude equation, Equation 8.52.

P8.4c: Find the intersections of the root loci with the imaginary axis and compute the value of K at these intersections.

P8.4d: Draw the root loci diagram by hand based on the information obtained from P8.4a to P8.4c.

P8.4e: Draw the root loci diagram using MATLAB command `rlocus` to verify your hand-drawn diagram from P8.4d.

P8.4f: Use the root loci diagram to locate the dominant roots that would render damping ratio $\varsigma = 0.707$.

P8.4g: Compute the value of K at the dominant root locations.

P8.4h: Find the closed-loop system transfer functions, $Y(s)/R(s)$ and $U(s)/R(s)$, with the K found in P8.4g.

P8.4i: Plot the step responses, $y(t)$ and $u(t)$, of the closed-loop system using the transfer functions in P8.4h.

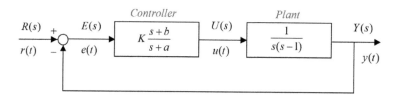

Fig. 8.46: Root locus design with phase-lead compensation.

P8.5a: Consider the feedback control system with phase-lead compensation on Figure 8.46. Before using the root locus design with phase-lead compensation, we would like to confirm that the proportional controller K and the PI controller $(K_p s + K_i)/s$ are unable to stabilize the system. Verify the confirmation using the root locus design theory.

P8.5b: Root locus design is not just about choosing the right value of the parameter K. The controller structure that determines the LTF (loop transfer function) pole-zero pattern is at least as important. Adding the phase-lead compensator $(s+b)/(s+a)$ with $b < a$ is equivalent to adding a zero at $s = -b$ and a pole $s = -a$ to the LTF pole-zero pattern that can change the location of the asymptotes, the break-out/break-in points, the moving direction of the roots trajectories, etc. If $b > a$ then the compensator $(s+b)/(s+a)$ will become a phase-lag compensator. Show that the phase-lag compensation will not work based on the root locus design theory.

P8.5c: Vary the values of b and a, one at a time, to observe how they will change the shape of the root loci diagram. Then find a best choice of K based on the closed-loop pole locations and their corresponding damping ratios, natural frequencies, and time constants.

P8.5d: Build a Simulink or MATLAB simulation program according to the feedback control system block diagram in Figure 8.46. Then conduct simulations by applying a step input to $r(t)$, and observe the steady-state and transient step responses at $y(t)$ and $u(t)$. You may need to determine a trade-off between the performance of $y(t)$ and the control effort constraint on $u(t)$ by modifying the value of K a few times. Finally, comment on your design and the simulation results.

P8.6a: For the feedback position control system shown in Figure 8.47, the plant, which is the system to be controlled, is an extremely lightly damped system with damping ratio $\varsigma = 0.0125$. In order to achieve zero steady-state tracking error, the controller needs to include an integrator. If there is no compensation, there would be no LTF zeros, only three LTF poles at the origin, and $-0.05 \pm j4$. The two branches of the root loci originating from the complex pair will jump into the right half of the complex plane right away and have no way of coming back. In order to bend the angle of departure of the two complex plant poles toward the left half of the complex plane and move the asymptotes to intersect with the negative real axis, two zeros, $s = -b$ and $s = -c$, and one pole, $s = -a$ with $b < a$ and $c < a$, need to be added to the controller. Show that the controller $K(s + b)/(s(s + a))$, an integral controller with phase-lead compensator, is still not able to stabilize the system.

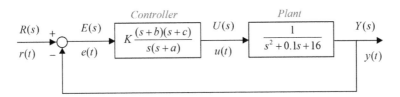

Fig. 8.47: Root locus design with double zeros compensation for an extremely lightly damped tracking control system.

P8.6b: Vary the values of the three compensator parameters b, c, and a, one at a time, to observe how they will change the shape of the root loci diagram. Then find a best choice of K based on the closed-loop pole locations and their corresponding damping ratios, natural frequencies, and time constants.

P8.6c: Build a Simulink or MATLAB simulation program according to the feedback control system block diagram in Figure 8.47. Then conduct simulations by applying a step input to $r(t)$, and observe the steady-state and transient step responses at $y(t)$ and $u(t)$. You may need to determine a trade-off between the performance of $y(t)$ and the control effort constraint on $u(t)$ by modifying the value of K a few times. Or you may even need to go back to readjust the compensator parameters b, c, and a. Finally, comment on your design and the simulation results.

P8.7a: The plant to be controlled in the feedback position control system shown in Figure 8.48(a) is exactly the same as that considered in Problem P8.6, where an integral controller structure with two zeros/one pole compensation was employed in the root locus design. This P8.6 solution resolves stability and the lightly damped issue; however, the response is slow with time constant larger than one second since the dominant real pole is too close to the imaginary axis. This issue can be resolved if the plant complex poles $-0.05 \pm j4$ can be relocated. The new approach will employ a state feedback to move this complex pair of poles to the new locations with damping ratio $\varsigma = 0.9$ and natural frequency $\omega_n = 10$ rad/s. Find the state-feedback gain matrix F.

P8.7b: Note that the two block diagrams in Figure 8.48(a) and (b) are equivalent. Show that the loop transfer function (LTF) of the system is $s^{-1}C[sI-(A+BF)]^{-1}B$.

P8.7c: Draw the root loci diagram associated with this LTF. Vary the damping ratio and the natural frequency to obtain a few corresponding F matrices, and then observe how F will affect the shape of the root loci diagram.

P8.7d: Build a Simulink or MATLAB simulation program according to the feedback control system block diagram shown in Figure 8.48(a). Then conduct simulations by applying a step input to $r(t)$, and observe the steady-state and transient step responses at $y(t)$ and $u(t)$. You may need to determine a trade-off between the performance of $y(t)$ and the control effort constraint on $u(t)$ by modifying the value of K a few times. Or you may even need to go back to readjust the state feedback gain matrix F. Finally, comment on your design and the simulation results.

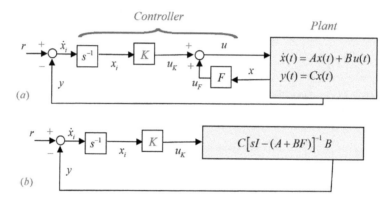

Fig. 8.48: Root locus design with state-feedback compensation for an extremely lightly damped tracking control system.

Time Delay, Plant Uncertainty, and Robust Stability

I N Chapter 8, we learned how to select a feedback control system structure to achieve steady-state disturbance response rejection and steady-state reference input tracking using the concept of the *type* of a system and the internal model principle. We have also studied, to a great extent, using root locus design technique to fine-tune the transient response of the closed-loop system. **In this chapter, we will consider the stability issues caused by time delay and plant uncertainties. The Nyquist stability criterion, developed by Nyquist in 1932, will be employed to characterize how the time delay and plant uncertainties affect the closed-loop system stability.** The Nyquist approach also provides two robust stability measures (i.e., gain and phase margins) to specify the allowable perturbations of the gain and the phase of the loop transfer function at two specific frequencies for the closed-loop system to remain stable. These two stability margin measures only reveal robust stability information at the two frequencies instead of the whole frequency spectrum. Furthermore, these two measures only work for SISO (single-input/single-output) systems. The attempt of extending the concept of gain/phase margins to MIMO (multi-input/multi-output) systems was not successful since there is no meaningful definition for the phase of a matrix loop transfer function.

The success of finding a more general robust stability measure that works for MIMO systems at all frequencies arrived shortly after the *small gain theorem*—a generalization of the Nyquist criterion to MIMO systems—was proved by George Zames in 1966 [Desoer and Vidyasagar, 1975]. The *generalized stability margin* is defined in terms of the maximum singular value (or the magnitude for SISO systems) of *complementary sensitivity function* matrix $T(j\omega) = L(j\omega)[I + L(j\omega)]^{-1}$, where $L(j\omega)$ is the loop transfer function matrix of the closed-loop system. **The generalized stability margin works for both SISO and MIMO systems and provides robust stability information for the entire frequency spectrum.** The frequency-dependent generalized stability margin function gives the maximum allowable variation of the maximum singular value (or the magnitude for SISO systems) of the plant for every frequency so that the closed-loop system can still remain stable.

9.1 Stability Issues Caused by Time Delay and Plant Uncertainty

The first and the most important requirement in the design of feedback control system is stability, since an unstable system is not only useless, it can be harmful or even potentially can cause a disaster. As discussed in Section 7.3, a linear time-invariant system is stable if and only if all the roots of its characteristic equation are in the strictly left half of the complex plane. Thus, in the design of feedback control systems as described in Chapter 8, the characteristic equation of the closed-loop system $1 + L(s) = 0$, where $L(s)$ is the loop transfer function of the closed-loop system, should have all its roots in the strictly left half of the complex plane.

The stability of feedback control systems can be affected by time delay and plant uncertainty; hence, it is imperative to incorporate the considerations of all possible time delays and plant uncertainties in the design process to ensure the system will remain stable under all worst-case scenarios. Nyquist stability criterion and the stability margins concept derived from the Nyquist approach were the first tools developed to address the two important stability issues.

9.1.1 Time Delay and Stability

In feedback control systems, time delay occurs in almost every sensing and actuation process. Hence, its effect on stability is an important practical issue. However, this issue was not resolved until 1932 when Nyquist published one of the most important control systems theories in [Nyquist, 1932], which is now known as Nyquist stability criterion. The obstacle that prevented the problem from being resolved earlier is that **a feedback control system with time delay is an infinite dimensional system, which has an infinite number of closed-loop system poles.**

If the system is finite dimensional, or, equivalently, the number of the roots of the characteristic equation is finite, then the stability of the closed-loop system can be determined based on if the characteristic equation has a root in the RHP, which stands for the right half of the complex plane.

One way to know if there exist closed-loop system poles in the RHP is to compute all these poles by solving for the roots of the associated characteristic equation, or to compute the eigenvalues of the corresponding state-space model. Alternatively, the Routh-Hurwitz stability criterion approach of Section 7.7 can be employed to check the number of poles in the RHP without the need of solving for the roots or the eigenvalues. Furthermore, the root locus design approach described in Section 8.4 provides ways of choosing controller parameters so that the closed-loop system will not have poles in the RHP. However, **these approaches do not work for the infinite-dimensional systems; therefore, they will not work for the systems with time delay either since the feedback control systems with time delays are infinite-dimensional systems.**

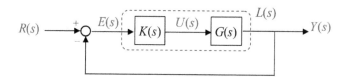

Fig. 9.1: A feedback control system with a loop transfer function $L(s)$ that includes a time delay.

Example 9.1 (A Closed-Loop System with Time Delay Is an Infinite-Dimensional System)

Consider the feedback control system shown in Figure 9.1. If the loop transfer function $L(s)$ is given as

$$L(s) = \frac{2}{s+1}$$

then the closed-loop characteristic equation will be

$$1 + L(s) = 1 + \frac{2}{s+1} = 0 \quad \rightarrow \quad s + 3 = 0$$

and the root of the equation can be found at $s = -3$ to assert that the closed-loop system is stable.

Recall that the loop transfer function $L(s)$ usually consists of the plant, which is the system to be controlled, the sensor, the actuator, and the controller. In practice, a time delay may occur in the sensing or actuating process. Now, assume the delay time is T. Then the loop transfer function will become

$$L(s) = \frac{2}{s+1} e^{-sT} \tag{9.1}$$

where the term e^{-sT} is the transfer function of a time delay element with delay time T as described in Theorem 2.22. Thus the closed-loop characteristic equation will turn out to be

$$F(s) = 1 + L(s) = \frac{1}{s+1} \left[3 + (1-2T)s + T^2 s^2 - \frac{1}{3} T^3 s^3 + \cdots \cdots \right] = 0 \tag{9.2}$$

which apparently is a polynomial equation with infinite numbers of roots. Since it is impossible to compute all the infinite number of roots, the stability analysis of feedback control system involving time delay was an unresolved issue before Nyquist stability criterion was discovered. ∎

9.1.2 Plant Uncertainty and Stability

A feedback control system usually is designed based on a mathematical model of the system to be controlled, which is called the *plant*. In practice, the real system to be controlled is not identical to the ideal plant model due to unmodelled plant dynamics, specification tolerance of components, and plant parameter perturbations influenced by the environment conditions. Hence, a feedback control system not only needs to be stable for the nominal system with the ideal plant model, it should be designed to achieve robust stability against all possible plant uncertainties.

The Nyquist stability criterion was developed by Nyquist in 1932 [Nyquist, 1932] based on Cauchy complex integral theorem presented by a French mathematician Augustin-Louis Cauchy in 1831 [Smithies, 1997]. The Nyquist approach not only resolves the stability analysis issue of infinite-dimensional feedback control systems, it also provides important concepts and tools for achieving *robust stability* of feedback control systems, which will be elaborated in later sections of this chapter.

9.2 Contour Mapping and Cauchy's Principle of the Argument

Nyquist stability analysis theory was developed based on Cauchy's principle of the argument, and the complex contour mapping was the underlying framework of Cauchy's complex variable theory, including the principle of the argument. Hence, we will **briefly review the complex function and complex contour mapping in the following subsection** before discussing Cauchy's principle of the argument.

9.2.1 Complex Contour Mapping

Complex contour mapping is a special complex function, such as $F(s)$, in which the domain of the complex function is a simple directional closed path on the complex plane. Here, "simple" means the closed path does not cross itself. **The complex variable s is supposed to travel along the closed contour for exactly one revolution.** For each value of s (e.g., s_1) on the contour, a corresponding complex function value $F(s_1)$ can be computed and plotted on the complex F-plane. That means the image of the contour on the s-plane is mapped onto the F-plane. As s traverses the simple closed contour once, the image or the trajectory of $F(s)$ on the F-plane will also be a closed path, but it may cross itself and may encircle a particular point N times, where N can be any integer, in the same (positive N) or in the opposite (negative N) encirclement direction with the contour on the s-plane.

To avoid confusion, the closed contour travel direction on the s-plane can be fixed to be either clockwise or counterclockwise. Counterclockwise contour direction has been considered the positive direction in almost all mathematics books. On the contrary, for some practical reasons, the majority of the control and systems community has decided to go the other way to adopt the clockwise encirclement direction as the positive direction. **One of the compelling reasons is that the clockwise encirclement of the right half complex plane is consistent with the positive frequency increasing direction in the Nyquist path. Therefore, we will follow the systems and control community's convention regarding the contour mapping encirclement direction. Note that this clockwise direction convention is only chosen for the contour encirclement counting. For other rotation angle measurements in degrees or radians, we still follow the universal convention: Counterclockwise direction is positive unless otherwise specified.**

To better understand complex contour mapping, in the following two examples, we will briefly review the real function mapping, and study their similarities and differences, which may enhance our learning experience of the complex contour mapping.

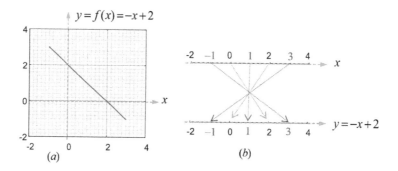

Fig. 9.2: A simple real function to demonstrate the mapping of a real variable.

Example 9.2 (A Simple Real Function Mapping)

Consider the simple real function

$$y = f(x) = -x + 2$$

which specifies how the variable x will affect the value of y. As the independent variable x varies, the dependent variable y will change accordingly. The mapping relationship between x and y can be represented by the tabulated chart,

$$
\begin{array}{c|ccccc}
x & -1 & 0 & 1 & 2 & 3 \\
\hline
y & 3 & 2 & 1 & 0 & -1
\end{array}
\tag{9.3}
$$

or by the graphs shown in Figure 9.2. A graphical representation of a function like the one shown in Figure 9.2(a) is an effective way to illustrate the mapping relationship from a real variable x to another real variable y. But this two-dimensional graph or even a three-dimensional graph cannot be applied to complex function mapping since a generalization of Figure 9.2(a)'s graphical representation to complex function mapping would need a four-dimensional space.

The graph in Figure 9.2(b) looks awkward for real function mapping. However, the concept can be easily generalized to complex function mapping. The two real number lines for the independent real variable x and the dependent real variables y can be generalized to the complex s-plane and the complex $F(s)$-plane. ∎

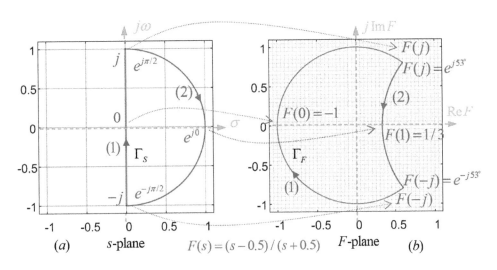

Fig. 9.3: A simple complex function to demonstrate the mapping of a complex contour.

Example 9.3 (An Illustration of Complex Function Contour Mapping)

Consider the simple complex function

$$F(s) = \frac{s - 0.5}{s + 0.5}$$

which specifies how the complex variable s will affect the value of the complex function $F(s)$. As the independent complex variable s varies on the complex s-plane, the dependent complex function variable $F(s)$ will change accordingly on the complex F-plane. The domain of the complex function in general can be any set of complex variables on the complex s-plane. The domain of the complex function we are interested, is a simple closed contour, similar to the one shown in Figure 9.3(a). For ease of explanation, this simple closed contour (or path) Γ_s is decomposed into two segments. Segment (1), in blue, is on the $j\omega$ axis (the imaginary axis) with $s = j\omega$, where $\omega = -1 \to 0 \to 1$. Segment (2), in red, is a semicircle $s = e^{j\phi}$, where $\phi = \pi/2 \to 0 \to -\pi/2$.

The $F(s)$ mappings of segments (1) and (2), respectively, will be

$$F(j\omega) = \frac{j\omega - 0.5}{j\omega + 0.5} = \frac{e^{j(\pi - \theta)}}{e^{j\theta}} = e^{j(\pi - 2\theta)}, \quad \text{where} \quad \theta = \tan^{-1}\frac{\omega}{0.5}, \quad \omega = -1 \to 0 \to 1$$

and

$$F(e^{j\phi}) = \frac{e^{j\phi} - 0.5}{e^{j\phi} + 0.5} = \frac{0.75 + j\sin\phi}{(\cos\phi + 0.5)^2 + \sin^2\phi}, \quad \text{where} \quad \phi = \frac{\pi}{2} \to 0 \to \frac{-\pi}{2}$$

The mapping relationship between s and $F(s)$ can be represented by the following tabulated chart:

$$
\begin{array}{c|ccccccccc}
s & -j & \to & -j0.5 & \to & 0 & \to & j0.5 & \to & j & \to & e^{j0} \\
\hline
F(s) & e^{-j53°} & \to & e^{-j\pi/2} & \to & -1 & \to & e^{j\pi/2} & \to & e^{j53°} & \to & 1/3
\end{array}
\tag{9.4}
$$

Now we have completed the $F(s)$ **mapping** Γ_F **of the closed contour** Γ_s **shown in Figure 9.3(b).** After obtaining the complex contour mapping Γ_F, we are particularly interested in **the number and direction of the encirclements of the origin by** Γ_F **on the** F**-plane.** It can be seen that Γ_F encircles the origin once clockwise, which is in the same direction of the Γ_s contour in the s-plane. Therefore, the number of encirclement is $N = 1$. In the case that the encirclement direction were counterclockwise, the number would have been $N = -1$. ∎

9.2.2 Cauchy's Principle of the Argument

One version of the Cauchy complex integral theorem is called Cauchy's principle of the argument or Cauchy's complex contour mapping theorem, which is given next.

Theorem 9.4 (Cauchy's Principle of the Argument)

Let Γ_s *be a simple closed curve in the (complex) s-plane, as shown in the left graph of Figure 9.4.* $F(s)$ *is a rational function having no poles or zeros on* Γ_s*. Let* Γ_F *be the image of* Γ_s *under the map* $F(s)$*. Then,*

$$N = Z - P$$

where

> N *is the number of clockwise encirclements of the origin by* Γ_F *as s traverses* Γ_s *once in the clockwise direction;*
> Z *is the number of zeros of* $F(s)$ *enclosed by* Γ_s*, counting multiplicities; and*
> P *is the number of poles of* $F(s)$ *enclosed by* Γ_s*, counting multiplicities.*

Proof: Note that the rational function

$$F(s) = K\frac{(s-z_1)(s-z_2)\cdots(s-z_m)}{(s-p_1)(s-p_2)\cdots(s-p_n)} \tag{9.5}$$

can be expressed as:

$$F(s) = K\frac{\rho_{z1}e^{j\theta_{z1}}\rho_{z2}e^{j\theta_{z2}}\cdots\rho_{zm}e^{j\theta_{zm}}}{\rho_{p1}e^{j\theta_{p1}}\rho_{p2}e^{j\theta_{p2}}\cdots\rho_{pn}e^{j\theta_{pn}}} = \frac{K\rho_{z1}\rho_{z2}\cdots\rho_{zm}}{\rho_{p1}\rho_{p2}\cdots\rho_{pn}}e^{j[(\theta_{z1}+\theta_{z2}+\cdots+\theta_{zm})-(\theta_{p1}+\theta_{p2}+\cdots+\theta_{pn})]} \tag{9.6}$$

where

$$\rho_{zi} = |s-z_i|, \quad i = 1,\cdots,m \quad \text{and} \quad \rho_{pj} = |s-p_j|, \quad j = 1,\cdots,n$$

are the magnitudes of the phasors $s - z_i$ and $s - p_j$, respectively, and

$$\theta_{zi} = \angle(s-z_i), \quad i = 1,\cdots,m \quad \text{and} \quad \theta_{pj} = \angle(s-p_j), \quad j = 1,\cdots,n$$

are the angles (arguments) of the phasors $s - z_i$ and $s - p_j$, respectively.

In view of Equation 9.6, as s traverses Γ_s once, its image Γ_F encircles the origin only if at least one of the angles θ_j undergoes a change of 2π radians. **Any pole or zero outside of** Γ_s **does not produce any angle change through a circuit of** Γ_s**. On the other hand, a pole or zero inside of** Γ_s **does produce a** 2π **angle change.** This is easily visualized in Figure 9.4. Equation 9.6 implies that for a complete clockwise transverse of Γ_s, each zero inside of Γ_s produces a clockwise 2π angle change and each pole inside of Γ_s produces a counterclockwise 2π angle change. Hence, the net number of clockwise encirclements of the origin by Γ_F is $Z - P$. ∎

Example 9.5 (Illustrate the Principle of the Argument)

The complex contour mapping example shown in Figure 9.4 is employed to illustrate the theorem on principle of the argument. Assume the complex rational function is

$$F(s) = \frac{s - z_1}{(s - p_1)(s - p_2)(s - p_3)} = \frac{s - 1}{(s + 1 - j)(s + 1 - j)(s - 3)} = \frac{s - 1}{s^3 - s^2 - 4s - 6} \tag{9.7}$$

and the simple closed path Γ_s is a circle centered at the origin of the s-plane with radius equals to 2. For clarity, Γ_s is partitioned into two segments: Segment (1) is in red, which starts from $s = 2$, clockwise along the semicircle to $s = 2e^{-j135°}$ and ends at $s = -2$. Immediately, segment (2), which is in blue, begins from $s = -2$, moving along the upper semicircle to go back to $s = 2$ to complete one revolution of the circle.

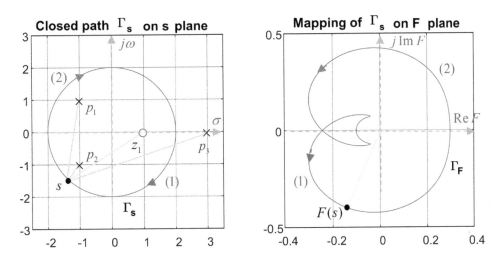

Fig. 9.4: Complex contour mapping and the principle of the argument.

The image of segment (1) of Γ_s is shown in the right graph of Figure 9.4 as segment (1) of Γ_F, also in red. It can be seen that the starting point $s = 2$ is mapped to $F(2) = -0.1$, $s = 2e^{-j135°}$ to $F(2e^{-j135°}) = -0.16212 - j0.38819$, and $s = -2$ finds its image at $F(-2) = 0.3$ on Γ_F. Similarly, the three points on segment (2) of Γ_s: $s = -2$, $s = 2e^{j135°}$, and $s = 2$ are mapped to $F(-2) = 0.3$, $F(2e^{j135°}) = -0.16212 + j0.38819$, and $F(2) = -0.1$, respectively, on Γ_F. Note that Γ_F is symmetrical with respect to the real axis, and **it encircles the origin of the F-plane once counterclockwise. Hence, the number of clockwise encirclements of the origin by Γ_F is $N = -1$.** Recall that the number of poles of $F(s)$ enclosed by Γ_s is $P = 2$, and the number of zeros of $F(s)$ enclosed by Γ_s is $Z = 1$. **Therefore, $N = -1 = Z - P = 1 - 2$, which is consistent with the result of Theorem 9.4.**

Now we will employ this example to illustrate why $N = Z - P$. Following the notations of Equation 9.6, Equation 9.7 can be rewritten as the following:

$$F(s) = \frac{s - z_1}{(s - p_1)(s - p_2)(s - p_3)} = |F(s)| \angle F(s) = \frac{\rho_{z1}}{\rho_{p1}\rho_{p2}\rho_{p3}} e^{j[\theta_{z1} - (\theta_{p1} + \theta_{p2} + \theta_{p3})]} \tag{9.8}$$

As the complex variable s traverses around Γ_s, both the magnitude and the phase (also called angle or argument) of $F(s)$ will change accordingly. However, the number N of clockwise encirclements of the origin by Γ_F in Theorem 9.4 is independent of the magnitudes ρ_{z1}, ρ_{p1}, ρ_{p2}, and ρ_{p3}. Furthermore, the poles and zeros of $F(s)$ that are not enclosed by Γ_s also do not contribute to the number N of clockwise encirclements of the origin by Γ_F. **As shown in the left graph of Figure 9.4, the pole p_3 is not enclosed by Γ_s. As s starts from $s = 2$, moving around Γ_s once through the points $s = -j2$, $s = -2$, $s = j2$, and back to $s = 2$, the phase of $\angle(s-p_3)$ will change from point to point, but the overall net change of the phase is zero, as it can be clearly seen from Equation 9.9.**

$$\frac{s}{\theta_{p3} = \angle(s-p_3)} \begin{array}{c|ccccccccc} & 2 & \to & -j2 & \to & -2 & \to & j2 & \to & 2 \\ \hline & -180° & \to & -146.3° & \to & -180° & \to & -213.7° & \to & -180° \end{array} \tag{9.9}$$

On the other hand, each zero or pole of $F(s)$ enclosed by Γ_s will contribute to increasing or decreasing the number of encirclements of the origin by Γ_F. The zero $z_1 = 1$ is enclosed by Γ_s. After s traverses around Γ_s once, the net change of the phase $\theta_{z1} = \angle(s-z_1)$ will be $-360°$, as shown in Equation 9.10.

$$\frac{s}{\theta_{z1} = \angle(s-z_1)} \begin{array}{c|ccccccccc} & 2 & \to & -j2 & \to & -2 & \to & j2 & \to & 2 \\ \hline & 0° & \to & -90° & \to & -180° & \to & -270° & \to & -360° \end{array} \tag{9.10}$$

Similarly, the net changes of the phases $\theta_{p1} = \angle(s-p_1)$ and $\theta_{p2} = \angle(s-p_2)$ will be also $-360°$, respectively, since these two poles are also enclosed by Γ_s. Hence, the net change of the phase of $F(s)$ and the number of encirclements N of the origin by Γ_F can be summarized as follows:

$$\theta_{z1} - (\theta_{p1} + \theta_{p2} + \theta_{p3}) = (-360°) - [(-360°) + (-360°) + 0°] \quad \leftrightarrow \quad N = Z - P = 1 - 2 = -1$$

Note that a $-360°$ phase change is equivalent to one clockwise encirclement of the origin by Γ_F. ∎

In this example, we have witnessed that the poles and zeros of $F(s)$ that are not enclosed by Γ_s will not affect the number of encirclements of the origin by Γ_F. However, they do affect the magnitude of $F(s)$, and consequently will change the shape of Γ_F. In the following example, we will see how the removal of the pole p_3 from the $F(s)$ of the previous example will affect the contour mapping.

Example 9.6 (A Pole or Zero Outside Γ_s Does Not Affect the Encirclement Number N, but Will Change the Shape of Contour Mapping Γ_F)

The complex rational function $F(s)$ under consideration here is almost the same as that considered in the previous example, except that the pole p_3 outside Γ_s is removed. That is,

$$F(s) = \frac{s - z_1}{(s - p_1)(s - p_2)} = \frac{s-1}{(s+1-j)(s+1-j)} = \frac{s-1}{s^2 + 2s + 2} \tag{9.11}$$

The simple closed path Γ_s is still the same, which is a circle centered at the origin of the s-plane with radius equal to 2. For the sake of clarity, Γ_s is partitioned into two segments: Segment (1) is in red, which is the lower half circle, starting from $s = 2$ and ending at $s = -2$, and segment (2) is in blue, which is the upper half circle, starting from $s = -2$ and ending at $s = 2$.

The image of segment (1) of Γ_s is shown in the right graph of Figure 9.5 as segment (1) of Γ_F, also in red. It can be seen that the starting point $s = 2$ is mapped to $F(2) = 0.1$, $s = -j2$ to $F(2e^{-j90°}) = 0.5$, and $s = 2e^{-j136.4°}$ to $F(2e^{-j136.4°}) = j1.978$, and $s = -2$ finds its image at $F(-2) = -1.5$ on Γ_F. Similarly, the four points on segment (2) of Γ_s: $s = -2$, $s = 2e^{j136.4°}$, $s = j2$, and $s = 2$ are mapped to $F(-2) = -1.5$, $F(2e^{j136.4°}) = -j1.978$, $F(j2) = F(2e^{-j90°}) = 0.5$ and $F(2) = 0.1$, respectively, on Γ_F. Note that Γ_F is symmetrical with respect to the real axis, and **it encircles the origin of the F-plane once, counterclockwise. Hence, the number of clockwise encirclements of the origin by Γ_F**

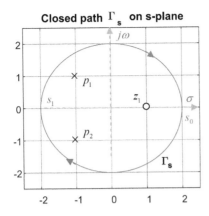
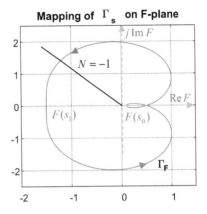

Fig. 9.5: Complex contour mapping for Example 9.6 .

is $N = -1$. Recall that the number of poles of $F(s)$ enclosed by Γ_s is $P = 2$, and the number of zeros of $F(s)$ enclosed by Γ_s, is $Z = 1$. **Therefore**, $N = -1 = Z - P = 1 - 2$, **which is consistent with the result of Theorem 9.4.**

Note that the N, Z, and P numbers are the same as those in Example 9.5, but the shape of contour mapping Γ_F is very different from that in Example 9.5. ∎

In the next example, we will observe how the contour mapping Γ_F and its clockwise encirclement number around the origin will be affected if the zero, z_1, inside Γ_s is removed.

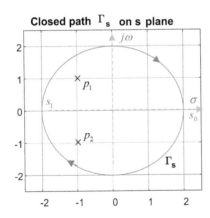
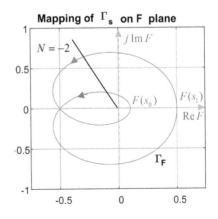

Fig. 9.6: Complex contour mapping for Example 9.7.

Example 9.7 (A Change of the Number of Poles or Zeros Inside Γ_s Will Affect the Encirclement Number N of Γ_F Around the Origin)

The complex rational function $F(s)$ under consideration here **is almost the same as that considered in the previous example, except that the zero, z_1, inside Γ_s is removed.** That is,

$$F(s) = \frac{1}{(s-p_1)(s-p_2)} = \frac{1}{(s+1-j)(s+1-j)} = \frac{1}{s^2+2s+2} \tag{9.12}$$

The simple closed path Γ_s is still the same, which is a circle centered at the origin of the s-plane with radius equal to 2. For the sake of clarity, Γ_s is partitioned into two segments: segment (1) is in red, which is the lower half circle, starting from $s = 2$ and ending at $s = -2$, and segment (2) is in blue, which is the upper half circle, starting from $s = -2$ and ending at $s = 2$.

The image of segment (1) of Γ_s is shown in the right graph of Figure 9.6 as segment (1) of Γ_F, also in red. It can be seen that the starting point $s = 2$ is mapped to $F(2) = 0.1$, $s = -j2$ to $F(2e^{-j90°}) = 0.1 + j0.2$, $s = 2e^{-j120°}$ to $F(2e^{-j120°}) = -0.5$, and $s = 2e^{-j144°}$ to $F(2e^{-j144°}) = -j0.688$, and $s = -2$ finds its image at $F(-2) = 0.5$ on Γ_F. Similarly, the image of segment (2) of Γ_s can be found as the conjugate of the image of segment (1), as shown in the right graph of Figure 9.6.

Note that Γ_F is symmetrical with respect to the real axis, and **it encircles the origin of the F-plane twice, counterclockwise.** Hence, the number of clockwise encirclements of the origin by Γ_F is $N = -2$. Recall that the number of poles of $F(s)$ enclosed by Γ_s is $P = 2$, and the number of zeros of $F(s)$ enclosed by Γ_s is $Z = 0$. Therefore, $N = -2 = Z - P = 0 - 2$, **which is consistent with the result of Theorem 9.4.**   ∎

9.3 Nyquist Path, Nyquist Plot, and Nyquist Stability Criterion

As mentioned in the beginning of the chapter, for the typical feedback control system shown in Figure 9.7, the closed-loop system stability is determined by the closed-loop system characteristic equation,

$$1 + L(s) = 0 \tag{9.13}$$

where $L(s) = G(s)K(s)$ **is the loop transfer function**, and $G(s)$ and $K(s)$ are the system to be controlled (called the plant) and the controller, respectively. The closed-loop system is stable if and only if all the roots of the characteristic equation are in the strictly left half of the complex plane. One way to check the stability of the closed-loop system is to solve the equation for all the roots. This approach may become tedious or even impossible if the equation is of high order or has infinite number of roots. As described in Example 9.1, a system with time delay is an infinite-dimensional system whose characteristic equation has an infinite number of roots.

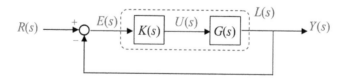

Fig. 9.7: A typical feedback control system block diagram for Nyquist stability analysis.

9.3.1 Nyquist Path

The Nyquist stability analysis approach provides an alternative way to check the closed-loop system stability without the need of finding the roots of the characteristic equation. The tool Nyquist employed to solve the very important engineering problem was the Cauchy complex integral theorem or Cauchy's principle of the argument, which was briefly reviewed in Section 9.2. **In order to find if there is any closed-loop system pole (the characteristic equation roots) in the right half of the complex plane,**

Nyquist took two brilliant steps: (1) Create a special simple closed path Γ_s, now called Nyquist path or Nyquist contour, to enclose the entire right half of the complex plane; (2) Define the mapping function

$$F(s) = 1 + L(s) \tag{9.14}$$

so that the zeros of $F(s)$ are the closed-loop system poles.

The Nyquist path is a simple closed path Γ_s that encloses the entire right half of the complex s-plane, as shown in Figure 9.8. The mapping function $F(s)$, which is the closed-loop characteristic function, is assumed to have no poles or zeros on Γ_s. If $F(s)$ has a pole on the imaginary axis of the s-plane, a tiny semicircle contour with radius ε will be employed to go around it, as shown in Figure 9.8b.

If $F(s)$ has no poles on the imaginary axis, the Nyquist path Γ_s will look like the one shown in Figure 9.8a. For clarity, the Nyquist path is divided into the following three segments:

1: Segment (1) starts from the origin of the s-plane, moving up on the imaginary axis with $s = j\omega$, $\omega = 0 \rightarrow \infty$.

2: Segment (2) is a huge semicircle with $s = \lim\limits_{R\to\infty} Re^{j\phi}$ and $\phi = 90° \rightarrow 0° \rightarrow -90°$.

3: Segment (3) is the complex conjugate of Segment (1), which starts from $s = -j\infty$, moving up on the imaginary axis back to the origin of the s-plane (i.e., $s = j\omega$, $\omega = -\infty \rightarrow 0$).

In the case that $F(s)$ has a pole at the origin, as shown in Figure 9.8b, the Nyquist path Γ_s will have four segments with a tiny semicircle segment (4) inserted between segments (3) and (1):

1: Segment (1) starts from $s = j\varepsilon$, moving up on the imaginary axis with $s = j\omega$, $\omega = \varepsilon \rightarrow \infty$.

2: Segment (2) is a huge semicircle with $s = \lim\limits_{R\to\infty} Re^{j\phi}$ and $\phi = 90° \rightarrow 0° \rightarrow -90°$.

3: Segment (3) is the complex conjugate of segment (1), which starts from $s = -j\infty$, moving up on the imaginary axis with $s = j\omega$, $\omega = -\infty \rightarrow -\varepsilon$.

4: Segment (4) is a tiny semicircle with $s = \lim\limits_{\varepsilon\to 0} \varepsilon e^{j\phi}$ and $\phi = -90° \rightarrow 0° \rightarrow 90°$.

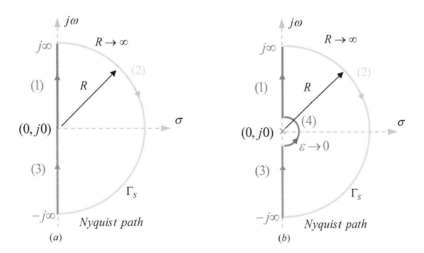

Fig. 9.8: The Nyquist path is a simple closed path that encloses the right half of the s-plane.

9.3.2 Nyquist Plot

Similar to the complex contour mapping we did in Section 9.2, **an $F(s)$ mapping of the Nyquist path Γ_s can be produced as Γ_F on another complex plane, the $F(s)$-plane. This Γ_F plot is called the Nyquist plot of $F(s)$.** Then, according to Cauchy's principle of the argument in Theorem 9.4, we have $N = Z - P$, where N is the number of clockwise encirclements of the origin by Γ_F, and Z and P are the numbers of zeros and poles of $F(s)$ enclosed by Γ_s in the s-plane. Since $F(s)$ and the loop transfer function $L(s)$ share the same poles, P is the number of the poles of $L(s)$ in the right half of the s-plane, which is usually given or can be easily computed. The encirclement number N can be counted from Γ_F, the Nyquist plot of $F(s)$. Therefore, we will have $Z = N + P$, which is the number of zeros of $F(s)$ enclosed by Γ_s, or, equivalently, the number of the closed-loop system poles in the right half of s-plane. The closed-loop system is stable if and only if $Z = 0$.

In the following example, we will construct the Nyquist plot for a simple feedback control system, and use it to determine the stability of the system.

Example 9.8 (Construction of Nyquist Plot of $F(s)$ for a Simple Feedback Control System)

Consider the feedback control system shown in Figure 9.7, where the loop transfer function $L(s)$ and the characteristic function $F(s)$ of the closed-loop system are given as

$$L(s) = 2\frac{s-1}{s+1} \quad \rightarrow \quad F(s) = 1 + L(s) = \frac{3s-1}{s+1} \tag{9.15}$$

respectively. It is easy to see that $F(s)$ has one zero, $s = 1/3$, in the right half of s-plane and, therefore the closed-loop system is unstable. However, we will employ this simple example to demonstrate how to use the Nyquist approach to determine the number of zeros of $F(s)$ enclosed by the Nyquist path Γ_s.

Since $F(s) = 1 + L(s)$, we will construct Γ_L, the Nyquist plot of $L(s)$ first, and then shift the graph of Γ_L to the right by one unit to obtain the Nyquist plot of $F(s)$. The procedure for constructing Γ_L, the Nyquist plot of $L(s)$, is given as follows:

1: **On segment (1) of the Nyquist path Γ_s, we have $s = j\omega$, and $\omega = 0 \rightarrow 1 \rightarrow \infty$.** Then the trajectory of

$$L(j\omega) = 2\frac{j\omega - 1}{j\omega + 1} = 2\frac{\sqrt{\omega^2 + 1}\ e^{j(\pi-\theta)}}{\sqrt{\omega^2 + 1}\ e^{j\theta}} = 2e^{j(\pi-2\theta)} \quad \text{where} \quad \theta = \tan^{-1}\omega \tag{9.16}$$

will be a **red upper semicircle, shown in Figure 9.9(b), with radius equal to 2, starting from** $L(j0) = 2e^{j\pi}$ **to** $L(j1) = 2e^{j\pi/2}$ **and ending at** $L(j\infty) = 2$.

2: **Segment (2) is a huge semicircle with** $s = \lim_{R\to\infty} Re^{j\phi}$ **and** $\phi = 90° \rightarrow 0° \rightarrow -90°$. **With** $s = Re^{j\phi}$, we have

$$\lim_{R\to\infty} L(Re^{j\phi}) = \lim_{R\to\infty} 2\frac{Re^{j\phi} - 1}{Re^{j\phi} + 1} = 2 \tag{9.17}$$

hence, **the entire segment (2) semicircle is mapped to the single point $(2, j0)$ on L-plane** indicated by a green dot in Figure 9.9(b).

3: **The image of segment (3) is the blue lower semicircle with radius equal to 2, starting from** $L(-j\infty) = 2$ **to** $L(-j1) = 2e^{-j\pi/2}$ **and ending at** $L(j0) = -2$, which is the complex conjugate of the image of segment (1).

Now we have the Nyquist plot of $L(s)$, Γ_L, on the L-plane, as shown in Figure 9.9b. Since $F(s) = 1 + L(s)$, the Nyquist plot of $F(s)$, Γ_F can be obtained by simply moving Γ_L to the right by one unit, as shown in Figure 9.9c. It can be observed that **the Nyquist plot of $F(s)$ on the F-plane, Γ_F, encircles** the origin $(0, j0)$ **clockwise one time, which indicates that the encirclement number is $N = 1$. Recall that $F(s)$ and $L(s)$ share the same poles, and the only pole of $L(s)$ is $s = -1$, which is not enclosed by Γ_s; hence, the number of poles of $F(s)$ enclosed by Γ_s is $P = 0$. Therefore, according to Theorem 9.4, principle of the argument, we have the number of zeros of $F(s)$ enclosed by Γ_s is $Z = N + P = 1 + 0 = 1$, which implies that the closed-loop system is unstable because it has one pole in the right half of the complex s-plane.** ∎

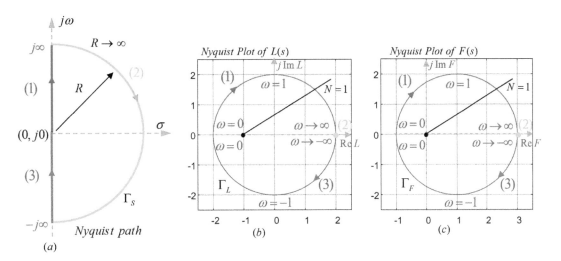

Fig. 9.9: Construction of Nyquist plots of $L(s)$ and $F(s)$ for the simple feedback control system in Example 9.8.

The Nyquist plot graph on Figure 9.9(b) is obtained using the following MATLAB code:

```
% CSD Fig9.9b Nyquist plot based on mapping
figure(5)
theta=linspace(0,pi/2,500); re_L=2*cos(pi-2.*theta);
im_L=2*sin(pi-2.*theta); plot(re_L,im_L,'r-'),
axis([-2.5,2.5,-2.5,2.5]), hold on, theta=linspace(pi/2,pi,500);
re_L=2*cos(pi-2.*theta); im_L=2*sin(pi-2.*theta);
plot(re_L,im_L,'b-'); axis([-2.5,2.5,-2.5,2.5]); grid,
```

The same Nyquist plot can also be obtained using the following MATLAB commands:

```
% CSD Fig9.9b Nyquist plot using nyquist(L)
s=tf('s'); L=2*(s-1)/(s+1); figure(21), nyquist(L)
```

Remark 9.9 (The Number of Encirclements of the Origin $(0, j0)$ by Γ_F Equals to That of the Critical Point $(-1, j0)$ by Γ_L)

From Figures 9.9c and 9.9b, it can be easily observed that the number of clockwise encirclements of the origin $(0, j0)$ by Γ_F is exactly the same as the number of clockwise encirclements of the critical point $(-1, j0)$ by Γ_L. For this reason, it is not necessary to construct the Nyquist plot of $F(s)$. **From now on, we will just employ the Nyquist plot of $L(s)$, Γ_L, together with the critical point $(-1, j0)$ to determine the stability of the closed-loop system.** ∎

9.3.3 Nyquist Stability Criterion

From these discussions, the Nyquist stability analysis can be summarized in the following theorem.

Theorem 9.10 (Nyquist Stability Criterion Theorem)

Suppose the s-plane Nyquist contour Γ_s has an image in the L-plane that encircles the critical point $-1 + j0$ clockwise N times. Moreover, suppose there are P poles of $L(s)$ in the right half s-plane. Then the number of unstable closed-loop system poles is $Z = N + P$ since $N = Z - P$, as shown in Theorem 9.4, Cauchy's principle of the argument.

Remark 9.11 (Comment on Proof of the Theorem)

Nyquist's theorem simply restates Cauchy's principle of the argument in Theorem 9.4 as the number of closed-loop system poles in the RHP equals the number of clockwise encirclements of the $-1 + j0$ point in the L-plane plus the number of the loop transfer function poles in the RHP. ∎

Example 9.12 (Nyquist Plot of $L(s)$ with a Pole at the Origin and a Parameter K)

Consider the feedback control system shown in Figure 9.7, where the loop transfer function $L(s)$ and the characteristic function $F(s)$ of the closed-loop system are given as

$$L(s) = \frac{K(s-1)}{s(s+1)} \quad \text{and} \quad F(s) = 1 + L(s) = 1 + \frac{K(s-1)}{s(s+1)} = \frac{s^2 + (K+1)s - K}{s(s+1)} \tag{9.18}$$

respectively. It is easy to see that the closed-loop characteristic equation is

$$s^2 + (K+1)s - K = 0$$

and according to Routh-Hurwitz stability criterion, the closed-loop system is stable if and only if the parameter K satisfies the following inequality:

$$K + 1 > 0 \quad \text{and} \quad -K > 0, \qquad \text{or equivalently,} \qquad -1 < K < 0$$

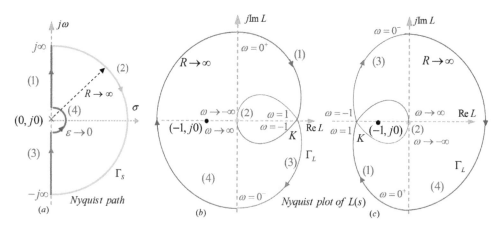

Fig. 9.10: Construction of Nyquist plot of $L(s)$ with a pole at origin and a parameter K for the feedback control system in Example 9.12.

However, this example is here mainly to demonstrate how to construct the Nyquist plot of the loop transfer function $L(s)$ that has a pole at the origin and a design parameter K. The Nyquist plot of $L(s)$ will then be used together with Theorem 9.10, the Nyquist stability criterion, to determine the number of closed-loop system poles in the RHP. Note that the Nyquist path Γ_s shown in Figure 9.10(a) consists of four segments. Segment (4), a tiny semicircle with radius ε around the pole at the origin, is added to fulfill the assumption that Γ_s should not have poles on it.

The procedure to constructing Γ_L, the Nyquist plot of $L(s)$ with $K > 0$, is given as follows:

1: On segment (1) of the Nyquist path Γ_s, the variable $s = j\omega$, is assumed to be moving along the imaginary axis following $\omega = \varepsilon \to 1 \to \infty$. The corresponding image on L-plane, Γ_L, will be

$$L(j\omega) = \frac{K(j\omega - 1)}{j\omega(j\omega + 1)} = \frac{K\sqrt{\omega^2 + 1}\ e^{j(\pi - \theta)}}{\omega\sqrt{\omega^2 + 1}\ e^{j\pi/2}e^{j\theta}} = \frac{K}{\omega}e^{j(\pi/2 - 2\theta)} \quad \text{where} \quad \theta = \tan^{-1}\omega \quad (9.19)$$

which is in red with label (1) passing through the following three points:

$$L(j\varepsilon) = \lim_{\varepsilon \to 0} \frac{K}{\varepsilon}e^{j\pi/2} = \infty e^{j\pi/2} \to L(j1) = K \to L(jR) = \lim_{R \to \infty}\left(\frac{K}{R}\right)e^{-j\pi/2} = 0e^{-j\pi/2} \quad (9.20)$$

Note that $L(j1) = K > 0$ means that when $\omega = 1$ rad/s, segment (1) of the Nyquist image Γ_L intersects the real axis of the L-plane at $(K, j0)$, as shown in Figure 9.10(b).

2: Segment (2) is a huge semicircle, with $s = \lim_{R \to \infty} Re^{j\phi}$ and $\phi = \pi/2 \to 0 \to -\pi/2$. With $s = Re^{j\phi}$, we have

$$\lim_{R \to \infty} L(Re^{j\phi}) = \lim_{R \to \infty} \frac{K(Re^{j\phi} - 1)}{Re^{j\phi}(Re^{j\phi} + 1)} = \lim_{R \to \infty} \frac{K}{R}e^{-j\phi} = 0e^{-j\phi}, \quad \text{where} \quad -\phi = \frac{-\pi}{2} \to 0 \to \frac{\pi}{2} \quad (9.21)$$

hence, the entire segment (2) semicircle is mapped to the single point $(0, j0)$ on the L-plane, indicated by a green dot in Figure 9.10(b).

3: The image of segment (3) is in blue with label (3) passing through the following three points:

$$L(-jR) = \lim_{R \to \infty} \frac{K}{R}e^{j\pi/2} = 0e^{j\pi/2} \to L(-j1) = K \to L(-j\varepsilon) = \lim_{\varepsilon \to 0} \frac{K}{\varepsilon}e^{-j\pi/2} = \infty e^{-j\pi/2} \quad (9.22)$$

4: **Segment (4) is a tiny semicircle with $s = \lim_{\varepsilon \to 0} \varepsilon e^{j\psi}$ and $\psi = -\pi/2 \to 0 \to \pi/2$. With $s = \varepsilon e^{j\psi}$ and $\psi = -\pi/2 \to 0 \to \pi/2$, we have**

$$\lim_{\varepsilon \to 0} L(\varepsilon e^{j\psi}) = \lim_{\varepsilon \to 0} \frac{K(\varepsilon e^{j\psi} - 1)}{\varepsilon e^{j\psi}(\varepsilon e^{j\psi} + 1)} = \lim_{\varepsilon \to 0} \frac{K}{\varepsilon}e^{j(\pi - \psi)} = \infty e^{j(\pi - \psi)}$$
$$\text{where} \quad \pi - \psi = \frac{3\pi}{2} \to \pi \to \frac{\pi}{2} \quad (9.23)$$

hence, the tiny semicircle, segment (4), is mapped to the huge semicircle with radius $R \to \infty$ passing through the following three points on the L-plane:

$$L(\varepsilon e^{-j\pi/2}) = \infty e^{j3\pi/2} \to L(\varepsilon e^{j0}) = \infty e^{j\pi} \to L(\varepsilon e^{j\pi/2}) = \infty e^{j\pi/2} \quad (9.24)$$

Now we have the Nyquist plot of $L(s)$, Γ_L, on the L-plane, as shown in Figure 9.10(b) for the case with $K > 0$. **The number of clockwise encirclements of the critical point $(-1, j0)$ by the Nyquist plot Γ_L is $N = 1$.** Meanwhile, the number of the poles of $L(s)$ enclosed by Γ_s is $P = 0$. Hence, according to Nyquist stability criterion, $Z = N + P = 1 + 0 = 1$, which implies that the closed-loop system has one pole in the RHP; therefore, the closed-loop system is unstable.

For the case with $K < 0$, this procedure can be used to obtain the Nyquist plot of $L(s)$, Γ_L, which is shown in Figure 9.10(c). Notice that the number N of clockwise encirclements of $(-1, j0)$ by the Nyquist plot Γ_L is dependent on the intersection of Γ_L with the real axis. If the intersection point is between $(-1, j0)$ and $(0, j0)$, or, equivalently, $-1 < K < 0$, the encirclement number is $N = 0$. Hence, according to Nyquist stability criterion, $Z = N + P = 0 + 0 = 0$, which implies that the closed-loop system has no pole in the RHP; therefore, the closed-loop system is stable when $-1 < K < 0$.

If $K < -1$, the intersection point of the Nyquist plot Γ_L with the real axis will be on the left side of the critical point $(-1, j0)$. Under this condition, the number of clockwise encirclements of $(-1, j0)$ by the Nyquist plot Γ_L will be $N = 2$, which leads to $Z = N + P = 2 + 0 = 2$. Therefore, the closed-loop system is unstable since it has two poles in the RHP.   ■

Segments (1) and (3) of the Nyquist plot graph on Figures 9.10(b) are obtained using the following MATLAB code:

```
% CSD Fig9.10b Nyquist plot Ex9.12
 figure(6),
 theta=linspace(pi/8,(pi+0.01)./2,500);
 re_L=(1./tan(theta)).*cos(pi/2-2.*theta);
 im_L=(1./tan(theta)).*sin(pi/2-2.*theta);
 plot(re_L,im_L,'r-'), hold on,
 theta=linspace(-(pi-0.01)/2,-pi./8,500);
 re_L=(1./tan(theta)).*cos(pi/2-2.*theta);
 im_L=(1./tan(theta)).*sin(pi/2-2.*theta);
 plot(re_L,im_L,'b-'), grid,
```

The same Nyquist plot graph also can be obtained using the following MATLAB commands:

```
% CSD Fig9.10b Nyquist plot Ex9.12 use nyquist(L)
K=1, s=tf('s'); L=K*(s-1)/(s*(s+1)); figure(22), nyquist(L)
```

Example 9.13 (Construction of Nyquist Plot of $L(s)$ with a Pole in RHP and a Parameter K)

For the feedback control system shown in Figure 9.7, assume the loop transfer function $L(s)$ is given as

$$L(s) = \frac{0.6K}{(s-0.5)(s^2+s+1)} \tag{9.25}$$

Then we have the characteristic function $F(s)$ of the closed-loop system as follows,

$$F(s) = 1 + L(s) = 1 + \frac{0.6K}{(s-0.5)(s^2+s+1)} = \frac{s^3 + 0.5s^2 + 0.5s + 0.6K - 0.5}{(s-0.5)(s^2+s+1)}$$

Note that the loop transfer function $L(s)$ has a pole in the RHP and a design parameter K, which is to be determined so that the closed-loop system is stable. The Nyquist stability analysis approach will be employed to achieve the objective.

As we did in the previous examples, the first step is to construct the Nyquist plot of $L(s)$ and then use it together with Theorem 9.10, the Nyquist stability criterion, to determine the number of closed-loop system poles in the RHP. Since the loop transfer function $L(s)$ has no poles on the $j\omega$-axis, the Nyquist path Γ_s consists of only three segments, as shown in Figure 9.11(a).

The procedure to constructing Γ_L, the Nyquist plot of $L(s)$ with $K = 1.3$, is given as follows:

1: On segment (1) of the Nyquist path Γ_s, the variable $s = j\omega$, is assumed to move along the imaginary axis following $\omega = 0 \to 0.707 \to \infty$. Then, the trajectory of

$$L(j\omega) = \frac{0.6K}{(j\omega - 0.5)(-\omega^2 + j\omega + 1)} = 0.6K\frac{-0.5(\omega^2 + 1) + j\omega(\omega^2 - 0.5)}{(0.5^2 + \omega^2)((\omega^2 - 1)^2 + \omega^2)} \tag{9.26}$$

will be a solid green curve labeled as (1), shown in Figure 9.11(b), starting from $L(j0) = -1.2K = -1.56$ to $L(j0.707) = -0.8K = -1.04$ and ending at $L(j\infty) = 0$. Note that segment (1) of the Nyquist plot Γ_L with $K = 1.3$, the solid green curve, intersects the negative real axis of the L-plane at these three points.

2: Segment (2) is a huge semicircle of Γ_s, with $s = \lim\limits_{R \to \infty} Re^{j\phi}$ and $\phi = \pi/2 \to 0 \to -\pi/2$. With $s = Re^{j\phi}$, we have

$$\lim_{R \to \infty} L(Re^{j\phi}) = \lim_{R \to \infty} \frac{0.6K}{(Re^{j\phi} - 0.5)(R^2e^{j2\phi} + Re^{j\phi} + 1)} = \lim_{R \to \infty} \frac{K}{R^3}e^{-j3\phi} = 0e^{-j3\phi} \tag{9.27}$$

where $-3\phi = \frac{\pi}{2} \to 0 \to \frac{-\pi}{2}$; hence, the entire segment (2) semicircle is mapped to the single point $(0, j0)$ on the L-plane, as shown in Figure 9.11(b).

3: The image of segment (3) with $K = 1.3$ is in dashed green with label (3) passing through the following three points:

$$L(-jR) = \lim_{R \to \infty} \frac{K}{R}e^{-j\pi/2} = 0e^{-j\pi/2} \to L(-j0.707) = -0.8K = -1.04$$
$$\to L(-j0) = -1.2K = -1.56 \tag{9.28}$$

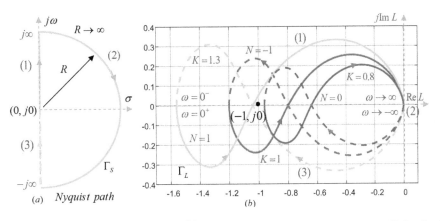

Fig. 9.11: Construction of Nyquist plot of $L(s)$ with an RHP pole and a parameter K for the feedback control system in Example 9.13.

With three K values, we have three corresponding double-crossing Nyquist plots of $L(s)$, Γ_L, on the L-plane, as shown in Figure 9.11(b). Note that each Nyquist plot intersects with the negative axis twice. The Nyquist plot in green is for the case with $K = 1.3$. The number of clockwise encirclements of the critical point $(-1, j0)$, marked as the black dot, by the Nyquist image Γ_L, is $N = 1$. Meanwhile, the number of the poles of $L(s)$ enclosed by Γ_s is $P = 1$. Hence, according to Nyquist stability criterion, $Z = N + P = 1 + 1 = 2$, which implies that the closed-loop system has two poles in the RHP;

therefore, the closed-loop system is unstable when $K = 1.3$.

For the case with $K = 1$, this procedure can be repeated to obtain the Nyquist image of $L(s)$, Γ_L, as shown in Figure 9.11(b) in red labeled with $K = 1$. The red mapping contour intersects the real axis at the following three points:

$$L(j0) = -1.2K = -1.2, \quad L(\pm j0.707) = -0.8K = -0.8, \quad L(\pm j\infty) = 0 \tag{9.29}$$

It also encircles the critical point $(-1, j0)$ once, counterclockwise; hence, the number of clockwise encirclement of $(-1, j0)$ by the red Γ_L is $N = -1$. With $P = 1$, we have the number of unstable closed-loop system poles $Z = N + P = (-1) + 1 = 0$. Therefore, the closed-loop system is stable when $K = 1$.

The Nyquist plot of $L(s)$, Γ_L, associated with $K = 0.8$ is in blue, labeled with $K = 0.8$, as shown in Figure 9.11(b). The blue mapping contour intersects the real axis at the following three points:

$$L(j0) = -1.2K = -0.96, \quad L(\pm j0.707) = -0.8K = -0.64, \quad L(\pm j\infty) = 0 \tag{9.30}$$

It does not encircle the critical point $(-1, j0)$, which implies $N = 0$. Thus, the number of unstable closed-loop system poles is one since $Z = N + P = 0 + 1 = 1$. Therefore the closed-loop system is unstable when $K = 0.8$.

Next, we would like to find the range of the design parameter K so that the closed-loop system is stable. It is observed that the Nyquist plot Γ_L consists of two loops attaching together on the negative real axis at the $L = -0.8K$ intersection point. The right end of the right loop is always connected to the origin of the L-plane, but the left end of the left loop is $L = -1.2K$. The encirclement direction of the left loop is counterclockwise, but the right loop is circling in the opposite direction. For the closed-loop system to be stable, the critical point $(-1, j0)$ has to be inside the left loop. Therefore, the closed-loop system is stable if and only if the following two inequalities are satisfied:

$$-1.2K < -1 \quad \text{and} \quad -1 < -0.8K \tag{9.31}$$

which is equivalent to

$$\frac{5}{6} < K < \frac{5}{4}$$

The intersection points of the Nyquist plot Γ_L with the real axis can be obtained from setting the imaginary part of Equation 9.26 to zero. That is,

$$\omega(\omega^2 - 0.5) = 0 \quad \rightarrow \quad \omega = 0 \quad \text{or} \quad \omega = \pm\sqrt{0.5} = \pm 0.707 \text{rad/s}$$

Then we have the two intersection points on the real axis at

$$L(j0) = 0.6K \frac{-0.5(0+1)}{(0.5^2+0)((0-1)^2+0)} = -1.2K$$

$$L(\pm j0.707) = 0.6K \frac{-0.5(0.5+1)}{(0.5^2+0.5)((0.5-1)^2+0.5)} = -0.8K$$

Furthermore, as $\omega \rightarrow \infty$, the Nyquist plot Γ_L will also intersect the real axis at the origin of the L-plane, since $L(\pm j\infty) = 0$. ∎

The Nyquist plot graph on Figure 9.11(b) is obtained using the following MATLAB code:

```
% CSD Fig9.11b Double-crossing Nyquist plot Ex9.13
figure(8)
K=1, num=0.6*K; den=[1 0.5 0.5 -0.5]; w=logspace(-3,2,500);
[re,im]=nyquist(num,den,w); plot(re,im,'r-'),
axis([-1.7,0.1,-0.4,0.4]), hold on, w=-w;
[re,im]=nyquist(num,den,w); plot(re,im,'r--'),
axis([-1.7,0.1,-0.4,0.4]), grid
```

The same Nyquist plot graph can also be obtained using the following MATLAB commands:

```
% CSD Fig9.11b Double-crossing Nyquist plot Ex9.13 use nyquist(L)
K=1, s=tf('s'); L=0.6*K/((s-0.5)*(s^2+s+1)); figure(22),
nyquist(L)
or
s=tf('s'); L=0.6/((s-0.5)*(s^2+s+1)); figure(23),
nyquist(L,1.3*L,0.8*L)
```

9.3.4 Stability Issue Arising from Feedback Control System with Time Delay

As briefly described in Section 9.1.1, time delay in a feedback control system may lead to instability if the delay time is over some limit. Since feedback control heavily depends on the measured or estimated information of reality to perform continuous control corrections to achieve stability and desired performances, the control system may not be able to perform correct control action in time if the sensor is too slow to provide accurate timely information. From the analysis in Example 9.1, we learned that a time delay can transform an originally simple first-order system to a complicated infinite dimensional system.

Since an infinite-dimensional system has infinite poles, there is no way to compute all of them and check if they are all in the left half of the complex plane. As we have studied in the previous sections, **the Nyquist stability criterion is capable of effectively counting the number of infinite-dimensional closed-loop system poles in the RHP without the need to compute all the poles. In the following, the Nyquist stability analysis approach will be employed to investigate how the delay time T will affect the stability of the closed-loop system.**

Example 9.14 (Construction of Nyquist Plot of $L(s)$ with a Time Delay Parameter T)

Consider the feedback control system shown in Figure 9.7, where the loop transfer function $L(s)$ and the characteristic function $F(s)$ of the closed-loop system are given as

$$L(s) = \frac{2e^{-sT}}{s+1}, \quad F(s) - 1 + L(s) = \frac{1}{s+1}\left[3 + (1-2T)s + T^2s^2 - \frac{1}{3}T^3s^3 + \cdots\cdots\right] \quad (9.32)$$

respectively. The loop transfer function $L(s)$ has a pole, but it is not in the RHP. Thus, the integer number P is zero in the Nyquist stability criterion equation $Z = N + P$. Therefore, the closed-loop system **is stable if and only if the number of clockwise encirclements N of the critical point $(-1, j0)$ by Γ_L, the Nyquist plot of $L(s)$, is zero.** Note that if the delay time T is nonzero, the characteristic function $F(s)$ will have infinite numbers of zeros, which means that the closed-loop system has an infinite number of poles.

The construction of the Nyquist plot for an infinite-dimensional system is basically the same as that for finite-dimensional systems. Since $L(s)$ has no poles on the $j\omega$-axis of the s-plane, the Nyquist path will include the same three segments, as shown in Figure 9.12(a).

The procedure to constructing Γ_L, the Nyquist plot of $L(s)$ with delay time $T = 1.0$ s, is given as follows. We will see how the variation of T affects the performance of the closed-loop system after the Nyquist plot is completed.

1: On segment (1) of the Nyquist path Γ_s, the variable $s = j\omega$ is assumed to move along the imaginary axis following $\omega = 0 \to 2.029 \to \infty$. Then the trajectory of the mapped contour will be determined by the following equation:

$$L(j\omega) = \frac{2e^{-j\omega T}}{1 + j\omega} = \frac{2}{\sqrt{1+\omega^2}\, e^{j\theta}} e^{-j\omega T} = \frac{2}{\sqrt{1+\omega^2}} e^{-j(\omega T + \theta)} \quad \text{where} \quad \theta = \tan^{-1}\omega \quad (9.33)$$

This polar form complex function can also be written in the following rectangular form:

$$L(j\omega) = \frac{2}{\sqrt{1+\omega^2}} \cos(\omega T + \theta) - j\frac{2}{\sqrt{1+\omega^2}} \sin(\omega T + \theta) \quad \text{where} \quad \theta = \tan^{-1}\omega \quad (9.34)$$

When ω increases from 0 to 4.913, the values of the complex function $L(j\omega)$ will change according to Equation 9.33 to generate the following tabulated chart:

ω	0 $\to$	0.861 $\to$	2.029 $\to$	3.426 $\to$	4.913	
$\angle L(j\omega)$	0 $\to$	$-\pi/2$ $\to$	$-\pi$ $\to$	$-3\pi/2$ $\to$	-2π	(9.35)
$|L(j\omega)|$	2 $\to$	1.516 $\to$	0.884 $\to$	0.56 $\to$	0.399	

It starts from $L(j0) = 2$ and will spiral around the origin clockwise, with decreasing radius via the points $L(j0.861) = 1.516e^{-j\pi/2}$, $L(j2.029) = -0.884$, $L(j3.426) = 0.56e^{-j3\pi/2}$, to arrive at $L(j4.913) = 0.399e^{-j2\pi}$ to complete the first spiraling cycle. As ω continues to increase, the Nyquist plot Γ_L will spiral around the origin infinite times and approach the origin as $\omega \to \infty$. The trajectory is shown in red, labeled as (1), shown in Figure 9.12(b).

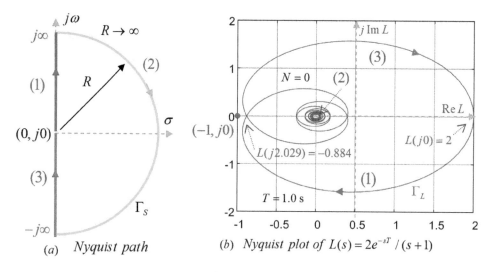

Fig. 9.12: Construction of Nyquist plot of $L(s)$ for a feedback control system with a time delay T in Example 9.14.

2: Segment (2) is a huge semicircle of Γ_s, with $s = \lim_{R \to \infty} Re^{j\phi}$ and $\phi = \pi/2 \to 0 \to -\pi/2$. With $s = Re^{j\phi}$, we have

$$\lim_{R \to \infty} L(Re^{j\phi}) = \frac{2}{\lim_{R \to \infty}\left(e^{RT(\cos\phi + j\sin\phi)}(Re^{j\phi} + 1)\right)} = 0 \quad (9.36)$$

hence, the entire segment (2) semicircle is mapped to the single point $(0, j0)$ on the L-plane, as shown in Figure 9.12(b).

3:   The image of segment (3) is in blue with label (3), which is the conjugate of the image of segment (1). The red and the blue Γ_L trajectories are symmetrical with respect to the real axis.

Now we have the complete Nyquist plot of $L(s)$, Γ_L, for the system with delay time $T = 1$ s. Since the leftmost intersection point of Γ_L with the negative real axis is on the right-hand side of the critical point $(-1 + j0)$, the number of clockwise encirclements of $(-1, j0)$, marked as the red dot, by the Nyquist image Γ_L, is $N = 0$. Meanwhile, the number of the poles of $L(s)$ in the RHP is $P = 0$. Hence, according to Nyquist stability criterion, $Z = N + P = 0 + 0 = 0$, which implies that the closed-loop system has no poles in the RHP; **therefore, the closed-loop system is stable when the delay time is $T = 1$ s or less.** ■

The Nyquist plot graph on Figure 9.12(b) is obtained using the following MATLAB code:

```
% CSD Fig9.12b Nyquist plot Ex9.14 Effect of time delay
K=1, T=1, w=linspace(0,50,1000);
re=K*2./sqrt(1+w.^2).*cos(w.*T+atan(w));
im=-K*2./sqrt(1+w.^2).*sin(w.*T+atan(w)); figure(30),
plot(re,im,'r-'),title('Nyquist plot'), hold on,
w=linspace(-50,0,1000); re=K*2./sqrt(1+w.^2).*cos(w.*T+atan(w));
im=-K*2./sqrt(1+w.^2).*sin(w.*T+atan(w)); figure(30),
plot(re,im,'b-'),title('Nyquist plot'), grid,
```

The same Nyquist plot graph also can be obtained using the following MATLAB commands:

```
% CSD Fig9.12b Nyquist plot Ex9.14 Time delay Use Nyquist(L)
T=1, num=2;  den=[1 1];
L=tf(num,den,'InputDelay',T), figure(25)
nyquist(L)
```

Critical Delay Time

From the Nyquist plot graph Γ_L in Figure 9.12(b), it is observed that the leftmost intersection point of Γ_L will move to the left if the delay time T increases. Based on Equations 9.33 and 9.34, we will have $L(j\omega) = -1$, which means Γ_L intersects the real axis at $(-1, j0)$, if there exists a delay time T_c and a frequency ω_c so that the following two equations are satisfied:

$$\frac{2}{\sqrt{1 + \omega_c^2}} = 1 \quad \text{and} \quad \omega_c T_c + \tan^{-1}\omega_c = \pi \tag{9.37}$$

The solution of the equations provides the smallest delay time that would destabilize the system:

$$\omega_c = \sqrt{3} = 1.732 \, \text{rad/s} \quad \text{and} \quad T_c = \frac{2\pi}{3\sqrt{3}} = 1.209 \, \text{s} \tag{9.38}$$

As shown in Figure 9.13(a), if the delay time is $T = T_c = 1.209$ s, the Nyquist plot Γ_L trajectory will intersect the negative real axis at $(-1, j0)$ when $\omega = \omega_c = 1.732$ rad/s (i.e., $L(j1.732) = -1$). If the delay time of the system is greater than the critical delay time, $T > T_c = 1.209$ s, the leftmost intersection point of Γ_L on the real axis will be on the left-hand side of $(-1, j0)$, as shown in Figure 9.13(b), and then the number of clockwise encirclements of $(-1, j0)$ by Γ_L will become $N = 1$. Hence, the number of closed-loop system poles in the RHP will be one since $Z = N + P = 1 + 0 = 1$ according to the Nyquist stability criterion. **Therefore, the closed-loop system is unstable if the delay time T is greater than the critical delay time $T_c = 1.209$ s.**

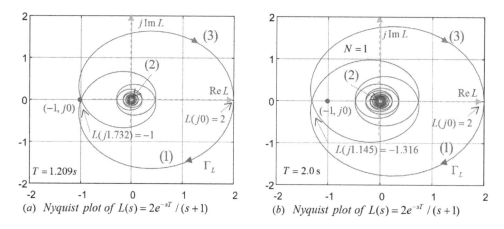

(a) *Nyquist plot of* $L(s) = 2e^{-sT}/(s+1)$ (b) *Nyquist plot of* $L(s) = 2e^{-sT}/(s+1)$

Fig. 9.13: Critical delay time that will destabilize the system.

Bode Plot Perspective

In Example 9.14, the Nyquist plot of the loop transfer function $L(s)$ and the Nyquist stability criterion were employed to investigate the stability issue caused by time delay in a feedback control system. In the following example we will consider the same system regarding the same stability issue, but the main tool is the Bode plot instead of the Nyquist plot.

Recall that the Bode plot were introduced in Section 2.5.4 and Section 3.7, respectively, for the first-order and the second-order systems in the study of steady-state sinusoidal response. For a quick review, consider a typical closed-loop system, as shown in the block diagram of Figure 9.7, where the loop transfer function is $L(s)$, and **the overall closed-loop transfer function between the input $R(s)$ and the output $Y(s)$ is $M(s)$ as described in the following:**

$$Y(s) = \frac{L(s)}{1+L(s)}R(s) := M(s)R(s) \tag{9.39}$$

For the output response $y(t)$ of a stable closed-loop system $M(s)$, due to an input $r(t)$, we usually are interested in both of its steady-state response $y_{ss}(t)$ and the transient response $y_{tr}(t)$. However, for many applications we may only be interested in the steady-state response **if the input $r(t)$ is a sinusoidal function (e.g., $r(t) = cos\omega(t)$). Then the steady-state output response can be easily obtained as**

$$y_{ss}(t) = A\cos(\omega t + \theta) \quad \text{where} \quad A = |M(j\omega)| \quad and \quad \theta = \angle M(j\omega) \tag{9.40}$$

Note that both the magnitude $|M(j\omega)|$ and the phase $\angle M(j\omega)$ are functions of the frequency ω. When the frequency of the sinusoidal input signal varies, the amplitude and the phase of the steady-state sinusoidal response will change accordingly. The Bode plot consist of the magnitude and phase plots to explicitly exhibit their values at each frequency of interest.

Example 9.15 (Bode Plot Perspective of the Stability Issues Caused by Time Delay)

In addition to being an effective graphical display of the frequency response of a system, Bode plot are important tools for feedback control systems design. However, **in almost all feedback control systems design and analysis, we employ the loop transfer function $L(s)$ instead of the closed-loop transfer function $M(s)$ in the design/analysis process. For the same reason, the Bode plot of the** loop transfer function $L(s)$ (**not the closed-loop transfer function** $M(s)$) **will be constructed to determine the stability margins of the closed-loop system.**

For the loop transfer function of a system with time delay T,

$$L(s) = \frac{2e^{-sT}}{s+1} \tag{9.41}$$

$L(j\omega)$ can be expressed in polar form as:

$$L(j\omega) = \frac{2e^{-j\omega T}}{1+j\omega} = \frac{2}{\sqrt{1+\omega^2}\, e^{j\theta}} e^{-j\omega T} = \frac{2}{\sqrt{1+\omega^2}} e^{-j(\omega T+\theta)}, \quad \text{where} \quad \theta = \tan^{-1}\omega \tag{9.42}$$

Then we have the magnitude and the phase of $L(j\omega)$ in dB and degree, respectively, as functions of frequency in rad/s in the following:

$$
\begin{aligned}
|L(j\omega)|_{dB} &= 20\log_{10}|L(j\omega)| = 20\log_{10}2 - 10\log_{10}(1+\omega^2) \\
\angle L(j\omega) &= -180(\omega T + \tan^{-1}\omega)/\pi
\end{aligned}
\tag{9.43}
$$

The Bode plot of the loop transfer function $L(s)$ for three delay times, $T = 1$s, $T = 1.209$s, and $T = 2$s, are shown in Figures 9.14(a), 9.14(b), and 9.14(c), respectively. These three Bode plot are associated with the three Nyquist plots shown in Figure 9.12(b), Figure 9.13(a), and Figure 9.13(b), respectively. **Note that the magnitude plots** $|L(j\omega)|_{dB}$ **versus** ω **are all identical, since the time delay only affects the phase. Larger delay time causes more phase shift.**

The Bode plot for the case with delay time $T = 1.209$s is shown in Figures 9.14(b). It can be seen that at the frequency $\omega = 1.732$ rad/s, the phase is $\angle L(j1.732) = -180°$ and the magnitude is $|L(j1.732)|_{dB} = 0_{dB}$, which means that **the Nyquist plot of the** $L(s)$ **with delay time** $T = 1.209$s **intersects the real axis of the** L**-plane at the critical point** $L(j1.732) = 1 \cdot e^{-j180°}$**, since** $0_{dB} = 1$**. This delay time is the critical delay time** T_c**, for the system to be stable, the delay time must be smaller than** $T_c = 1.209$s.

The Bode plot for the case with delay time $T = 1$s are shown in Figures 9.14(a). When the phase is $-180°$, the frequency is $\omega = 2.029$ rad/s, and the magnitude is $|L(j2.029)|_{dB} = -1.07$dB, which means that $L(j2.029) = 0.884 \cdot e^{-j180°}$, since $-1.07_{dB} = 0.884$. **This** $1.07_{dB} = 1.131$ **gain margin means that the magnitude is allowed to increase by 1.131 times before the system become unstable.** The definition of the stability gain margin will be officially defined in the next section.

The Bode plot for the case with delay time $T = 2$s are shown in Figure 9.14(c). When the phase is $-180°$, the frequency is $\omega = 1.145$ rad/s, and the magnitude is $|L(j1.145)|_{dB} = 2.385$dB, which means that $L(j1.145) = 1.316 \cdot e^{-j180°}$, since $2.385_{dB} = 1.316$. **This** $-2.385_{dB} = 0.76$ **gain margin means that the magnitude needs to decrease to 76% for the system to become stable.**

■

The Bode plot graphs in Figure 9.14(a)(b)(c) are obtained using the following MATLAB code:

```
% CSD Fig9.14 Bode plot Ex9.15 Time delay and stability
K=1, T=1, w=logspace(-1,0.36,500); mag=K*2./sqrt(1+w.^2);
phase=-(w.*T+atan(w))*180/pi; magb=20*log10(mag); figure(31),
subplot(2,1,1), semilogx(w,magb,'r-'),
title('Magnitude response in dB'), grid, subplot(2,1,2),
semilogx(w,phase,'r-'),title('Phase response in deg'), grid,
```

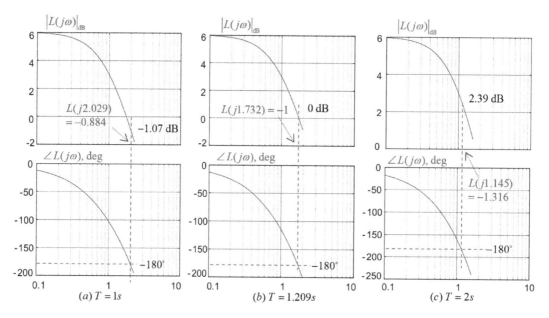

Fig. 9.14: Bode plot of the loop transfer function $L(s) = 2e^{-sT}/(s+1)$ with delay time $T = 1\,\text{s}$, $T = 1.209\,\text{s}$, and $T = 2\,\text{s}$, respectively.

The same Bode plot can be obtained using the following MATLAB commands:

```
% CSD Fig9.14 Bode plot Ex9.15 Time delay Use bode(L,w)
K=1, T=1, num=2; den=[1 1]; w=logspace(-1,0.36,500);
L=tf(num,den,'InputDelay',T), figure(25), bode(L,w), grid
```

Remark 9.16 (Bode Plot and Nyquist Plot)

The Bode plot and the Nyquist plot are both important frequency-domain graphical tools for control systems design and analysis. Either one alone has its pros and cons, but they compensate for each other very well. The Nyquist plot, together with the Nyquist stability criterion, successfully address the stability issue of the infinite-dimensional systems and provide a meaningful measure of robust stability for control systems. However, **the Nyquist plot does not explicitly display the magnitude, the phase, and the frequency as clearly as the Bode plot**. On the other hand, the information provided by the Bode plot alone is not enough for stability analysis because it only considers $s = j\omega$, the positive imaginary axis of the s-plane, not the whole Nyquist contour.

In some cases, the Bode plot can be a more precise and effective tool in control systems design. For a feedback control system with time delay, usually the system is assumed stable when the delay time is negligible. Then it is clear that the increase of the delay time can only make the system less stable. In this case, the Bode plot can be very effective in the design of a compensator to offset the influence of the time delay on the closed-loop system.   ■

A Simple Compensation to Improve the Stability of a System with Time Delay

Example 9.17 (A Simple Compensator to Offset the Time Delay Influence on the Closed-loop System Stability)

From the stability analysis of the system considered in Examples 9.14 and 9.15, we have learned that the closed-loop system will become unstable if the delay time is greater than the critical delay time $T_c = 1.209$ s. For the case with delay time $T = 2$ s, the closed-loop system is apparently unstable, as shown in the Nyquist plot in Figure 9.13(b) and the Bode plot in Figure 9.14(c).

By comparing the Bode plots in Figures 9.14(a) and 9.14(c), we can see that the difference is in the sign of $|L(j\omega)|_{dB}$ at the phase-crossover frequency. When the sign is negative, as in Figure 9.14(a), $|L(j\omega)|_{dB} = -1.07$ dB, the closed-loop system is stable. On the other hand, when the sign is positive, as in Figure 9.14(c), $|L(j\omega)|_{dB} = 2.39$ dB, the closed-loop system is unstable. Thus, it is possible to find a compensator to reduce the $|L(j\omega)|_{dB}$ to a negative value so that the closed-loop system will become stable.

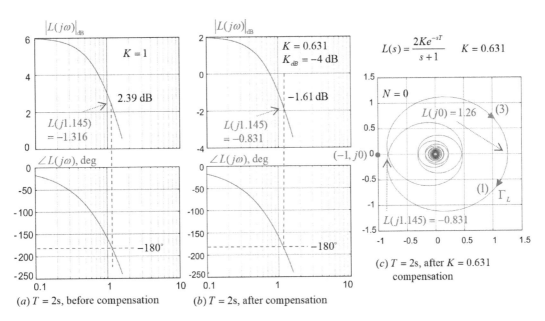

Fig. 9.15: Bode plot of the loop transfer function $L(s) = 2Ke^{-sT}/(s+1)$ with delay time $T = 2$ s and the proportional control $K = 1$ and $K = 0.631$, respectively.

Later in Section 9.6, the concept of frequency loop-shaping will be introduced in control system design, which can be employed to target some specific frequency range. For now, we will just insert a simple constant proportional controller K to the loop transfer function so that $L(s)$ will be

$$L(s) = \frac{2Ke^{-sT}}{s+1} \tag{9.44}$$

Then the magnitude in dB and the phase in degree of $L(j\omega)$ will become

$$|L(j\omega)|_{dB} = 20\log_{10}|L(j\omega)| = 20\log_{10}2 + 20\log_{10}K - 10\log_{10}(1+\omega^2)$$
$$\angle L(j\omega) = -180(\omega T + \tan^{-1}\omega)/\pi \tag{9.45}$$

Note that adding the proportional controller K only changes the magnitude while the phase remains unchanged. If $20\log_{10}K$ is chosen to be -4 dB, which is equivalent to $K = 0.631$, then the $|L(j\omega)|_{dB}$

magnitude plot curve will move down by $4\,\mathrm{dB}$, as shown in **Figure 9.15(b)**. Since the phase plot $\angle L(j\omega)$ **remains the same, and the phase-crossover frequency is still at** $\omega = 1.145$ **rad/s, the value of** $|L(j\omega)|_{dB}$ **at the phase-crossover frequency will be** $|L(j1.145)|_{dB} = -1.61\,\mathrm{dB}$. Therefore, the insertion of the proportional control compensation with $20\log_{10}K = -4\,\mathrm{dB}$ has transformed an unstable system to a stable system with a $1.61\,\mathrm{dB}$ stability gain margin.

The Nyquist plot associated with the Bode plot of the compensated system is shown in Figure 9.15(c). **The intersection of** Γ_L **with the negative real axis is now at** $L(j1.145) = -0.831$, **which is on the right-hand side of the critical point (marked as a red dot). Thus, the number of the clockwise encirclements of** $(-1, j0)$ **by** Γ_L **has changed from** $N = 1$ **to** $N = 0$, and therefore the closed-loop system has become stable since the number of unstable closed-loop system poles is now $Z = N + P = 0 + 0 = 0$. ∎

9.4 Robust Stability

Now let us consider the essential value of Nyquist's theorem; it allows us a direct method of evaluating stability robustness with respect to variations in the loop transfer function variation. Our concern is not so much with intentional variations, such as compensator gain or pole and zero locations, but with unintended and uncertain deviations of the plant parameters from the design model. We begin with the assumption that the system is stable (i.e., it satisfies the Nyquist criterion). The Nyquist criterion gives us two direct and useful measures of robustness. The first, as noted, is the admissible variation of loop gain without the loss of closed-loop stability. This is called the *gain margin*.

Recall that the gain margin concept derives from the fact that multiplication of the loop transfer function $L(s)$ by the positive number K expands or contracts the Nyquist image to a point where it crosses over the $(-1, j0)$ point in the L-plane. Alternatively, we can consider rotating the image until the image crosses the $(-1, j0)$ point, thereby changing the number of encirclements and violating the stability criterion. Note that because of symmetry of the Nyquist image with respect to the real axis, the rotation can be clockwise or counterclockwise. **The admissible rotation angle is called the** *phase margin*. **The phase margin indicates the additional phase lag of the loop transfer function that can be tolerated without destabilizing the closed-loop system.**

The gain and phase margins can be determined from either the Nyquist or Bode plot, as indicated in Figure 9.16(a) and (b).

9.4.1 Gain and Phase Margins

The gain and phase margins can be obtained either from the Nyquist plot, or from the Bode plot. The Nyquist plot exhibits clear physical meaning of the gain and phase margins, but its visual presentation does not provide precise readings of the margins and the frequencies at which these margins are measured. On the other hand, **the Bode plot alone do not provide enough information to determine if the system is stable. However, if the system has been known stable, the Bode plot can be employed to provide precise readings of the gain and phase margins and the frequencies at which these margins are measured.**

Reading Gain Margin from Nyquist Plot

In the partial Nyquist plot of $L(s)$ shown in Figure 9.16(a), the gain margin is determined by the position of the intersection (the blue dot) of the Nyquist image Γ_L (the blue curve) and the negative real axis. The intersection position is represented by the complex number on the L-plane

$$\left|L(j\omega_p)\right|\angle 180° \tag{9.46}$$

where ω_p is called the *phase-crossover frequency* at which the phase of $L(j\omega_p)$ is $180°$. The gain margin is defined by the following equation:

$$GM = -\left|L(j\omega_p)\right|_{dB} = -20\log_{10}\left|L(j\omega_p)\right| \tag{9.47}$$

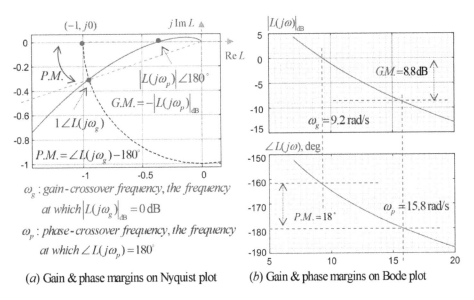

(a) Gain & phase margins on Nyquist plot   (b) Gain & phase margins on Bode plot

Fig. 9.16: Positive gain and phase margins defined on Nyquist plot in (a), and the corresponding gain and phase margins shown on Bode plot in (b).

If this intersection point is between the origin $(0, j0)$ and the critical point $(-1, j0)$ (the red dot), which means the intersection is on the right-hand side of $(-1, j0)$, then the magnitude $\left|L(j\omega_p)\right|$ will be less than 1 and the gain margin (GM) will be positive. **A closed-loop system with a positive gain margin does not mean it is stable. However, if the system is stable when the intersection point is between $(-1, j0)$ and $(0, j0)$, then the same system will continue to be stable as long as the intersection point remains inside the interval.**

The gain margin is a good indication on how much gain variation is allowed for the system to stay stable. For example, if the intersection is at $(-0.1, j0)$ or $0.1\angle 180°$, the gain margin will be

$$GM = -20\log_{10}0.1 = 20 \text{ dB}$$

and the system will remain stable if the system gain will not increase to ten times of its original gain. On the other hand, if the intersection point is at $(-0.8, j0)$ or $0.8\angle 180°$, the gain margin will be

$$GM = -20\log_{10}0.8 = 1.94 \text{ dB}$$

and the system gain will only need to increase by 25% (or become 1.25 times of its original value) to move the intersection point to the other side of the critical point $(-1, j0)$ to destabilize the system. If the intersection point moves to the other side of the critical point $(-1, j0)$, the number of encirclements of

$(-1, j0)$ by the Nyquist image contour will change; hence, the stability status of the closed-loop system will change according to the Nyquist stability criterion.

Therefore, the system will be more stable if the absolute value of gain margin is larger, or if the intersection point $|L(j\omega_p)| \angle 180°$ is further away from the critical point $(-1, j0)$.

Reading Gain Margin From Bode Plot

Although the Nyquist plot clearly shows the intersection point of the Nyquist image Γ_L with the negative real axis, it does not reveal the phase-crossover frequency. Since the Bode plot explicitly show both the magnitude and the phase of $L(j\omega)$ as functions of the frequency, they provide more detailed information. As defined in Equation 9.47, the gain margin is determined by the magnitude of $|L(j\omega_p)| \angle 180°$. The phase-crossover frequency, ω_p, is the frequency at which the phase of $L(j\omega)$ is $180°$ or $-180°$. From the Bode plot shown in Figure 9.16(b), it is easy to see that the $\angle L(j\omega)$ **phase curve intersects the** $-180°$ **horizontal line when the frequency** ω **is the** *phase-crossover frequency* ω_p. Draw a vertical straight line at the phase-crossover frequency, $\omega_p = 15.8$ rad/s, and extend this line up to intersect the $|L(j\omega)|_{\mathrm{dB}}$ magnitude curve. Then, the value of $|L(j\omega)|_{\mathrm{dB}}$ at $\omega_p = 15.8$ rad/s can be read from the graph as $|L(j\omega_p)|_{\mathrm{dB}} = -8.8$ dB. Therefore, the gain margin is

$$GM = -|L(j\omega_p)|_{dB} = 8.8 \text{ dB}$$

Reading Phase Margin From Nyquist Plot

In the partial Nyquist plot of $L(s)$, shown in Figure 9.16(a), the phase margin is determined by the intersection (the purple dot) of the Nyquist image Γ_L and the unit circle centered at the origin. The intersection position is represented by the complex number on the L-plane

$$1 \angle L(j\omega_g) \tag{9.48}$$

where ω_g **is called the** *gain-crossover frequency* **at which the magnitude of** $L(j\omega_g)$ **is** *one*, **or** $|L(j\omega_g)|_{\mathrm{dB}} = 0$ dB. The phase margin is defined by the following equation:

$$P.M. = \angle L(j\omega_g) - 180° \tag{9.49}$$

Just like the perturbation of the gain, the variation of the phase of the loop transfer function $L(s)$ can also destabilize a system. Recall that in Section 9.3.4, a time delay will cause a phase lag in the Nyquist plot of $L(s)$. **A system with larger absolute value of phase margin will be more robust against the phase variations of the system.**

Reading Phase Margin From Bode Plot

As defined in Equation 9.49, the phase margin is determined by the phase of $L(j\omega)$ at the gain-crossover frequency ω_g, the frequency at which the magnitude $|L(j\omega_g)|$ is 1, or $|L(j\omega_g)|_{\mathrm{dB}} = 0$ dB. The first step is to find the gain-crossover frequency ω_g. From the Bode plot shown in Figure 9.16(b), it is easy to see that **the intersection of the** $|L(j\omega)|_{dB}$ **curve with the** 0 dB **horizontal line on the magnitude plot occurs when the frequency** ω **is the** *gain-crossover frequency* ω_g. Draw a vertical straight line at the gain-crossover frequency, $\omega_g = 9.2$ rad/s, and extend this line down to the phase plot to intersect the $\angle L(j\omega)$ curve. The value of $\angle L(j\omega)$ at $\omega_g = 9.2$ rad/s can be read from the phase plot that $\angle L(j\omega_g)$ is $-162°$. Therefore, the phase margin is $P.M. = -162° - (180°) = 18°$.

9.4.2 Effect of the Gain of Loop Transfer Function on Gain and Phase Margins

In this section, we will consider two examples that exhibit how the gain of the loop transfer function $L(s)$ will affect the stability of the closed-loop system.

Example 9.18 (Stabilize an Originally Unstable System to a Desired Gain Margin)

Consider a closed-loop system with the following loop transfer function:

$$L(s) = \frac{20000}{s^3 + 55s^2 + 250s} \tag{9.50}$$

From the partial Nyquist plot and the Bode plot in Figures 9.17(a) and 9.17(b), respectively, we have found the gain and phase margins of the system as follows:

$$GM = -\left|L(j\omega_p)\right|_{\text{dB}} = -3.4 \text{ dB} \quad \text{where} \quad \omega_p = 15.8 \text{ rad/s}$$

$$P.M. = \angle L(j\omega_g) - 180° = -6° \quad \text{where} \quad \omega_g = 19 \text{ rad/s} \tag{9.51}$$

Note that the system has negative gain and phase margins, since the Nyquist image Γ_L intersects the negative real axis at the left-hand side of the critical point $(-1, j0)$. **In general, a system with negative gain or phase margin does not mean the closed-loop system is unstable. The information given by the partial Nyquist plot and the Bode plot is not enough to determine if the closed-loop system is stable.** However, it is quite straightforward to check the closed-loop stability by solving the three roots of the characteristic equation or using the Routh-Hurwitz criterion, or the Nyquist stability criterion based on the complete Nyquist plot. The system is indeed unstable, but both the gain and phase margins are small. **A gain margin of -3.4 dB means that it only requires a small gain reduction of $L(s)$ to 67% of its original gain to stabilize the closed-loop system.**

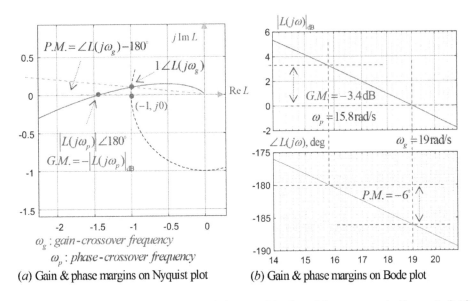

ω_g: gain-crossover frequency

ω_p: phase-crossover frequency

(a) Gain & phase margins on Nyquist plot   (b) Gain & phase margins on Bode plot

Fig. 9.17: The gain and phase margins of the unstable closed-loop system in Example 9.18

Assume the loop transfer function $L(s)$ structure is slightly modified to

$$L(s) = \frac{20000K}{s^3 + 55s^2 + 250s} \tag{9.52}$$

where K is a constant gain to be designed. The system is the same as the original one if $K = 1$. **In general, this K can be a function of s, or $K(j\omega)$ is a function of frequency ω, so that the system can be designed to satisfy multiple design objectives like robust stability, disturbance reduction, and control-input constraints.** Here, we will assume K is just a constant parameter to be determined so that a robust stability objective can be achieved.

Now the closed-loop system is unstable with gain margin -3.4 dB and phase margin $-6°$. We would like to **design a simple constant controller K so that the closed-loop system is stable with gain margin improved to** 14.6 dB.

Since the change of K will not affect the phase, the phase plot will remain the same. From the Bode plot in Figure 9.18(b), it can be seen that the gain and phase margins will improve if the $|L(j\omega)|_{dB}$ curve is moved down on the magnitude plot while the phase plot remains unchanged.

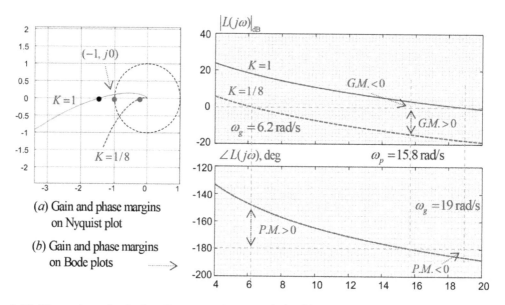

(a) Gain and phase margins on Nyquist plot

(b) Gain and phase margins on Bode plots

Fig. 9.18: Illustration of reducing K to move down the $|L(j\omega)|_{dB}$ curve to improve the gain and phase margins of an originally unstable closed-loop system in Example 9.18.

The graphs in Figures 9.18(a) and (b) show the differences between the original system (with $K = 1$) and the modified system (with $K = 1/8$) in the Nyquist plot and in the Bode plot. The Nyquist plot shows that the Nyquist image Γ_L has moved its intersection point with the negative real axis from the black dot position, crossing over the red dot critical point $(-1, j0)$, to become stable toward the blue dot position. The Nyquist plot shows clearly that an obvious robust stability improvement has been achieved, but it does not reveal the details quantitatively.

The Bode plot shows clearly that if the objective is to achieve a gain margin of 14.6 dB, then K **needs to be reduced to a level so that the $|L(j\omega)|_{dB}$ curve can move down by 18 dB on the magnitude plot.** The 18 dB reduction of gain is approximately equivalent to reducing K from 1 to $1/8$.

With $K = 1/8$, the Nyquist plot and the Bode plot have been modified to those shown in Figures 9.19(a) and (b), respectively. It can be seen that **the phase-crossover frequency is still at $\omega_p = 15.8$ rad/s, but due to the 18 dB reduction of $\left|L(j\omega_p)\right|_{\text{dB}}$, the gain margin has improved from -3.4 dB to 14.6 dB. Although the phase plot remains unchanged, the gain-crossover frequency has changed from $\omega_g = 19$ rad/s to $\omega_g = 6.2$ rad/s, and the phase margin has improved from $-6°$ to $31°$.**

■

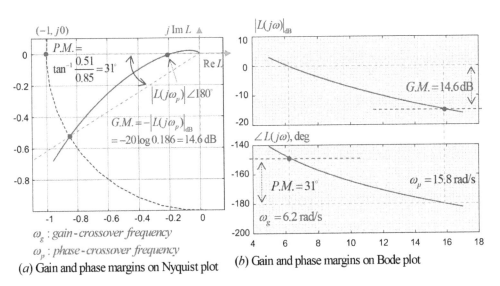

(*a*) Gain and phase margins on Nyquist plot

(*b*) Gain and phase margins on Bode plot

Fig. 9.19: Illustration of reducing K from 1 to $1/8$ to improve the gain margin by 18 dB and the phase margin by $37°$ in Example 9.18.

The Nyquist plot graph in Figure 9.19(a) is produced using the following MATLAB code:

```
% CSD Fig9.19a Nyquist plot Ex9.18 Gain & phase margins
K=1/8; num=20000*K; den=[1 55 250 0]; w=linspace(5,100);
[re,im]=nyquist(num,den,w); figure(103), plot(re,im,'-r'),
title('Nyquist plot'), hold on, t=2.9:pi/20:4.8;
[x,y]=meshgrid(t); plot(cos(t),sin(t),'k--'); axis equal; grid
```

The Bode plot graphs in Figure 9.19(b) are obtained using the following MATLAB code:

```
% CSD Fig9.19b Bode plot Ex9.18 Gain & phase margins
K=1/8; num=20000*K; den=[1 55 250 0]; w=linspace(4,20);
[mag,phase]=bode(num,den,w); magb=20*log10(mag); figure(104),
subplot(2,1,1), plot(w,magb,'-r'), title('Magnitude in dB'), grid,
subplot(2,1,2), plot(w,phase,'-r'), title('Phase in deg'), grid
```

In the following example, we will revisit the system considered in Example 9.13. The system has a double-crossing Nyquist image that intersects the negative real axis twice. Recall that, according to the Nyquist stability criterion, the closed-loop system will be stable when these two intersections are at the opposite sides of the critical point $(-1, j0)$. Furthermore, the gain margins are determined by the two intersection positions. **The gain margin for the intersection on the right is positive while the other has a negative gain margin.**

Example 9.19 (A System with Double-crossing Nyquist Image Has Positive and Negative Gain Margins at the Same Time)

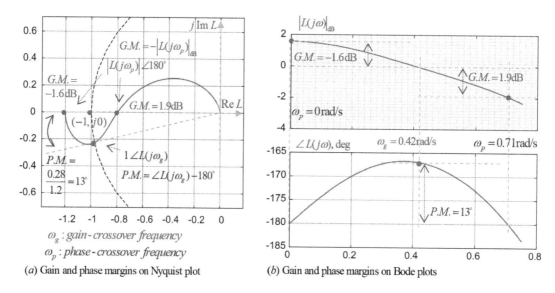

(a) Gain and phase margins on Nyquist plot

(b) Gain and phase margins on Bode plots

Fig. 9.20: Revisit the double-crossing Nyquist image of Example 9.13 that has positive and negative gain margins at the same time in Example 9.19.

The system considered in Example 9.13 has a double-crossing Nyquist image, as shown in Figure 9.11. Its loop transfer function is

$$L(s) = \frac{0.6K}{(s-0.5)(s^2+s+1)}$$

A partial Nyquist plot and the Bode plot of $L(s)$ with $K = 1$ are shown in Figures 9.20(a) and (b), respectively. **Note that the Nyquist image Γ_L intersects the negative real axis of the L-plane at the following two points:**

$$L(j0) = -1.2 \quad \text{and} \quad L(j\sqrt{0.5}) = -0.8$$

It has been shown in Example 9.13 that the system is stable. According to the definition of gain and phase margins, the system has phase margin $PM = 13°$ but has two gain margins

$$GM_1 = -20\log_{10}0.8 = 1.9382 \text{ dB} \quad \text{and} \quad GM_2 = -20\log_{10}1.2 = -1.5836 \text{ dB}$$

The positive gain margin on the right is $GM_1 = 1.9382$ dB. It means that the gain of the loop transfer function K is allowed to increase to $K = 1.25$ without destabilizing the closed-loop system. On the other hand, the negative gain margin $GM_2 = -1.5836$ dB indicates that the closed-loop system can stay stable as long as K is not reduced to below $K = 5/6$. In other words, the closed-loop system is stable if and only if

$$5/6 < K < 1.25$$

Note that the stability range of K derived in terms of the two gain margins is consistent with the inequality in Equation 9.31, which was found based on the Nyquist stability criterion.   ∎

The Nyquist plot graph in Figure 9.20(a) is produced using the following MATLAB code:

```
% CSD Fig9.20a Nyquist plot Ex9.19 Double-crossing Two gain margins
figure(105),
K=1, num=0.6*K; den=[1 0.5 0.5 -0.5];
w=linspace(0,10,500);
[re,im]=nyquist(num,den,w); plot(re,im,'r-'),
axis([-1.7,0.1,-0.4,0.4]), grid
```

The Bode plot graphs on Figure 9.20(b) are obtained using the following MATLAB code:

```
% CSD Fig9.20b Bode plot Ex9.19 Double-crossing Two gain margins
K=1, num=0.6*K; den=[1 0.5 0.5 -0.5]; w=linspace(0,0.8,100);
[mag,phase]=bode(num,den,w); magb=20*log10(mag); figure(106),
subplot(2,1,1), plot(w,magb,'-r'),
title('Magnitude response in dB'),
grid, subplot(2,1,2), plot(w,phase,'-r'), grid
```

9.5 Generalized Stability Margins

As described in the previous section, the gain and phase margins are good indications of how much gain perturbation is allowed at the phase-crossover frequency and how much phase variation is permitted at the gain-crossover frequency, respectively. **However, these two stability margin measures only reveal the robust stability information at two frequencies, not the whole frequency spectrum. Furthermore, these two measures only work for SISO (single-input/single-output) systems.** The attempt of extending the concept of robust stability margins to MIMO (multi-input, multi-output) systems was not successful until 1966 when the small gain theorem was discovered.

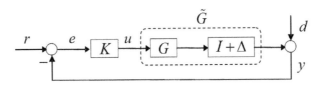

Fig. 9.21: A typical feedback control system with unstructured norm-bounded plant uncertainties.

9.5.1 Small Gain Theorem and Robust Stability

Consider the feedback control system with plant uncertainties shown in Figure 9.21. The nominal plant model is represented by G, and the set of uncertain plants is described by

$$\mathscr{G} = \left\{ \tilde{G} : \; \tilde{G} = (I+\Delta)G, \; \text{where } \Delta(s) \in RH_\infty \text{ and } \bar{\sigma}\left[\Delta(j\omega)\right] \le \ell(\omega) \right\} \tag{9.53}$$

Here, RH_∞ represents the set of rational function matrices with real coefficients that are analytic (have no poles) in the closed right half complex plane, and $\bar{\sigma}[X]$ stands for the maximum singular value of X, or, equivalently, the square root of the maximum eigenvalue of X^*X, where X^* is the conjugate transpose of the complex matrix X. **The positive real scalar function $\ell(\omega)$ prescribes the maximum magnitude variation of the uncertain plant dynamics at all frequencies** according to the practical system and its working environment. In reality, the discrepancy between the nominal model and the real system is larger at higher frequencies, and, thus, extra care needs to be given for high-frequency uncertainties in dealing with robust stability issues.

The unstructured plant uncertainties include unmodeled dynamics and any variation caused by environmental parameters, which are unknown except the bounded norm information in $\ell(\omega)$. To determine a necessary and sufficient condition so that the uncertain closed-loop system is stable seems to be a very difficult problem. Surprisingly, this challenging robust stability design problem was solved in an effective and elegant fashion, as shown below in the Small Gain Theorem.

First, let us introduce the concept of sensitivity function and complementary sensitivity function.

Remark 9.20 (The Sensitivity and Complementary Sensitivity Functions)

Consider the feedback control system shown in Figure 9.21, where G and $\tilde{G}$ are the nominal and the perturbed models of the system to be controlled, respectively, and Δ represents a set of plant uncertainties. In general, the controller K is designed so that the closed-loop system has desired performance. There are two closed-loop transfer functions that are central to understanding the performance of feedback systems. **These are the** *sensitivity function*, $S(s)$, **and the** *complementary sensitivity function*, $T(s)$. **Let the loop transfer function (LTF) be denoted by**

$$L(s) = G(s)K(s) \tag{9.54}$$

and define

$$S(s) = [I + L(s)]^{-1} \quad \text{and} \quad T(s) = L(s)[I + L(s)]^{-1} \tag{9.55}$$

For the feedback control system of Figure 9.21, if $\Delta = 0$ and $d = 0$, where d is the disturbance input, then the relationship between the reference input $R(s) = \mathscr{L}[r(t)]$ and **the tracking error** $E(s) = \mathscr{L}[e(t)]$ **is**

$$E(s) = [I + L(s)]^{-1}R(s) = S(s)R(s)$$

Thus, a smaller $S(s)$ **will lead to a smaller tracking/regulation error.** Similarly, if $\Delta = 0$ and $r = 0$, then the relationship between the disturbance input $D(s) = \mathscr{L}[d(t)]$ and **the output disturbance response** $Y(s) = \mathscr{L}[y(t)]$ **is**

$$Y(s) = [I + L(s)]^{-1}D(s) = S(s)D(s)$$

Hence, a smaller $S(s)$ **will also imply a smaller disturbance response.**

On the other hand, as will be seen in the Small Gain Theorem below that **a smaller complementary sensitivity function** $T(s)$ **will produce better robust stability.** That is, to achieve smaller tracking/regulation error, less disturbance response, and better robust stability, we would like to design a controller so that the sensitivity function and the complementary sensitivity function are both small, if possible.

However, it is impossible to reduce both at the same time and at the same frequency since the sum of $S(s)$ and $T(s)$ is a constant:

$$S(s) + T(s) = [I + L(s)]^{-1} + L(s)[I + L(s)]^{-1} = [I + L(s)][I + L(s)]^{-1} = I$$

Nevertheless, **plant uncertainties are more significant in high frequency range than low frequencies while the disturbances and the reference inputs usually occur in low frequency range. Therefore, the controller can be designed to minimize** $|S(j\omega)|$ **in low frequency range while reducing** $|T(j\omega)|$ **at high frequencies.** ■

Theorem 9.21 (Small Gain Theorem for Robust Stability)

Consider the feedback control system with plant uncertainty described by the block diagram shown in Figure 9.21 and by the set of uncertain plants satisfying the bounded norm condition described in Equation 9.53. The loop transfer function matrix $L(s)$ and the complementary sensitivity function matrix $T(s)$ of the nominal closed-loop system are defined in Equations 9.54 and 9.55, respectively.

If the nominal closed-loop system $\mathscr{C}(G,K)$, which is the closed-loop system with $\Delta = 0$ or $\tilde{G} = G$, is stable, then the uncertain closed-loop system $\mathscr{C}(\tilde{G},K)$ is stable if and only if the following inequality is satisfied:

$$\bar{\sigma}[T(j\omega)] < \frac{1}{\ell(\omega)} \qquad \text{for all} \ \ \omega \tag{9.56}$$

∎

Note that the small gain theorem for robust stability works for both MIMO and SISO systems, and the plant $G(s)$ is not restricted to be a square matrix. The theorem also covers the whole spectrum of frequencies. Therefore, it provides much more general applications than the classical gain and phase margins. The physical sense of the maximum singular value, which is the norm employed in the theorem, may not be very clear to most of the undergraduate students at this moment. However, for the application of the theorem to SISO systems, the maximum singular values $\bar{\sigma}[T(j\omega)]$ and $\bar{\sigma}[\Delta(j\omega)]$ are simply the magnitudes $|T(j\omega)|$ and $|\Delta(j\omega)|$, respectively, as shown in the following corollary.

Corollary 9.22 (Special Case of the Small Gain Theorem for SISO Systems)

Consider the same feedback control system with plant uncertainties described by Figure 9.21 and Equation 9.53 except that all matrix functions are replaced by their scalar function counterparts and $\bar{\sigma}[\Delta(j\omega)] \leq \ell(\omega)$ is regarded as

$$|\Delta(j\omega)| \leq \ell(\omega)$$

Then the uncertain closed-loop system $\mathscr{C}(\tilde{G},K)$ is stable if and only if the following inequality is satisfied:

$$|T(j\omega)| < \frac{1}{\ell(\omega)} \qquad \text{for all} \ \ \omega \tag{9.57}$$

∎

9.5.2 Interpretation of the Generalized Stability Margins

In the previous subsection, Section 9.5.1, we learned that a generalized frequency-dependent stability margin function can be obtained from the small gain theorem. The uncertain closed-loop system $\mathscr{C}(\tilde{G},K)$ is stable if and only if

$$|T(j\omega)| < \frac{1}{\ell(\omega)} \quad \text{where} \quad |\Delta(j\omega)| \leq \ell(\omega) \quad \text{for all} \ \ \omega$$

For example, if $|T(j\omega_1)| = 0.5$, then the maximum allowable variation of $|\Delta(j\omega_1)|$ has to be less than 2. Otherwise, the system will become unstable. To guarantee the closed-loop system to be robustly stable, the maximum allowable variation of $|\Delta(j\omega)|$ has to be less than $1/|T(j\omega)|$ for all ω. Hence, naturally, a generalized stability margin function $\mathscr{M}(\omega)$ can be defined as follows:

$$\mathscr{M}(\omega) = 1/\bar{\sigma}[T(j\omega)] = 1/|T(j\omega)| \tag{9.58}$$

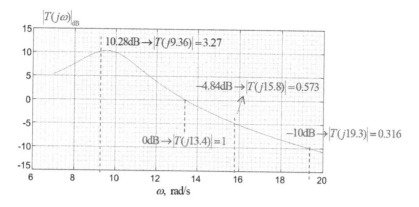

Fig. 9.22: The generalized stability margin function $\mathscr{M}(\omega)$ is the inverse of $|T(j\omega)|$.

Example 9.23 (Generalized Stability Margin Function $\mathscr{M}(\omega)$ and $|T(j\omega)|$)

Consider the feedback control system with plant uncertainties shown in Figure 9.21. The loop transfer function of the system is given as

$$L(s) = G(s)K(s) = \frac{5000}{s(s^2 + 55s + 250)} \qquad (9.59)$$

The complementary sensitivity function of the system is

$$T(s) = L(s)[I + L(s)]^{-1}$$

and the magnitude plot of $T(j\omega)$, $|T(j\omega)|_{\mathrm{dB}}$, can be obtained, as shown in Figure 9.22. For MIMO systems, this plot would have been the maximum singular value plot of $\bar{\sigma}[T(j\omega)]$.

On this complementary sensitivity plot, it can be seen that at $\omega = 9.36\,\mathrm{rad/s}$, we have

$$|T(j9.36)|_{\mathrm{dB}} = 10.28\,\mathrm{dB} \quad \rightarrow \quad |T(j9.36)| = 3.27 \quad \rightarrow \quad \mathscr{M}(9.36) = 1/3.27 = 0.306$$

which means that the maximum allowable magnitude variation of $|\Delta(j9.36)|$, to avoid destabilizing the system, is 0.306. If the variation of $|\Delta(j9.36)|$ is more than 0.306, the system will become unstable. Similarly, the values of $|T(j\omega)|$ at $\omega = 13.4\,\mathrm{rad/s}$, $\omega = 15.8\,\mathrm{rad/s}$, and $\omega = 19.3\,\mathrm{rad/s}$ are computed respectively as follows:

$$|T(j13.4)|_{\mathrm{dB}} = 0\,\mathrm{dB} \quad \rightarrow \quad |T(j13.4)| = 1 \quad \rightarrow \quad \mathscr{M}(13.4) = 1/1 = 1$$
$$|T(j15.8)|_{\mathrm{dB}} = -4.84\,\mathrm{dB} \quad \rightarrow \quad |T(j15.8)| = 0.573 \quad \rightarrow \quad \mathscr{M}(15.8) = 1/0.573 = 1.745$$
$$|T(j19.3)|_{\mathrm{dB}} = -10\,\mathrm{dB} \quad \rightarrow \quad |T(j19.3)| = 0.316 \quad \rightarrow \quad \mathscr{M}(19.3) = 1/0.316 = 3.165$$

Therefore, the maximum allowable magnitude variations of $|\Delta(j\omega)|$ at these three frequencies so that the system will remain stable are $|\Delta(j13.4)| = 1$, $|\Delta(j15.8)| = 1.745$, and $|\Delta(j19.3)| = 3.165$, respectively.

Note that a **smaller $|T(j\omega)|$ allows more magnitude perturbation at that frequency, and the generalized stability margin function is the reciprocal of the magnitude of the complementary sensitivity function.** It is also observed that $|T(j\omega)|$ is decreasing at the high frequency region, which means the high frequency components of the system are allowed larger uncertainties. ∎

The $|T(j\omega)|$ **plot graph on Figure 9.22 is obtained using the following MATLAB code:**

```
% CSD Fig9.22 |T(jw)| plot Ex9.23 Generalized stability margin
 num=5000; den=[1 55 250 0]; L=tf(num,den);
% Complementary function T=L*inv(1+L);
 T = feedback(L,1); w1=linspace(1,35); figure(100), svT=sigma(T,w1);
 svTb=20*log10(svT); plot(w1,svTb), title('sigma of T'), grid on,
 grid minor
```

From these discussions, we learn that the maximum singular value of the complementary sensitivity function, $\bar{\sigma}\left[T(j\omega)\right]$ for MIMO systems, or the magnitude of the complementary sensitivity function, $|T(j\omega)|$ for SISO systems, provides important stability margin information for the whole frequency spectrum. This information is critical in the loop-shaping control system design to ensure robust stability.

In the next subsection, we will discuss the differences between the complementary sensitivity function $T(j\omega)$ and the loop transfer function $L(j\omega)$ in terms of their ability to provide robust stability information. We will show that the gain and phase margins can also be obtained from the magnitude of the complementary sensitivity function.

9.5.3 Relationship Between Gain/Phase Margins and the Generalized Stability Margins

In the following we will show that the gain and phase margins can be computed based on the magnitude of the complementary sensitivity function.

Theorem 9.24 (Use $|T(j\omega_p)|$ and $|T(j\omega_g)|$ to Compute the Gain and Phase Margins)

Consider the feedback control system in Figure 9.21 with the loop transfer function $L(s) = G(s)K(s)$ and the complementary sensitivity function $T(s) = L(s)[I+L(s)]^{-1}$. Assume ω_p and ω_g are the phase-crossover frequency and the gain-crossover frequency, respectively. Then the gain margin (GM) and the phase margin (PM) of the system can be computed using $|T(j\omega_p)|$ and $|T(j\omega_g)|$.

(a) If $|L(j\omega_p)| < 1$, the gain margin is

$$GM = 20\log_{10}\left(1 + 1\big/\big|T(j\omega_p)\big|\right) \tag{9.60}$$

(b) If $|L(j\omega_p)| > 1$, the gain margin is

$$GM = 20\log_{10}\left(1 - 1\big/\big|T(j\omega_p)\big|\right) \tag{9.61}$$

(c) If $\angle L(j\omega_g) > \pi$, the phase margin is

$$PM = 2\sin^{-1}\left(0.5\big/\big|T(j\omega_g)\big|\right) \tag{9.62}$$

(d) If $\angle L(j\omega_g) < \pi$, the phase margin is

$$PM = -2\sin^{-1}\left(0.5\big/\big|T(j\omega_g)\big|\right) \tag{9.63}$$

Proof:

(a) *According to the definition of the gain margin, we have $L(j\omega_p) = |L(j\omega_p)|e^{j\pi}$ and $GM = -20\log_{10}|L(j\omega_p)|$. Since $|L(j\omega_p)| < 1$, the equation relating the complementary sensitivity function to the loop transfer function at $\omega = \omega_p$ will become*

$$\frac{1}{|T(j\omega_p)|} = \left|\frac{1+L(j\omega_p)}{L(j\omega_p)}\right| = \frac{1-|L(j\omega_p)|}{|L(j\omega_p)|} = \frac{1}{|L(j\omega_p)|} - 1 \quad \rightarrow \quad \frac{1}{|L(j\omega_p)|} = 1 + \frac{1}{|T(j\omega_p)|}$$

Therefore, the gain margin is

$$GM = -20\log_{10}|L(j\omega_p)| = 20\log_{10}\left(1 + \frac{1}{|T(j\omega_p)|}\right)$$

(b) *The proof is similar to part (a) except that now the intersection of the Nyquist plot of $L(j\omega)$ with the real axis is at the left of $(-1, j0)$. Thus,*

$$\frac{1}{|T(j\omega_p)|} = \left|\frac{1+L(j\omega_p)}{L(j\omega_p)}\right| = \frac{|L(j\omega_p)|-1}{|L(j\omega_p)|} = 1 + \frac{-1}{|L(j\omega_p)|} \quad \rightarrow \quad \frac{1}{|L(j\omega_p)|} = 1 - \frac{1}{|T(j\omega_p)|}$$

Therefore, the gain margin is

$$GM = -20\log_{10}|L(j\omega_p)| = 20\log_{10}\left(1 - \frac{1}{|T(j\omega_p)|}\right)$$

(c) *Since $\angle L(j\omega_g) > \pi$, we have $|L(j\omega_g)| = 1$, $\angle L(j\omega_g) = \pi + \phi$, and the phase margin is $PM = \phi$. The equation relating the complementary sensitivity function to the loop transfer function at $\omega = \omega_g$ becomes*

$$\frac{1}{|T(j\omega_g)|} = \left|\frac{1+L(j\omega_g)}{L(j\omega_g)}\right| = \frac{|1+L(j\omega_g)|}{|L(j\omega_g)|} = |1+L(j\omega_g)|$$

From the Nyquist plot graph in Figure 9.23, it can be seen that the length of the straight line connecting points A and C is $|1+L(j\omega_g)|$. Points A, O, and B are on the same straight line whose length is the diameter of the circle, which is 2. The triangle $\triangle ABC$ is a right triangle and the angle $\angle ABC$ is 2ϕ, where the angle ϕ is the phase margin. Hence,

$$\sin\frac{\phi}{2} = \frac{|1+L(j\omega_g)|}{2} = \frac{0.5}{|T(j\omega_g)|}$$

and therefore the phase margin is

$$PM = \phi = 2\sin^{-1}\left(\frac{0.5}{|T(j\omega_g)|}\right)$$

(d) *The proof is similar to Part (c) and is left as an exercise.*

■

Example 9.25 (The Magnitude Plot of the Complementary Sensitivity Function and Its Relationship with the Gain and Phase Margins)

The system considered in Example 9.23 with the loop transfer function:

$$L(s) = G(s)K(s) = \frac{5000}{s(s^2+55s+250)} \tag{9.64}$$

will be employed in the following to compare the Nyquist plot, Bode plot, and the magnitude plot of $T(j\omega)$, which is the complementary sensitivity function, and identify **the relationship among the gain margin GM, the phase margin PM, the magnitude of the complementary sensitivity function $|T(j\omega)|$, and the generalized stability margin function $\mathcal{M}(\omega)$.**

The Nyquist plot and Bode plot of the feedback control system with loop transfer function $L(s)$, given by Equation 9.64, are shown in Figure 9.23. These plots were shown in Figure 9.16 earlier in Section 9.4.1 to introduce how to read gain and phase margins in the Nyquist plot and Bode plot. The plots in Figure 9.23 show more detailed geometric information that are essential for the proof in Theorem 9.24.

Now, **from Figure 9.23, we have the gain-crossover frequency $\omega_g = 9.36\,\text{rad/s}$ at which**

$$L(j\omega_g) = 1e^{j(\pi+\phi)}$$

and the phase margin is $PM = \phi = 17.5°$. The phase-crossover frequency is $\omega_p = 15.8\,\text{rad/s}$ at which we have

$$L(j\omega_p) = |L(j\omega_p)|e^{j\pi}$$

and the gain margin can be found as $GM = -20\log_{10}|L(j\omega_p)| = 8.77\,\text{dB}$.

The $|T(j\omega)|$ plot, the magnitude of the complementary sensitivity function, is shown in Figure 9.24. As discussed in Example 9.23, this magnitude function $|T(j\omega)|$ is the reciprocal of the generalized stability margin function $\mathcal{M}(\omega)$, which specifies the maximum allowable variations of $\Delta(j\omega)$ for each ω so that the system can remain stable.

In Figure 9.24, when the frequency is at $\omega = \omega_g$, the gain-crossover frequency, we have $|T(j\omega_g)|_{\text{dB}} = 10.28\,\text{dB}$, which gives $|T(j\omega_g)| = 3.27$ and its reciprocal, the generalized stability margin function $\mathcal{M}(\omega_g) = 1/3.27 = 0.306$. This 0.306 stability margin at the frequency ω_g means that the variation of $\Delta(j\omega_g) < 0.306$ will not cause the system to become unstable. In addition to this robust stability information regarding the maximal variation of $\Delta(j\omega_g)$, the $|T(j\omega_g)| = 3.27$ value can be employed to compute the phase margin, as promised by Theorem 9.24. **Plugging $|T(j\omega_g)| = 3.27$ into Equation 9.62, we have the phase margin**

$$PM = \phi = 2\sin^{-1}\left(\frac{0.5}{|T(j\omega_g)|}\right) = 2\sin^{-1}\left(\frac{0.5}{3.27}\right) = 17.6°$$

which is consistent with the result obtained from the Bode plot.

At the frequency ω_p, the phase-crossover frequency, we have $|T(j\omega_p)|_{\text{dB}} = -4.84\,\text{dB}$, which gives $|T(j\omega_p)| = 0.573$. The reciprocal of this, $\mathcal{M}(\omega_p) = 1/0.573 = 1.745$, is the generalized stability margin. This 1.745 stability margin at the frequency ω_p means that the variation of $\Delta(j\omega_p) < 1.745$ will not destabilize the system. The $|T(j\omega_p)| = 0.573$ value can be employed to compute the gain margin using Equation 9.60,

$$GM = 20\log_{10}\left(1 + 1/|T(j\omega_p)|\right) = 20\log_{10}\left(1 + 1.745\right) = 8.77\,\text{dB}$$

which is consistent with the result obtained from the Bode plot. ■

The Nyquist plot graph on Figure 9.23(a) is produced using the following MATLAB code:

```
% CSD Fig9.23a Nyquist plot Ex9.25 |T(jw)| & Gain/phase margins
num=5000; den=[1 55 250 0]; L=tf(num,den);
w2=logspace(0.85,2); [re,im]=nyquist(num,den,w2); figure(103),
```

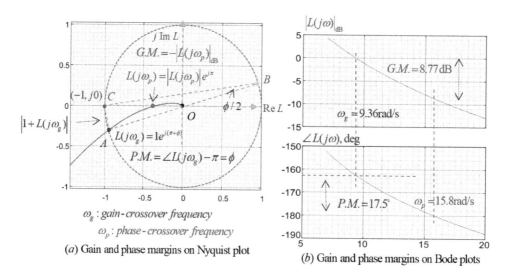

(a) Gain and phase margins on Nyquist plot

(b) Gain and phase margins on Bode plots

Fig. 9.23: Gain and phase margins on Nyquist and Bode plots.

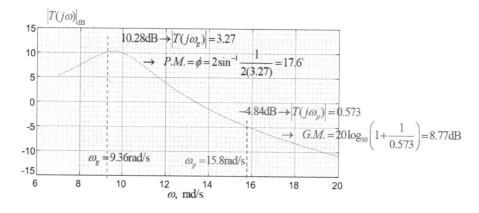

Fig. 9.24: Gain and phase margins on the $|T(j\omega)|$ plot.

```
plot(re,im,'r-'), title('Nyquist plot'), hold on, t = 0:pi/80:6.28;
[x,y] = meshgrid(t); plot(cos(t),sin(t),'m--'); axis equal;
grid on, grid minor
```

The Bode plot graphs on Figure 9.23(b) are obtained using the following MATLAB code:

```
% CSD Fig9.23b Bode plot Ex9.25 |T(jw)| & Gain/phase margins
num=5000; den=[1 55 250 0];
w3=linspace(7,20); [mag,phase]=bode(num,den,w3); magb=20*log10(mag);
figure(104), subplot(2,1,1),
title('Magnitude response in dB'), plot(w3,magb),
title('Magnitude response in dB'), grid on, grid  minor,
subplot(2,1,2),
title('Phase response in deg'), plot(w3,phase),
title('Phase response in deg'), grid on, grid minor
```

9.6 Essential Closed-Loop Transfer Functions and Loop Shaping

In the previous section, Section 9.5, we learned that the robust stability of a closed-loop system is closely related with the complementary sensitivity function

$$T(s) = L(s)[1+L(s)]^{-1} \tag{9.65}$$

where $L(s) = G(s)K(s)$ is the loop transfer function (LTF) of the closed-loop system, as shown in Figure 9.25.

On the other hand, as discussed in Section 8.1.2, the tracking error response $E(s)$, due to the reference input $R(s)$ and the disturbance input $D(s)$ of the same closed-loop system, shown in Figure 9.25, is given by Equation 8.4:

$$E(s) = [1+L(s)]^{-1}R(s) - [1+L(s)]^{-1}D(s)$$

Note that the tracking performance is mainly determined by the sensitivity function,

$$S(s) = [1+L(s)]^{-1} \tag{9.66}$$

where $L(s) = G(s)K(s)$, again, is the loop transfer function (LTF) of the closed-loop system.

It can be seen that the tracking error and the disturbance response will be better if the sensitivity function $S(s)$ can be made smaller. We also learned that the robust stability margin will be larger if the complementary sensitivity function $T(s)$ can be reduced. However, the two functions S and T can not be reduced at the same time since $S+T = 1$. Fortunately, the tracking reference input signal $r(t)$ and the disturbance input $d(t)$ usually occur in the low frequency range while the plant uncertainties only become issues at high frequencies. For this reason, it has been a common practice to **design a controller** $K(s)$ **so that the sensitivity function** $S(j\omega)$ **is small in the low frequency range, while keeping the complementary sensitivity function** $T(j\omega)$ **small at the high frequency end**. This control system design is called a *loop shaping approach*.

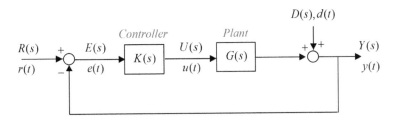

Fig. 9.25: A typical feedback control system structure.

At low frequencies, the magnitude of the loop transfer function, $|L|$, usually is much greater than 1 so that the sensitivity function $S = (1+L)^{-1}$ is approximately equal to L^{-1}; hence, we have

$$|L(j\omega)| \approx \frac{1}{|S(j\omega)|} \qquad \text{at low frequencies when} \quad |L| \gg 1 \tag{9.67}$$

On the other hand, at the high frequency region, the magnitude of the loop transfer function, $|L|$, is much less than 1 so that the complementary sensitivity function $T = L(1+L)^{-1}$ is approximately equal to L; hence, we have

$$|L(j\omega)| \approx |T(j\omega)| \qquad \text{at high frequencies when} \quad |L| \ll 1 \qquad (9.68)$$

Therefore, the loop shaping design can be accomplished by choosing a controller $K(s)$ so that the magnitude of the loop transfer function $L(s) = G(s)K(s)$ is large in the low frequency range, but small at high frequencies.

Recall that in Examples 9.23 and 9.25, we selected a controller K to manipulate the loop transfer function $L = KG$, and thus the complementary sensitivity function $T = L(1+L)^{-1}$, to achieve an acceptable robust stability requirement. In the following, we will evaluate the tracking error and disturbance response performance of the system in terms of the sensitivity function $S = (1+L)^{-1}$.

Example 9.26 (Loop Shaping for Tracking Performance and Robust Stability)

The system considered in Example 9.23 with loop transfer function

$$L(s) = G(s)K(s) = \frac{5000}{s(s^2 + 55s + 250)} \qquad (9.69)$$

is revisited in the following to reveal the tracking performance and the robust stability margin on the same loop shaping diagram.

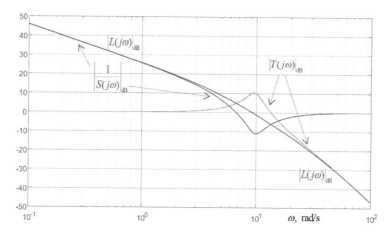

Fig. 9.26: A loop shaping diagram showing $|T(j\omega)|_{\mathrm{dB}}$, $|1/S(j\omega)|_{\mathrm{dB}}$, and $|L(j\omega)|_{\mathrm{dB}}$.

Three graphs—$|1/S(j\omega)|_{\mathrm{dB}}$ in blue, $|T(j\omega)|_{\mathrm{dB}}$ in green, and $|L(j\omega)|_{\mathrm{dB}}$ in red—are shown on the loop shaping diagram in Figure 9.26. These graphs verify that $|1/S(j\omega)|_{\mathrm{dB}} \approx |L(j\omega)|_{\mathrm{dB}}$ when $\omega < 4$ rad/s and $|T(j\omega)|_{\mathrm{dB}} \approx |L(j\omega)|_{\mathrm{dB}}$ when $\omega > 20$ rad/s. **The controller designer would like to make $|L(j\omega)|_{\mathrm{dB}}$ large (i.e., to decrease $|S(j\omega)|$) in the low frequency range and at the same time make $|L(j\omega)|_{\mathrm{dB}}$ small (i.e., to decrease $|T(j\omega)|$) in the high frequency range.**

The high frequency portion ($\omega > 6$ rad/s) of the $|T(j\omega)|_{\mathrm{dB}}$ graph was employed in Examples 9.23 and 9.25 to respectively obtain the generalized stability margin function $\mathscr{M}(\omega)$ and the gain/phase margins.

In the low frequency portion of the $|L(j\omega)|_{\mathrm{dB}}$ or $|1/S(j\omega)|_{\mathrm{dB}}$ graph, for instance, when $\omega = 1$ rad/s, we have

$$|L(j1)|_{dB} = |1/S(j1)|_{dB} = 26 \text{ dB} \quad \rightarrow \quad |S(j1)| = 0.05$$

which means the tracking error of the reference input signal at the frequency $\omega = 1$ rad/s will be only 5%. Similarly, when $\omega = 0.1$ rad/s, we have

$$|L(j0.1)|_{dB} = |1/S(j0.1)|_{dB} = 46 \text{ dB} \quad \rightarrow \quad |S(j0.1)| = 0.005$$

which means the tracking error of the reference input signal at the frequency $\omega = 0.1$ rad/s will be only 0.5%. ∎

The loop shaping graphs on Figure 9.26 are obtained using the following MATLAB code:

```
% Fig9.26 CSD_LoopShaping_Ex9.26
num=5000; den=[1 55 250 0]; L=tf(num,den);
% Complementary function T
T = feedback(L,1);
% Sensitivity function S
S=1-T;
figure(34),
sigma(inv(S),'b',T,'g',L,'r',{.1,100}),
grid on
```

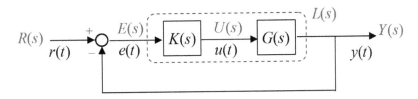

Fig. 9.27: The loop transfer function (LTF) $L(s)$ of a typical feedback control system.

9.7 Exercise Problems

In the typical feedback control system shown in Figure 9.27, $G(s)$ is the plant—the system to be controlled—and $K(s)$ is the controller to be designed to improve the performance and robust stability of the closed-loop system subject to control-input constraints. In the following exercise problems we will particularly focus on the robust stability requirement. Notice that $L(s) = G(s)K(s)$ is the loop transfer function (LTF), which has been playing a key role in the root locus design and Nyquist stability analysis.

P9.1a: In this exercise problem, we will revisit the dual-loop motor speed tracking control system considered in Example 6.1. The block diagram of the feedback control system is shown in Figure 9.28. The plant is a DC motor with transfer function

$$G(s) = \frac{b}{s+a}$$

where the output $y(t)$ and the control input $u(t)$ represent the motor speed and the electric voltage, respectively. The controller is composed of one integrator s^{-1} and two constant parameters K_1 and K_2.

The integrator is included to guarantee zero steady-state error due to step tracking input, and K_1 and K_2 are to be determined based on the desired transient performance and robust stability subject to control-input constraints. First of all, show that the loop transfer function is

$$L(s) = \frac{bK_2}{s(s+a-bK_1)}$$

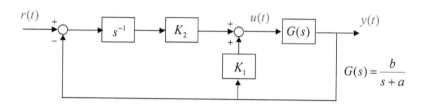

Fig. 9.28: A dual-loop motor speed tracking control system.

P9.1b: Let $b = 145.5$ and $a = 43.14$. Find the characteristic equation of the closed-loop system, and determine the values of K_1 and K_2 so that the damping ratio and the natural frequency of the closed-loop system are $\varsigma = 0.9$ and $\omega_n = 50$ rad/s, respectively.

P9.1c: With the K_1 and K_2 designed in P9.1b, we are ready to evaluate the performance of the closed-loop system. Assume the control input $u(t)$ is required to be less than 15V to avoid actuator saturation, and the reference input is expected to be below 40 rad/s. Let the reference input be $r(t) = 40u_s(t)$ rad/s. Plot the closed-loop responses $y(t)$ and $u(t)$. Inspect the performance of $y(t)$ in terms of steady-state error, rise time, maximum overshoot, and settling time. Also check if the control-input constraint is satisfied for $u(t)$.

P9.1d: Draw the Nyquist plot and the Bode plot of the loop transfer function $L(s)$, and find the phase-crossover frequency ω_p, the gain margin GM, the gain-crossover frequency ω_g, and the phase margin PM of the system.

P9.1e: Find the complementary sensitivity function

$$T(s) = L(s)[1+L(s)]^{-1}$$

Plot the maximum singular value of $T(j\omega)$, which is equal to the magnitude $|T(j\omega)|$ in this SISO case,

$$\bar{\sigma}[T(j\omega)] = |T(j\omega)|$$

and comment on the physical meaning of this plot.

P9.1f: Use the gain-crossover frequency ω_g from the solution of P9.1d, and the value of $|T(j\omega_g)|$ from the $|T(j\omega)|$ plot obtained in P9.1e to compute the phase margin of the system based on Equation 9.62 or Equation 9.63. Verify this result with the PM value obtained from P9.1d.

P9.1g: In almost all practical control systems, time delay may occur in the process of measurement, decision making, and actuator actuation, and the loop transfer function needs to be modified as $L(s)e^{-sT_d}$, where T_ds is the delay time. Let $T_d = 0.01$s, draw the Nyquist plot and the Bode plot of $L(s)e^{-sT_d}$, and find the phase-crossover frequency ω_p, the gain margin GM, the gain-crossover frequency ω_g, and the phase margin PM of the delayed system. Is the system stable?

P9.1h: Find the critical delay time T_c at which the system will become unstable. Draw the Nyquist plot and the Bode plot of $L(s)e^{-sT_c}$, and use these plots to verify that T_c is indeed the critical delay time.

P9.1i: Comment on the controller designed in P9.1b especially based on its ability to address the robust stability issue caused by time delay.

P9.2a: In this exercise problem, we will still consider the same dual-loop integral control system structure shown in Figure 9.28, the same plant

$$G(s) = \frac{b}{s+a} = \frac{145.5}{s+43.14}$$

but the controller parameters K_1 and K_2 will be designed differently so that the closed-loop system has a better robust stability against time delay. The loop transfer function will have the same form, as shown in P9.1a. Find the characteristic equation of the closed-loop system in terms of the parameters K_1 and K_2, and then determine the values of K_1 and K_2 so that the damping ratio and the natural frequency of the closed-loop system are $\varsigma = 0.9$ and $\omega_n = 10$ rad/s, respectively. Notice that we keep the same damping ratio, but reduce the natural frequency by a factor of 5 in order to slow down the tracking response.

P9.2b: With the new K_1 and K_2 designed in P9.2a, we are ready to evaluate the performance of the new closed-loop system. Let the reference input be $r(t) = 40u_s(t)$ rad/s. Plot the closed-loop responses $y(t)$ and $u(t)$. Inspect the performance of $y(t)$ in terms of steady-state error, rise time, maximum overshoot, and settling time. Also check if the control-input constraint is satisfied for $u(t)$. Compare the simulation results with those obtained in P9.1c.

P9.2c: Draw the Nyquist plot and the Bode plot of the loop transfer function $L(s)$ and find the phase-crossover frequency ω_p, the gain margin GM, the gain-crossover frequency ω_g, and the phase margin PM of the system.

P9.2d: Find the complementary sensitivity function

$$T(s) = L(s)[1+L(s)]^{-1}$$

Plot the maximum singular value of $T(j\omega)$,

$$\bar{\sigma}[T(j\omega)] = |T(j\omega)|$$

and comment on the physical meaning of this plot. Compare this plot with that in P9.1e.

P9.2e: Use the gain-crossover frequency ω_g from the solution of P9.2c, and the value of $|T(j\omega_g)|$ from the $|T(j\omega)|$ plot obtained in P9.2d to compute the phase margin of the system based on Equation 9.62 or Equation 9.63. Verify this result with the PM value obtained from P9.2c.

P9.2f: Assume there exists a time delay in the system and the loop transfer function needs to be modified to $L(s)e^{-sT_d}$, where $T_d s$ is the delay time. Let $T_d = 0.01$s, draw the Nyquist plot and the Bode plot of $L(s)e^{-sT_d}$, and find the phase-crossover frequency ω_p, the gain margin GM, the gain-crossover frequency ω_g, and the phase margin PM of the delayed system. Is the system stable? Compare the results with those obtained in P9.1g.

P9.2g: Find the critical delay time T_c at which the system will become unstable. Draw the Nyquist plot and the Bode plot of $L(s)e^{-sT_c}$, and use these plots to verify that T_c is indeed the critical delay time. Compare the critical delay time with that obtained in P9.1h, and give your comment.

P9.2h: Comment on the advantages and the deficiencies of the gain and phase margins as measures of robust stability.

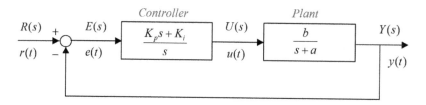

Fig. 9.29: A PI motor speed tracking control system.

P9.3a: In this exercise problem, we will consider the same DC motor speed tracking control problem with the same plant

$$G(s) = \frac{b}{s+a} = \frac{145.5}{s+43.14}$$

as in P9.1, but the controller structure is different. It is the well-known PI (proportional plus integral) controller

$$K_p + \frac{K_i}{s}$$

as shown in Figure 9.29. First of all, show that the loop transfer function is

$$L(s) = \frac{bK_ps + bK_i}{s(s+a)}$$

Note that this loop transfer function has a zero at $-K_i/K_p$ while the loop transfer functions in P9.1 and P9.2 have no zeros.

P9.3b: Let $b = 145.5$ and $a = 43.14$. Find the characteristic equation of the closed-loop system, and determine the values of K_p and K_i so that the damping ratio and the natural frequency of the closed-loop system are $\varsigma = 0.9$ and $\omega_n = 50$ rad/s, respectively. Notice that the poles of this PI control system are placed at the same locations as the poles of the system in P9.1.

P9.3c: Now we are ready to evaluate the performance of the closed-loop system with the K_p and K_i obtained in P9.3b. Assume the control input $u(t)$ is required to be less than 15V to avoid actuator saturation, and the reference input is expected to be below 40 rad/s. Let the reference input be $r(t) = 40u_s(t)$ rad/s. Plot the closed-loop responses $y(t)$ and $u(t)$. Inspect the performance of $y(t)$ in terms of steady-state error, rise time, maximum overshoot, and settling time, and check if the control-input constraint is satisfied for $u(t)$. Compare the simulation results with those obtained in P9.1c, and give your comments.

P9.3d: Draw the Nyquist plot and the Bode plot of the loop transfer function $L(s)$, and find the phase-crossover frequency ω_p, the gain margin GM, the gain-crossover frequency ω_g, and the phase margin PM of the system.

P9.3e: Find the complementary sensitivity function

$$T(s) = L(s)[1 + L(s)]^{-1}$$

Plot the maximum singular value of $T(j\omega)$,

$$\bar{\sigma}[T(j\omega)] = |T(j\omega)|$$

and comment on the physical meaning of this plot.

P9.3f: Use the gain-crossover frequency ω_g from the solution of P9.1d, and the value of $|T(j\omega_g)|$ from the $|T(j\omega)|$ plot obtained in P9.3e to compute the phase margin of the system based on Equation 9.62 or Equation 9.63. Verify this result with the PM value obtained from P9.3d.

P9.3g: Assume there exists a time delay in the system and the loop transfer function needs to be modified to $L(s)e^{-sT_d}$, where $T_d s$ is the delay time. Let $T_d = 0.01s$, draw the Nyquist plot and the Bode plot of $L(s)e^{-sT_d}$, and find the phase-crossover frequency ω_p, the gain margin GM, the gain-crossover frequency ω_g, and the phase margin PM of the delayed system. Is the system stable?

P9.3h: Find the critical delay time T_c at which the system will become unstable. Draw the Nyquist plot and the Bode plot of $L(s)e^{-sT_c}$ and use these plots to verify that T_c is indeed the critical delay time.

P9.3i: Comment on the PI controller designed in P9.3b, especially on its differences from the dual-loop controller designed in P9.1b.

P9.4a: In this exercise problem, we will revisit the first-order closed-loop control system with a time delay in Example 9.14. The loop transfer function of the system is

$$L(s) = \frac{2}{s+1}e^{-sT}$$

where T is the delay time. First of all, assume there is no time delay (i.e., $T = 0$). Draw the Nyquist plot and the Bode plot of $L(s)$ with $T = 0$, and determine the gain-crossover frequency $]\omega_g$ rad/s, and the phase margin PM in degrees.

P9.4b: Recall that we computed the critical delay time T_c based on Equations 9.37 and 9.38. The delay time also can be obtained using the information of the phase margin and the gain-crossover frequency. Use the phase margin PM and the gain-crossover frequency ω_g in P9.4a to verify that the critical delay time is $T_c = 1.209s$.

P9.5a: Consider the feedback control system shown in Figure 9.27 whose loop transfer function $L(s)$ is described by the following first-order linear system with time delay,

$$L(s) = \frac{b}{s+a}e^{-sT}$$

where b and a are real constant parameters and T is the delay time. Show that the critical delay time T_c can be computed using the following formula if $b > a$:

$$T_c = \frac{1}{\sqrt{b^2 - a^2}}\left(\pi - \tan^{-1}\left(\frac{\sqrt{b^2 - a^2}}{a}\right)\right)$$

P9.5b: What does it mean when the condition $b > a$ is not satisfied?

P9.5c: Vary the parameters b and a, one at a time, and observe how they would affect the value of the critical delay time T_c.

State Feedback and Linear Quadratic Optimization

I N this chapter and the next we will focus on feedback control analysis and design based on the state-space models. The state-space approach became popular in the early 1960s beginning with the publications of Rudolf Kalman, [Kalman, 1960a,b, Kalman and Bertram, 1960, Kalman and Bucy, 1961]. Instead of frequency-domain methods (i.e., Laplace transform approaches), attention returned to the earlier methods of analysis and design using differential equations (e.g., [Maxwell, 1868]).

The main reasons of this revolutionary paradigm shift are the following: (1) The state-space approach resolved basic theoretical problems that had impeded the extension of frequency-domain tools to MIMO systems; (2) The nonlinear system state-space representation is elegant and versatile, allowing systematic ways to identify the equilibriums of the system, to find a local (linear or nonlinear) model at each equilibrium of interest that can be employed in analysis and controller design; (3) The state-space framework makes it easier to formulate the control problems as constrained optimization problems like the LQR (linear quadratic regulation), the LQG (linear quadratic Gaussian), the H_2 optimization, and the H_∞ optimization control problems; (4) The computing capability and the miniaturization of the digital computer has facilitated the applications of the state-space control approaches in almost every product and every manufacturing process to achieve automation, precision, reliability, and performance enhancement.

However, the rise of the state-space approach does not mean the end of the frequency-domain approach. Instead, the state-space model framework has made it possible to incorporate frequency-domain performance requirement into design of large-scale MIMO control systems. The frequency-domain properties and the time-domain properties are still the two important aspects of any system. They are inseparable. In fact, the time-domain responses, stability, and robustness are dictated by the pole locations and the frequency response of the system, as we have witnessed in Sections 2.5, 3.3, 3.4, 8.4, 8.6, 9.3, and 9.4.

In the following section, we will have a brief review of what we have learned in the previous chapters regarding the control systems fundamentals related to the state-space approach. We will reinforce these key concepts and employ them in new control system design applications. Then we will incorporate performance optimization with control-input constraints in the state-feedback control problem formulation and discuss the solution to the optimization problem. In the next chapter, the observer theory will be introduced and employed to optimally estimate the state variables so that the linear quadratic optimization approach can be extended to the more general output feedback case.

10.1 Brief Review of the State-Space Approach

The nonlinear state-space model was employed to describe the dynamics of the simple inverted pendulum system in Section 4.4 because **it provides the best possible framework to compute the equilibriums and to obtain the linearized state-space model at the equilibriums of interest via Jacobian matrices approach**, as shown in Equations 4.41 and 4.42. The linear state-space model at each equilibrium is described in the form:

$$\dot{x}(t) = Ax(t) + Bu(t)$$
$$y(t) = Cx(t) + Du(t)$$

where $x(t)$ is the 2×1 state vector consisting the angular displacement and the angular velocity of the pendulum, $u(t)$ is the control input representing the applied force, $y(t)$ is the output representing the angular displacement of the pendulum, and the dimensions of the matrices A, B, C, and D are assumed comparable.

The poles of the inverted pendulum system at the equilibrium associated with the upright pendulum position were shown to be the eigenvalues of the A matrix, which verifies the equilibrium is unstable since one of the two poles is in the right half of the complex plane, as shown in Equation 4.42. **The linear state-space model can be further employed to design a state-feedback controller $u(t) = Fx(t)$ to place the closed-loop system poles, which are the eigenvalues of the matrix $A + BF$, at desired locations in the left half of the complex plane to stabilize the closed-loop system and achieve desired performances.**

Although the state variables assignments are not unique, usually for mechanical systems the physical variables like displacements and velocities are chosen to be state variables, if possible. Similarly, for electrical systems, the currents through the inductors and the voltages across the capacitors are practical candidates to serve as state variables. In the control system design or analysis, **for computational reasons, a state-space similarity transformation may be employed to change the state variables so that the state-space model is in some special form, like the company form or the diagonal form.** On most occasions, state variables are chosen after a differential equation model is obtained. However, it is possible to assign state variables before constructing the dynamics model. In Section 5.5, a direct state-space modeling approach was presented to obtain a state-space model for electrical circuits, as demonstrated in Examples 5.12 and 5.13.

Chapter 6 covers systems representations of interconnected systems including block diagrams, signal flow graphs, transfer functions, state-space models, state diagrams, and the relationships among them. Mason's gain formula, the state transition matrix, the Cayely-Hamilton theorem, and the solution of the state equation are also the main topics of the chapter. A state diagram is a graphical representation of a state-space model in the form of signal flow graph or block diagram. Hence, it is trivial to find the state-space model given a state diagram and vice versa. Furthermore, **the transfer function can be computed directly from the state-space model using the formula $G(s) = C(sI - A)^{-1}B + D$ in Equation 6.24 or obtained indirectly from the state diagram using Mason's gain formula, as demonstrated in Example 6.23.** Conversely, given a transfer function there are infinitely many corresponding state diagrams or state-space models. Depending on the need or preference, the corresponding state diagram can be in the companion form via direction realization, or in the diagonal form via parallel connection, or in any other form associated with cascade connection or feedback connection, as demonstrated in Examples 6.24, 6.25, 6.26, and 6.27.

In Chapter 7, more fundamental concepts and tools of feedback control systems are provided to prepare for the more advanced control systems design and analysis, especially in the state space. **These include advantages and limitations of feedback control, characteristic equations, poles and zeros,**

BIBO stability, internal stability, similarity transforms in state space, state-feedback pole placement and their applications to control systems design and analysis. Note that the internal stability is defined based on the status of every state in the state-space model while the BIBO stability was defined only in terms of the input-output relationship of the system; hence, the internal stability in general is stronger than the BIBO stability. We will discuss more about the difference of these two stability definitions after *controllability* and *observability* are officially defined later in this chapter.

Since the performance and behavior of the system are mainly determined by its pole locations and the pole locations can be altered via feedback control, it is a common practice to utilize pole placement to improve the characteristics of the closed-loop system. As demonstrated in Section 3.6, the variation of the proportional controller K will move the closed-loop system pole locations, as shown in the right graph of Figure 3.16. Due to the movement of the poles, the damping ratio ς, the natural frequency ω_n, and the corresponding time responses will change accordingly, as shown in left graph of Figure 3.16. A similar idea was applied to the state-space models in Section 7.5 using state feedback. **The state-space pole placement can be achieved by the direct approach or the transform approach. The direct approach is conceptually simple, but computationally can become very complicated when the order of the system is higher than three. The transform approach requires a similarity transformation to transform the state-space model to a special companion form initially, but after that the computation becomes extremely simple, even the order of the system is as high as 100.** The transform approach was employed in Section 7.6.4 to place the poles of the closed-loop cart-inverted pendulum system in the left half of the complex plane at $s = -2, -8$, and $-4 \pm j3$ to convert an originally unstable system to become stable.

In Section 8.6, an aircraft longitudinal flight path tracking control problem was considered. The initial attempt was to use the classical control approach with a PI controller together with root locus design (Figure 8.35) to achieve the closed-loop system stability, zero steady-state tracking error, and acceptable transient response. Due to the RHP zeros and the phugoid (long-period) mode poles, the associated root locus diagram (Figure 8.36) does not allow much option to choose an acceptable set of closed-loop system poles to deliver an acceptable performance. The response was either extremely slow or too much oscillation, as shown in Figure 8.37.

To address the issue, a state-feedback integral tracking control structure (Figure 8.38) together with root locus design was employed to achieve the objective. Since all the four state variables are assumed available for feedback to provide more information than the PI controller case where only the flight path angle is assumed available for feedback, the state-feedback controller is expected to do better. Like any other viable feedback control scheme, the state feedback could not change the RHP zero positions; however, it did replace the poles of the loop transfer function to the new locations, $-1.7, -5.9$, $-1.6 \pm j1.8$, and $s = 0$, which provides a much more favorable root locus diagram, as shown in Figure 8.39. Consequently, an optimal tracking integrator constant K was selected to lead to a much better tracking performance, as shown in Figures 8.40 and 8.41.

Although we still have more to learn about the state-space approaches later in this chapter and the following one, **we have already experienced the benefit of employing state feedback, internal model principle, and the root locus technique to design a stabilizing, tracking/regulating closed-loop control system.** In the following section, we will employ a rather simple second-order lightly damped position control system to demonstrate the state space/root locus pole placement approach and compare it with the traditional PID (proportional integral and derivative) control approach.

10.2 Control of a Lightly Damped Positioning System

The poor performance of a lightly damped system, which can easily drift from its operating equilibrium and oscillate with large amplitude, is common in practice; for example, the aircraft flight dynamics like the phugoid (long-period) mode of F/A-18 has a very small damping ratio, $\varsigma = 0.1$, and a quite long (62.3 seconds) oscillation period, as described in Equation 8.68. **If the system is not adequately compensated, moderate turbulence would cause unacceptably long and large up and down oscillations in longitudinal motion and make the aircraft very difficult, if not impossible, to maneuver.**

10.2.1 A Simple Pendulum Positioning System

In the following, **a rather simple nonlinear lightly damped pendulum positioning system, as shown in Figure 10.1, will be employed to demonstrate how to stabilize and improve the performance of the system using the state space/root locus pole placement approach.** One end of the rod is connected to a pivot with bearing so that the rod can perform one degree-of-freedom swing motion without much friction. The other end of the rod is attached with a motor/propeller, which serves as an actuator to produce the torque, T, required in the control system.

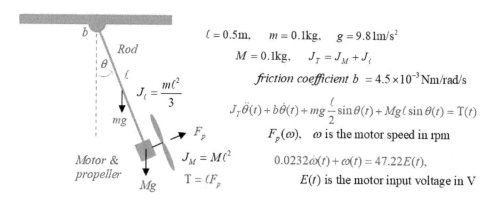

$\ell = 0.5\text{m}, \quad m = 0.1\text{kg}, \quad g = 9.81\text{m/s}^2$

$M = 0.1\text{kg}, \quad J_T = J_M + J_\ell$

friction coefficient $b = 4.5 \times 10^{-3}\,\text{Nm/rad/s}$

$J_T \ddot{\theta}(t) + b\dot{\theta}(t) + mg\dfrac{\ell}{2}\sin\theta(t) + Mg\ell\sin\theta(t) = \text{T}(t)$

$F_p(\omega), \quad \omega$ is the motor speed in rpm

$0.0232\dot{\omega}(t) + \omega(t) = 47.22E(t),$

$E(t)$ is the motor input voltage in V

$J_\ell = \dfrac{m\ell^2}{3}$

$J_M = M\ell^2$

$\text{T} = \ell F_p$

Fig. 10.1: A nonlinear, lightly damped pendulum positioning system.

Equations of Motion

The procedure of deriving the dynamics model of the pendulum positioning system is similar to those discussed in Section 4.4 and Section 4.5. By either the Newtonian or the Lagrange equation approach, the equation of motion for the pendulum can be found as follows:

$$J\ddot{\theta}(t) + b\dot{\theta}(t) + 0.5mg\ell\sin\theta(t) + Mg\ell\sin\theta(t) = \text{T}(t) \qquad (10.1)$$

The total moment of inertia is $J = J_\ell + J_M = m\ell^2/3 + M\ell^2$, where $\ell = 0.5$ m is length of the rod and $m = 0.1$ kg and $M = 0.1$ kg are the mass of the rod and the motor, respectively. The friction coefficient of the pivot is assumed $b = 4.5 \times 10^{-3}$ Nm/rad/s and the gravity is $g = 9.81$ m/s^2. The output θ (rad) is the angular displacement of the rod, the control input is the applied torque $\text{T} = \ell F_p(\omega)$ (Nm), and the propeller force $F_p(\omega)$ is determined by the motor speed ω (rad/s). The DC motor dynamics is described by the following equation,

$$0.0232\,\dot{\omega}(t) + \omega(t) = 47.22E(t) \tag{10.2}$$

where E (V) is the DC motor input voltage.

Nonlinear State Equations and Equilibriums

With the physical data given, the pendulum equation, Equation 10.1 becomes

$$\ddot{\theta}(t) + a_1\,\dot{\theta}(t) + a_0\sin\theta(t) = b_0\mathrm{T}(t) \tag{10.3}$$

where $a_1 = 0.135$, $a_0 = 22.073$, and $b_0 = 30$. Let the state variables be $x_1(t) = \theta(t)$ and $x_2(t) = \dot{\theta}(t)$, then the nonlinear state equation associated with Equation 10.3 can be written as

$$\dot{x} = \begin{bmatrix} \dot{x}_1 \\ \dot{x}_2 \end{bmatrix} = \begin{bmatrix} x_2 \\ -a_0\sin x_1 - a_1x_2 + b_0\mathrm{T} \end{bmatrix} = f(x,\mathrm{T}) = \begin{bmatrix} f_1(x_1,x_2,\mathrm{T}) \\ f_2(x_1,x_2,\mathrm{T}) \end{bmatrix} \tag{10.4}$$

Assume the operating equilibrium is chosen to keep the angular displacement of the pendulum at $\theta(t) = \theta^* = 15° = \pi/12$ rad. Then the equilibrium of the system can be found by solving the state equations with the derivative of the state variables set to zero. Now, we have

$$\begin{bmatrix} \dot{x}_1 \\ \dot{x}_2 \end{bmatrix} = 0 \quad\rightarrow\quad \begin{matrix} x_2 = 0 \\ -a_0\sin 15° - a_1x_2 + b_0\mathrm{T} = 0 \end{matrix} \quad\rightarrow\quad \begin{bmatrix} x_1^* \\ x_2^* \end{bmatrix} = \begin{bmatrix} 15° \\ 0 \end{bmatrix}, \quad \mathrm{T}^* = 0.19043\text{Nm}$$

Linearized State-Space Model

Next, we will find a linearized state-space model for the $\theta^* = 15°$ equilibrium. At this equilibrium $(x_1^*, x_2^*, \mathrm{T}^*) = (15°, 0°/\text{s}, 0.19043\text{ Nm})$, we have the linearized state-space model

$$\dot{\bar{x}}(t) = A\bar{x}(t) + B\bar{\mathrm{T}}(t) \tag{10.5}$$

where the matrices A and B are computed via Jacobian matrices J_x and J_T, respectively, as follows:

$$A = J_x = \left[\frac{\partial f}{\partial x}\right]_{x^*,\mathrm{T}^*} = \begin{bmatrix} \partial f_1/\partial x_1 & \partial f_1/\partial x_2 \\ \partial f_2/\partial x_1 & \partial f_2/\partial x_2 \end{bmatrix}_{x^* = \begin{bmatrix} \pi/12 \\ 0 \end{bmatrix},\mathrm{T}^*} = \begin{bmatrix} 0 & 1 \\ -a_0\cos(\pi/12) & -a_1 \end{bmatrix}$$

and

$$B = J_\mathrm{T} = \left[\frac{\partial f}{\partial \mathrm{T}}\right]_{x^*,\mathrm{T}^*} = \begin{bmatrix} \partial f_1/\partial \mathrm{T} \\ \partial f_2/\partial \mathrm{T} \end{bmatrix}_{x^*,\mathrm{T}^*} = \begin{bmatrix} 0 \\ b_0 \end{bmatrix}$$

That is,

$$\dot{\bar{x}}(t) = \begin{bmatrix} \dot{\bar{x}}_1(t) \\ \dot{\bar{x}}_2(t) \end{bmatrix} = \begin{bmatrix} 0 & 1 \\ -21.32 & -0.135 \end{bmatrix} \begin{bmatrix} \bar{x}_1(t) \\ \bar{x}_2(t) \end{bmatrix} + \begin{bmatrix} 0 \\ 30 \end{bmatrix} \bar{\mathrm{T}}(t) = A\bar{x}(t) + B\bar{\mathrm{T}}(t) \tag{10.6}$$

Note that the relationship among the real values $x(t)$, $\mathrm{T}(t)$, the equilibrium values x^*, T^*, and the differential (perturbed) values $\bar{x}(t)$, $\bar{\mathrm{T}}$ are shown in the following:

$$x(t) = \bar{x}(t) + x^*, \quad \mathrm{T}(t) = \bar{\mathrm{T}}(t) + \mathrm{T}^* \tag{10.7}$$

For instance, $\bar{x}^T = \begin{bmatrix} 20° & 0°/\text{s} \end{bmatrix}$ means that the real state vector is $x^T = \begin{bmatrix} 35° & 0°/\text{s} \end{bmatrix}$, and a $\bar{\mathrm{T}} = 0$ Nm reveals that the real torque is $\mathrm{T} = \mathrm{T}^* = 0.19043$ Nm.

Analysis of the Open-Loop System

Recall that the eigenvalues of the A matrix, or the poles of the system are the roots of the following characteristic equation:

$$|sI - A| = \begin{vmatrix} s & -1 \\ 21.32 & s + 0.135 \end{vmatrix} = s^2 + 0.135s + 21.32 := s^2 + 2\varsigma\omega_n s + \omega_n^2 = 0 \qquad (10.8)$$

The roots of this characteristic equation are

$$-\alpha \pm j\omega = -0.0675 \pm j4.6169$$

and the corresponding damping ratio and the natural frequency are

$$\varsigma = 0.0146 \quad \text{and} \quad \omega_n = 4.6174 \, \text{rad/s}$$

respectively. We have learned from the previous chapters, especially Section 3.4.3, that the time-domain behavior of the system is closely related to the damping factor α, the frequency ω, the damping ratio ς, and the natural frequency ω_n, which are derived from the roots of the characteristic equation. Hence, it is possible to get a general idea of how the system will behave based on the information of the system poles, or, equivalently, the roots of the characteristic equation.

Before conducting a computer simulation using the mathematical model, we can perform a simple virtual experiment. Imagine that a pendulum positioning system, as shown in Figure 10.1 is operating at the $\theta = \theta^* = 15°$ equilibrium. That is, the motor propeller is providing a constant torque $T^* = 0.19043$ Nm to keep θ at the 15° equilibrium. Now, let's perturb the system a little bit by moving the pendulum up to the 35° position while the applied torque remains the same at $T^* = 0.19043$ Nm. Then release the pendulum at $t = 0$ s and observe the pendulum angular displacement $\theta(t)$ as a function of time. What will you see? The system is stable, so eventually the pendulum will go back to the equilibrium. But since the damping factor α and the damping ratio ς are very small, the pendulum will go down toward the equilibrium, pass it with a large overshoot, and then swing back and forth about the equilibrium many times until it is stabilized at the equilibrium.

The oscillation frequency is $\omega = 4.6169$ rad/s, and thus the oscillation period is $P = 2\pi/\omega = 1.361$ s. The damping factor $\alpha = 0.0675$ reveals that the oscillation amplitude will decrease exponentially with time constant $\tau = 1/\alpha = 14.81$ s. That is, the oscillation amplitude will reduce to 36.8% of its original value after $t = \tau = 14.81$ s, or, equivalently, reduce to 1.83% of its original value after $4\tau = 59.2$ s of time. The oscillation amplitude decreasing rate can also be computed using the damping ratio $\varsigma = 0.0146$. The maximum overshoot is $OS = e^{-\varsigma\pi/\sqrt{1-\varsigma^2}} = 0.95516$, which means that the oscillation amplitude reduces to 95.516% of its value after a half period $P/2 = 0.68$ s of time. Hence, after 87 half periods, which is 59.16s, the oscillation amplitude will reduce to 1.84% of its original value.

A Simulink simulation of the pendulum positioning system of Equation 10.3 or Equation 10.4 with initial angular displacement at $\theta(0) = 35°$, which is 20° away from the equilibrium position $\theta^* = 15°$, can be conducted to obtain the oscillatory time response, as shown on the left graph of Figure 10.2, while the control-input torque is kept at the equilibrium torque $T^* = 0.19043$ Nm, as shown on the right graph. The oscillation period P can be measured from the peak-to-peak time on the left graph. The time at the seventh peak is approximately 9.55s, which implies $P = 9.55/7 = 1.364$ s. The maximum overshoot OS can be computed based on the measure of the amplitude at the seventh peak, which is 10.5°, or, equivalently 10.5/20 = 52.5% of the initial amplitude after 14 half periods. Therefore, we have $OS^{14} = 0.525$, which implies that $OS = 0.955$.

The simulation results are fairly consistent with the virtual experiment and the prediction based on the pole location $-\alpha \pm j\omega$, the damping ratio ς, and the natural frequency ω_n.

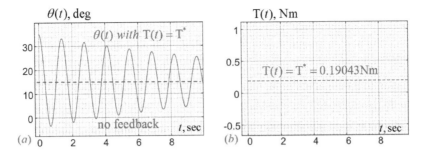

Fig. 10.2: An oscillatory time response of the nonlinear lightly damped pendulum system due to a perturbed initial condition.

10.2.2 State-Feedback Stabilization of the Pendulum Positioning System

From this analysis and the simulation results of the pendulum positioning system, the open-loop system can drift out of its equilibrium easily due to a small disturbance, and it also requires a long period of time to recover back to the equilibrium. Furthermore, **the lightly damping feature may make it difficult or even impossible for manual control due to the oscillations and man-machine interface miscommunication and time delay.** One may suggest to fundamentally change the mechanical design to make it more heavily damped. Well, it is like a double-edged sword. Increasing the friction to make the system less sensitive to disturbances will at the same time cause the system to be less responsive to control commands. **One effective way to resolve this dilemma is to employ feedback control.**

Recall that at the equilibrium $(x_1^*, x_2^*, T^*) = (15°, 0°/s, 0.19043 \text{ Nm})$, we have the linearized state-space model

$$\dot{\bar{x}}(t) = A\bar{x}(t) + B\bar{T}(t)$$

where the matrices A and B are given by Equation 10.6:

$$A = \begin{bmatrix} 0 & 1 \\ -21.32 & -0.135 \end{bmatrix}, \quad B = \begin{bmatrix} 0 \\ 30 \end{bmatrix}$$

Now, we will close the loop using the state feedback

$$\bar{T}(t) = F\bar{x}(t) \tag{10.9}$$

so that the closed-loop system poles are at $s = -10, -11$.

The characteristic equation of the closed-loop system will be

$$(s+10)(s+11) = s^2 + 21s + 110 = s^2 + 2\varsigma\omega_n s + \omega_n^2 \quad \rightarrow \quad \varsigma = 1.0011, \quad \omega_n = 10.49 \text{ rad/s}$$

which implies the closed-loop system response will be slightly overdamped with no overshoot and no oscillations. The closed-loop control system thus designed will yield the state-feedback gain matrix as

$$F = \begin{bmatrix} -2.956 & -0.6955 \end{bmatrix} \tag{10.10}$$

and the state equation of the closed-loop system will become

$$\dot{\bar{x}}(t) = (A+BF)\bar{x}(t) = \begin{bmatrix} 0 & 1 \\ -110 & -21 \end{bmatrix}\bar{x}(t) \tag{10.11}$$

Assume the initial condition

$$\bar{x}(0)^T = \begin{bmatrix} 20° & 0°/s \end{bmatrix} = \begin{bmatrix} 0.349 & 0 \end{bmatrix}$$

The solution of the closed-loop system state equation, Equation 10.11 can be found as

$$\begin{bmatrix} \bar{x}_1(t) \\ \bar{x}_2(t) \end{bmatrix} = e^{(A+BF)t} \begin{bmatrix} 0.349 \\ 0 \end{bmatrix} = \begin{bmatrix} 11e^{-10t} - 10e^{-11t} & e^{-10t} - e^{-11t} \\ -110e^{-10t} + 110e^{-11t} & -10e^{-10t} + 10e^{-11t} \end{bmatrix} \begin{bmatrix} 0.349 \\ 0 \end{bmatrix}$$

where $e^{(A+BF)t}$ is the state transition matrix of the closed-loop system that can be computed using the inverse Laplace transform,

$$e^{(A+BF)t} = \mathscr{L}^{-1}\left[(sI - (A+BF))^{-1} \right]$$

or utilizing the Cayley-Hamilton approach in Section 6.4.2. Hence, the pendulum angular position $\theta(t)$ and the applied torque $T(t)$ will be

$$\theta(t) = x_1^* + \bar{x}_1(t) = 15° + 220°e^{-10t} - 200°e^{-11t}$$

and

$$T(t) = T^* + \bar{T}(t) = T^* + F\bar{x} = 0.19043 + 15.3522e^{-10t} - 16.3838e^{-11t} \text{ Nm}$$

respectively. **Note that we always use rad, rad/s as units in the computation, and convert them back to deg and deg/s in display for ease of human reading.**

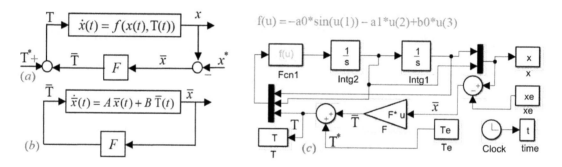

Fig. 10.3: The nonlinear, linearized, and simulation models of the pendulum positioning system.

The Simulink simulation diagram in Figure 10.3(c) with the nonlinear plant is employed to conduct the closed-loop initial state response simulation. In the Simulink simulation diagram, you will see a function block named `Fcn1`. Double click the function block to open the pop-up window, called `Function Block Parameters: Fcn1`, and type

```
-a0*sin(u(1))-a1*u(2)+b0*u(3)
```

into the Parameters Expression box. Note that this function f(u)=-a0*sin(u(1))-a1*u(2)+b0*u(3) is a function of the three inputs: u(1), u(2), and u(3) that represent x_1, x_2, and T, respectively.

The value of the function then serves as the input to the Intg2 integrator; that is, $\dot{x}_2 = f(u)$. The initial state $x_1(0) = 35° = 0.6109$ rad, which is equivalent to $\bar{x}_1(0) = 20° = 0.349$ rad, is chosen by double clicking the Intg1 integrator to open the pop-up window, called `Function Block Parameters:`

`Intg1`, and type the radian number 0.6109 onto to Initial Condition box. The input constant boxes named `xe` and `Te` should be assigned as 0.2618, the radian number of the equilibrium position $x_1^* = 15°$, and 0.19043, the equilibrium torque, respectively. Of course, F is the state-feedback gain, as shown in Equation 10.10.

The simulation results are shown in Figure 10.4. It can be seen that the results are consistent with the analysis and computations. **The state-feedback control has brought the pendulum from the perturbed $35°$ position back to the $15°$ equilibrium within 2% vicinity in just** 0.6 **seconds, which is** 100 **times faster than the slowly decayed oscillatory response without feedback, as shown in Figure 10.2.** The required torque T(t) to complete the control action shown on the right graph of Figure 10.4 is between −0.8 Nm and 0.5 Nm, which is within a practical range.

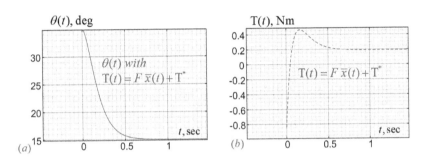

Fig. 10.4: An impressive disturbance response reduction accomplished by state feedback.

10.2.3 Stabilization of the Motor/Propeller-Driven Pendulum Positioning System

In Section 10.2.2, a state-feedback control was employed to greatly improve the stability of the originally lightly damped system. For simplicity, the torque was considered as the control input. **In practice, the torque can be provided by a motor control subsystem.** In the motor/propeller-driven pendulum positioning system shown in Figure 10.1, the torque applied to the pendulum is

$$T(t) = \ell F_p(t) \quad \text{and} \quad F_p(t) \text{ is proportional to } \omega^2(t) \tag{10.12}$$

where ℓ (m) is the length of the pendulum and $\omega(t)$ (rad/s) is the rotational speed of the motor/propeller. The motor dynamics and the torque applied to the pendulum are described by the equation,

$$\dot{\omega}(t) = -a_m \omega(t) + b_m E(t) := f(\omega, E)$$
$$T(t) = (1/k_2)\omega^2(t) := h(\omega, E) \tag{10.13}$$

where $a_m = 43.1$ (1/s), $b_m = 2034.5$ (1/Vs^2), and $k_2 = 26345$ (1/Nms^2). Note that the state equation of the motor is linear, but the relationship between the torque T and the motor speed ω is nonlinear. When the system is operating at the $15°$ pendulum equilibrium,

$$[x^* \ T^*]^T = [x_1^* \ x_2^* \ T^*]^T = [0.2618 \text{ rad} \ 0\text{rad}/s \ 0.19043\text{Nm}]^T$$

the corresponding motor speed equilibrium ω^* and the motor input voltage equilibrium E^* can be computed based on Equation 10.13 as follows:

$$T^* = 0.19043 = (1/k_2)(\omega^*)^2 \quad \rightarrow \quad \omega^* = \sqrt{0.19043k_2} = 70.83\text{rad}/s$$

$$0 = -a_m\omega^* + b_mE^* \quad \rightarrow \quad E^* = (a_m/b_m)\omega^* = 1.5\text{V}$$

The linearized model of the nonlinear motor/propeller dynamics shown in Equation 10.13 can be obtained using the Jacobian matrices approach in Section 4.4.2 as follows:

$$\dot{\bar{\omega}}(t) = -a_m\bar{\omega}(t) + b_m\bar{E}(t)$$

$$\bar{T}(t) = (1/k_2)\left.\frac{\partial\omega^2}{\partial\omega}\right|_{\omega^*}\bar{\omega}(t) = (2/k_2)\omega^*\bar{\omega}(t)$$

(10.14)

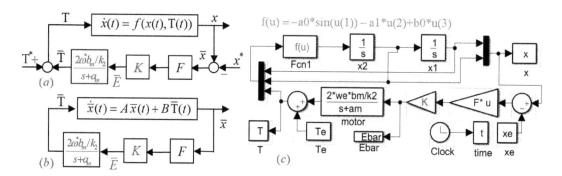

Fig. 10.5: The nonlinear, linearized, and simulation models of the closed-loop pendulum positioning system with motor/propeller as the actuator.

With the motor/propeller as the actuator, the model diagrams of the closed-loop pendulum positioning system shown in Figure 10.3 are now redrawn as those shown in Figure 10.5. Figure 10.5(a) shows the closed-loop block diagram of the nonlinear pendulum system with the linear controller including F, K, and the transfer function of the motor/propeller $(2\omega^*b_m/k_2)/(s+a_m)$. **Note that the output of the nonlinear plant is the real state vector x while the input to the linear controller is the differential (or perturbed) state vector $\bar{x} = x - x^*$, where x^* is the equilibrium state vector. Similarly, the output of the linear controller is the differential (or perturbed) torque $\bar{T}$ while the input to the nonlinear plant is the real torque $T = \bar{T} + T^*$, where T^* is the equilibrium torque.**

Figure 10.5(c) is a Simulink simulation diagram constructed based on the block diagram of Figure 10.5(a). In fact, this simulation diagram is almost the same as that in Figure 10.3(c) except for the insertion of the motor/propeller transfer function and the additional design parameter K. **The insertion of the motor/propeller transfer function is for the practical reason of generating the torque. But the motor/propeller dynamics is a low-pass filter, which will slow down the desired feedback action intended by the original F state-feedback design. For this reason, the K parameter is inserted for compensation purposes. An optimal value of K can be determined using the root locus design approach.**

Figure 10.5(b) is the closed-loop block diagram of the linearized pendulum system with the linear controller including F, K, and the transfer function of the motor/propeller. Note that this linear closed-loop block diagram is almost the same as that in Figure 10.3(b) except for the insertion of the motor/propeller transfer function and the K parameter.

Recall that the root locus design approach starts from the pole-zero diagram of the loop transfer function of the closed-loop system shown in Figure 8.17 and Definition 8.14. **The loop transfer function (LTF) of the closed-loop system in Figure 10.5(b) is $KG(s)$, where $G(s)$ is**

$$G(s) = -F(sI - A)^{-1}B \cdot \frac{2\omega^* b_m / k_2}{s + a_m}$$

The root locus diagram based on the three poles, p_1, $p_2 = -0.0675 \pm j4.62$, $p_3 = -43.1$ and one zero $z_1 = -4.25$ of $G(s)$, can be constructed as shown in Figure 10.6.

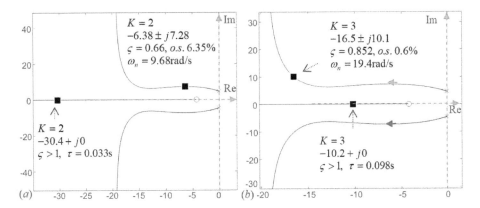

Fig. 10.6: The closed-loop pole locations for $K = 2$ and $K = 3$ on the root loci diagrams of the system shown in Figure 10.5(b).

As shown in Figure 10.6, if the controller parameter is chosen to be $K = 2$, the closed-loop system poles will be

$$-6.38 \pm j7.28 \quad \text{and} \quad -30.4$$

where the two complex conjugate poles are the dominant poles with damping ratio $\varsigma = 0.66$, which implies the system response will be slightly underdamped with about 6% overshoot. On the other hand, if the controller parameter is chosen to be $K = 3$, the three closed-loop system poles will be

$$-10.2 \quad \text{and} \quad -16.5 \pm j10.1$$

where the real pole with damping factor $\alpha = 10.2$ is the dominant pole, which implies the system response will be slightly overdamped.

The disturbance recovery simulation results based on the Simulink diagram of Figure 10.5(c) are shown in Figure 10.7. The simulation results are fairly consistent with the root locus design analysis. The $K = 2$ design will lead to a slightly underdamped response that brings the pendulum down from $\theta = 35°$ toward the desired equilibrium position $\theta = 15°$ more quickly than the $K = 3$ response, but it overshot to $\theta = 13°$ before returning to the $\theta = 15°$ later, around $t = 0.7$ s. On the other hand, the $K = 3$ response is slightly overdamped that comes down from $\theta = 35°$ rather slowly to reach the desired equilibrium position $\theta = 15°$ around $t = 0.65$ s without overshoot or oscillations. It turns out that the $K = 2.5$ design is an approximately optimal choice. It reaches $\theta = 15°$ at $t = 0.4$ s with an unnoticeable overshoot. When $K = 2.5$, the three closed-loop system poles locations are at

$$-9.49 \pm j6.92 \quad \text{and} \quad -24.3$$

where the complex conjugate poles are the dominant poles with damping ratio $\varsigma = 0.808$, which implies the overshoot is just 1.35%.

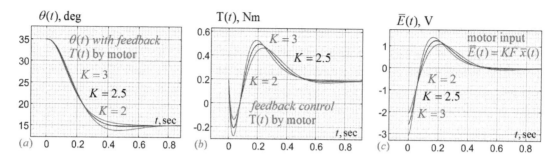

Fig. 10.7: The disturbance recovery responses accomplished by the motor driven state-feedback control system shown in Figure 10.5(c).

Remark 10.1 (The Insertion of Motor/Propeller Dynamics Into the Feedback Loop and the K Compensation)

It is noted that the $K = 3$ disturbance recovery response in Figure 10.7(a) is about the same as that shown in Figure 10.4(a). The $K = 2.5$ response in Figure 10.7(a) is better than that shown in Figure 10.4(a). But if the value of the controller parameter reduces to $K = 1$, the disturbance recovery response will be oscillatory with 26% overshoot and won't reach the steady state until $t = 2$ s. This $K = 1$ poor performance actually is foretold by the root locus analysis that the three closed-loop system poles are at

$$-2.72 \pm j6.53 \quad \text{and} \quad -37.8$$

and the complex conjugate poles are the dominant poles with damping ratio $\varsigma = 0.385$ that implies the overshoot is about 27%.

The insertion of the motor/propeller dynamics into the feedback loop without the K compensation will slow down the feedback correction and degrade the performance due to the inherent low-pass filter property of the motor. However, the performance can be recovered or even made better with an adequate K compensation at $K = 2.5$. ∎

The two graphs of the same root locus plot shown on Figure 10.6 are generated using the following MATLAB code:

```
% CSD Fig10.5b 10.6 rlocus(GK) State-feedback Pendulum positioning system
 % Construction of root locus diagram for the systems
 % shown in Fig. 10.5(b)
am=43.1, bm=2035, xe=[0.2618  0]', Te=0.19043,
 % Linearized model at this equilibrium, xe, Te
A=[0 1; -21.32 -0.135], B=[0; 30], damp(A),
 % State feedback
F=[-2.956   -0.6955], damp(A+B*F),
 % Motor speed equilibrium
k2=26345, we=sqrt(k2*Te), Ee=(am/bm)*we,
 % Root Locus Design
s=tf('s'); sysG_F=ss(A,B,F,0); G_F=tf(sysG_F),
G_M=(2*we*bm/k2)/(s+am), G=-G_M*G_F, figure(12)
K=logspace(-3,2,1000); rlocus(G,K)
```

10.2.4 Tracking Control of the Pendulum Positioning System Using State-Space Pole Placement

In the previous two subsections, Sections 10.2.2 and 10.2.3, a state feedback/root locus design approach was employed to improve the stability and performance at a specified operating equilibrium. In many practical applications, the operating equilibrium may depend on an external command or reference input, which is usually unknown *a priori*, and the controller is required to be designed to achieve closed-loop system stability, zero steady-state tracking error, and an optimal transient performance subject to control-input constraints. **The regulation/tracking issues arise in almost every engineering problem involved with precision, automation, guidance, navigation, and control. In fact, we have addressed these is-sues in Sections 8.1, 8.5, 8.6, and 8.7 regarding the internal model principle, type of systems, and their applications in DC motor speed control, sinusoidal position tracking control, F/A-18 flight path control, and aircraft altitude regulation.**

In the following, we will consider the tracking control of the pendulum positioning system using the internal model principle, the state-feedback pole placement, and the root locus design approaches.

The system to be controlled is still the pendulum positioning system with the same dynamics as de-scribed by Equation 10.4 and the same operating equilibrium at $(x_1^*, x_2^*, T^*) = (15°, 0°/s, 0.19043\text{Nm})$. The difference is in the structure and capability of the tracking/regulation control system. The structure of the tracking/regulation controller is shown in Figure 10.8. The controller is designed based on the block diagram in Figure 10.8(b), where the controller is connected to the linearized model

$$\dot{\bar{x}}(t) = A\bar{x}(t) + B\bar{T}(t)$$

where the matrices A and B are given in Equation 10.6. **After the design of the controller is completed, the controller will be connected with the nonlinear model or the real system, as shown in Figure 10.8(a), for simulation or real-time testing.**

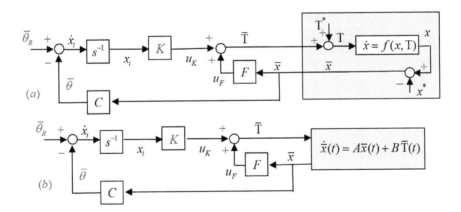

Fig. 10.8: The state feedback and integral tracking control for the pendulum positioning system.

The integrator internal model structure will guarantee the step tracking error to be zero at steady state; hence, the design of F and K will focus on the stability and the transient response. There are several ways of designing F and K to enhance the performance of the closed-loop system. **One simple, effective way is to first find a state-feedback gain matrix F so that the eigenvalues** of $A + BF$ are placed at favorable locations on the complex plane and then employ the root locus design approach to find a value of the integrator constant K so that the closed-loop system poles are at desired locations to achieve a best possible performance.

LTF Pole-Zero Pattern and Construction of Root Locus Diagram

The root locus design of K can only do as good as the LTF (loop transfer function) pole-zero pattern can provide. We will see that the eigenvalues of $A + BF$ will be main part of the LTF pole-zero pattern; therefore, the choice of F is critical to the success of the overall design. Recall that we placed the eigenvalues of $A + BF$ at $s_1 = -10$ and $s_2 = -11$ to obtain $F = \begin{bmatrix} -2.956 & -0.6955 \end{bmatrix}$. We will continue to use it and call this design as *Design b*. For comparison, we will have another design, called *Design a*, which places the eigenvalues of $A + BF$ at $s_1, s_2 = -10 \pm j5$. *Design a* gives $F = \begin{bmatrix} -3.456 & -0.6622 \end{bmatrix}$.

To apply the root locus design to a simple closed-loop system structure, as shown in Figure 10.9(b), the LTF pole-zero pattern required is just the pole-zero pattern of the open-loop system $G(s)$. However, for a more complicated closed-loop system like Figure 10.9(a), the LTF pole-zero pattern required for root locus design in general is not the same as the pole-zero pattern of the open-loop system.

Recall that the loop transfer function of the closed-loop system in Figure 10.9(b), before the K is cut off the loop, is $KG(s)$, where $G(s)$ can be seen as the transfer function from u to e multiplied by a negative sign. Similarly, **for the closed-loop system in Figure 10.9(a), the loop transfer function should be $KG(s)$, where $G(s)$ is the transfer function from u_K to x_i multiplied by a negative sign.** Hence, $G(s)$ can be represented by the following state-space model with u_K and $-x_i$ as the input and the output, respectively.

$$G(s): \quad \begin{aligned} \begin{bmatrix} \dot{\bar{x}} \\ \dot{x}_i \end{bmatrix} &= \begin{bmatrix} A + BF & 0 \\ -C & 0 \end{bmatrix} \begin{bmatrix} \bar{x} \\ x_i \end{bmatrix} + \begin{bmatrix} B \\ 0 \end{bmatrix} u_K := A_G \begin{bmatrix} \bar{x} \\ x_i \end{bmatrix} + B_G u_K \\ -x_i &= \begin{bmatrix} 0 & -1 \end{bmatrix} \begin{bmatrix} \bar{x} \\ x_i \end{bmatrix} := C_G \begin{bmatrix} \bar{x} \\ x_i \end{bmatrix} \end{aligned} \tag{10.15}$$

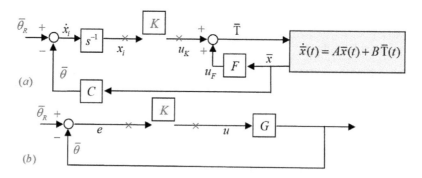

Fig. 10.9: Derivation of the loop transfer function for the closed-loop state feedback and integral tracking control system shown in Figure 10.8.

Based on Equation 10.15, the root locus diagrams for *Design a* and *Design b* can be constructed, as shown in Figure 10.10(a) and Figure 10.10(b), respectively. From Equation 10.15, the state-space

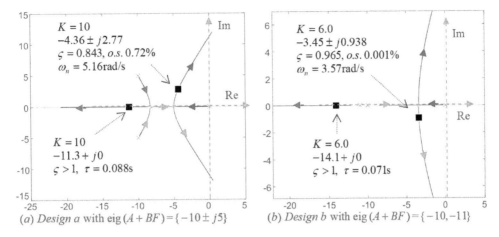

(a) *Design a* with eig$(A+BF)=\{-10\pm j5\}$ (b) *Design b* with eig$(A+BF)=\{-10,-11\}$

Fig. 10.10: Root locus diagrams associated with the integral tracking control system shown in Figure 10.8.

representation of the loop transfer function, it can be seen that the LTF poles are the eigenvalues of A_G, which are the eigenvalues of $A+BF$ together with the integrator pole at $s=0$. Thus, for *Design a*, the loop transfer function will have three poles and no zeros. The three poles are

$$\begin{matrix} p_1 \\ p_2 \end{matrix} = -10\pm j5, \quad p_3 = 0$$

where the pair of complex poles are the eigenvalues of $A+BF$, and the pole at the origin is the pole of the integrator.

When $K=0$, the closed-loop system poles (the roots of the closed-loop characteristic equation) will be at the three LTF pole locations, as $K\to\infty$ the three roots will be on the three asymptotes: the three straight lines with angles $\pi/3$, π, and $-\pi/3$ intersecting the real axis at $\sigma=(p_1+p_2+p_3)/3=-6.667$. The two root loci branches originated from the complex conjugates, p_1 and p_2, will move toward the real axis with departure angles $-63.6°$ and $63.6°$, respectively. These two branches will break into the real axis at $s=-8.34$ when $K=7.71$ and split into two branches on the real axis, one toward the left all the way to the negative infinity of the real axis, and the other moving to the right to meet the third branch coming from p_3 at the origin. These two branches meet at $s=-5$ when $K=8.33$ and break away immediately into the complex plane toward the $\pi/3$ and the $-\pi/3$ asymptotes, respectively. These two branches will cross the imaginary axis at $\pm j11.2$ into the right half of the complex plane when $K=83.3$.

On the other hand, for *Design b*, the loop transfer function will have three poles and no zeros. The three poles are

$$p_1 = -11, \quad p_2 = -10, \quad p_3 = 0,$$

all on the real axis. There are three asymptotes: the three straight lines with angles $\pi/3$, π, and $-\pi/3$ intersecting the real axis at $\sigma=(p_1+p_2+p_3)/3=-7$. The root loci branch originated from $p_1=-11$ will move left toward the negative infinity of the real axis. The two branches started from $p_2=-10$ and $p_3=0$ will move toward each other on the real axis until they meet at $s=-3.48$ when $K=5.67$ and break away immediately into the complex plane toward the $\pi/3$ and the $-\pi/3$ asymptotes, respectively. These two branches will cross the imaginary axis at $\pm j10.5$ into the right half of the complex plane when $K=77.1$.

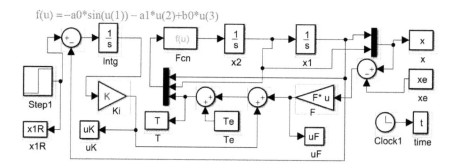

Fig. 10.11: Simulation diagram associated with the state feedback and integral tracking control system shown in Figure 10.8.

Determination of K in Root Locus Design

In Figure 10.10(a), the root locus diagram for *Design a*, by moving the little black square cursor we can see how the K value affects the closed-loop system poles trajectories and their associated damping ratios and natural frequencies. When $K = 10$, the three closed-loop system poles are at

$$\begin{matrix} s_1 \\ s_2 \end{matrix} = -4.36 \pm j2.77, \quad s_3 = -11.3$$

where the pair of complex poles are the dominant poles and their corresponding damping ratio and natural frequency are $\varsigma = 0.843$ and $\omega_n = 5.16 \mathrm{rad/s}$, respectively. There will be a little bit overshoot at the peak time $t_{ap} = \pi/2.77 = 1.13$ s, but this less-than-1% overshoot is a worthwhile tradeoff for a faster response, as will be seen in the simulation results graphs of Figure 10.12.

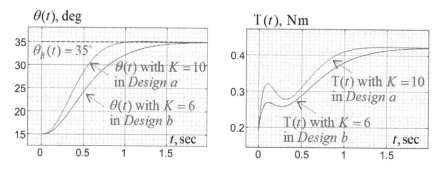

Fig. 10.12: Simulation results of the state feedback and integral tracking control system.

In the root locus diagram of Figure 10.10(b) for *Design b*, when $K = 6$, the three closed-loop system poles are at

$$\begin{matrix} s_1 \\ s_2 \end{matrix} = -3.45 \pm j0.938, \quad s_3 = -14.1$$

where the pair of complex poles are the dominant poles and their corresponding damping ratio and natural frequency are $\varsigma = 0.965$ and $\omega_n = 3.57 \mathrm{rad/s}$, respectively. There is an unnoticeable overshoot at the peak time $t_{ap} = \pi/2.77 = 1.13\text{s}$ and $t_{bp} = \pi/0.938 = 3.35$ s, respectively, which is slower than *Design a*, as will be verified in the simulation results graphs of Figure 10.12.

The Simulink simulation diagram of Figure 10.11 is constructed based on the block diagram shown in Figure 10.8. The only difference is that in the Simulink program the real pendulum angle θ, instead of $\bar{\theta}$, is fed back to compare with the desired real angle position θ_R instead of $\bar{\theta}_R$. This discrepancy does not affect the simulation results since the required correction error sent to the tracking integrator is essentially the same.

The simulation results of both *Design a* and *Design b* are shown in Figure 10.12. Figure 10.12(a) shows that *Design a* **response is faster than** *Design b* **since the peak times of** *Design a* **and** *Design b* **are**

$$t_{ap} = \pi/2.77 = 1.13 \text{ s} \quad \text{and} \quad t_{bp} = \pi/0.938 = 3.35 \text{ s}$$

respectively. Recall that the peak time is computed based on Equation 3.69, $t_p = \pi/\omega$, where ω is the imaginary part of the dominant complex poles. Increasing ω may not always help since it may cause the damping ratio to decrease to enlarge the overshoot and oscillations.

The control-input torques required to complete the tracking/regulation for *Design a* and *Design b* are shown in Figure 10.12(b), and the required real torques for both cases are between 0.19 Nm and 0.42 Nm, which are in a reasonable applicable range.

The *Design a* root locus diagram on Figure 10.10(a) is generated using the following MATLAB code. The *Design b* root locus diagram on Figure 10.10(b) can be generated by simply replacing `F=[-3.456 -0.6622]` with `F=[-2.956 -0.6966]`:

```
% CSD Fig10.10 Root loci Design a & Design b
% Root loci for the system in Fig10.9(b) with F=[-3.456 -0.6622]
 A=[0  1;-21.32  -0.135]; B=[0;30];
 F=[-3.456   -0.6622];   %F=[-2.956  -0.6966];
 s=tf('s'); C=[1 0]; A_G=[A+B*F zeros(2,1);-C 0], B_G=[B;0],
 C_G=[zeros(1,2) -1], D_G=0, sysG=ss(A_G,B_G,C_G,D_G); G=tf(sysG),
 pole_G=pole(G), [zero_G,gain_G]=zero(G), figure(13),
 K=logspace(-1,2,1000); rlocus(G,K)
```

In the root locus diagram construction, the main MATLAB command is `rlocus(G,K)` in which `K` is the root locus gain parameter to be determined, and `G` is the state-space representation of the loop transfer function given by Equation 10.15. This tool is versatile and helpful. However, a control system designer is still required to be proficient in the materials covered in Chapter 8. Knowing how a change of the LTF pole-zero pattern will affect the trajectories of the root locus diagram is even more important than constructing the root loci diagram. **The root locus design actually starts from finding a favorable LTF pole-zero pattern rather than starting from a given LTF pole-zero pattern.**

If a SISO (single-input/single-output) system is described by a rational function $G(s) = N(s)/D(s)$, where both $N(s)$ and $D(s)$ are polynomial functions with real coefficients and $deg(D(s)) \geq deg(N(s))$, then the poles and zeros of the system are the roots of $D(s) = 0$ and the roots of $N(s) = 0$, respectively. If a system is given by a state-space representation $G(s) = (A,B,C,D)$, the poles and zeros can be directly computed in the state space without the need of converting to polynomial functions. The poles are the eigenvalues of the A matrix, and **the zeros can be computed based on the solution of the generalized eigenvalue problem as described in Remark 10.2.**

Remark 10.2 (Zeros of State-Space Model (A, B, C, D)**)**

The zeros of the state-space model (A,B,C,D) are the generalized eigenvalues λ_i so that

$$\begin{bmatrix} \lambda_i I - A & B \\ -C & D \end{bmatrix} v_i = \begin{bmatrix} \lambda_i \begin{bmatrix} I & 0 \\ 0 & 0 \end{bmatrix} - \begin{bmatrix} A & -B \\ C & -D \end{bmatrix} \end{bmatrix} v_i = [\lambda_i E - Z] v_i \qquad (10.16)$$

where v_i are the corresponding generalized eigenvectors. The MATLAB command

```
>> [Vz,Dz]=eig(Z,E)
```

can be employed to obtain the generalized eigenvalues in Dz and the generalized eigenvectors in Vz. ∎

Example 10.3 (Find the Zeros of a System in State-Space Representation)

Consider the system with transfer function, $G(s) = \frac{s+2}{s+1}$, which obviously has a zero at $s = -2$. A state-space model of the system can be found, $G(s) = C(sI - A)^{-1}B + D$ with $A = -1$, $B = 1$, $C = 1$, $D = 1$. Now, we would like to employ this state-space model to demonstrate how to compute the zeros of a system in state space using Equation 10.16.

The zeros of $C(sI - A)^{-1}B + D$ are the complex numbers λ_i so that the rank of $\begin{bmatrix} \lambda_i I - A & B \\ -C & D \end{bmatrix}$ drops below its normal rank. It can be solved as a generalized eigenvalue problem:

$$\begin{bmatrix} \lambda_i + 1 & 1 \\ -1 & 1 \end{bmatrix} v_i = 0, \quad \rightarrow \quad \lambda_i = -2 \quad \rightarrow \quad \begin{bmatrix} -2+1 & 1 \\ -1 & 1 \end{bmatrix} v_i = 0 \quad \rightarrow \quad v_i = \begin{bmatrix} 1 \\ 1 \end{bmatrix} \qquad (10.17)$$

This generalized eigenvalue problem can also be solved using the following MATLAB code:

```
>> A=-1; B=1; C=1; D=1; E=[1  0; 0  0];   Z=[A  -B; C  -D];
[Vz,Dz]=eig(Z,E)
Vz =
      1      0
      1     -1
Dz =
     -2      0
      0    Inf
```

This generalized eigenvalue/eigenvector problem has an eigenvalue at $\lambda_i = -2$ and its corresponding eigenvector $v_i = [1 \ 1]^T$. ∎

10.2.5 Tracking Control of the Pendulum Positioning System Using PID Control

In the previous subsection, Section 10.2.4, we employed the state-feedback pole placement together with integral tracking compensation to address the tracking/regulation control problem for the pendulum positioning system. The state-feedback pole placement is employed to replace the poles of the plant so that the pole-zero pattern of the loop transfer function will become more favorable for root locus design. In this subsection, we will try to design the best possible PID controller for the lightly damped pendulum position tracking control problem. Before getting into the PID control system design, we will explore if the PI controller can do the job.

Can PI Controller Work for the Pendulum Positioning System?

The PI controller shown in Figure 10.13(a) and 10.13(b) is expressed as

$$\frac{s + c_0}{s} K = K_P + K_I \frac{1}{s} \quad \rightarrow \quad K_P = K, \quad K_I = c_0 K$$

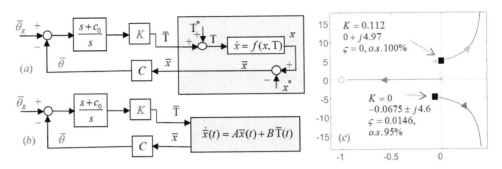

Fig. 10.13: Block diagram and root locus diagram for the PI control of the pendulum positioning system.

where K_P and K_I are the proportional and the integral coefficients, respectively, of the PI controller. That is, **inserting a PI controller to the feedback loop is equivalent to adding a pole at the origin and a zero at $s = -c_0$ to the pole-zero pattern of the root locus diagram**, and hoping a choice of K value in the root locus design will lead to a desirable closed-loop system performance. From Figure 10.13(b), it can be seen that the transfer function of the linearized plant is $C(sI - A)^{-1}B$. Thus, the loop transfer function for the root locus design will be

$$G(s) = \frac{s + c_0}{s} KC(sI - A)^{-1}B$$

which has three poles and one zero. They are

$$\begin{matrix} p_1 \\ p_2 \end{matrix} = -0.0675 \pm j4.6, \quad p_3 = 0, \quad z_1 = -c_0$$

where **the pair of complex poles p_1, p_2 are the poles of the lightly damped pendulum system.** The pole at the origin, $p_3 = 0$, is the pole of the integrator and the zero, $z_1 = -c_0$, is associated with the integrator gain. If $c_0 > 0.135$ is chosen, the root locus diagram will look like the one shown in Figure 10.13(c), in which the two asymptotes will be in the RHP and the real part of the complex roots can only be between -0.0675 and 0 for the closed-loop system to stay stable. But **the damping ratio for any of these complex roots is extremely small, so these complex roots cannot serve as dominant poles. On the other hand, for the real root sitting between 0 and $-c_0$ to be the dominant pole, it needs to move to a position extremely close to the imaginary axis that will make the control action too slow to be practical. Therefore, there exists no viable PI control solution for the lightly damped pendulum position control system.**

PID Controller Structure

The PID controller $K_D s + K_P + K_I/s$, together with the low-pass filter $w/(s+w)$, can be expressed as

$$\frac{K_D s^2 + K_P s + K_I}{s} \frac{w}{s+w} = \frac{(s+c_0)(s+c_1)}{s(s+w)} K \tag{10.18}$$

and, therefore, the nonlinear and the linearized closed-loop pendulum position systems with PID controller are depicted in Figure 10.14(a) and 10.14(b), respectively. Note that **the insertion of the PID controller and the low-pass filter to the feedback loop is equivalent to adding two poles, $s = 0$ and $s = -w$, and two zeros, $s = -c_0$ and $s = -c_1$ to the pole-zero pattern of the root locus diagram.**

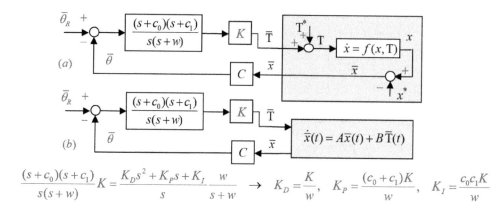

Fig. 10.14: Block diagram for the PID control of the pendulum positioning system.

Construction of Root Locus Diagram for PID Controller Design

From Figure 10.14(b), it can be seen that the transfer function of the linearized plant is $C(sI-A)^{-1}B$, and thus **the loop transfer function for the root locus design will be**

$$G(s) = \frac{(s+c_0)(s+c_1)}{s(s+w)} KC(sI-A)^{-1}B \tag{10.19}$$

which has four poles and two zeros,

$$\begin{matrix} p_1 \\ p_2 \end{matrix} = -0.0675 \pm j4.6, \quad p_3 = 0, \quad p_4 = -w, \quad z_1 = -c_0, \quad z_2 = -c_1 \tag{10.20}$$

where **the pair of complex poles p_1, p_2 are the poles of the lightly damped pendulum system. The pole at the origin, $p_3 = 0$, is the pole of the integrator. The pole $p_4 = -w$ is determined by the bandwidth of the low-path filter, which is usually chosen to be larger than the actuator bandwidth. The zeros $z_1 = -c_0$ and $z_2 = -c_1$ are free design parameters to be selected to obtain a favorable root locus diagram ready for the design of the K parameter.**

The parameters w, c_0, and c_1 are chosen so that $p_4 = -50$, $z_1 = -1.5$, and $z_2 = -2$ lead to the root locus diagram shown in Figure 10.15. Since the loop transfer function has four poles and two zeros, there are four root loci branches and two of them will approach to the two asymptotes with angles $\pi/2$ and $-\pi/2$ that intersect the real axis at $\sigma = -23.32$ when $K \to \infty$. The two branches originating from p_1 and p_2 will leave the two poles with $\pm 140°$ departure angles moving to the left and then bending toward the real axis. These two branches will meet at $s = -10.3$ when $K = 23.5$ and split immediately on the real axis, one moving to the right toward $z_2 = -2$, and the other to the left, which will meet the branch that came from p_4 at $s = -21.2$ when $K = 25.2$, and then break away into the complex plane, one going up toward the asymptote with angle $\pi/2$, and the other going down toward the asymptote with angle $-\pi/2$. The branch out of $p_3 = 0$ is moving to the left toward $z_1 = -1.5$.

Determination of K in Root Locus Design

Now we have the four complete root trajectories on the root locus diagram, as shown in Figure 10.15. If $K = 30$ is selected, the four closed-loop system poles will be at

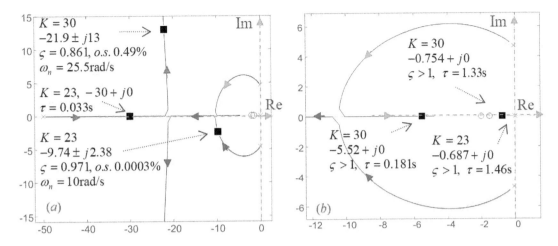

Fig. 10.15: Root Locus diagram for the PID control of the pendulum positioning system.

$$s_3 = -0.754, \quad s_1 = -5.52, \quad \begin{matrix} s_4 \\ s_2 \end{matrix} = -21.9 \pm j13 \qquad (10.21)$$

where $s_3 = -0.754$ is the dominant pole.

If $K = 23$ is selected, the four closed-loop system poles will be at

$$s_3 = -0.687, \quad \begin{matrix} s_1 \\ s_2 \end{matrix} = -9.74 \pm j2.38, \quad s_4 = -30 \qquad (10.22)$$

where $s_3 = -0.687$ **is the dominant pole.**

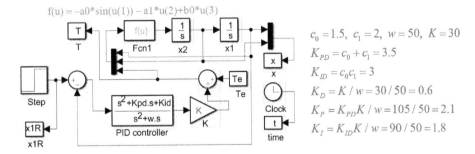

Fig. 10.16: Simulation diagram for the PID control of the pendulum positioning system.

The Simulink simulation diagram shown in Figure 10.16 is similar to that in Figure 10.11 except the controller part is replaced by the PID controller. Two simulations were conducted: One is for the PID controller associated with $K = 30$, and the other is for the PID controller with $K = 23$.

The step tracking responses for both cases $K = 30$ and $K = 23$ are shown in Figure 10.17(a). Both responses exhibit resemblance in waveform, although the $K = 23$ is a little bit slower. For the $K = 30$ case, the real pole at $s_3 = -0.754$ is called the dominant pole because the responses due to the other three poles will decay much more quickly. **But it does not mean the non-dominant responses are negligible. In fact, the response associated with a pole with larger damping factor (the absolute value of the real part) or smaller time constant will respond to command/disturbance faster although they will also decay faster.** As shown in Figure 10.17(a), the $K = 30$ step tracking response (in blue) shoots up from $\theta = 15°$ to $\theta = 35°$ within 0.1 s. This fast response to the step command in the first 0.15 s is mainly contributed by the pair of complex poles at $-21.9 \pm j13$. But it also decays fast to dip the response down to $31°$ before the dominant response catches up at around 0.6 s. Then the response thereafter is due to the dominant pole $s_3 = -0.754$ with time constant $\tau_3 = 1/0.754 = 1.33$ s, which will take another 3 s to reach the steady state.

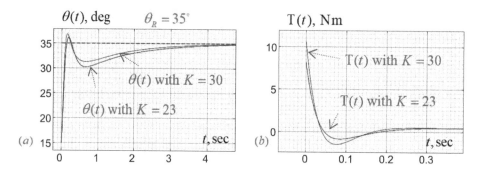

Fig. 10.17: Simulation results of the PID control of the pendulum positioning system.

For the $K = 23$ case, the real pole at $s_3 = -0.687$ is the dominant pole. It is a little bit closer to the imaginary axis than the $K = 30$ case; hence, it will take longer time to reach the steady state. Similar to the $K = 30$ case, the $K = 23$ **step tracking response (in red, as shown in Figure 10.17(a)) shoots up from $\theta = 15°$ to $\theta = 35°$ within** 0.12 s. **This fast response to the step command in the first** 0.2 s **is mainly contributed by the pair of complex poles at** $-9.74 \pm j2.38$. **But it also decays fast to dip the response down to** $30°$ **before the dominant response catches up at around** 0.7 s. Then the response thereafter is due to the dominant pole $s_3 = -0.687$ with time constant $\tau_3 = 1/0.687 = 1.46$ s, which will take another 3.4 s to reach the steady state.

Control-Input Constraint

The limitation of control input always needs to be considered in all control systems designs. If a control system requires a control-input magnitude beyond the capability of the actuator, the controller output and the input to the plant (the system to be controlled) will be different. The input to the plant will be the saturation value of the actuator for all controller outputs with magnitude greater than the saturation value. **That means the controller loses its ability to control the plant, and the system may become unstable. For this reason, a good control system design should avoid control-input saturation.**

The required control-input torque $T(t)$ to provide the tracking performance in Figure 10.17(a) is shown in Figure 10.17(b). The range of the control-input torque for the $K = 30$ case is between -1.5 Nm and 10.5 Nm. The range for the $K = 23$ case is a little bit better, but still between -1 Nm and 8.2 Nm. For comparison, the required control-input torque $T(t)$ to provide the tracking performance of the state feedback/integral tracking control system in Figure 10.12(a) is shown in Figure 10.12(b). Note that the range of the control-input torque is between 0.19 Nm and 0.42 Nm, which is more than 25 times less than that of the PID control system.

The surge of torque at $t = 0$ from $T = 0.19$ Nm to $T = 10.5$ Nm in Figure 10.17(b) is to provide the shoot-up from $\theta = 15°$ to $\theta = 35°$ within 0.1 s in Figure 10.17(a). **This quick response at the early time is unnecessary since the dominant pole response is too slow to catch up.**

Remark 10.4 (An Unfair Comparison of the PID Control with the State Feedback/Inetgral Tracking Control)

The state feedback/integral tracking control is supposed to do better than the PID control since the former employs more information (all the states information) than the latter, which only utilizes the output feedback. **By using the state feedback, the original plant poles can be replaced by favorable ones. On the other hand, by using the PID controller, the original plant poles remain part of the pole-zero pattern for root locus design.** The only modification the PID control can do is to choose the locations of the two added zeros and the low-pass filter pole. **The presence of the original lightly damped plant poles prevents the PID control from obtaining a root locus pole-zero pattern as favorable as that of the state feedback/integral tracking control approach.**

■

10.3 Controllability

Recall that in Section 7.6 we learned that the cart-inverted pendulum system is unstable, but the system can be stabilized. A sufficient condition is given in the paragraph right after Equation 7.108: "If the system is controllable, then the closed-loop system poles can be placed anywhere on the complex plane. The definition of controllability and relevant issues will be discussed in later chapters."

The concept of controllability is discussed in the following. Consider a system with state equation

$$\dot{x}(t) = Ax(t) + Bu(t), \quad x \in R^n, \ u \in R^m \tag{10.23}$$

Definition 10.5 (Controllability)

The system is (completely) controllable if there exists a control input $u(t)$ defined on a finite time interval $[0, t_f]$ for some $t_f > 0$ that steers the system from any initial state x_0 to any final state x_f.

Equivalently, there exists $t_f > 0$ and $u(t)$ for any x_0 and x_f, such that

$$x_f = e^{At_f}x_0 + \int_0^{t_f} e^{A(t_f-\tau)}Bu(\tau)\,d\tau \tag{10.24}$$

Equation 10.24 will be employed to prove the controllability rank theorem.

10.3.1 Controllability Rank Test

Theorem 10.6 (Controllability Rank Condition)

Consider the following $n \times nm$ controllability matrix:

$$\mathscr{C} = \begin{bmatrix} B & AB & A^2B & \cdots & A^{n-1}B \end{bmatrix} \tag{10.25}$$

The system (10.23), or the matrix pair (A, B), is (completely) controllable if and only if

$$rank\ \mathscr{C} = n$$

Proof: *First, we will show that*

$$(A, B) \text{ is controllable} \quad \rightarrow \quad \text{rank } \mathscr{C} = n.$$

In many cases, it is easier to prove by contradiction for a false statement than directly prove a true statement. If (A, B) is controllable but rank $\mathscr{C} < n$, then there exists a nonzero vector v such that

$$v^T \mathscr{C} = v^T \begin{bmatrix} B & AB & A^2 B & \cdots & A^{n-1} B \end{bmatrix} = 0$$

or

$$v^T B = 0, \quad v^T A B = 0, \quad v^T A^2 B = 0, \quad \cdots, \quad v^T A^{n-1} B = 0$$

Recall that by Theorem 6.15 (Cayley-Hamilton theorem) and Equation 6.14,

$$e^{At} = \sum_{i=0}^{n-1} \alpha_i(t) A^i = \alpha_0(t) I + \alpha_1(t) A + \alpha_2(t) A^2 + \cdots + \alpha_{n-1}(t) A^{n-1}$$

Hence,

$$v^T e^{At} B = v^T \left(\alpha_0(t) B + \alpha_1(t) A B + \alpha_2(t) A^2 B + \cdots + \alpha_{n-1}(t) A^{n-1} B \right) = 0$$

Now, from Equation 10.24, if $x_0 = 0$, the final state x_f will be

$$x_f = \int_0^{t_f} e^{A(t_f - \tau)} B u(\tau) d\tau$$

and

$$v^T x_f = v^T \int_0^{t_f} e^{A(t_f - \tau)} B u(\tau) d\tau = 0$$

for all $u(t)$, $t \geq 0$. This means that the controllable subspace is orthogonal to the vector v, which contradicts the assumption that (A, B) is controllable. Therefore, the rank of the controllability matrix $\mathscr{C}$ has to be n.

Next, conversely we will show that

$$(A, B) \text{ is controllable} \quad \leftarrow \quad \text{rank } \mathscr{C} = n$$

Again, we will prove it based on the contradiction approach. Assume rank $\mathscr{C} = n$ but (A, B) is not controllable; then there exists a nonzero vector v such that

$$v^T \int_0^{t_f} e^{A(t_f - \tau)} B u(\tau) d\tau = 0$$

which implies that

$$v^T e^{A(t_f - \tau)} B = 0, \quad 0 \leq \tau \leq t_f$$

Differentiate this equation to obtain the following derivatives,

$$v^T e^{A(t_f - \tau)} A B = 0, \quad v^T e^{A(t_f - \tau)} A^2 B = 0, \quad \cdots, \quad v^T e^{A(t_f - \tau)} A^{n-1} B = 0, \quad 0 \leq \tau \leq t_f$$

Let $\tau = t_f$, and we have

$$v^T B = 0, \quad v^T A B = 0, \quad v^T A^2 B = 0, \quad \cdots, \quad v^T A^{n-1} B = 0$$

This contradicts the assumption that rank $\mathscr{C} = n$. Therefore, (A, B) has to be controllable. ∎

Example 10.7 (Controllability of a MIMO System)

Consider a three-state two-input linear system described by the following state equation:

$$\frac{d}{dt}\begin{bmatrix} x_1 \\ x_2 \\ x_3 \end{bmatrix} = \begin{bmatrix} -9 & 3 & 7 \\ -5 & 1 & 5 \\ -5 & 3 & 3 \end{bmatrix} \begin{bmatrix} x_1 \\ x_2 \\ x_3 \end{bmatrix} + \begin{bmatrix} 2 & 1 \\ 1 & 1 \\ 1 & 1 \end{bmatrix} \begin{bmatrix} u_1 \\ u_2 \end{bmatrix} = Ax + Bu$$

$$\begin{bmatrix} y_1 \\ y_2 \end{bmatrix} = \begin{bmatrix} 1 & 0 & -1 \\ -1 & 1 & 1 \end{bmatrix} \begin{bmatrix} x_1 \\ x_2 \\ x_3 \end{bmatrix} = Cx$$

The controllability matrix can be found as

$$\mathscr{C} = \begin{bmatrix} B & AB & A^2B \end{bmatrix} = \begin{bmatrix} 2 & 1 & -8 & 1 & 32 & 1 \\ 1 & 1 & -4 & 1 & 16 & 1 \\ 1 & 1 & -4 & 1 & 16 & 1 \end{bmatrix}$$

We easily recognize that the rank of $\mathscr{C}$ is 2. Thus, the system is not controllable.   ∎

If a system fails to be controllable it is imperative to identify the uncontrollable physical modes. For example, an uncontrollable mode may be stable and does not interfere with achieving the performance we desire for this system. On the other hand, if the uncontrollable mode is unstable or has a harmful effect on the system performance, identifying it may provide clues to modifying the system actuation structure to resolve the problem. One way to easily make such an identification is to transform the system to diagonal form (or, more generally into Jordan form). In the following, the system considered in the previous example will be employed to illustrate which part of the system is uncontrollable.

Example 10.8 (Controllable Modes)

Consider the system of Example 10.7. We will compute the eigenvalues $\lambda_1, \lambda_2, \lambda_3$ and corresponding eigenvectors v_1, v_2, v_3. From the latter define the similarity transformation matrix $T = [v_1, v_2, v_3]$ and implement the transformation from the original state x to the new state $\hat{x}$, $\hat{x} = T^{-1}x$ to obtain the transformed system

$$\dot{\hat{x}} = \begin{bmatrix} T^{-1}AT \end{bmatrix}\hat{x} + \begin{bmatrix} T^{-1}B \end{bmatrix}u \tag{10.26}$$

The eigenvalue-eigenvector pairs of A are:

$$\lambda_1 = -4, \ v_1 = \begin{bmatrix} 2 \\ 1 \\ 1 \end{bmatrix}, \quad \lambda_2 = -2, \ v_2 = \begin{bmatrix} 1 \\ 0 \\ 1 \end{bmatrix}, \quad \lambda_3 = 1, \ v_3 = \begin{bmatrix} 1 \\ 1 \\ 1 \end{bmatrix}$$

Note that there are three real eigenvalues and two of the modes are stable. The third is unstable. Using the three eigenvectors we set up the transformation matrix T and obtain the transformed state equations

$$\dot{\hat{x}} = \begin{bmatrix} -4 & 0 & 0 \\ 0 & -2 & 0 \\ 0 & 0 & 1 \end{bmatrix}\hat{x} + \begin{bmatrix} 1 & 0 \\ 0 & 0 \\ 0 & 1 \end{bmatrix}u$$

We begin with the knowledge (from Example 10.7) that there is one uncontrollable mode. The new states, $\hat{x}_1, \hat{x}_2, \hat{x}_3$ denote the motion associated with modes 1, 2, and 3, respectively. Observe that the state equations are decoupled. They can be solved one at a time, each independent of the others. **Inspection of the transformed B matrix shows that neither of the control inputs affects $\hat{x}_2$, indicating that $\hat{x}_2$ is the uncontrollable mode.**   ∎

10.3.2 The Controllability Decomposition Form

The ability to identify the controllable part of a system has control design implications beyond the interpretive mode implications. Here, we discuss the decomposition introduced by Kalman [Kalman, 1963] that separates the controllable and the uncontrollable parts of a linear system.

Theorem 10.9 (Controllability Decomposition Form)

Given a linear system in the form

$$\dot{x}(t) = Ax(t) + Bu(t)$$
$$y(t) = Cx(t)$$

with $x \in R^n, u \in R^m, y \in R^p$, if the system is not controllable and

$$rank\ \mathscr{C} = r < n$$

then there exists a nonsingular similarity transformation matrix T that transforms the original state x to the new state $\hat{x}$, $\hat{x} = T^{-1}x$ such that the transformed system

$$\dot{\hat{x}} = [T^{-1}AT]\hat{x} + [T^{-1}B]u = \hat{A}\hat{x} + \hat{B}u$$
$$y = [CT]\hat{x} = \hat{C}\hat{x}$$

has the form

$$\hat{A} = \begin{bmatrix} \hat{A}_{11} & \hat{A}_{12} \\ 0 & \hat{A}_{22} \end{bmatrix}, \quad \hat{B} = \begin{bmatrix} \hat{B}_1 \\ 0 \end{bmatrix}, \quad \hat{C} = \begin{bmatrix} \hat{C}_1 & \hat{C}_2 \end{bmatrix} \tag{10.27}$$

where $\hat{A}_{11} \in R^{r \times r}$, $\hat{B}_1 \in R^{r \times m}$, $\hat{C}_1 \in R^{p \times r}$ and the subsystem $\{\hat{A}_{11}, \hat{B}_1, \hat{C}_1\}$ is controllable.

Proof: *Hint: Choose $T = \begin{bmatrix} T_1 & T_2 \end{bmatrix}$ with*

$$T_1 = \begin{bmatrix} f_1 & f_2 & ... & f_r \end{bmatrix}$$

where f_1, f_2, ... f_r are linearly independent and span the r-dimensional range space of $\mathscr{C}(A,B)$. The columns of T_2 are chosen so that together with the columns of T_1 span the whole n-dimensional space. ∎

Example 10.10 (Controllability Decomposition Form)

Recall that the system considered in Example 10.7 is

$$\frac{d}{dt}\begin{bmatrix} x_1 \\ x_2 \\ x_3 \end{bmatrix} = \begin{bmatrix} -9 & 3 & 7 \\ -5 & 1 & 5 \\ -5 & 3 & 3 \end{bmatrix}\begin{bmatrix} x_1 \\ x_2 \\ x_3 \end{bmatrix} + \begin{bmatrix} 2 & 1 \\ 1 & 1 \\ 1 & 1 \end{bmatrix}\begin{bmatrix} u_1 \\ u_2 \end{bmatrix} = Ax + Bu$$

$$\begin{bmatrix} y_1 \\ y_2 \end{bmatrix} = \begin{bmatrix} 1 & 0 & -1 \\ -1 & 1 & 1 \end{bmatrix}\begin{bmatrix} x_1 \\ x_2 \\ x_3 \end{bmatrix} = Cx$$

The controllability matrix of the system is

$$\mathscr{C} = \begin{bmatrix} 2 & 1 & -8 & 1 & 32 & 1 \\ 1 & 1 & -4 & 1 & 16 & 1 \\ 1 & 1 & -4 & 1 & 16 & 1 \end{bmatrix}$$

Since *rank* $\mathscr{C} = 2 < 3$, any two linearly independent column vectors of $\mathscr{C}$ will span the two-dimensional range space of $\mathscr{C}$. Let

$$T_1 = [f_1 \quad f_2] = \begin{bmatrix} 2 & 1 \\ 1 & 1 \\ 1 & 1 \end{bmatrix}$$

The choice of T_2 is arbitrary as long as it makes $T = [T_1 \quad T_2]$ nonsingular. Let T_2 be chosen so that

$$T = [T_1 \quad T_2] = \begin{bmatrix} 2 & 1 & 0 \\ 1 & 1 & 0 \\ 1 & 1 & 1 \end{bmatrix}$$

Then the transformed state-space model will be

$$\dot{\hat{x}} = \begin{bmatrix} \hat{A}_{11} & \hat{A}_{12} \\ 0 & \hat{A}_{22} \end{bmatrix} \hat{x} + \begin{bmatrix} \hat{B}_1 \\ 0 \end{bmatrix} u = \begin{bmatrix} -4 & 0 & 3 \\ 0 & 1 & 3 \\ 0 & 0 & -2 \end{bmatrix} \hat{x} + \begin{bmatrix} 1 & 0 \\ 0 & 1 \\ 0 & 0 \end{bmatrix} u$$

$$y = [\hat{C}_1 \quad \hat{C}_2] \hat{x} = \begin{bmatrix} 1 & 0 & -1 \\ 0 & 1 & 1 \end{bmatrix} \hat{x}$$

Note that neither u_1 or u_2 has effect on $\hat{A}_{22} = -2$. Hence, the dynamics associated with $\hat{A}_{22}$ are not controllable, while the dynamics associated with $\hat{A}_{11}$ can be modified via state feedback. ∎

Remark 10.11 (Controllable and Uncontrollable Subspaces)

The controllable subspace is the range space of the controllability matrix $\mathscr{C}$, while the uncontrollable subspace is the null space of $\mathscr{C}^T$. The null space of $\mathscr{C}^T$ is the orthogonal complement of the range space of $\mathscr{C}$.

For the system in Example 10.10, the controllable subspace is a two-dimensional space spanned by any two linearly independent vectors that are the linear combinations of the column vectors of the controllability matrix $\mathscr{C}$. Hence, the two vectors, $[1 \quad 0 \quad 0]^T$ and $[0 \quad 1 \quad 1]^T$ can serve as the basis vectors of the range space of $\mathscr{C}$, which is the controllable subspace:

$$\text{Range}(\mathscr{C}) \sim \begin{bmatrix} 1 & 0 \\ 0 & 1 \\ 0 & 1 \end{bmatrix}$$

The uncontrollable subspace is the one-dimensional null space of $\mathscr{C}^T$ spanned by the vector $[0 \quad -1 \quad 1]^T$:

$$\text{Null}(\mathscr{C}^T) \sim \begin{bmatrix} 0 \\ -1 \\ 1 \end{bmatrix}$$

which is orthogonal to the range space of $\mathscr{C}$.

Note that the space spanned by the vector $T_2 = [0 \; 0 \; 1]^T$ of Example 10.10 is not the uncontrollable subspace although its associated similarity transform T still achieves controllability decomposition.

If the similarity transformation matrix $T = [T_1 \; T_2]$ is chosen according to the basis vectors of the range space of $\mathscr{C}$ and the null space of $\mathscr{C}^T$ as

$$T = [T_1 \quad T_2] = \begin{bmatrix} 1 & 0 & 0 \\ 0 & 1 & -1 \\ 0 & 1 & 1 \end{bmatrix}$$

then the transformed state-space model will be

$$\dot{\hat{x}} = \begin{bmatrix} \hat{A}_{11} & \hat{A}_{12} \\ 0 & \hat{A}_{22} \end{bmatrix} \hat{x} + \begin{bmatrix} \hat{B}_1 \\ 0 \end{bmatrix} u = \begin{bmatrix} -9 & 10 & 4 \\ -5 & 6 & 2 \\ 0 & 0 & -2 \end{bmatrix} \hat{x} + \begin{bmatrix} 2 & 1 \\ 1 & 1 \\ 0 & 0 \end{bmatrix} u$$

$$y = [\hat{C}_1 \quad \hat{C}_2] \hat{x} = \begin{bmatrix} 1 & -1 & -1 \\ -1 & 2 & 0 \end{bmatrix} \hat{x}$$

Although the numbers are slightly different, the structure of the controllability decomposition form remains the same and the eigenvalues of $\hat{A}_{11}$ and $\hat{A}_{22}$, respectively, are identical to those obtained in Example 10.10. ∎

Example 10.12 (Controllable Subspace and Stabilizability)

Consider a system described by the following state equation:

$$\frac{d}{dt} \begin{bmatrix} x_1 \\ x_2 \end{bmatrix} = \begin{bmatrix} 0 & 1 \\ 1 & 0 \end{bmatrix} \begin{bmatrix} x_1 \\ x_2 \end{bmatrix} + \begin{bmatrix} 1 \\ 1 \end{bmatrix} u = Ax + Bu$$

The controllability matrix of the system is

$$\mathscr{C} = [B \quad AB] = \begin{bmatrix} 1 & 1 \\ 1 & 1 \end{bmatrix}$$

Since $rank\ \mathscr{C} = 1 < 2$, the range space of $\mathscr{C}$ is the one-dimensional subspace spanned by the vector $[1 \quad 1]^T$, and the null space of $\mathscr{C}^T$ is the other one-dimensional subspace spanned by the vector $[-1 \quad 1]^T$:

$$Range\,(\mathscr{C}) \sim \begin{bmatrix} 1 \\ 1 \end{bmatrix} \quad and \quad Null\,(\mathscr{C}^T) \sim \begin{bmatrix} -1 \\ 1 \end{bmatrix}$$

These vectors can be employed to form a similarity transformation matrix to transform old coordinates x to new coordinates $\hat{x}$, $\hat{x} = T^{-1}x$.

$$T = [T_1 \quad T_2] = \begin{bmatrix} 1 & -1 \\ 1 & 1 \end{bmatrix}$$

Then the transformed state-space equations are

$$\dot{\hat{x}} = \begin{bmatrix} \hat{A}_{11} & \hat{A}_{12} \\ 0 & \hat{A}_{22} \end{bmatrix} \hat{x} + \begin{bmatrix} \hat{B}_1 \\ 0 \end{bmatrix} u = \begin{bmatrix} 1 & 1 \\ 0 & -1 \end{bmatrix} \hat{x} + \begin{bmatrix} 1 \\ 0 \end{bmatrix} u$$

Note that the control input u has no effect on $\hat{A}_{22} = -1$. Hence, the dynamics associated with $\hat{A}_{22}$ are not controllable, while the dynamics associated with $\hat{A}_{11} = 1$ can be modified via state feedback as follows. With the state feedback,

$$u = \hat{F}\hat{x} = [\hat{f}_1 \quad \hat{f}_2] \begin{bmatrix} \hat{x}_1 \\ \hat{x}_2 \end{bmatrix}$$

the closed-loop system state equation will be

$$\begin{bmatrix} \dot{\hat{x}}_1 \\ \dot{\hat{x}}_2 \end{bmatrix} = \begin{bmatrix} 1+\hat{f}_1 & 1+\hat{f}_2 \\ 0 & -1 \end{bmatrix} \begin{bmatrix} \hat{x}_1 \\ \hat{x}_2 \end{bmatrix}$$

Note that the uncontrollable yet stable eigenvalue $\hat{A}_{22} = -1$ is unchanged, while the controllable unstable eigenvalue $\hat{A}_{11} = 1$ has been changed to $\hat{A}_{11} = 1 + \hat{f}_1$. The system will become stable if $\hat{f}_1$ is chosen to be less than -1. Therefore, **a system can be stabilized if the uncontrollable part of the system is stable.**

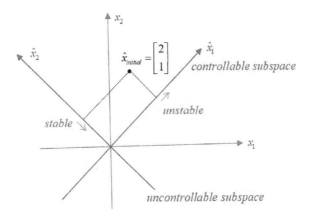

Fig. 10.18: Controllable and uncontrollable subspaces.

The controllable and uncontrollable subspaces of the system are illustrated in Figure 10.18. Assume the initial state is $\hat{x}_{initial}$ at $[2 \quad 1]^T$ position. Since the eigenvalue associated with the uncontrollable subspace spanned by $\hat{x}_2$ is stable, the position of the state on the $\hat{x}_2$ axis will move from 1 to 0, although it is not controllable. On the other hand, the eigenvalue associated with the controllable subspace spanned by $\hat{x}_1$ is unstable; hence, the position of the state on the $\hat{x}_1$ axis will grow without bound if no control action is taken. However, a control action can be taken to convert the unstable state $\hat{x}_1$ to become stable. ∎

10.4 Poles and Zeros of MIMO Systems

We have learned that the behavior of a system is mainly determined by its pole locations on the complex plane, and if the system is controllable and observable (the definition of observability will be given in the next chapter) a feedback controller can be designed to move the poles to more favorable locations to improve the stability and performance. The zeros also have effect on system performance, as revealed in Chapter 8 on how they would influence the root locus diagram to shape up the closed-loop system performance. It is noted that the zeros in the right half of the complex plane are notorious in limiting the performance of the closed-loop system, as described in Remark 8.23.

For SISO systems, the poles and zeros can be easily found if their transfer functions are available. For MIMO systems with state-space model (A, B, C, D), the poles of the system can be evaluated as the eigenvalues of the matrix A if (A, B, C, D) is controllable and observable. However, the computation of the zeros of MIMO systems is more complicated. In the following, we will explain the physical meaning of system zeros, give a precise definition of MIMO system zeros accordingly, and convert

the computation of zeros to a generalized eigen problem that can be solved efficiently.

The poles and zeros of MIMO systems can also be computed based on their transfer function matrices in the form of $G(s) = N(s)/d(s)$, where $G(s)$ is a $p \times m$ rational function matrix with p outputs and m inputs. The denominator $d(s)$ is the least common denominator of all entries of $G(s)$ and $N(s)$ is a $p \times m$ polynomial matrix. However, the polynomial approach is involved and beyond the scope of the book. The book by Kailath [Kailath, 1980] provides more detailed discussion on MIMO system poles and zeros.

The general linear state-space model is described by

$$\dot{x}(t) = Ax(t) + Bu(t)$$
$$y(t) = Cx(t) + Du(t)$$

(10.28)

where $x \in R^n, u \in R^m, y \in R^p$. Recall that the transfer function of the state-space model was derived in Section 6.6.1 as

$$G(s) = C(sI - A)^{-1}B + D$$

For SISO cases, the transfer function is a rational function $G(s) = N(s)/D(s)$, where both $N(s)$ and $D(s)$ are polynomial function of s. The poles of the system are the roots of $D(s) = 0$, and the zeros of the system are the roots of $N(s) = 0$.

10.4.1 Revisit Poles and Zeros of SISO Systems

Consider the state-space model (A,B,C,D) with one input and one output so that $x \in R^n, u \in R^1, y \in R^1$. Then B is a column vector of length n, denoted b; C is a row vector of length n, denoted c; and D is a scalar, denoted d. The transfer function can be written

$$G(s) = c[sI - A]^{-1}b + d = \frac{c\text{Adj}[sI - A]b + d|sI - A|}{|sI - A|} = k\frac{n(s)}{d(s)}$$

(10.29)

where $n(s)$ is a polynomial of degree less than or equal to n and $d(s)$ is a polynomial of degree n. The gain parameter k is a normalizing parameter such that the highest order coefficients of both $n(s)$ and $d(s)$ are both equal to one. **The poles of the transfer function are the roots of $d(s) = 0$ and its zeros are the roots of $n(s) = 0$.** This is a simple and conventional definition of single-input/single-output (SISO) poles and zeros.

Example 10.13 (F/A-18 Revisited, Poles and Zeros of a SISO System)

Recall the F/A-18 longitudinal flight dynamics model of Equation 8.64 from which if only the elevator control δ_e is considered as the input and the flight path angle $\gamma = \theta - \alpha$ as the output we will have

$$A = \begin{bmatrix} -0.02389 & -28.32 & 0 & -32.2 \\ -0.00033 & -0.362 & 1 & 0 \\ 0 & -2.212 & -0.2532 & 0 \\ 0 & 0 & 1 & 0 \end{bmatrix}, \quad b = \begin{bmatrix} -3.8114 \\ -0.05145 \\ -2.8791 \\ 0 \end{bmatrix}$$

$$c = \begin{bmatrix} 0 & -1 & 0 & 1 \end{bmatrix}, \quad d = 0$$

With this data we can evaluate the transfer function $G(s) = c[sI - A]^{-1}b + d$ using Mathematica or use the MATLAB command: `ss2tf` (state space to transfer function). Now the characteristic equation of the system is

$$|sI - A| = s^4 + 0.63916s^3 + 2.3086s^2 + 0.052669s + 0.023445 = 0$$

whose roots are the poles of the system. Equation 10.29 yields the transfer function, shown in factored form:

$$G(s) = 0.051453 \frac{(s + 4.393)(s - 4.106)(s - 0.03491)}{(s^2 + 0.02027s + 0.01026)(s^2 + 0.6189s + 2.286)}$$

We clearly see the fourth-order denominator and its roots, the system poles $-0.0101 \pm j0.101$ and $-0.309 \pm j1.48$, as well as the third-order numerator and its roots, the system zeros -4.393, 4.106, and 0.03491. ∎

The computational results in Example 10.13 are generated using the following MATLAB code:

```
% CSD Ex10.13 Eq8.64 State model of F/A-18 Poles Zeros
A =[ -2.3893e-02  -2.8317e+01           0  -3.2200e+01;
     -3.2923e-04  -3.6208e-01  1.0000e+00           0;
      4.0491e-11  -2.2115e+00  -2.5319e-01          0;
               0            0  1.0000e+00           0];
B =[ -3.8114e+00   9.5196e-04;
     -5.1453e-02  -3.8506e-07;
     -2.8791e+00           0;
               0           0];
b = B(:,1);
c = [0 -1  0  1];    d = 0;
[NUM,DEN] = ss2tf(A,b,c,d)
eig(A)
damp(A)
sys = ss(A,b,c,d)
zpk(sys)
```

10.4.2 Physical Meaning of System Zeros

For MIMO case, the transfer function

$$G(s) = C[sI - A]^{-1}B + D$$

can be rewritten as

$$G(s) = C\frac{\mathrm{Adj}[sI - A]}{|sI - A|}B + D = \frac{C\,\mathrm{Adj}[sI - A]B + |sI - A|D}{|sI - A|} = \frac{N(s)}{d(s)} \tag{10.30}$$

Notice that that $N(s)$ is a $p \times m$ matrix. The elements of $N(s)$ are polynomials in s of degree at most n. $G(s)$ is a $p \times m$ matrix whose elements are rational functions with least common denominator $d(s)$. Thus, we see that the poles of the system are easily identified as the roots of the polynomial $d(s)$, which is also the characteristic polynomial of the matrix A. Identifying the zeros of the transfer matrix $G(s)$ is more complicated.

During the 1970s an extension of the concept of zeros to MIMO systems was a substantive topic of discussion (e.g., [Rosenbrock, 1973, 1974, Davison and Wang, 1974, Kouvaritakis and MacFarlane, 1976a,b, Kalnitsky and Kwatny, 1977]). We can establish an alternative, but equivalent view to our earlier definition of SISO system zeros that does two things. First, it provides a new physical interpretation of a system zero, and second it can be extended to multiple-input/multiple-output (MIMO) systems. The basic idea is the following theorem.

Theorem 10.14 (Physical Meaning of SISO System Zeros)

Consider a linear SISO state-space system defined by Equation 10.28. If the complex number λ is a system zero then there exists an input $u(t) = e^{\lambda t}$ and an initial state $x(t_0) = x_0$ such that $y(t) \equiv 0$ for all $t \geq t_0$.

Proof: Recall that in Equation 6.23 of Section 6.6.1, we have

$$Y(s) = C[sI - A]^{-1}x_0 + \left\{ C[sI - A]^{-1}B + D \right\} U(s)$$

In the SISO case, C is a row vector, B is a column vector and D is a scalar. Consequently,

$$G(s) := \left\{ C[sI - A]^{-1}B + D \right\} = k\frac{n(s)}{d(s)}$$

where

$$d(s) = |sI - A|$$

Suppose $u(t) = e^{\lambda t}$, equivalently,

$$U(s) = \frac{1}{s - \lambda}$$

Thus,

$$Y(s) = \frac{C\text{Adj}[sI - A]x_0}{d(s)} + k\frac{n(s)}{d(s)}\frac{1}{s - \lambda}.$$

Because $G(s)$ is realizable, the second term is a proper rational function. Take the second term and perform an (incomplete) partial fraction expansion:

$$k\frac{n(s)}{d(s)}\frac{1}{s - \lambda} = \frac{a(s)}{d(s)} + \frac{b}{s - \lambda}$$

From the basic results of the partial fraction expansion, $a(s)$ is a polynomial of degree $n - 1$ and b is a constant. Our goal is to determine the constant b in the usual way:

$$\lim_{s \to \lambda} \left((s - \lambda)\frac{kn(s)}{d(s)}\frac{1}{s - \lambda} \right) = \lim_{s \to \lambda} \frac{(s - \lambda)a(s)}{d(s)} + \lim_{s \to \lambda} \frac{(s - \lambda)b}{s - \lambda}$$

From this we determine b as

$$b = k\frac{n(\lambda)}{d(\lambda)} = G(\lambda)$$

Hence,

$$Y(s) = \frac{C\text{Adj}[sI - A]x_0}{d(s)} + k\frac{n(s)}{d(s)}\frac{1}{s - \lambda} = \left(\frac{C\text{Adj}[sI - A]x_0}{d(s)} + \frac{a(s)}{d(s)} \right) + \frac{G(\lambda)}{s - \lambda}$$

It is always possible to determine x_0 so that

$$\left(\frac{C\text{Adj}[sI - A]x_0}{d(s)} + \frac{a(s)}{d(s)} \right) = 0$$

This follows from the fact that $C\text{Adj}[sI - A]x_0$ is a polynomial of order $n - 1$ and the n components of x_0 can be used to match its n coefficients to those of $a(s)$. As a result, we have

$$Y(s) = \frac{G(\lambda)}{s - \lambda}$$

If λ is a zero of $G(s)$, then $Y(s) = 0$ and $y(t) = 0$.   ∎

Remark 10.15 (Another Interpretation of SISO System Zeros)

Theorem 10.14 asserts that if a SISO system has a zero at $s = \lambda$ (or a pair complex conjugate zeros) there exists a control input and an initial state such that the resultant state trajectory maintains the output at zero. Another interpretation is that regardless of the initial state, the system output contains only the homogeneous response (i.e., the specific input is blocked from having any affect on the output).   ■

The importance of this theorem is that it can be extended to MIMO systems and gives us the answer to the question, "What are the zeros of a MIMO system?" Consider once again Equation 10.28, but this time $x \in R^n, u \in R^m, y \in R^p$. This time we ask if there is a λ, a $g \in R^m$ for a control $u(t) = ge^{\lambda t}$ and an initial state $x_0 \in R^n$ such that $x(t) = x_0 e^{\lambda t}$ and $y(t) \equiv 0$, $t \geq t_0$. Such a solution must satisfy

$$\lambda x_0 e^{\lambda t} = A x_0 e^{\lambda t} + B g e^{\lambda t}$$

and

$$0 = C x_0 e^{\lambda t} + D g e^{\lambda t}$$

Putting these together we get

$$\begin{bmatrix} \lambda I - A & B \\ -C & D \end{bmatrix} \begin{bmatrix} -x_0 \\ g \end{bmatrix} = 0. \tag{10.31}$$

Definition 10.16 (MIMO System Zeros)

The complex number λ is a zero of the system

$$\dot{x}(t) = Ax(t) + Bu(t)$$
$$y(t) = Cx(t) + Du(t)$$

with $x \in R^n, u \in R^m, y \in R^p$ if Equation 10.31 has a nontrivial solution for x_0 and g.   ■

The matrix equation, Equation 10.31 represents $n + p$ linear equations in the $n + m$ unknowns, the elements of the vectors x_0 and g. **A nontrivial solution exists if and only if there exists a complex value λ so that**

$$\begin{bmatrix} \lambda I - A & B \\ -C & D \end{bmatrix}$$

drops below its normal rank, and this λ is a zero of the system (A, B, C, D).

The matrix

$$S(\lambda) = \begin{bmatrix} \lambda I - A & B \\ -C & D \end{bmatrix} \tag{10.32}$$

is called the *system matrix* or *Rosenbrock system matrix* [Rosenbrock, 1969]. It is the degeneracy of the system matrix that leads to system zeros. If $Rank(B) = m$ and $Rank(C) = p$ then the generic rank of $S(\lambda)$ (i.e., for generic values of λ) is $n + \min(m, p)$. $Rank(B) = m$ means that the m controls are independent. $Rank(C) = p$ means that the p outputs are independent. If all controls and outputs are independent, then all zeros are associated with specific values of λ that reduce the rank of S from $n + min(m, p)$. In the following discussion we assume independent controls and outputs.

We can identify different conditions under which nontrivial solutions of Equation 10.31 exist, which leads to categorization of system zeros into several types. This is accomplished by examining various conditions that lead to degeneracy of the system matrix $S(\lambda)$.

Those particular values of λ for which the rank of the Rosenbrock system matrix $S(\lambda)$ drops below its normal rank are called *invariant zeros*. Invariant zeros can be of three different types:

1. **Input decoupling zeros:** The eigenvalues associated with uncontrollable modes. The values of λ that satisfy

$$\text{rank} \begin{bmatrix} \lambda I - A & B \end{bmatrix} < n$$

2. **Output decoupling zeros:** The eigenvalues associated with unobservable modes. The values of λ that satisfy

$$\text{rank} \begin{bmatrix} \lambda I - A \\ C \end{bmatrix} < n$$

3. **Transmission zeros:** All other invariant zeros.

The problem of finding the values λ that make the system matrix of Equation 10.32 lose its normal rank is a special case of the generalized eigenvalue problem. The computation of the zeros of a state-space model (A, B, C, D) based on the Rosenbrock system matrix $S(\lambda)$ is summarized in the following theorem.

Theorem 10.17 (Computation of the Zeros of State-Space Model (A, B, C, D))

The zeros of the state-space model (A, B, C, D) are the generalized eigenvalues λ_i so that

$$\begin{bmatrix} \lambda_i I - A & B \\ -C & D \end{bmatrix} v_i = \left[\lambda_i \begin{bmatrix} I & 0 \\ 0 & 0 \end{bmatrix} - \begin{bmatrix} A & -B \\ C & -D \end{bmatrix} \right] v_i = [\lambda_i E - Z] v_i \qquad (10.33)$$

where v_i are the corresponding generalized eigenvectors.   ■

The MATLAB command

```
Dz=eig(Z,E)   or   [Vz,Dz]=eig(Z,E)
```

can be employed to obtain the generalized eigenvalues and the generalized eigenvectors in Dz and Vz, respectively. This state-space approach was employed to find the zero of a simple first-order SISO system in Example 10.3. In Example 10.13, we obtained the poles and zeros of a fourth-order F/A–18 SISO system by converting the state-space model to a transfer function. We will verify the zeros of the fourth-order F/A–18 SISO system in the next example by the Theorem 10.17 approach.

Example 10.18 (F/A–18 SISO Longitudinal Revisited, Computation of Zeros of a SISO System in State Space)

Recall that the F/A–18 longitudinal flight dynamics model considered in Example 10.13 is given by

$$A = \begin{bmatrix} -0.02389 & -28.32 & 0 & -32.2 \\ -0.00033 & -0.362 & 1 & 0 \\ 0 & -2.212 & -0.2532 & 0 \\ 0 & 0 & 1 & 0 \end{bmatrix}, \quad b = \begin{bmatrix} -3.8114 \\ -0.05145 \\ -2.8791 \\ 0 \end{bmatrix}$$

$$c = \begin{bmatrix} 0 & -1 & 0 & 1 \end{bmatrix}, \quad d = 0$$

With the data (A, b, c, d) obtained from running the Example 10.13 program, we can compute the zeros of the system using the following MATLAB command:

```
% CSD Ex10.18 Eq8.64 Compute F/A-18 SISO zeros
Z=[A  -b; c  -d];
E=blkdiag(eye(4),zeros(1))
Dz=eig(Z,E)
```

And the results will be:

```
E  =
       1      0      0      0      0
       0      1      0      0      0
       0      0      1      0      0
       0      0      0      1      0
       0      0      0      0      0
Dz  =
    3.4907e-02
   -4.3935e+00
    4.1059e+00
          -Inf
           Inf
```

As expected, we have obtained the same three zeros, 0.034907, −4.3935, and 4.1059, for the SISO system by either the direct computation of the transfer function or computing the generalized eigenvalues of the system matrix.   ∎

Example 10.19 (F/A–18 MIMO Longitudinal Revisited, Computation of Zeros of a MIMO System in State Space)

Recall the F/A–18 longitudinal flight dynamics model of Equation 8.64, from which both of the elevator and thrust controls, δ_e and δ_T, are considered as the inputs and both the flight path angle $\gamma = \theta - \alpha$ and the air speed V are the outputs, and we will have

$$A = \begin{bmatrix} -0.02389 & -28.32 & 0 & -32.2 \\ -0.00033 & -0.362 & 1 & 0 \\ 0 & -2.212 & -0.2532 & 0 \\ 0 & 0 & 1 & 0 \end{bmatrix}, \quad B = \begin{bmatrix} -3.8114 & 9.5196*10^{-4} \\ -0.05145 & -3.8506*10^{-7} \\ -2.8791 & 0 \\ 0 & 0 \end{bmatrix}$$

$$C = \begin{bmatrix} 0 & -1 & 0 & 1 \\ 1 & 0 & 0 & 0 \end{bmatrix}, \quad D = \begin{bmatrix} 0 & 0 \\ 0 & 0 \end{bmatrix}$$

Run the Example 10.13 program to obtain the data A, B, then we can find the 2-input/2-output transfer function matrix using the following MATLAB command:

```
% CSD Ex10.19 Eq8.64 F/A-18 Poles Zeros
C=[0 -1 0 1; 1 0 0 0]; D=zeros(2); sys=ss(A,B,C,D), zpk(sys)
```

Then we have the transfer functions from the two inputs to the two outputs:

```
From input 1 to output...
             0.051453 (s+4.393) (s-4.106) (s-0.03491)
     1:  -------------------------------------------------------
         (s^2 + 0.02027s + 0.01026) (s^2 + 0.6189s + 2.286)

             -3.8114 (s-6.57) (s+6.623) (s+0.1803)
     2:  -------------------------------------------------------
         (s^2 + 0.02027s + 0.01026) (s^2 + 0.6189s + 2.286)

From input 2 to output...
             3.8506e-07 (s+0.8378) (s^2 + 0.2532s + 2.212)
```

```
1:    -----------------------------------------------------
          (s^2 + 0.02027s + 0.01026) (s^2 + 0.6189s + 2.286)


          0.00095196 (s-0.01245) (s^2 + 0.6392s + 2.314)
2:    -----------------------------------------------------
          (s^2 + 0.02027s + 0.01026) (s^2 + 0.6189s + 2.286)
```

Notice that the four elements that make up the 2×2 transfer function matrix are rational functions with a common denominator that provides a clear identification of the poles. However, **the zeros of each individual numerators are not the zeros of the system.** Although the zeros can be obtained as the complex values of s that make the numerator matrix $N(s)$ lose its normal rank, the computation is complicated and numerically unreliable. **We obtain the zeros by determining the generalized eigenvalues of the system matrix.** With the MATLAB command:

```
Z=[A  -B; C  -D];
E=blkdiag(eye(4),zeros(2))
Dz=eig(Z,E)
```

we will have the following results:

```
E =
          1    0    0    0    0    0
          0    1    0    0    0    0
          0    0    1    0    0    0
          0    0    0    1    0    0
          0    0    0    0    0    0
          0    0    0    0    0    0
Dz =
               -Inf
        -4.4631e+00
         4.2099e+00
                Inf
                Inf
                Inf
```

We have the two zeros: -4.4631 and 4.2099. We can go further and confirm that the system is both controllable and observable. **Thus, the two system zeros are transmission zeros.** ∎

10.5 State-Feedback Control via Linear Quadratic Regulator Design

Consider a system described by the following state equation

$$\dot{x}(t) = Ax(t) + Bu(t) \tag{10.34}$$

where $x \in R^n, u \in R^m$, and all the state variables in $x(t)$ are available for feedback. Recall that the behavior and performance of the system are mainly determined by the poles of the system, which are the eigenvalues of the A matrix. Using the state-feedback control to close the loop,

$$u(t) = Fx(t) \tag{10.35}$$

the state equation of the closed-loop system will become

$$\dot{x}(t) = (A + BF)x(t) \tag{10.36}$$

and then the behavior and performance of the closed-loop system will be dictated by the eigenvalues of $A + BF$.

If the system is controllable, or the rank of the controllability matrix

$$\mathscr{C} = [B \; AB \; A^2B \; \cdots \; A^{n-1}B]$$

is n, then the eigenvalues of $A + BF$ can be placed anywhere of the complex plane. The concept of the state feedback was first applied in Section 4.4.3 of the book to stabilize the originally unstable simple inverted pendulum system. More detailed discussions of the state-feedback pole placement approach were given later in Sections 7.5.1 and 7.5.2, respectively, for the direct approach and the transform approach. The direct approach is implemented according to Equations 10.35 and 10.36, which are conceptually simple but computationally can become very complicated for high-order systems. On the other hand, the transform approach requires the state equation be transformed into the companion form, but the effort of the transformation certainly is worthwhile since it has made the computation for high-order computations as easy as that for the low-order systems.

In addition to stabilizing a system at an originally unstable equilibrium, as demonstrated in Section 7.6.4, the state-space pole placement approach can work together with tracking/regulation theory and root locus design, as shown in Section 8.6.3 and Section 8.7, respectively, to achieve aircraft flight path angle tracking control and aircraft altitude regulation.

The reasoning behind the pole placement approach is that the performance of the system is quite related to the pole locations on the complex plane. For example, the typical second-order system underdamped step response is determined by the two complex poles $-\alpha \pm \omega$ or their associated damping ratio ς and natural frequency ω_n, as shown in Section 3.4, particularly demonstrated in Figures 3.10 and 3.11. However, in general, especially for high order systems, the pole locations may not precisely reflect the desired time-domain performance. Furthermore, control-input constraints are not explicitly considered in the pole placement design process. Hence, substantial simulations usually are required to verify the design.

The linear quadratic regulator (LQR) design is a time-domain performance index optimization approach in which the performance index consists of two parts: one accounting for the performance and the other representing the control-input effort. With a chosen weighting function, an optimal trade-off solution can be found by solving the optimization problem.

10.5.1 Performance Index and LQR State Feedback

Consider the system described by the state equation Equation 10.34. Assume the system is stabilizable; then the LQR control design problem is to determine a state-feedback control law $u(t) = Fx(t)$ so that the closed-loop system is stable and the performance index,

$$PI = \int_0^\infty \left(x^T(t)Qx(t) + u^T(t)Ru(t) \right) \, dt \qquad (10.37)$$

is minimized, where $Q \in R^{n \times n}$ is positive semi-definite and $R \in R^{m \times m}$ is positive definite. The definitions of positive definite and positive semi-definite matrices are given in Appendix E.6.

Theorem 10.20 (Linear Quadratic Regulator State Feedback)

Assume the system with the state equation Equation 10.34 is stabilizable, then the optimal state-feedback control that stabilizes the closed-loop system and minimizes the performance index PI of Equation 10.37 for any initial state $x(0) = x_0$ is

$$u = Fx \quad with \quad F = -R^{-1}B^T X \tag{10.38}$$

where $X = X^T \geq 0$ is the unique positive semi-definite stabilizing solution of the algebraic Riccati equation [Zhou et al., 1995, Kailath, 1980],

$$A^T X + XA - XBR^{-1}B^T X + Q = 0 \tag{10.39}$$

and the optimal performance index is $PI_{opt} = x_0^T X x_0$. ∎

10.5.2 Stabilizing Solution of the Algebraic Riccati Equation

One way to solving for the stabilizing solution of the algebraic Riccati equation, Equation 10.39, is to use its corresponding Hamiltonian matrix [Zhou et al., 1995, Kailath, 1980],

$$H = \begin{bmatrix} A & -BR^{-1}B^T \\ -Q & -A^T \end{bmatrix} \tag{10.40}$$

The eigenvalue structure of the Hamiltonian matrix has the following interesting property.

Theorem 10.21 (Eigenvalues of the Hamiltonian Matrix)

The set of the 2n eigenvalues of the Hamiltonian matrix H are symmetric with respect to the imaginary axis. That is, λ is an eigenvalue of H if and only if $-\lambda$ is. ∎

Assume the Hamiltonian matrix H has no eigenvalues on the imaginary axis; then H has n stable eigenvalues in the left half of the complex plane and another n unstable eigenvalues in the right half of the complex plane. The n eigenvectors associated with the stable eigenvalues can be stacked to form a $2n \times n$ complex matrix $T \in C^{2n \times n}$ with partition as follows:

$$T = \begin{bmatrix} T_1 \\ T_2 \end{bmatrix} \tag{10.41}$$

where T_1 and T_2 are both $n \times n$ complex matrices. If T_1 is invertible, then the stabilizing solution of the Riccati equation is

$$X = T_2 T_1^{-1} \tag{10.42}$$

The stabilizing solution X is real, symmetric, positive semi-definite, and unique.

Notice that **the stabilizing solution exists only if the two conditions are satisfied: (1) The Hamiltonian matrix has no eigenvalues on the imaginary axis, and (2) the matrix T_1 is invertible.** These two conditions are satisfied under the two assumptions of the LQR problem formulation, which are: **(1) (A,B) is stabilizable, and (2) the weighting matrices Q and R are positive semi-definite and positive definite, respectively.**

Example 10.22 (The Stabilizing Solution of an Algebraic Riccati Equation)

Consider the system

$$\dot{x}(t) = Ax(t) + Bu(t) = \begin{bmatrix} -2 & -2 \\ 2 & 3 \end{bmatrix} x(t) + \begin{bmatrix} -1 \\ 1 \end{bmatrix} u(t)$$

which was employed in Examples 7.27 and 7.28 to demonstrate the pole-placement state-feedback approaches. Here, we will use the LQR Riccati equation approach to find a state feedback $u(t) = Fx(t)$ so that the closed-loop system is stable and the performance index

$$PI = \int_0^\infty \left(x^T(t)Qx(t) + u^T(t)Ru(t) \right) \, dt$$

is minimized, where the weighting matrices are chosen as

$$Q = \begin{bmatrix} 1 & 0 \\ 0 & 1 \end{bmatrix}, \quad R = 1$$

Note that the open-loop system has poles at -1 and 2; hence, it is unstable. (A, B) is stabilizable since it is controllable. The Hamiltonian matrix corresponding to the algebraic Riccati equation, Equation 10.39, is

$$H = \begin{bmatrix} A & -BR^{-1}B^T \\ -Q & -A^T \end{bmatrix} = \begin{bmatrix} -2 & -2 & -1 & 1 \\ 2 & 3 & 1 & -1 \\ -1 & 0 & 2 & -2 \\ 0 & -1 & 2 & -3 \end{bmatrix}$$

whose eigenvalues are

$$-2.4885, \quad -0.89856, \quad 2.4885, \quad 0.89856$$

and the eigenvectors associated with the stable eigenvalues are

$$T = \begin{bmatrix} T_1 \\ T_2 \end{bmatrix} = \begin{bmatrix} 0.28724 & 0.41001 \\ -0.2049 & -0.19405 \\ -0.3267 & 0.59762 \\ -0.8768 & 0.66112 \end{bmatrix}$$

hence, the stabilizing Riccati solution is

$$X = T_2 T_1^{-1} = \begin{bmatrix} 6.5737 & 10.81 \\ 10.81 & 19.433 \end{bmatrix}$$

The state-feedback gain is thus

$$F = -R^{-1}B^T X = \begin{bmatrix} -4.2361 & -8.6231 \end{bmatrix}$$

and the closed-loop system poles are now the eigenvalues of $A + BF$, which are

$$-2.4885, \quad -0.89856$$

exactly the same as the stable eigenvalues of the Hamiltonian matrix. ∎

These numerical results are obtained by running the following MATLAB code:

```
% CSD Ex10.22 State feedback Riccati Hamiltonian
A=[-2 -2;2 3]; B=[-1;1]; eig_A=eig(A), Q=eye(2); R=1;
H=[A  -B*inv(R)*B'; -Q  -A'], [V,D]=eig(H), T1=V(1:2,1:2),
T2=V(3:4,1:2), X=T2*inv(T1),
Riccati_Eq_Check=A'*X+X*A-X*B*inv(R)*B'*X+Q,
F=-inv(R)*B'*X, eig_ABF=eig(A+B*F)
```

A MATLAB command: `lqr` can also be employed to find an LQR solution:

```
>> [K,S,E]=lqr(A,B,Q,R)
   K =
      4.2361e+00    8.6231e+00
   S =
      6.5737e+00    1.0810e+01
      1.0810e+01    1.9433e+01
   E =
     -2.4885e+00
     -8.9856e-01
```

Note that $K = -F$, $S = X$, and E gives the eigenvalues of $A - BK$ or $A + BF$. If only the solution of the algebraic Riccati equation is of interest, the MATLAB command: are can be applied as follows:

```
>> X=are(A,B*inv(R)*B',Q)
   X =
      6.5737e+00    1.0810e+01
      1.0810e+01    1.9433e+01
```

10.5.3 Weighting Matrices Q and R in the Performance Index Integral

To employ the LQR state-feedback control design approach, usually we start with the knowledge of a nonlinear dynamics model of the system to be controlled, the desired operating equilibrium, disturbances and measurement noises, system model uncertainties, and actuator limitations. **To demonstrate the design process, we will use the simple inverted pendulum system discussed in Section 4.4 to demonstrate how to formulate a state-feedback control problem as an LQR optimization problem.**

The schematic of the simple inverted pendulum system is depicted in Figure 4.8, where the two state variables $x_1 = \theta$ and $x_2 = \dot{\theta}$ are the angular displacement and the angular velocity of the pendulum, respectively, and the control input $u = f_a$ is the external control force perpendicular to the gravity. The nonlinear dynamics model of the system is represented by the following nonlinear state equation:

$$\begin{bmatrix} \dot{x}_1 \\ \dot{x}_2 \end{bmatrix} = \begin{bmatrix} x_2 \\ \frac{g}{\ell}\sin x_1 - \frac{b}{m\ell^2}x_2 + \frac{1}{m\ell}\cos x_1 \cdot u \end{bmatrix} \tag{10.43}$$

The equilibrium of interest is at $x^* = \begin{bmatrix} 0 & 0 \end{bmatrix}^T$, which represents the stick at the upright position $\theta = 0$ with zero angular velocity $\dot{\theta} = 0$. Assume $g = 9.8$ m/s^2, $\ell = 1.089$ m, $m = 0.918$ kg, $b = 0.551$ Ns so that

$$\frac{g}{\ell} = 9, \quad \frac{b}{m\ell^2} = 0.6, \quad \frac{1}{m\ell} = 1$$

hence, the state equation of the linearized model at the upright stick equilibrium $x^* = \begin{bmatrix} 0 & 0 \end{bmatrix}^T$ can be found as

$$\dot{x}(t) = Ax(t) + Bu(t) = \begin{bmatrix} 0 & 1 \\ 9 & -0.6 \end{bmatrix} x(t) + \begin{bmatrix} 0 \\ 1 \end{bmatrix} u(t) \tag{10.44}$$

Note that the uncompensated system is not stable at this equilibrium since the eigenvalues of the A matrix are 2.715 and -3.315. Recall that in Section 4.4.3, a state-feedback controller $u = Fx = \begin{bmatrix} -34 & -7.4 \end{bmatrix} x$ was designed based on the pole placement approach to place the closed-loop system poles at $-4 \pm j3$ so that the damping ratio and the natural frequency are $\varsigma = 0.8$ and $\omega_n = 5$ rad/s, respectively. A simulation that demonstrates the performance of this pole-placement state-feedback controller was shown in Figure 4.11.

In the following, we will employ the LQR approach to design a state-feedback controller to stabilize the system and minimize the performance index *PI*,

$$PI = \int_0^\infty \left(x^T(t)Qx(t) + u^T(t)Ru(t) \right) dt$$

where Q and R are positive semi-definite and positive definite, respectively. As long as (A,B) is stabilizable and the Q and R requirements are satisfied, any state-feedback controller designed based on the LQR approach theorem, Theorem 10.20, will stabilize the system. However, to achieve a desired closed-loop system performance the weighting matrices Q and R need to be chosen carefully according to the performance requirement and the control-input constraint.

In the following examples, we will not only design an LQR state-feedback controller to stabilize the system at the originally unstable equilibrium, $x^* = \begin{bmatrix} 0 & 0 \end{bmatrix}^T$. **We would like the controller to be able to bring the system from a perturbed state, say $x(0) = x_0 = \begin{bmatrix} 0.2618 & 0 \end{bmatrix}^T$, back to the equilibrium $x^* = \begin{bmatrix} 0 & 0 \end{bmatrix}^T$ as quickly and smoothly as possible within control-input constraint.** Note that $x_1 = \theta = 0.2618$ rad is $15°$.

Since the controllability matrix

$$[B \ \ AB] = \begin{bmatrix} 0 & 1 \\ 1 & -0.6 \end{bmatrix}$$

is of full rank, the system is controllable and thus stabilizable. There exists a state-feedback control strategy, $u(t) = Fx(t)$, so that the closed-loop system poles or the eigenvalues of $A + BF$, are in the left complex plane as well as the control-input constraints are satisfied. **In the following three examples, we will consider three sets of Q and R weighting matrices, respectively. For each set, there exists a unique stabilizing optimal controller. By evaluating the performance of each controller, we may see how the choice of Q and R would affect the performance of the system.**

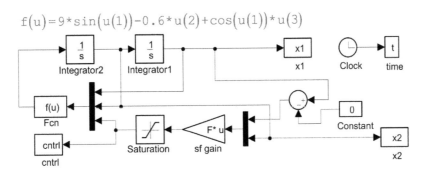

Fig. 10.19: Simulation diagram to evaluate LQR controller performance.

Although the controller is designed based on the linearized model, Equation 10.44, the nonlinear model Equation 10.43 is employed in the simulation, as shown in Figure 10.19. The function block Fcn is defined by

$$f(u) = 9 * sin(u(1)) - 0.6 * u(2) + cos(u(1)) * u(3)$$

where $u(1)$, $u(2)$, and $u(3)$, respectively, represent the state variables x_1, x_2, and the control-input u of Equation 10.43. The initial condition of the state variables are assigned as x20=0 and

x10=0.2618, respectively, inside the integrator blocks. This initial condition means that the pendulum stick has deviated from the equilibrium by 15 degrees to the right with zero angular velocity.

Example 10.23 (Case 1 LQR State Feedback Controller for the Simple Inverted Pendulum)

Consider the state equation, Equation 10.44, which is the linearized state-space model of the nonlinear simple inverted pendulum dynamics of Equation 10.43 at the unstable equilibrium $x^* = \begin{bmatrix} 0 & 0 \end{bmatrix}^T$. Let the weighting matrices Q and R be

$$Q = \begin{bmatrix} q_1 & 0 \\ 0 & q_2 \end{bmatrix}, \quad R = r_1$$

then

$$x^T Q x = q_1 x_1^2 + q_2 x_2^2, \quad u^T R u = r_1 u^2$$

and the performance index (also called cost function) will be

$$PI = \int_0^\infty \left(q_1 x_1^2 + q_2 x_2^2 + r_1 u^2 \right) dt = q_1 \int_0^\infty x_1^2 \, dt + q_2 \int_0^\infty x_2^2 \, dt + r_1 \int_0^\infty u^2 \, dt$$

The three terms on the right-hand side of the equation are the weighted total energies of the angular displacement ($x_1 = \theta$), the angular velocity ($x_2 = \dot{\theta}$), and the control-input force ($u = f_a$), respectively. For Q to be positive semi-definite and R positive definite, q_1 and q_2 have to be greater or equal to zero and r_1 is required to be greater than zero. **The control-input weight r_1 cannot be zero since $r_1 = 0$ means that infinity feedback is allowed, which of course is not practically possible.** Making r_1 larger will put more constraint on the control-input energy consumption. **Similarly, the weight q_1 may need to be made larger if the reduction of the energy of x_1 would improve the performance.**

We will begin with the selection of the weights $q_1 = q_2 = 1$ and $r_1 = 1$, find the unique stabilizing controller that minimizes the performance index associated with this particular weight selection, evaluate the performance of the closed-loop system, and then revise the weight selection according to the performance evaluation.

With this Q, R selection,

$$Q = \begin{bmatrix} 1 & 0 \\ 0 & 1 \end{bmatrix}, \quad R = 1$$

the unique stabilizing solution for the algebraic Riccati equation can be found as

$$X = \begin{bmatrix} 60.831 & 18.055 \\ 18.055 & 5.5213 \end{bmatrix}$$

The state-feedback gain is thus

$$F = -R^{-1} B^T X = \begin{bmatrix} -18.055 & -5.5213 \end{bmatrix}$$

and the closed-loop system poles are at -2.5018 and -3.6195. Since the initial state is $x(0) = x_0 = \begin{bmatrix} 0.2618 & 0 \end{bmatrix}^T$, **the minimal performance index is**

$$PI_{opt} = x_0^T X x_0 = 4.1693$$

Based on Equation 10.43 and the simulation diagram in Figure 10.19, a Simulink program is assembled to conduct simulations to observe the time-domain responses due to the initial conditions of x_1 and x_2. The time-domain responses of the two state variables $x_1(t) = \theta(t)$ and $x_2(t) = \dot{\theta}(t)$ due to the initial conditions $x_1(0) = 0.2618$ rad and $x_2(0) = 0$ rad/s, are shown on the left-hand side of Figure 10.20. Meanwhile, the control-input action is recorded on the right graph of the figure. The pendulum initially is tilted to the right by $15°$ (0.2618 rad). The deviation of the pendulum position from the equilibrium $x^* = \begin{bmatrix} 0 & 0 \end{bmatrix}^T$ prompted the control-input $u(t)$ to react immediately, changing **from 0 N to** -4.7 **N** and then gradually reducing to zero so that the angular velocity x_2 and the angular displacement x_1 can change accordingly to bring the pendulum back to the equilibrium. **It takes about** 2.8 **seconds to bring the pendulum back to the equilibrium.** ∎

Comparing the simulation results of Case 1 LQR state-feedback controller with those of the pole placement state-feedback controller shown in Figure 4.11, we observe that the latter only takes about 1.7 seconds to converge to the equilibrium while using more control-input, -8.8N. In the next example, we will reduce the control-input weight r_1 to allow using more control-input energy and then observe if this change will improve the performance.

Case 1:

$$Q = \begin{bmatrix} 1 & 0 \\ 0 & 1 \end{bmatrix}, \ R=1$$

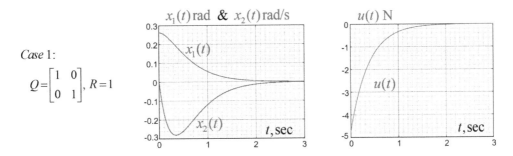

Fig. 10.20: Simulation results of the Case 1 LQR controller performance.

Before getting into the next example, it is interesting to see if multiplying Q and R by the same constant would change the outcome of the LQR state-feedback controller design. Let the Q and R in Case 1 design be multiplied by 10 to become

$$Q = \begin{bmatrix} 10 & 0 \\ 0 & 10 \end{bmatrix}, \quad R = 10$$

and repeat the LQR controller design in Example 10.23. We will see the stabilizing solution X to the algebraic Riccati equation becomes 10 times of the solution obtained in Example 10.23, and thus, the minimal performance index PI_{opt} will increase 10 times accordingly to

$$J_{opt} = x_0^T X x_0 = 41.693$$

However, the stabilizing state-feedback gain matrix F remains the same as

$$F = -R^{-1}B^T X = \begin{bmatrix} -18.055 & -5.5213 \end{bmatrix}$$

since the same variation in R and X cancels each other. Therefore, **only the relative weights are important, and the value of the minimal performance index** PI_{opt} **does not reflect the performance** of the closed-loop system.

Example 10.24 (Case 2 LQR State Feedback Controller for the Simple Inverted Pendulum)

In this example, we consider the same simple inverted pendulum control problem with the same LQR state-feedback control design as in Example 10.23. The only difference is in the selection of the weighting matrices Q and R.

Let the weighting matrices Q and R be

$$Q = \begin{bmatrix} q_1 & 0 \\ 0 & q_2 \end{bmatrix} = \begin{bmatrix} 1 & 0 \\ 0 & 1 \end{bmatrix}, \quad R = r_1 = 0.001$$

in which the Q matrix is the same as that in Case 1, only the weight r_1 is reduced to 0.001 to allow more usage of control-input energy that may improve the closed-loop system performance by shortening the convergence time to the equilibrium.

With the Q, R thus selected, the unique stabilizing solution for the algebraic Riccati equation can be found as

$$X = \begin{bmatrix} 1.088 & 0.041879 \\ 0.041879 & 0.032326 \end{bmatrix}$$

The state-feedback gain is now

$$F = -R^{-1}B^T X = \begin{bmatrix} -41.879 & -32.326 \end{bmatrix}$$

and the closed-loop system poles are at -1.0308 and -31.895. Since the initial state is $x(0) = x_0 = \begin{bmatrix} 0.2618 & 0 \end{bmatrix}^T$, **the minimal performance index is**

$$PI_{opt} = x_0^T X x_0 = 0.074568$$

The time-domain responses of the two state variables $x_1(t) = \theta(t)$, $x_2(t) = \dot{\theta}(t)$, and the control input $u(t)$ due to the initial condition: $x_1(0) = 0.2618$ rad and $x_2(0) = 0$ rad/s, are shown in Figure 10.21. **It does utilize more control-input magnitude with -11 N of force compared with -4.7 N in Case 1. However, the performance is not improved. Actually it gets worse—neither x_1 nor x_2 converges to the equilibrium within 3 seconds.** ∎

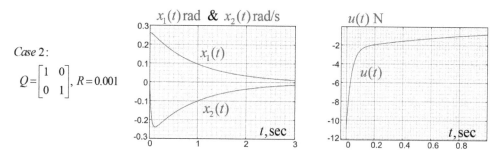

Fig. 10.21: Simulation results of the Case 2 LQR controller performance.

The choice of q_1 (the weight for $x_1 = \theta$) and q_2 (the weight for $x_2 = \dot{\theta}$) to be identical in Cases 1 and 2 may not be a good one. Although eventually both x_1 and x_2 shall converge to zero, limiting the energy of x_2 (angular velocity) will slow down the convergence of x_1 (angular displacement). For this reason, q_2 should be chosen much smaller than q_1. With the weights being chosen as $q_1 = 1000$,

$q_2 = 0$, and $r_1 = 1$, we saw a great improvement in performance. After a few minor revisions, it seems that the weight selection of $q_1 = 1{,}000$, $q_2 = 20$, and $r_1 = 1.2$ will give an optimal performance. The LQR controller design associated with this Case 3 weighting matrices

$$Q = \begin{bmatrix} q_1 & 0 \\ 0 & q_2 \end{bmatrix} = \begin{bmatrix} 10^3 & 0 \\ 0 & 20 \end{bmatrix}, \quad R = r_1 = 1.2$$

and the performance evaluation of the closed-loop system will be given in the following example.

Example 10.25 (Case 3 LQR State Feedback Controller for the Simple Inverted Pendulum)

In this example, we consider the same simple inverted pendulum control problem with the same LQR state-feedback control design as in Example 10.23. The only difference is in the selection of the weighting matrices Q and R. Let the weighting matrices Q and R be

$$Q = \begin{bmatrix} q_1 & 0 \\ 0 & q_2 \end{bmatrix} = \begin{bmatrix} 10^3 & 0 \\ 0 & 20 \end{bmatrix}, \quad R = r_1 = 1.2,$$

in which the weight q_1 is much larger than the weight q_2 to emphasize the minimization of the x_1 energy while allowing enough energy for x_2 to speed up the convergence to the equilibrium. The weight r_1 is selected to make sure the control-input constraint condition is met.

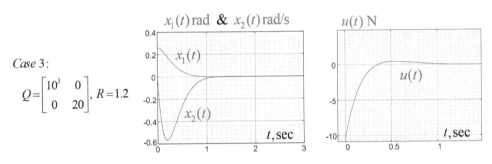

Fig. 10.22: Simulation results of the Case 3 LQR controller performance.

With the Q, R thus selected, the unique stabilizing solution for the algebraic Riccati equation can be found as

$$X = \begin{bmatrix} 361.08 & 47.086 \\ 47.086 & 11.007 \end{bmatrix}$$

The state-feedback gain is now

$$F = -R^{-1}B^T X = \begin{bmatrix} -39.238 & -9.1725 \end{bmatrix}$$

and the closed-loop system poles are at $-4.8863 \pm j2.5224$. Since the initial state is $x(0) = x_0 = [0.2618 \quad 0]^T$, the minimal performance index is

$$PI_{opt} = x_0^T X x_0 = 24.748$$

The time-domain responses of the two state variables, $x_1(t) = \theta(t)$, $x_2(t) = \dot{\theta}(t)$, and the control input $u(t)$ due to the initial condition, $x_1(0) = 0.2618$ rad and $x_2(0) = 0$ rad/s, are shown in Figure

10.22. With this LQR state-feedback controller, **it only takes** 1.15 **seconds by using less than** $10.3N$ **of control input to bring the perturbed pendulum state at the 15-degree tilted angular position back to the equilibrium state—the upright pendulum position.**

With this state-feedback control law $u = Fx$, the closed-loop system poles are the eigenvalues of $A + BF$, which are $-4.8863 \pm j2.5224$. The damping ratio and the natural frequency associated with the closed-loop system poles are $\varsigma = 0.889$ and $\omega_n = 5.499$rad/s. ∎

10.6 Exercise Problems

P10.1: In this exercise problem, we will review how to find equilibriums of a nonlinear system, and how to obtain a linearized state-space model of the nonlinear system at a chosen equilibrium. Then we will study the system characteristics at and around the equilibrium. Assume the nonlinear state equation of a lightly damped pendulum system, which is similar to the one in Equation 10.4, is given below,

$$\dot{x} = \begin{bmatrix} \dot{x}_1 \\ \dot{x}_2 \end{bmatrix} = \begin{bmatrix} x_2 \\ -a_0 \sin x_1 - a_1 x_2 + b_0 u \end{bmatrix} = f(x,u) = \begin{bmatrix} f_1(x_1,x_2,u) \\ f_2(x_1,x_2,u) \end{bmatrix} \qquad (10.45)$$

where $a_1 = 0.1$, $a_0 = 20$, and $b_0 = 40$. The state variables x_1 and x_2 represent the angular displacement and the angular velocity of the pendulum system, respectively. The control input u is the applied torque to drive the system.

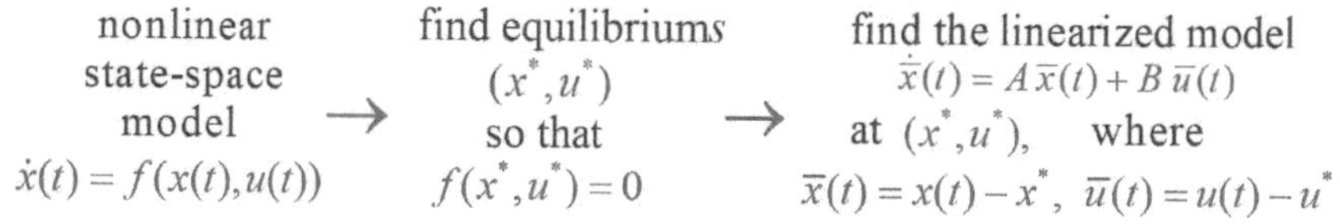

nonlinear state-space model
$\dot{x}(t) = f(x(t), u(t))$

$\rightarrow$

find equilibriums
(x^*, u^*)
so that
$f(x^*, u^*) = 0$

$\rightarrow$

find the linearized model
$\dot{\bar{x}}(t) = A\bar{x}(t) + B\bar{u}(t)$
at (x^*, u^*),   where
$\bar{x}(t) = x(t) - x^*, \ \bar{u}(t) = u(t) - u^*$

Fig. 10.23: Identify equilibriums and find the linearized model at a chosen equilibrium.

P10.1a: As a brief recap of the linearization process, Figure 10.23 shows that the first step is to find the equilibriums. Assume the operating equilibrium is chosen to keep the angular displacement of the pendulum at $18° = 0.1\pi$ rad, which is $x_1 = x_1^* = 0.1\pi$ rad and $x_2 = x_2^* = 0$ rad/s. Find the corresponding control input $u = u^*$ Nm at the equilibrium.

P10.1b: Find the linearized state equation

$$\dot{\bar{x}}(t) = A\bar{x}(t) + B\bar{u}(t) \qquad (10.46)$$

at the equilibrium (x_1^*, x_2^*, u^*) chosen in P10.1a.

P10.1c: Find the characteristic equation of the linearized model and the poles of the system, and comment on the system characteristics based on the damping ratio, natural frequency, and the location of the poles on the complex plane.

P10.1d: Build a simulation program according to the linearized state-space model in Equation 10.46. Conduct the simulation with the following conditions: $\bar{u}(t) = 0$, $\bar{x}_1(0) = 9° = 0.05\pi$rad, and $\bar{x}_2(0) =$

0rad/s. Plot the simulation results $\bar{x}_1(t)$ and $\bar{x}_2(t)$ for $t \geq 0$.

P10.1e: Build a simulation program according to the nonlinear state-space model in Equation 10.45. Apply the equilibrium control input $u(t) = u^*$ Nm to the system, and observe the values of the state variables $x_1(t)$ and $x_2(t)$ after the system reaches the steady state. What are the values of $x_1(t)$ and $x_2(t)$ at the equilibrium state?

P10.1f: With the nonlinear simulation program at the equilibrium $(18°, 0, u^*)$, manually move x_1 from $18°$ to the $27°$ position, and release at $t = 0$. Plot the state variables $x_1(t)$, $x_2(t)$, and the control input $u(t)$. Compare the nonlinear simulation responses $x_1(t)$, $x_2(t)$ with the linear simulation responses $\bar{x}_1(t)$ and $\bar{x}_2(t)$ obtained in P10.1d.

P10.2a: This exercise problem is a continuation of Problem P10.1. As revealed from the solutions of P10.1, the time response of the uncompensated pendulum system is oscillatory with large overshoot. In the following we would design a controller, also called a compensator, to improve the performance of the system. First of all, let us check the controllability of the system. Show that the system represented by Equation 10.46 is controllable.

P10.2b: Find a state feedback $\bar{u}(t) = F\bar{x}(t)$ so that

$$|sI - (A + BF)| = s^2 + 2\varsigma\omega_n s + \omega_n^2 = s^2 + 18s + 100$$

That is, the closed-loop system poles will be placed at $-9 \pm j4.359$, or, equivalently, the damping ratio and the natural frequency are $\varsigma = 0.9$ and $\omega_n = 10$rad/s, respectively.

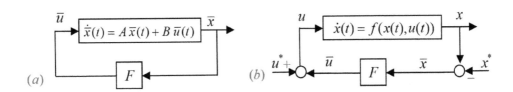

Fig. 10.24: Closed-loop system with state feedback.

P10.2c: Build a simulation program according to Figure 10.24(a), which includes the linearized state-space model and the state-feedback controller obtained in P10.2b. Conduct the simulation with the initial condition $\bar{x}_1(0) = 9° = 0.05\pi$rad, and $\bar{x}_2(0) = 0$rad/s. Plot the state response $\bar{x}_1(t)$ and $\bar{x}_2(t)$ for $t \geq 0$.

P10.2d: Build a simulation program according to Figure 10.24(b), which includes the nonlinear state-space model and the state-feedback controller obtained in P10.2b. Conduct the simulation with the initial condition: $x_1(0) = 27° = 0.15\pi$rad, and $x_2(0) = 0$rad/s. Plot the state response $x_1(t)$ and $x_2(t)$ for $t \geq 0$.

P10.2e: Compare the nonlinear simulation results $x_1(t)$ and $x_2(t)$ in P10.2d with the linear simulation results $\bar{x}_1(t)$ and $\bar{x}_2(t)$ obtained in P10.2c, and give your comments.

P10.3: Consider a set of linear algebraic equations, which is represented in the following matrix form,

$$Ax = b, \quad \text{where} \quad A = \begin{bmatrix} 1 & 2 & 1 \\ 2 & 1 & -1 \\ 3 & 0 & -3 \\ 4 & -1 & -5 \end{bmatrix}$$

A systematic way of investigating the solution existence and uniqueness is to find the range space and the null space of the matrix.

P10.3a: Find the range space of the matrix A, Range (A).

P10.3b: Find the null space of the matrix A, Null (A).

P10.3c: Find the condition on the vector b such that the equation has solutions.

P10.3d: Assume $b^T = \begin{bmatrix} 5 & 4 & 3 & 2 \end{bmatrix}$. Does the equation have a solution? Is the solution unique? If the equation has more than one solution, find the full set of solutions.

P10.4: Recall that the controllable subspace is the range space of the controllability matrix $\mathscr{C}$, while the uncontrollable subspace is the null space of $\mathscr{C}^T$. The null space of $\mathscr{C}^T$ is the orthogonal complement of the range space of $\mathscr{C}$. Consider a system represented by the following state equation:

$$\dot{x}(t) = Ax(t) + Bu(t) = \begin{bmatrix} -14 & -19 & -23 \\ 19 & 27 & 33 \\ -6 & -9 & -11 \end{bmatrix} x(t) + \begin{bmatrix} -1 \\ 0 \\ 1 \end{bmatrix} u(t)$$

P10.4a: Find the controllability matrix $\mathscr{C}$, and determine if the system is controllable.

P10.4b: Find the controllable subspace of the system, which is the range space of the controllability matrix, Range $(\mathscr{C})$.

P10.4c: Find the uncontrollable subspace of the system, which is the null space of the transpose of the controllability matrix, Null $(\mathscr{C}^T)$.

P10.4d: Use the basis vectors of the range space of $\mathscr{C}$ and the null space of $\mathscr{C}^T$ to construct a similarity transformation matrix $T = \begin{bmatrix} T_1 & T_2 \end{bmatrix}$ to transform the state equation into the controllability decomposition form, as shown in Theorem 10.9.

P10.4e: Is the system stabilizable? Explain.

P10.4f: Design a state-feedback controller so that the closed-loop system is internally stable.

P10.4g: Find the closed-loop system poles.

P10.4h: Assume the initial state of the system is $x(0) = \begin{bmatrix} 1 & -1 & 3 \end{bmatrix}^T$. Plot the state response $x(t)$ of the closed-loop system.

P10.5: For a SISO system, the zeros can be found easily from its transfer function. However, that is not the case for MIMO systems. In this exercise, you will apply Theorem 10.17 to a simple SISO state-space model to find the zeros of the system. Then verify the result using the zeros of the transfer function of the system.

P10.5a: Consider a SISO system described by the following state-space model

$$\dot{x}(t) = Ax(t) + Bu(t)$$
$$y(t) = Cx(t) + Du(t)$$

where $A = -1$, $B = 1$, $C = -3$, and $D = 1$. Determine the pole and zero of the system directly using the state-space model. That is, use Theorem 10.17 to determine the zero, and compute the eigenvalue of the A matrix to obtain the pole.

P10.5b: Find the transfer function of the system and use it to determine the zero and the pole of the system.

P10.5c: Comment on the relationship of the poles and zeros obtained in P10.5b and P10.5c.

P10.6: Consider a MIMO system described by the following state-space model

$$\dot{x}(t) = Ax(t) + Bu(t)$$
$$y(t) = Cx(t) + Du(t)$$

where

$$A = \begin{bmatrix} 0 & 4 & 0 & 0 & 0 \\ 1 & 0 & 0 & 0 & 0 \\ 0 & 0 & -2 & 4 & 8 \\ 0 & 0 & 1 & 0 & 0 \\ 0 & 0 & 0 & 1 & 0 \end{bmatrix}, \quad B = \begin{bmatrix} 1 & 0 \\ 0 & 0 \\ 0 & 1 \\ 0 & 0 \\ 0 & 0 \end{bmatrix}, \quad C = \begin{bmatrix} 0 & 1 & 0 & 1 & 3 \\ 1 & 0 & 0 & -1 & 0 \end{bmatrix}$$

P10.6a: Find the poles of the system by computing the eigenvalues of the A matrix, and determine the zeros of the system by using Theorem 10.17.

P10.6b: Find the transfer function matrix of the system, and use it to determine the poles and zeros for each entry of the transfer function matrix.

P10.6c: Comment on the relationship of the poles and zeros obtained in P10.6b and P10.6c.

P10.7: In this exercise problem, we would like to revisit the lightly damped pendulum positioning system considered in Section 10.2.2. Recall that at the equilibrium

$$(x_1^*, x_2^*, T^*) = (15°, 0°/s, 0.19043\text{Nm})$$

we have the linearized state-space model

$$\dot{\bar{x}}(t) = A\bar{x}(t) + B\overline{T}(t)$$

where the matrices A and B are given by Equation 10.6,

$$A = \begin{bmatrix} 0 & 1 \\ -21.32 & -0.135 \end{bmatrix}, \quad B = \begin{bmatrix} 0 \\ 30 \end{bmatrix}$$

A pole placement approach was employed to improve the damping ratio from $\varsigma = 0.0146$ to $\varsigma = 1.0011$. In the following, we will utilize the LQR approach to design a state-feedback controller so that a performance index is optimized.

P10.7a: For notational simplicity, the state vector $\bar{x}(t)$ and the control input $\bar{T}(t)$ will be replaced by $x(t)$ and $u(t)$, respectively. That is, the linearized state-space model of the system to be controlled is

$$\dot{x}(t) = Ax(t) + Bu(t) = \begin{bmatrix} 0 & 1 \\ -21.32 & -0.135 \end{bmatrix} x(t) + \begin{bmatrix} 0 \\ 30 \end{bmatrix} u(t) \qquad (10.47)$$

The objective is to design a state-feedback controller $u(t) = Fx(t)$ so that the closed-loop system is stable and the following performance index

$$PI = \int_0^\infty \left(x^T(t)Qx(t) + u^T(t)Ru(t) \right) dt$$

is minimized. The solution of this optimization problem is

$$u(t) = Fx(t) \quad \text{with} \quad F = -R^{-1}B^TX$$

where X is the positive semi-definite stabilizing solution of the following algebraic Riccati equation:

$$A^TX + XA - XBR^{-1}B^TX + Q = 0$$

Let the weighting matrices in the performance index integral be

$$Q = \begin{bmatrix} 1 & 0 \\ 0 & 1 \end{bmatrix}, \quad R = 1$$

Find X, which is the positive semi-definite stabilizing solution of the above algebraic Riccati equation, and then use it to determine the optimal state-feedback gain matrix $F = -R^{-1}B^TX$.

P10.7b: Find the closed-loop system poles, which are the eigenvalues of $A + BF$, and the corresponding damping ratio and natural frequency.

P10.7c: Let the initial state be

$$x(0)^T = \begin{bmatrix} 20° & 0°/s \end{bmatrix} = \begin{bmatrix} 0.349 \,\text{rad} & 0 \,\text{rad}/s \end{bmatrix}$$

Plot the state response $x(t)$ and the control input $u(t)$.

P10.7d: Comment on the pole location and the simulation results of the closed-loop system.

P10.7e: Change the weight matrices Q and R, repeat the above design and simulations, and comment on how the weighting matrices affect the performance.

11

Observer Theory and Output Feedback Control

U P to now, we have learned how to employ the state-space model and state-feedback control with pole placement, linear quadratic optimization, and internal model principle to achieve stabilization, tracking, regulation, and performance enhancement. The state-space approach can also work together with the classical root locus design approach to achieve precise pole placement performance. However, the state-feedback approach requires direct access to all the system state variables, which may not be possible in many applications. Consequently, we need to generate suitable estimates of the states based on the available information. The observer theory provides a brilliant full-state observer structure to efficiently estimate the states using the inputs, the measurable outputs, and the state-space model.

The main computation involved in the design of the observer is the determination of the observer gain matrix, which in fact is a dual problem of finding the state-feedback gain matrix. In other words, the algorithm for computing the state-feedback gain matrix can be employed to find the observer gain matrix. Furthermore, the observer can be integrated seamlessly together with the state-feedback gain matrix to construct the output feedback controller, and the overall closed-loop system poles will be the observer poles together with the regulator poles, which are the eigenvalues of $A + BF$ we obtained using state feedback. Therefore, the observer and the state feedback can be designed separately. Similar to the state-feedback design, the observer can be designed using the pole placement approach or the quadratic performance index minimization approach. The output feedback controller consisting of the observer and the state-feedback gain is referred as the H_2 controller if the quadratic performance index minimization approach is involved in the design process.

11.1 Observability

Duality is an interesting property of nature. For example, human's left and right hands are dual to each other. We will soon find out that **observability and controllability are a duality pair, and the observer gain and the state-feedback gain are also a dual.** Understanding either one of the dual will make the learning of its counterpart very easy. With the concept of controllability and the design of the state-feedback gain we have covered the previous chapter, it will be a breeze in learning their counterparts in this chapter.

Although observability, controllability, and stability are technical terms, they actually are related to our daily life. For example, assume a person has a tumor but it is not observable. Without knowing what the problem is, there is no way to fix it. If the tumor is growing, the system will become unstable and eventually cease working. On the other hand, if it is observable, it is still required to be controllable for the problem to be fixed. The doctors need to have means, either by surgical procedure or by injecting medicine or through some other treatment to remove or contain the tumor.

For a control system to work, the system to be controlled is required to be stabilizable and detectable. As defined in the previous chapter, **a system is stabilizable if the uncontrollable part of the system is stable.** Similarly, **a system is detectable if the unobservable part of the system is stable.** In the "tumor" example, if the tumor is benign (stable) it is considered as detectable even it is unobservable.

11.1.1 Observability Rank Test

Consider a system with the linear state-space model

$$\dot{x}(t) = Ax(t) + Bu(t)$$
$$y(t) = Cx(t) + Du(t) \tag{11.1}$$

with $x \in R^n, u \in R^m, y \in R^p$. The basic concept of observability is to identify the state x given observation of the output y over some time interval $[0, t_f]$, $t_f > 0$.

Definition 11.1 (Observability)

The linear time-invariant system described by Equation 11.1 is said to be (completely) observable if the initial state $x(0_-)$ can be uniquely determined using the measurements of the output $y(t)$ and the knowledge of the input $u(t)$, which can be zero, over a finite interval of time $0_- \le t \le t_f$. ∎

Note that once $x(0_-)$ is known, $x(t)$ can be determined. Similar to the controllability rank test of Theorem 10.6, observability can be determined using the following theorem.

Theorem 11.2 (Observability Rank Condition)

Consider the following $np \times n$ observability matrix:

$$\mathcal{O} = \begin{bmatrix} C \\ CA \\ \vdots \\ CA^{n-1} \end{bmatrix} \tag{11.2}$$

The system described by Equation 11.1 or the matrix pair (A,C) is (completely) observable if and only if

$$rank \; \mathcal{O} = n$$

∎

Notice that the matrices B and D play no role in determining observability, thereby implying that the control input $u(t)$ is not relevant.

Example 11.3 (Observe the Initial State)

Consider the following simple two-state one-output linear system:

$$\dot{x}(t) = Ax(t) + Bu(t) = \begin{bmatrix} 0 & 1 \\ 1 & 0 \end{bmatrix} x(t) + \begin{bmatrix} 1 \\ 1 \end{bmatrix} u(t)$$
$$y(t) = Cx(t) = \begin{bmatrix} 1 & -1 \end{bmatrix} x(t)$$

The observability matrix of the system is

$$\mathscr{O} = \begin{bmatrix} C \\ CA \end{bmatrix} = \begin{bmatrix} 1 & -1 \\ -1 & 1 \end{bmatrix}$$

Since *rank* $\mathscr{O} = 1 < 2$, the system is not observable based on Theorem 11.2.

The unobservability of the system can also be verified based on the relationship between the output response and the initial state according to the definition of observability. The output response due to the initial state is

$$y(t) = Ce^{At}x(0) = 0.5 \begin{bmatrix} 1 & -1 \end{bmatrix} \begin{bmatrix} e^t + e^{-t} & e^t - e^{-t} \\ e^t - e^{-t} & e^t + e^{-t} \end{bmatrix} x(0) = \begin{bmatrix} e^{-t} & -e^{-t} \end{bmatrix} x(0)$$

Taking a derivative of the equation, we obtain

$$\dot{y}(t) = \begin{bmatrix} -e^{-t} & e^{-t} \end{bmatrix} x(0)$$

Combine the two equations into a matrix form:

$$\begin{bmatrix} y(t) \\ \dot{y}(t) \end{bmatrix} = \begin{bmatrix} e^{-t} & -e^{-t} \\ -e^{-t} & e^{-t} \end{bmatrix} x(0)$$

Since the matrix $\begin{bmatrix} e^{-t} & -e^{-t} \\ -e^{-t} & e^{-t} \end{bmatrix}$ **is singular, the initial state** $x(0)$ **cannot be uniquely determined from the information of** $y(t)$ **and its derivatives.** Therefore, according to the definition of observability the system is not observable. ∎

If a system is not observable it is necessary to identify the unobservable physical modes. One way to easily make such an identification is to transform the system to diagonal form (or, more generally into Jordan form). In the following, the system considered in the previous example will be employed to illustrate which part of the system is unobservable.

Example 11.4 (Observable Modes)

Consider the system of Example 11.3. We will compute the eigenvalues λ_1, λ_2 and corresponding eigenvectors v_1, v_2. From the latter define the similarity transformation matrix $T = [v_1, v_2]$ and implement the transformation from the original state x to the new state $\hat{x}$, $\hat{x} = T^{-1}x$ to obtain the transformed system

$$\begin{aligned} \dot{\hat{x}} &= \begin{bmatrix} T^{-1}AT \end{bmatrix} \hat{x} + \begin{bmatrix} T^{-1}B \end{bmatrix} u \\ y &= \begin{bmatrix} CT \end{bmatrix} \hat{x} \end{aligned} \tag{11.3}$$

The eigenvalue-eigenvector pairs of A are:

$$\lambda_1 = -1, \ v_1 = \frac{1}{\sqrt{2}} \begin{bmatrix} -1 \\ 1 \end{bmatrix}, \quad \lambda_2 = 1, \ v_2 = \frac{1}{\sqrt{2}} \begin{bmatrix} 1 \\ 1 \end{bmatrix}$$

Note that there are two real eigenvalues and the first mode is stable. The second one is unstable. Using the two eigenvectors we set up the transformation matrix T and obtain the transformed state equations

$$\dot{\hat{x}} = \begin{bmatrix} -1 & 0 \\ 0 & 1 \end{bmatrix} \hat{x} + \begin{bmatrix} 0 \\ \sqrt{2} \end{bmatrix} u$$

$$y = \begin{bmatrix} \sqrt{2} & 0 \end{bmatrix} \hat{x}$$

We begin with the knowledge (from Example 11.3) that there is one unobservable mode. The new states, $\hat{x}_1, \hat{x}_2$ denote the motion associated with modes 1 and 2, respectively. Observe that the state equations are decoupled. They can be solved one at a time, each independent of the other. Inspection of the transformed CT matrix shows that **the output is not affected by** $\hat{x}_2$, indicating that $\hat{x}_2$ **is the unobservable mode.** ∎

11.1.2 The Observability Decomposition Form

The ability to identify the observable part of a system has control design implications beyond the interpretive mode implications. Here, we discuss the decomposition introduced by Kalman [Kalman, 1963] that separates the observable and the unobservable parts of a linear system.

Theorem 11.5 (Observability Decomposition Form)

Given a linear system in the form

$$\dot{x}(t) = Ax(t) + Bu(t)$$
$$y(t) = Cx(t)$$

with $x \in R^n, u \in R^m, and\, y \in R^p$. If the system is not observable and

$$rank\ \mathcal{O} = r < n$$

then there exists a nonsingular similarity transform matrix T that transforms the original state x to the new state $\hat{x}$, $\hat{x} = T^{-1}x$ such that the transformed system

$$\dot{\hat{x}} = \left[T^{-1}AT\right]\hat{x} + \left[T^{-1}B\right]u = \hat{A}\hat{x} + \hat{B}u$$
$$y = [CT]\hat{x} = \hat{C}\hat{x}$$

has the form

$$\hat{A} = \begin{bmatrix} \hat{A}_{11} & 0 \\ \hat{A}_{21} & \hat{A}_{22} \end{bmatrix}, \quad \hat{B} = \begin{bmatrix} \hat{B}_1 \\ \hat{B}_2 \end{bmatrix} \tag{11.4}$$
$$\hat{C} = \begin{bmatrix} \hat{C}_1 & 0 \end{bmatrix}$$

where $\hat{A}_{11} \in R^{r \times r}$, $\hat{B}_1 \in R^{r \times m}$, $\hat{C}_1 \in R^{p \times r}$, and the subsystem $\{\hat{A}_{11}, \hat{B}_1, \hat{C}_1\}$ is observable.

Proof: *Hint: Choose T such that*

$$T^{-1} = \begin{bmatrix} U_1 \\ U_2 \end{bmatrix} \tag{11.5}$$

where the rows of U_1 are any r linearly independent row vectors of the observability matrix $\mathcal{O}(C,A)$. The rows of U_2 together with those of U_1 span the whole n-dimensional space. ∎

Example 11.6 (Observability Decomposition Form)

Recall that the system considered in Example 11.3 is

$$\dot{x}(t) = Ax(t) + Bu(t) = \begin{bmatrix} 0 & 1 \\ 1 & 0 \end{bmatrix} x(t) + \begin{bmatrix} 1 \\ 1 \end{bmatrix} u(t)$$
$$y(t) = Cx(t) = \begin{bmatrix} 1 & -1 \end{bmatrix} x(t)$$

The observability matrix of the system is

$$\mathcal{O} = \begin{bmatrix} C \\ CA \end{bmatrix} = \begin{bmatrix} 1 & -1 \\ -1 & 1 \end{bmatrix}$$

Since *rank* $\mathcal{O} = 1 < 2$, there is only one linearly independent row vector in $\mathcal{O}$; U_1 is chosen as

$$U_1 = \begin{bmatrix} 1 & -1 \end{bmatrix}$$

and U_2 should be chosen so that the similarity transformation matrix

$$T^{-1} = \begin{bmatrix} U_1 \\ U_2 \end{bmatrix}$$

is nonsingular. Hence, we choose $U_2 = \begin{bmatrix} 0 & 1 \end{bmatrix}$ so that we have

$$T^{-1} = \begin{bmatrix} U_1 \\ U_2 \end{bmatrix} = \begin{bmatrix} 1 & -1 \\ 0 & 1 \end{bmatrix} \quad \rightarrow \quad T = \begin{bmatrix} 1 & 1 \\ 0 & 1 \end{bmatrix}$$

Then the transformed state-space model will be

$$\dot{\hat{x}} = \begin{bmatrix} \hat{A}_{11} & 0 \\ \hat{A}_{21} & \hat{A}_{22} \end{bmatrix} \hat{x} + \begin{bmatrix} \hat{B}_1 \\ \hat{B}_2 \end{bmatrix} u = \begin{bmatrix} -1 & 0 \\ 1 & 1 \end{bmatrix} \hat{x} + \begin{bmatrix} 0 \\ 1 \end{bmatrix} u$$

$$y = \begin{bmatrix} \hat{C}_1 & 0 \end{bmatrix} \hat{x} = \begin{bmatrix} 1 & 0 \end{bmatrix} \hat{x}$$

Note that $\hat{x}_2$ has no effect on the output y; hence, the dynamics associated with $\hat{A}_{22} = 1$ are not observable, while the dynamics associated with $\hat{A}_{11} = -1$ are observable. ∎

Remark 11.7 (Observable and Unobservable Subspaces)

The observable subspace is the range space of the transpose of the observability matrix $\mathcal{O}^T$, while the unobservable subspace is the null space of $\mathcal{O}$. The null space of $\mathcal{O}$ is the orthogonal complement of the range space of $\mathcal{O}^T$.

For the system in Example 11.6, the observable subspace is a one-dimensional space spanned by the linearly independent column vectors of $\mathcal{O}^T$, which is

$$\text{Range}\left(\mathcal{O}^T\right) \quad \sim \quad \begin{bmatrix} 1 \\ -1 \end{bmatrix}$$

The unobservable subspace is

$$\text{Null}\left(\mathcal{O}\right) \quad \sim \quad \begin{bmatrix} 1 \\ 1 \end{bmatrix}$$

which is orthogonal to the range space of $\mathcal{O}^T$.

Note that the space spanned by the vector $U_2^T = [0 \ 1]^T$ of Example 11.6 is not the unobservable subspace although its associated similarity transform T still achieves observability decomposition.

If the similarity transformation matrix

$$T^{-1} = \begin{bmatrix} U_1 \\ U_2 \end{bmatrix}$$

is chosen according to the basis vectors of the range space of $\mathcal{O}^T$ and the null space of $\mathcal{O}$ as

$$T^{-1} = \begin{bmatrix} U_1 \\ U_2 \end{bmatrix} = \begin{bmatrix} 1 & -1 \\ 1 & 1 \end{bmatrix}$$

then the transformed state-space model will be

$$\dot{\hat{x}} = \begin{bmatrix} \hat{A}_{11} & 0 \\ \hat{A}_{21} & \hat{A}_{22} \end{bmatrix} \hat{x} + \begin{bmatrix} \hat{B}_1 \\ \hat{B}_2 \end{bmatrix} u = \begin{bmatrix} -1 & 0 \\ 0 & 1 \end{bmatrix} \hat{x} + \begin{bmatrix} 0 \\ 2 \end{bmatrix} u$$

$$y = \begin{bmatrix} \hat{C}_1 & 0 \end{bmatrix} \hat{x} = \begin{bmatrix} 1 & 0 \end{bmatrix} \hat{x}$$

Although the numbers are slightly different, the structure of the observability decomposition form remains the same and the eigenvalues of $\hat{A}_{11}$ and $\hat{A}_{22}$, respectively, are identical to those obtained in Example 11.6.

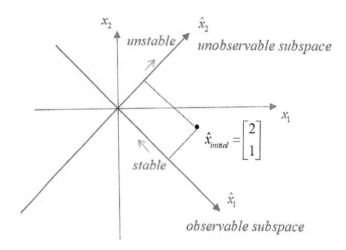

Fig. 11.1: Observable and unobservable subspaces.

The observable and unobservable subspaces of the system are illustrated in Figure 11.1. Assume the initial state is $\hat{x}_{initial}$ is at $[2 \ 1]^T$ position. Since the eigenvalue associated with **the observable subspace spanned by** $\hat{x}_1$ is stable, the position of the state on the $\hat{x}_1$ axis will move from 2 to 0. On the other hand, the eigenvalue associated with **the unobservable subspace spanned by** $\hat{x}_2$ is unstable; hence, the position of the state on the $\hat{x}_2$ axis will grow without bound. Furthermore, no control action can be taken to convert the unstable state $\hat{x}_2$ to become stable because it is unobservable. ∎

11.2 Duality in State Space

For a feedback control system to work, it needs to observe and gather the relevant information for decision making, and once a decision is made, it requires control actions to accomplish the objective. The observation and control processes seem to be completely different; yet surprisingly they are dual to each other, just like left and right hands! We will see that observability and controllability are a duality pair, and the observer design and the state-feedback control design are also a dual. Understanding either one will make it easy to learn the counterpart.

11.2.1 Duality of Controllability and Observability

Recall that for the linear system represented by the state-space model in Equation 11.1,

$$\dot{x}(t) = Ax(t) + Bu(t)$$
$$y(t) = Cx(t) + Du(t)$$

with $x \in R^n, u \in R^m, y \in R^p$. The controllability and observability of the system are, respectively, determined by the rank of the controllability matrix

$$\mathscr{C} = [B \ AB \ A^2B \ \cdots \ A^{n-1}B] \tag{11.6}$$

and by the rank of the observability matrix

$$\mathscr{O} = \begin{bmatrix} C \\ CA \\ \vdots \\ CA^{n-1} \end{bmatrix} \tag{11.7}$$

Since a matrix and its transpose have exactly the same rank, we have

$$rank \ \mathscr{O}^T = rank \ [C^T \ A^T C^T \ (A^T)^2 C^T \ \cdots \ (A^T)^{n-1} C^T] \tag{11.8}$$

which has the same form as the controllability matrix $\mathscr{C}$. Therefore, observability and controllability is a duality pair. **The basic concept and theory developed based on controllability can be easily extended for observability, and the computing resources available for analysis and design relevant to controllability can also be applied to those relevant to observability.**

As we have learned from Example 10.12, the controllable subspace is the range space of the controllability matrix $\mathscr{C}$ and the uncontrollable subspace is the null space of $\mathscr{C}^T$, or

$$Controllable \ subspace \ = \ \text{Range} \ (\mathscr{C}), \quad Uncontrollable \ subspace \ = \ \text{Null} \ (\mathscr{C}^T) \tag{11.9}$$

Owing to duality, it is not surprising to have the following deductions,

$$Observable \ subspace \ = \ \text{Range} \ (\mathscr{O}^T), \quad Unobservable \ subspace \ = \ \text{Null} \ (\mathscr{O}) \tag{11.10}$$

as described in Remark 11.7.

11.2.2 State-Space Models in Controller Form and Observer Form

Recall that a given system can have many state-space models depending on how the state variables are defined. Usually physical variables like displacements, velocities, voltages, and currents are chosen as state variables so that the state-space model can directly reflect the status of the physical variables of interest. However, for computational reasons in the design process, the state-space model may need to be transformed to a special form like a companion form or a diagonal form, discussed in Sections 6.6.2, 7.4.1, and 7.4.2.

The signal flow graph shown in Figure 11.2(a) is a state diagram of the following state-space model:

$$\begin{bmatrix} \dot{x}_1 \\ \dot{x}_2 \end{bmatrix} = \begin{bmatrix} 0 & 1 \\ -a_0 & -a_1 \end{bmatrix} \begin{bmatrix} x_1 \\ x_2 \end{bmatrix} + \begin{bmatrix} 0 \\ 1 \end{bmatrix} u = Ax + Bu$$

$$y = \begin{bmatrix} b_0 & b_1 \end{bmatrix} \begin{bmatrix} x_1 \\ x_2 \end{bmatrix} = Cx \tag{11.11}$$

Note that this state-space model is in companion form, which is also called controller form since state-space model in this form is always controllable. The transfer function associated with the state-space model can be found using either the state-space to transfer function formula,

$$G(s) = C(sI - A)^{-1}B = \frac{\begin{bmatrix} b_0 & b_1 \end{bmatrix} \begin{bmatrix} s+a_1 & 1 \\ -a_0 & s \end{bmatrix} \begin{bmatrix} 0 \\ 1 \end{bmatrix}}{s^2 + a_1 s + a_0} = \frac{b_1 s + b_0}{s^2 + a_1 s + a_0}$$

or Mason's gain formula,

$$G(s) = \frac{M_1 \Delta_1 + M_2 \Delta_2}{\Delta} = \frac{b_1 s^{-1} + b_0 s^{-2}}{1 - (-a_1 s^{-1} - a_0 s^{-2})} = \frac{b_1 s + b_0}{s^2 + a_1 s + a_0}$$

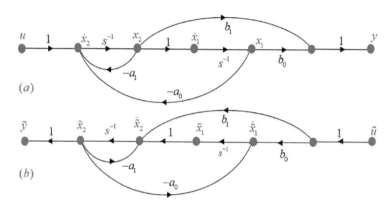

Fig. 11.2: Duality between the controller form and observer form realizations.

Now let us take a look at **the signal flow graph shown in Figure 11.2(b). Its shape is identical to the one shown in Figure 11.2(a), but the signal flow directions are all reversed and the input** u **and output** y **have exchanged positions. For ease of distinction, the state variables in Figure 11.2(b) are marked with** $\tilde{x}_1$ **and** $\tilde{x}_2$. **These two signal flow graphs are dual to each other from a graphical point of view. We would like to investigate the mathematical relationship between the two systems.**

The state-space model associated with the state diagram in Figure 11.2(b) can be found in terms of the state variables $\tilde{x}_1$ and $\tilde{x}_2$:

$$\begin{bmatrix} \dot{\tilde{x}}_1 \\ \dot{\tilde{x}}_2 \end{bmatrix} = \begin{bmatrix} 0 & -a_0 \\ 1 & -a_1 \end{bmatrix} \begin{bmatrix} \tilde{x}_1 \\ \tilde{x}_2 \end{bmatrix} + \begin{bmatrix} b_0 \\ b_1 \end{bmatrix} u = \tilde{A}\tilde{x} + \tilde{B}\tilde{u}$$

$$\tilde{y} = \begin{bmatrix} 0 & 1 \end{bmatrix} \begin{bmatrix} \tilde{x}_1 \\ \tilde{x}_2 \end{bmatrix} = \tilde{C}\tilde{x} \tag{11.12}$$

Notice that the two state-space models have the following relationship:

$$\tilde{A} = A^T, \quad \tilde{B} = C^T, \quad \tilde{C} = B^T \tag{11.13}$$

Hence, the two state-space models, Equations 11.11 and 11.12, or the two state diagrams in Figure 11.2(a) and Figure 11.2(b), are dual to each other. Since the state-space model in controller form is controllable, its dual—the state-space model in Equation 11.12 or the state diagram in Figure 11.2(b)—is referred as the observer form.

The relationship between the two state-space models can be found in the following:

$$\tilde{G}(s) = \tilde{C}(sI - \tilde{A})^{-1}\tilde{B} = B^T (sI - A^T)^{-1}C^T = \left[C(sI - A)^{-1}B \right]^T = G^T(s) \tag{11.14}$$

For the SISO case, these two transfer functions are identical, but for MIMO case, they in general are different.

11.3 Minimal Realization and Controllability and Observability

A minimal state-space model, also referred as minimal realization, means that the number of state variables or the dimension of the A matrix is minimal. **A minimal state-space model is controllable and observable.**

Theorem 11.8 (Minimal Realization and Controllability and Observability)

Given the state-space model (A,B,C),

$$\dot{x}(t) = Ax(t) + Bu(t)$$
$$y(t) = Cx(t)$$

the following three statements are equivalent:

(a) The state-space model (A,B,C) is controllable and observable.

(b) The state-space model (A,B,C) is a minimal realization.

(c) The transfer function $N(s)D^{-1}(s)$ or $D^{-1}(s)N(s)$ associated with (A,B,C) is irreducible.

∎

Remark 11.9 (The Computation Involved in Obtaining an Irreducible Transfer Function Is Complicated and Numerically Unreliable for High-Order Large MIMO Systems)

For SISO cases, the two fractional descriptions, $N(s)D^{-1}(s)$ and $D^{-1}(s)N(s)$, are identical and can be written as $N(s)/D(s)$, which is irreducible if and only if $N(s)$ and $D(s)$ have no common polynomial factors, or, equivalently, there is no possible pole-zero cancellation in $N(s)/D(s)$. However, for MIMO cases, $N(s)D^{-1}(s)$ and $D^{-1}(s)N(s)$ are in general different, and they are called right MFD (matrix fractional description) and left MFD, respectively. An irreducible left or right MFD can be obtained by removing the greatest common left or right divisor from $N(s)$ and $D(s)$, but the computation involved is complicated and may be numerically untrustworthy, especially for high-order, large MIMO systems. **For this reason, we will only employ the first two statements of Theorem 11.8 to determine if a given MIMO state-space model is a minimal realization—in other words, based on the controllability and observability of the model instead of the irreducibility of the MFD.** ∎

Example 11.10 (How Controllability and Observability Affect Minimal Realization)

Consider a system that is represented by the following state-space model in diagonal form:

$$\begin{bmatrix} \dot{x}_1 \\ \dot{x}_2 \\ \dot{x}_3 \end{bmatrix} = \begin{bmatrix} \lambda_1 & 0 & 0 \\ 0 & \lambda_2 & 0 \\ 0 & 0 & \lambda_3 \end{bmatrix} \begin{bmatrix} x_1 \\ x_2 \\ x_3 \end{bmatrix} + \begin{bmatrix} b_1 \\ b_2 \\ b_3 \end{bmatrix} u = Ax + Bu, \quad y = \begin{bmatrix} c_1 & c_2 & c_3 \end{bmatrix} \begin{bmatrix} x_1 \\ x_2 \\ x_3 \end{bmatrix} = Cx$$

According to Theorem 11.8, **the state-space model is a minimal realization if and only if it is controllable and observable.** The controllability matrix of the system is

$$\mathscr{C} = \begin{bmatrix} B \ AB \ A^2B \end{bmatrix} = \begin{bmatrix} b_1 & \lambda_1 b_1 & \lambda_1^2 b_1 \\ b_2 & \lambda_2 b_2 & \lambda_2^2 b_2 \\ b_3 & \lambda_3 b_3 & \lambda_3^2 b_3 \end{bmatrix}$$

The determinant of the controllability matrix is

$$\det \mathscr{C} = b_1 b_2 b_3 \left(\lambda_1 - \lambda_2 \right) \left(\lambda_2 - \lambda_3 \right) \left(\lambda_3 - \lambda_1 \right)$$

Hence, **the system is controllable if and only if** $\det \mathscr{C} \neq 0$, or, **equivalently,** λ_1, λ_2, **and** λ_3 **are distinct and** b_1, b_2, **and** b_3 **are nonzero.** Similarly, we have

$$\det \mathscr{O} = c_1 c_2 c_3 \left(\lambda_1 - \lambda_2 \right) \left(\lambda_2 - \lambda_3 \right) \left(\lambda_3 - \lambda_1 \right)$$

and so the system is observable if and only if λ_1, λ_2, and λ_3 are distinct, and c_1, c_2, and c_3 are nonzero. **Therefore, the state-space model is a minimal realization if and only if** λ_1, λ_2, **and** λ_3 **are distinct, and** b_1, b_2, b_3, c_1, c_2, **and** c_3 **are nonzero.**   ∎

These facts regarding the controllability, observability, and minimal realization can also be interpreted graphically in the following example using the state diagram.

Example 11.11 (Graphical Interpretation of Controllability, Observability, Minimal Realization)

The diagonal state-space model considered in the previous example can be graphically represented by the state diagram shown in Figure 11.3.

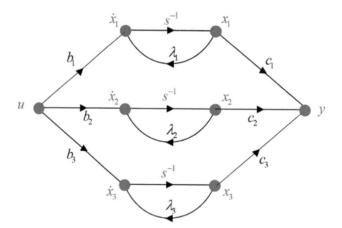

Fig. 11.3: The state-space model is a minimal realization if and only if it is controllable and observable.

It is clear that the system is composed of three subsystems in parallel connection, and the three subsystems are decoupled. The transfer function of the system can be found as

$$\frac{Y(s)}{U(s)} = G(s) = \frac{b_1 c_1}{s - \lambda_1} + \frac{b_2 c_2}{s - \lambda_2} + \frac{b_3 c_3}{s - \lambda_3} \tag{11.15}$$

If one of the input branches, b_1, b_2, b_3, is zero, say $b_1 = 0$, then the branch associated with b_1 in the state diagram will disappear and the control input u will have no effect on the dynamics of the subsystem with eigenvalue λ_1; hence, the system becomes uncontrollable. Meanwhile, the transfer function of Equation 11.15 will become

$$G(s) = \frac{b_2 c_2}{s - \lambda_2} + \frac{b_3 c_3}{s - \lambda_3}$$

which is a second-order system now, and therefore the third-order state-space model is not a minimal realization anymore.

If one of the output branches, c_1, c_2, c_3, is zero, say $c_2 = 0$, then the branch associated with c_2 in the state diagram will disappear and the state x_2 will have no influence on the output y, which means the state of the subsystem with eigenvalue λ_2 becomes unobservable; hence, the system is unobservable. Meanwhile, the transfer function of Equation 11.15 will become

$$G(s) = \frac{b_1 c_1}{s - \lambda_1} + \frac{b_3 c_3}{s - \lambda_3}$$

which is a second-order system now, and so the third-order state-space model is not a minimal realization any longer.

If the eigenvalues λ_1, λ_2, and λ_3, are not distinct, say $\lambda_2 = \lambda_1$, then the top two subsystems in the state diagram will collapse into one subsystem because their eigenvalues are identical. Consequently, the disappeared subsystem will become uncontrollable and unobservable. Meanwhile, the transfer function will become

$$G(s) = \frac{b_1 c_1}{s - \lambda_1} + \frac{b_2 c_2}{s - \lambda_1} + \frac{b_3 c_3}{s - \lambda_3} = \frac{b_1 c_1 + b_2 c_2}{s - \lambda_1} + \frac{b_3 c_3}{s - \lambda_3}$$

which is a second-order system now; hence, the third-order state-space model is not a minimal realization.

Therefore, the state-space model is a minimal realization if and only if λ_1, λ_2, and λ_3 are distinct and b_1, b_2, b_3, c_1, c_2, and c_3 are nonzero. ∎

Remark 11.12 (Minimal Realization and Pole-Zero Cancellation)

Consider the state-space model with the transfer function, Equation 11.15, shown in Example 11.11. Let

$$\lambda_1 = -1, \quad \lambda_2 = -2, \quad \lambda_3 = -3, \quad b_2 = b_3 = c_1 = c_2 = c_3 = 1$$

while keeping b_1 as a free parameter so that the transfer function can be rewritten:

$$\frac{Y(s)}{U(s)} = G(s) = \frac{b_1}{s+1} + \frac{1}{s+2} + \frac{1}{s+3} = \frac{(b_1 + 2)s^2 + (5b_1 + 7s) + (6b_1 + 5)}{(s+1)(s+2)(s+3)}$$

Then the system is controllable and observable and the associated state-space model is a minimal realization if and only if $b_1 \neq 0$ or the transfer function $G(s)$ is irreducible, which means that there is no pole-zero cancellation in $G(s)$. In case that $b_1 = 0$, the transfer function will become

$$G(s) = \frac{2s^2 + 7s + 5}{(s+1)(s+2)(s+3)} = \frac{(s+1)(2s+5)}{(s+1)(s+2)(s+3)}$$

Notice that the denominator and numerator have a common factor $s + 1$. In other words, the transfer function has a pole and a zero at the same location of complex plane. After the pole-zero cancellation, the transfer function will become

$$G(s) = \frac{2s+5}{(s+2)(s+3)}$$

which means that the transfer function before the pole-zero cancellation was reducible.

Similarly, there will be a pole-zero cancellation at $s = \lambda_2$ if c_2 is zero. For another case that has double eigenvalues at λ_1 and the third eigenvalue at λ_2, the pole-zero cancellation will occur at $s = \lambda_1$.

For SISO systems, the irreducibility of the transfer function $N(s)D^{-1}(s)$ can be easily determined by inspecting if the denominator and numerator polynomials have common factors. **However, for MIMO systems, the denominator and numerator of the transfer function are matrices, and it usually requires a more involved procedure to determine if $N(s)D^{-1}(s)$ is irreducible.** ∎

11.4 State-Space Models and Minimal Realizations of MIMO Systems

One of the advantages of the state-space control system analysis and design approaches over the classical control is that they can be applied to MIMO systems as easily as SISO systems if the state-space models are available. Our emphasis up to now has been on SISO systems; however, the knowledge of assembling state-space models, concept of controllability, observability, and minimal realization regarding SISO systems certainly can be extended to MIMO systems, although there are some differences.

In this section, we will discuss how to assemble state-space models based on transfer function matrices or interconnected subsystems with multiple inputs and outputs. The signal flow graph shown in Figure 11.4 represents a MIMO system with two inputs and two outputs consisting of four SISO subsystems $G_{11}(s)$, $G_{12}(s)$, $G_{21}(s)$, and $G_{22}(s)$.

The MIMO system in Figure 11.4 can also be represented by the following transfer function matrix:

$$\begin{bmatrix} y_1(s) \\ y_2(s) \end{bmatrix} = \begin{bmatrix} G_{11}(s) & G_{12}(s) \\ G_{21}(s) & G_{22}(s) \end{bmatrix} \begin{bmatrix} u_1(s) \\ u_2(s) \end{bmatrix} \tag{11.16}$$

11.4.1 Direct Realization Approach to Assemble a MIMO State-Space Model

Assume we have a state-space model for each subsystem of the MIMO system in Figure 11.4. Then by stacking the state vectors of all the subsystems into one we integrate the four subsystems into one state-space model. The order of the overall model should be the sum of the orders of the four subsystems. **However, we will see that even though the subsystem models are all minimal realizations, the overall model is not necessarily a minimal realization.**

Example 11.13 (Direct Realization of a MIMO System)

Consider the MIMO system shown in Figure 11.4, where the transfer functions of the four SISO subsystems are given as

$$G_{11}(s) = \frac{-1}{s+3}, \quad G_{12}(s) = \frac{1}{s+3}, \quad G_{21}(s) = \frac{1}{s}, \quad G_{22}(s) = \frac{1}{s(s+3)}$$

Following the state-space model construction procedure in Section 6.6.2, each state-space model of the four SISO subsystems can be assembled as follows:

(i) $G_{11}(s) = \frac{-1}{s+3}$ $\rightleftarrows$ $(s+3)y_{11}(s) = -u_1(s)$ $\rightleftarrows$ $\begin{aligned}\dot{x}_1 &= -3x_1 - u_1 \\ y_{11} &= x_1\end{aligned}$

(ii) $G_{12}(s) = \frac{1}{s+3}$ $\rightleftarrows$ $(s+3)y_{12}(s) = u_2(s)$ $\rightleftarrows$ $\begin{aligned}\dot{x}_2 &= -3x_2 + u_2 \\ y_{12} &= x_2\end{aligned}$

(iii) $G_{21}(s) = \frac{1}{s}$ $\rightleftarrows$ $sy_{21}(s) = u_1(s)$ $\rightleftarrows$ $\begin{aligned}\dot{x}_3 &= u_1 \\ y_{21} &= x_3\end{aligned}$

(iv) $G_{22}(s) = \frac{1}{s(s+3)}$ $\rightleftarrows$ $(s^2 + 3s)y_{22}(s) = u_2(s)$ $\rightleftarrows$ $\begin{aligned}\begin{bmatrix}\dot{x}_4 \\ \dot{x}_5\end{bmatrix} &= \begin{bmatrix}0 & 1 \\ 0 & -3\end{bmatrix}\begin{bmatrix}x_4 \\ x_5\end{bmatrix} + \begin{bmatrix}0 \\ 1\end{bmatrix}u_2 \\ y_{22} &= \begin{bmatrix}1 & 0\end{bmatrix}\begin{bmatrix}x_4 \\ x_5\end{bmatrix}\end{aligned}$

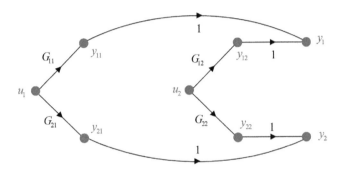

Fig. 11.4: A MIMO system can be an interconnected system of several subsystems with multiple inputs and outputs.

With these state-space models of the four SISO subsystems and the interconnected graph in Figure 11.4, we have the following state-space model for the overall MIMO system:

$$\begin{bmatrix}\dot{x}_1 \\ \dot{x}_2 \\ \dot{x}_3 \\ \dot{x}_4 \\ \dot{x}_5\end{bmatrix} = \begin{bmatrix}-3 & 0 & 0 & 0 & 0 \\ 0 & -3 & 0 & 0 & 0 \\ 0 & 0 & 0 & 0 & 0 \\ 0 & 0 & 0 & 0 & 1 \\ 0 & 0 & 0 & 0 & -3\end{bmatrix}\begin{bmatrix}x_1 \\ x_2 \\ x_3 \\ x_4 \\ x_5\end{bmatrix} + \begin{bmatrix}-1 & 0 \\ 0 & 1 \\ 1 & 0 \\ 0 & 0 \\ 0 & 1\end{bmatrix}\begin{bmatrix}u_1 \\ u_2\end{bmatrix} := Ax + Bu$$

$$\begin{bmatrix}y_1 \\ y_2\end{bmatrix} = \begin{bmatrix}1 & 1 & 0 & 0 & 0 \\ 0 & 0 & 1 & 1 & 0\end{bmatrix}\begin{bmatrix}x_1 \\ x_2 \\ x_3 \\ x_4 \\ x_5\end{bmatrix} := Cx$$

(11.17)

The poles of the MIMO model are simply the eigenvalues of the A matrix, while the zeros can be computed based on the algorithm in Theorem 10.17. By the MATLAB codes:

```
% CSD Ex11.13 MIMO poles zeros
A11=-3; A22=-3; A33=0; A44=[0 1;0 -3]; A=blkdiag(A11,A22,A33,A44);
B=[-1 0;0 1;1 0;0 0;0 1]; C=[1 1 0 0 0;0 0 1 1 0]; D=[0 0;0 0];
```

```
Z=[A  -B;C  -D]; E=blkdiag(eye(5),zeros(2,2));
poles_G=eig(A); disp('Poles of the MIMO state-space model are:'),
poles_G', zeros_G=eig(Z,E);
disp('Zeros of the MIMO state-space model (ignore Inf) are:'), zeros_G'
```

we will have the following results,

```
>>
Poles of the MIMO state-space model are:
   -3    -3     0     0    -3
Zeros of the MIMO state-space model (ignore Inf) are:
     -Inf   -4.0000   -0.0000      Inf       Inf       Inf   -3.0000
```

Therefore, the MIMO state-space model has five poles at $s = -3, -3, -3, 0, 0$, **and three zeros at** $s = -4, -3, 0$.

Next, we will determine if the MIMO state-space model is a minimal realization. This MIMO state-space model is a minimal realization if and only if it is controllable and observable according to Theorem 11.8. In the case that the model is not minimal, the Kalman decomposition approach of Sections 10.3.2 and 11.1.2 will be employed to find a minimal realization of the system by removing the uncontrollable and unobservable modes.

The controllability matrix is

$$
\mathscr{C} = \begin{bmatrix} B\ AB\ A^2B\ A^3B\ A^4B \end{bmatrix} = \begin{bmatrix}
-1 & 0 & 3 & 0 & -9 & 0 & 27 & 0 & -81 & 0 \\
0 & 1 & 0 & -3 & 0 & 9 & 0 & -27 & 0 & 81 \\
1 & 0 & 0 & 0 & 0 & 0 & 0 & 0 & 0 & 0 \\
0 & 0 & 0 & 1 & 0 & -3 & 0 & 9 & 0 & -27 \\
0 & 1 & 0 & -3 & 0 & 9 & 0 & -27 & 0 & 81
\end{bmatrix}
$$

and

$$rank\ \mathscr{C} = 4 < 5 \quad \to \quad system\ is\ uncontrollable$$

The observability matrix is

$$
\mathscr{O} = \begin{bmatrix} C \\ CA \\ CA^2 \\ CA^3 \\ CA^4 \end{bmatrix} = \begin{bmatrix}
1 & 1 & 0 & 0 & 0 \\
0 & 0 & 1 & 1 & 0 \\
-3 & -3 & 0 & 0 & 0 \\
0 & 0 & 0 & 0 & 1 \\
9 & 9 & 0 & 0 & 0 \\
0 & 0 & 0 & 0 & -3 \\
-27 & -27 & 0 & 0 & 0 \\
0 & 0 & 0 & 0 & 9 \\
81 & 81 & 0 & 0 & 0 \\
0 & 0 & 0 & 0 & -27
\end{bmatrix}
$$

and

$$rank\ \mathscr{O} = 3 < 5 \quad \to \quad system\ is\ unobservable$$

There are **two unobservable modes and one uncontrollable mode. We will first perform observability decomposition to remove the two unobservable modes** so that the observable model will be of third order. The uncontrollable mode may be overlapped with the unobservable ones. If that is the case, the observable model will be also controllable, and, therefore the observable model is a minimal realization. Otherwise, controllability decomposition is needed to remove the uncontrollable mode.

Let U_1 and U_2 be

$$U_1 = \begin{bmatrix} 1 & 1 & 0 & 0 & 0 \\ 0 & 0 & 1 & 1 & 0 \\ 0 & 0 & 0 & 0 & 1 \end{bmatrix}, \quad U_2 = \begin{bmatrix} 1 & -1 & 0 & 0 & 0 \\ 0 & 0 & 1 & -1 & 0 \end{bmatrix}$$

where the three row vectors of the U_1 matrix are any three linearly independent row vectors of the observability matrix $\mathcal{O}$, or, in other words, the three column vectors of U_1^T span the three-dimensional observable subspace or the range space of $\mathcal{O}^T$. On the other hand, the two row vectors of U_2 are chosen so that the similarity transformation matrix

$$T^{-1} = \begin{bmatrix} U_1 \\ U_2 \end{bmatrix}$$

is nonsingular and $U_1 U_2^T = 0$. In other words, the column vectors of U_2^T form a basis of the null space of $\mathcal{O}$, which is the orthogonal complement of the observable subspace. This similarity transformation

$$\hat{x} = T^{-1}x$$

transforms the state-space model into the following observability decomposition form:

$$\dot{\hat{x}} = \begin{bmatrix} \hat{A}_{11} & 0 \\ \hat{A}_{21} & \hat{A}_{22} \end{bmatrix}\hat{x} + \begin{bmatrix} \hat{B}_1 \\ \hat{B}_2 \end{bmatrix} u = \begin{bmatrix} -3 & 0 & 0 & 0 & 0 \\ 0 & 0 & 1 & 0 & 0 \\ 0 & 0 & -3 & 0 & 0 \\ 0 & 0 & 0 & -3 & 0 \\ 0 & 0 & -1 & 0 & 0 \end{bmatrix}\hat{x} + \begin{bmatrix} -1 & 1 \\ 1 & 0 \\ 0 & 1 \\ -1 & -1 \\ 1 & 0 \end{bmatrix} u$$

$$y = \begin{bmatrix} \hat{C}_1 & 0 \end{bmatrix}\hat{x} = \begin{bmatrix} 1 & 0 & 0 & 0 & 0 \\ 0 & 1 & 0 & 0 & 0 \end{bmatrix}\hat{x}$$

After deleting the unobservable modes, we have the third-order model $(\hat{A}_{11}, \hat{B}_1, \hat{C}_1)$ for the system, which is observable. Since this third-order observable model is also controllable, it is a minimal realization of the system.

$$\dot{\hat{x}}_{\min} = \hat{A}_{11}\hat{x}_{\min} + \hat{B}_1 u = \begin{bmatrix} -3 & 0 & 0 \\ 0 & 0 & 1 \\ 0 & 0 & -3 \end{bmatrix}\hat{x}_{\min} + \begin{bmatrix} -1 & 1 \\ 1 & 0 \\ 0 & 1 \end{bmatrix} u$$

$$y = \hat{C}_1 \hat{x}_{\min} = \begin{bmatrix} 1 & 0 & 0 \\ 0 & 1 & 0 \end{bmatrix}\hat{x}_{\min}$$

which has three poles at $s = -3, 0, -3$ and one zero at $s = -4$. These three poles are the eigenvalues of the matrix $\hat{A}_{11}$, and the zero $s = -4$ is computed based on the algorithm in Theorem 10.17.

In summary, the fifth-order MIMO state-space model obtained by this direct realization approach is not a minimal realization even though the four individual subsystems' state-space models were all minimal individually. Apparently, one of the two unobservable modes is also uncontrollable. Hence, after removing the unobservable modes we obtained a third-order minimal realization for the MIMO system. ∎

11.4.2 MIMO State-Space Models in Block Controller and Block Observer Forms

In addition to the direct realization approach discussed in Section 11.4.1, there are many ways to construct MIMO state-space models. Recall that in Section 11.2.2, we learned how to construct a state-space model in controller form or in observer form for a given SISO transfer function. These controller form and observer form construction procedures can be extended to MIMO cases.

Block Controller Form

Consider a MIMO system represented by the $p \times m$ transfer function matrix $G(s)$ shown in Figure 11.5. The transfer function matrix $G(s)$ can be rewritten in the form of right MFD (matrix fractional description) as

$$G(s) = \frac{N(s)}{d(s)} = N(s) \cdot D_R^{-1}(s) \quad \text{where} \quad D_R(s) = d(s)I_m \tag{11.18}$$

Let $\xi(s) = D_R(s)^{-1}u(s)$. Then we have the following two equations:

$$D_R(s)\xi(s) = u(s) \tag{11.19a}$$

$$y(s) = N(s) \cdot D_R(s)^{-1}u(s) = N(s) \cdot \xi(s) \tag{11.19b}$$

Assume

$$d(s) = s^2 + a_1 s + a_0 \quad \text{and} \quad N(s) = N_1 s + N_0$$

Then Equations 11.19a and 11.19b will lead to the following:

$$D_R(s)\xi(s) = u(s) \quad \rightarrow \quad (s^2 + a_1 s + a_0)\xi(s) = u(s) \quad \rightleftarrows \quad \ddot{\xi} = -a_1\dot{\xi} - a_0\xi + u \tag{11.20a}$$

$$y(s) = N(s) \cdot \xi(s) \quad \rightarrow \quad y(s) = (N_1 s + N_0)\xi(s) \quad \rightleftarrows \quad y = N_1\dot{\xi} + N_0\xi \tag{11.20b}$$

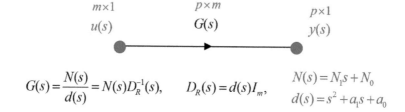

$$G(s) = \frac{N(s)}{d(s)} = N(s)D_R^{-1}(s), \quad D_R(s) = d(s)I_m, \quad \begin{aligned} N(s) &= N_1 s + N_0 \\ d(s) &= s^2 + a_1 s + a_0 \end{aligned}$$

Fig. 11.5: A MIMO transfer function in right MFD for block controller form realization.

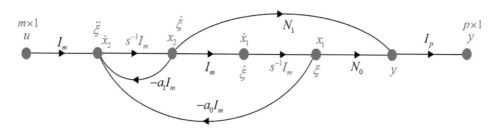

Fig. 11.6: A block controller form realization of a MIMO transfer function in right MFD.

Based on Equations 11.20a and 11.20b, a block controller form realization of the MIMO transfer function in right MFD is constructed and shown in Figure 11.6. With the state vectors x_1 and x_2 assigned at the outputs of the integrators $s^{-1}I_m$, we have the following state-space model equations:

$$\begin{bmatrix} \dot{x}_1 \\ \dot{x}_2 \end{bmatrix} = \begin{bmatrix} 0 & I_m \\ -a_0 I_m & -a_1 I_m \end{bmatrix} \begin{bmatrix} x_1 \\ x_2 \end{bmatrix} + \begin{bmatrix} 0 \\ I_m \end{bmatrix} u := Ax + Bu$$

$$y = \begin{bmatrix} N_0 & N_1 \end{bmatrix} \begin{bmatrix} x_1 \\ x_2 \end{bmatrix} := Cx$$

(11.21)

Example 11.14 (Block Controller Form Realization of a MIMO System)

In this example, we will employ the same MIMO system considered in Example 11.13 to demonstrate the block controller form realization approach. The transfer function matrix of the MIMO system is rewritten in the following in the form of right MFD:

$$G(s) = \begin{bmatrix} -1/(s+3) & 1/(s+3) \\ 1/s & 1/(s(s+3)) \end{bmatrix} = \begin{bmatrix} -s & s \\ s+3 & 1 \end{bmatrix} \begin{bmatrix} s(s+3) & 0 \\ 0 & s(s+3) \end{bmatrix}^{-1} := N(s) \cdot D_R^{-1}(s)$$

That is,

$$a_0 = 0, \quad a_1 = 3, \quad N_0 = \begin{bmatrix} 0 & 0 \\ 3 & 1 \end{bmatrix}, \quad N_1 = \begin{bmatrix} -1 & 1 \\ 1 & 0 \end{bmatrix}$$

Then according to Equation 11.21, we have a state-space model in block controller form for the MIMO system:

$$\dot{x} = \begin{bmatrix} 0 & 0 & 1 & 0 \\ 0 & 0 & 0 & 1 \\ 0 & 0 & -3 & 0 \\ 0 & 0 & 0 & -3 \end{bmatrix} x + \begin{bmatrix} 0 & 0 \\ 0 & 0 \\ 1 & 0 \\ 0 & 1 \end{bmatrix} u := Ax + Bu$$

$$y = \begin{bmatrix} 0 & 0 & -1 & 1 \\ 3 & 1 & 1 & 0 \end{bmatrix} x = Cx$$

The poles of the MIMO model are the eigenvalues of the A matrix, which are $s = -3, -3, 0, 0$. The zeros can be computed based on the algorithm in Theorem 10.17, which are $-4, 0$.

Next, we will determine if the MIMO state-space model is a minimal realization. This MIMO state-space model is a minimal realization if and only if it is controllable and observable according to Theorem 11.8. Since the state-space model is in block controller form, which is always controllable, only the observability of the model needs to be examined.

The observability matrix is

$$\mathcal{O} = \begin{bmatrix} C \\ CA \\ CA^2 \\ CA^3 \end{bmatrix} = \begin{bmatrix} 0 & 0 & -1 & 1 \\ 3 & 1 & 1 & 0 \\ 0 & 0 & 3 & -3 \\ 0 & 0 & 0 & 1 \\ 0 & 0 & -9 & 9 \\ 0 & 0 & 0 & -3 \\ 0 & 0 & 27 & -27 \\ 0 & 0 & 0 & 9 \end{bmatrix}$$

and

$$rank\ \mathcal{O} = 3 < 4 \quad \rightarrow \quad system\ is\ unobservable$$

There is one unobservable mode. The Kalman decomposition approach of Section 11.1.2 will be employed to find a minimal realization of the system by removing the unobservable mode.

Let U_1 and U_2 be

$$U_1 = \begin{bmatrix} 0 & 0 & -1 & 1 \\ 3 & 1 & 1 & 0 \\ 0 & 0 & 0 & 1 \end{bmatrix}, \quad U_2 = \begin{bmatrix} -1 & 3 & 0 & 0 \end{bmatrix}$$

where the three row vectors of the U_1 matrix are any three linearly independent row vectors of the observability matrix $\mathcal{O}$, or, in other words, the three column vectors of U_1^T span the three-dimensional observable subspace or the range space of $\mathcal{O}^T$. On the other hand, the row vector of U_2 is chosen so that the similarity transformation matrix

$$T^{-1} = \begin{bmatrix} U_1 \\ U_2 \end{bmatrix}$$

is nonsingular and $U_1 U_2^T = 0$. In other words, the column vectors of U_2^T form a basis of the null space of $\mathcal{O}$, which is the orthogonal complement of the observable subspace. This similarity transform

$$\hat{x} = T^{-1}x$$

transforms the state-space model into the following observability decomposition form:

$$\dot{\hat{x}} = \begin{bmatrix} \hat{A}_{11} & 0 \\ \hat{A}_{21} & \hat{A}_{22} \end{bmatrix} \hat{x} + \begin{bmatrix} \hat{B}_1 \\ \hat{B}_2 \end{bmatrix} u = \begin{bmatrix} -3 & 0 & 0 & 0 \\ 0 & 0 & 1 & 0 \\ 0 & 0 & -3 & 0 \\ 1 & 0 & 2 & 0 \end{bmatrix} \hat{x} + \begin{bmatrix} -1 & 1 \\ 1 & 0 \\ 0 & 1 \\ 0 & 0 \end{bmatrix} u$$

$$y = \begin{bmatrix} \hat{C}_1 & 0 \end{bmatrix} \hat{x} = \begin{bmatrix} 1 & 0 & 0 & 0 \\ 0 & 1 & 0 & 0 \end{bmatrix} \hat{x}$$

where the third-order subsystem $(\hat{A}_{11}, \hat{B}_1, \hat{C}_1)$ is observable. Note that this third-order observable model is also controllable. **After removing the unobservable mode, we have a minimal realization of the system**

$$\dot{\hat{x}}_{min} = \hat{A}_{11} \hat{x}_{min} + \hat{B}_1 u = \begin{bmatrix} -3 & 0 & 0 \\ 0 & 0 & 1 \\ 0 & 0 & -3 \end{bmatrix} \hat{x}_{min} + \begin{bmatrix} -1 & 1 \\ 1 & 0 \\ 0 & 1 \end{bmatrix} u$$

$$y = \hat{C}_1 \hat{x}_{min} = \begin{bmatrix} 1 & 0 & 0 \\ 0 & 1 & 0 \end{bmatrix} \hat{x}_{min}$$

which has three poles at $s = -3, 0, -3$ and one zero at $s = -4$. These three poles are the eigenvalues of the matrix $\hat{A}_{11}$, and the zero $s = -4$ is computed based on the algorithm in Theorem 10.17.

In summary, although the fourth-order MIMO state-space model obtained by the block controller form realization approach is still not minimal, it has less order than that of the direct realization approach. After removing the unobservable mode, we have obtained a third-order minimal realization. ∎

Block Observer Form

Consider a MIMO system represented by the $p \times m$ transfer function matrix $G(s)$ shown in Figure 11.7. The transfer function matrix $G(s)$ can be rewritten in the form of left MFD (matrix fractional description) as

$$G(s) = \frac{N(s)}{d(s)} = D_L^{-1}(s) \cdot N(s) \quad \text{where} \quad D_L(s) = d(s)I_p \tag{11.22}$$

Recall that the state-space model in block controller form shown in Equation 11.21 was derived from a MIMO transfer function in right MFD following a procedure similar to that of the SISO controller form.

Now, to find the counterpart of the block controller form associated with a MIMO transfer function in left MFD, we want to take advantage of the duality property instead of deriving it from scratch. In the following, we will use the short-hand notation

$$G(s) = N(s) \cdot (d(s)I_m)^{-1} \quad \rightleftarrows \quad \left(\begin{bmatrix} 0 & I_m \\ -a_0 I_m & -a_1 I_m \end{bmatrix}, \begin{bmatrix} 0 \\ I_m \end{bmatrix}, [N_0 \ N_1] \right) \tag{11.23}$$

to represent the relationship between the right MFD, $N(s) \cdot (d(s)I_m)^{-1}$, and the state-space model in block controller form shown in Equation 11.21.

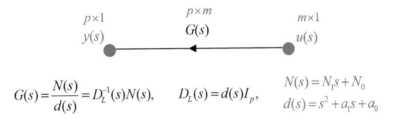

$$G(s) = \frac{N(s)}{d(s)} = D_L^{-1}(s)N(s), \qquad D_L(s) = d(s)I_p, \qquad \begin{aligned} N(s) &= N_1 s + N_0 \\ d(s) &= s^2 + a_1 s + a_0 \end{aligned}$$

Fig. 11.7: A MIMO transfer function in left MFD for block observer form realization.

Now, the transpose of $G(s) = (d(s)I_p)^{-1} \cdot N(s)$ is $G^T(s) = N^T(s) \cdot (d(s)I_p)^{-1}$, which is in the form of right MFD. Hence, by using the relationship in Equation 11.23 we have the following:

$$G^T(s) = N^T(s) \cdot (d(s)I_p)^{-1} \quad \rightleftarrows \quad \left(\begin{bmatrix} 0 & I_p \\ -a_0 I_p & -a_1 I_p \end{bmatrix}, \begin{bmatrix} 0 \\ I_p \end{bmatrix}, [N_0^T \ N_1^T] \right) \tag{11.24}$$

Then, taking transpose on both sides of the relationship will give the block observer form associated with the left MFD $G(s) = (d(s)I_p)^{-1} \cdot N(s)$:

$$G(s) = (d(s)I_p)^{-1} \cdot N(s) \quad \rightleftarrows \quad \left(\begin{bmatrix} 0 & -a_0 I_p \\ I_p & -a_1 I_p \end{bmatrix}, \begin{bmatrix} N_0 \\ N_1 \end{bmatrix}, [0 \ I_p] \right) \tag{11.25}$$

Therefore, the MIMO transfer function in left MFD $(d(s)I_p)^{-1} \cdot N(s)$ has a state-space model in block observer form as the following:

$$\begin{bmatrix} \dot{x}_1 \\ \dot{x}_2 \end{bmatrix} = \begin{bmatrix} 0 & -a_0 I_p \\ I_p & -a_1 I_p \end{bmatrix} \begin{bmatrix} x_1 \\ x_2 \end{bmatrix} + \begin{bmatrix} N_0 \\ N_1 \end{bmatrix} u = Ax + Bu$$
$$y = [0 \ I_p] \begin{bmatrix} x_1 \\ x_2 \end{bmatrix} = Cx \tag{11.26}$$

The state diagram associated with the state-space model in block observer form is shown in Figure 11.8. Notice that the shape of the graphs in Figure 11.8 is the same as that of Figure 11.6, but the directions of the signal flow are reversed and the positions of the input and the output have exchanged. These two state diagrams are dual to each other.

Example 11.15 (Block Observer Form Realization of a MIMO System)

In this example, we will employ the same MIMO system considered in Example 11.13 and Example 11.14 to demonstrate the block observer form realization approach. The transfer function matrix of the MIMO system is rewritten in the following in the form of left MFD:

$$G(s) = \begin{bmatrix} -1/(s+3) & 1/(s+3) \\ 1/s & 1/(s(s+3)) \end{bmatrix} = \begin{bmatrix} s(s+3) & 0 \\ 0 & s(s+3) \end{bmatrix}^{-1} \begin{bmatrix} -s & s \\ s+3 & 1 \end{bmatrix} := D_L^{-1}(s) \cdot N(s)$$

That is,

$$a_0 = 0, \quad a_1 = 3, \quad N_0 = \begin{bmatrix} 0 & 0 \\ 3 & 1 \end{bmatrix}, \quad N_1 = \begin{bmatrix} -1 & 1 \\ 1 & 0 \end{bmatrix}$$

Then according to Equation 11.26, we have a state-space model in block observer form for the MIMO system:

$$\dot{x} = \begin{bmatrix} 0 & 0 & 0 & 0 \\ 0 & 0 & 0 & 0 \\ 1 & 0 & -3 & 0 \\ 0 & 1 & 0 & -3 \end{bmatrix} x + \begin{bmatrix} 0 & 0 \\ 3 & 1 \\ -1 & 1 \\ 1 & 0 \end{bmatrix} u := Ax + Bu$$

$$y = \begin{bmatrix} 0 & 0 & 1 & 0 \\ 0 & 0 & 0 & 1 \end{bmatrix} x = Cx$$

The poles of the MIMO model are the eigenvalues of the A matrix, which are $s = -3, -3, 0, 0$. The zeros can be computed based on the algorithm in Theorem 10.17, which are $-4, 0$.

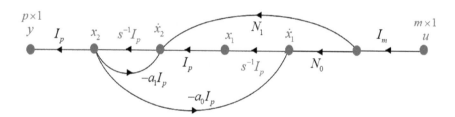

Fig. 11.8: A block observer form realization of a MIMO transfer function in left MFD.

Next, we will determine if the MIMO state-space model is a minimal realization. This MIMO state-space model is a minimal realization if and only if it is controllable and observable according to Theorem 11.8. Since the state-space model is in block observer form, which is always observable, only the controllability of the model needs to be examined.

The controllability matrix is

$$\mathscr{C} = \begin{bmatrix} B & AB & A^2B & A^3B \end{bmatrix} = \begin{bmatrix} 0 & 0 & 0 & 0 & 0 & 0 & 0 & 0 \\ 3 & 1 & 0 & 0 & 0 & 0 & 0 & 0 \\ -1 & 1 & 3 & -3 & -9 & 9 & 27 & -27 \\ 1 & 0 & 0 & 1 & 0 & -3 & 0 & 0 \end{bmatrix}$$

and

$$rank\ \mathscr{C} = 3 < 4 \quad \rightarrow \quad system\ is\ uncontrollable$$

There is one uncontrollable mode. The Kalman decomposition approach of Section 10.3.2 will be employed to find a minimal realization of the system by removing the uncontrollable mode.

Let T_1 and T_2 be

$$T_1 = \begin{bmatrix} 0 & 0 & 0 \\ 1 & 0 & 0 \\ 1 & 3 & -3 \\ 0 & 0 & 1 \end{bmatrix}, \quad T_2 = \begin{bmatrix} 1 \\ 0 \\ 0 \\ 0 \end{bmatrix}$$

where the three column vectors of the T_1 matrix are any three linearly independent column vectors of the controllability matrix $\mathscr{C}$, or, in other words, the three column vectors of T_1 span the three-dimensional controllable subspace or the range space of $\mathscr{C}$.

On the other hand, the column vector of T_2 is chosen so that the similarity transformation matrix

$$T = \begin{bmatrix} T_1 & T_2 \end{bmatrix}$$

is nonsingular and $T_1^T \cdot T_2 = 0$. In other words, the column vectors of T_2 form a basis of the null space of $\mathscr{C}^T$, which is the orthogonal complement of the controllable subspace. This similarity transformation

$$\hat{x} = T^{-1}x$$

transforms the state-space model into the controllability decomposition form

$$\dot{\hat{x}} = \begin{bmatrix} \hat{A}_{11} & \hat{A}_{12} \\ 0 & \hat{A}_{22} \end{bmatrix}\hat{x} + \begin{bmatrix} \hat{B}_1 \\ 0 \end{bmatrix}u = \begin{bmatrix} 0 & 0 & 0 & 0 \\ 0 & -3 & 0 & 1/3 \\ 1 & 0 & -3 & 0 \\ 0 & 0 & 0 & 0 \end{bmatrix}\hat{x} + \begin{bmatrix} 3 & 1 \\ -1/3 & 0 \\ 1 & 0 \\ 0 & 0 \end{bmatrix}u$$

$$y = \begin{bmatrix} \hat{C}_1 & \hat{C}_2 \end{bmatrix}\hat{x} = \begin{bmatrix} 1 & 3 & -3 & 0 \\ 0 & 0 & 1 & 0 \end{bmatrix}\hat{x}$$

where the third-order subsystem $(\hat{A}_{11}, \hat{B}_1, \hat{C}_1)$ is controllable. Note that this third-order controllable model is also observable.

After removing the uncontrollable mode, we have a minimal realization of the system,

$$\dot{\hat{x}}_{min} = \hat{A}_{11}\hat{x}_{min} + \hat{B}_1 u = \begin{bmatrix} 0 & 0 & 0 \\ 0 & -3 & 0 \\ 1 & 0 & -3 \end{bmatrix}\hat{x}_{min} + \begin{bmatrix} 3 & 1 \\ -1/3 & 0 \\ 1 & 0 \end{bmatrix}u$$

$$y = \hat{C}_1\hat{x}_{min} = \begin{bmatrix} 1 & 3 & -3 \\ 0 & 0 & 1 \end{bmatrix}\hat{x}_{min}$$

which has three poles at $s = -3, 0, -3$ and one zero at $s = -4$. These three poles are the eigenvalues of the matrix $\hat{A}_{11}$, and the zero $s = -4$ is computed based on the algorithm in Theorem 10.17.

In summary, although the fourth-order MIMO state-space model obtained by this block observer form realization approach is still not minimal, it has less order than that of the direct realization approach. After removing the uncontrollable mode, we have obtained a third-order minimal realization. ∎

11.4.3 MIMO State-Space Models in Gilbert Diagonal Form

Gilbert diagonal realization is a natural generalization of the SISO diagonal realization. Consider a $p \times m$ MIMO system with a transfer function matrix

$$G(s) = \frac{N(s)}{d(s)} \tag{11.27}$$

where $d(s) = (s - \lambda_1)(s - \lambda_2)\cdots(s - \lambda_\ell)$, $\lambda_i \neq \lambda_j$, $\deg N(s) < \ell$. Let $G(s)$ be written as

$$G(s) = \frac{R_1}{s - \lambda_1} + \frac{R_2}{s - \lambda_2} + \cdots + \frac{R_\ell}{s - \lambda_\ell} \quad \text{where} \quad R_i = \lim_{s \to \lambda_i}(s - \lambda_i)G(s) \tag{11.28}$$

and assume R_i can be decomposed as

$$R_i = C_i B_i \quad \text{where} \quad C_i \in R^{p \times r_i}, \quad B_i \in R^{r_i \times m} \quad \text{and} \quad r_i = \operatorname{rank} R_i \tag{11.29}$$

Then it is easy to verify that the state-space model (A, B, C) with

$$A = \begin{bmatrix} \lambda_1 I_{r_1} & 0 & \cdots & 0 \\ 0 & \lambda_2 I_{r_2} & \cdots & 0 \\ 0 & 0 & \ddots & 0 \\ 0 & 0 & \cdots & \lambda_\ell I_{r_\ell} \end{bmatrix}, \quad B = \begin{bmatrix} B_1 \\ B_2 \\ \vdots \\ B_\ell \end{bmatrix}, \quad C = \begin{bmatrix} C_1 & C_2 & \cdots & C_\ell \end{bmatrix} \tag{11.30}$$

is a state-space model of $G(s)$, and the dimension of the state space is $n = \sum_{i=1}^{\ell} r_i$.

Example 11.16 (Gilbert Diagonal Realization of a MIMO System)

In this example, we will employ the same MIMO system considered in Example 11.13, Example 11.14, and Example 11.15 to demonstrate the Gilbert diagonal realization approach. The transfer function matrix of the MIMO system is rewritten

$$G(s) = \begin{bmatrix} -1/(s+3) & 1/(s+3) \\ 1/s & 1/(s(s+3)) \end{bmatrix} = \frac{1}{s(s+3)}\begin{bmatrix} -s & s \\ s+3 & 1 \end{bmatrix} = \frac{R_1}{s} + \frac{R_2}{s+3}$$

where

$$R_1 = \lim_{s \to 0} sG(s) = \begin{bmatrix} 0 & 0 \\ 1 & 1/3 \end{bmatrix} = \begin{bmatrix} 0 \\ 1 \end{bmatrix}\begin{bmatrix} 1 & 1/3 \end{bmatrix} := C_1 B_1$$

$$R_2 = \lim_{s \to -3}(s+3)G(s) = \begin{bmatrix} -1 & 1 \\ 0 & -1/3 \end{bmatrix} I_2 := C_2 B_2$$

Hence, the state-space model (A, B, C) with

$$A = \begin{bmatrix} 0 & 0 \\ 0 & -3I_2 \end{bmatrix} = \begin{bmatrix} 0 & 0 & 0 \\ 0 & -3 & 0 \\ 0 & 0 & -3 \end{bmatrix}, \quad B = \begin{bmatrix} B_1 \\ B_2 \end{bmatrix} = \begin{bmatrix} 1 & 1/3 \\ 1 & 0 \\ 0 & 1 \end{bmatrix}$$

$$C = \begin{bmatrix} C_1 & C_2 \end{bmatrix} = \begin{bmatrix} 0 & -1 & 1 \\ 1 & 0 & -1/3 \end{bmatrix}$$

is a Gilbert diagonal realization, which has three poles at $s = -3, -3$, and 0, and one zero at $s = -4$.

The controllability matrix is

$$\mathscr{C} = \begin{bmatrix} B & AB & A^2B \end{bmatrix} = \begin{bmatrix} 1 & 1/3 & 0 & 0 & 0 & 0 \\ 1 & 0 & -3 & 0 & 9 & 0 \\ 0 & 1 & 0 & -3 & 0 & 9 \end{bmatrix}$$

and

$$rank\ \mathscr{C}\ =\ 3 \quad \rightarrow \quad system\ is\ controllable$$

The observability matrix is

$$\mathscr{O} = \begin{bmatrix} C \\ CA \\ CA^2 \end{bmatrix} = \begin{bmatrix} 0 & -1 & 1 \\ 1 & 0 & -1/3 \\ 0 & 3 & -3 \\ 0 & 0 & 1 \\ 0 & -9 & 9 \\ 0 & 0 & -3 \end{bmatrix}$$

and

$$rank\ \mathscr{O}\ =\ 3 \quad \rightarrow \quad system\ is\ observable$$

Therefore, the Gilbert diagonal realization is minimal. ∎

Theorem 11.17 (Gilbert Realization is Minimal)

Gilbert realization is controllable and observable and therefore is a minimal realization.

Proof: *Based on the Gilbert diagonal realization defined by Equations 11.28, 11.29, and 11.30, the controllability matrix can be written as*

$$\mathscr{C} = \begin{bmatrix} B & AB & \cdots & A^{n-1}B \end{bmatrix} = \begin{bmatrix} B_1 & \lambda_1 B_1 & \cdots & \lambda_1^{n-1} B_1 \\ B_2 & \lambda_2 B_2 & \cdots & \lambda_2^{n-1} B_2 \\ \vdots & \vdots & \cdots & \vdots \\ B_\ell & \lambda_\ell B_\ell & \cdots & \lambda_\ell^{n-1} B_\ell \end{bmatrix}$$

which can be decomposed into a product of two matrices as

$$\mathscr{C} = \begin{bmatrix} B_1 & 0 & \cdots & 0 \\ 0 & B_2 & \cdots & 0 \\ 0 & 0 & \ddots & 0 \\ 0 & 0 & \cdots & B_\ell \end{bmatrix} \begin{bmatrix} I_m & \lambda_1 I_m & \cdots & \lambda_1^{n-1} I_m \\ I_m & \lambda_2 I_m & \cdots & \lambda_2^{n-1} I_m \\ \vdots & \vdots & \cdots & \vdots \\ I_m & \lambda_\ell I_m & \cdots & \lambda_\ell^{n-1} I_m \end{bmatrix} := \mathscr{B} \cdot \mathscr{U}$$

Note that the dimensions of $\mathscr{B}$ and $\mathscr{U}$ are $n \times \ell m$ and $\ell m \times \ell m$, respectively, where $n = \sum_{i=1}^{\ell} r_i$. It is easy to see that the rank of $\mathscr{U}$ is ℓm; hence, $\mathscr{U}$ is nonsingular. By Sylvester's inequality,

$$\text{rank}(\mathscr{B}) + \text{rank}(\mathscr{U}) - \ell m \leq \text{rank}(\mathscr{C}) \leq \min\{\text{rank}(\mathscr{B}), \text{rank}(\mathscr{U})\}$$

we have $\text{rank}(\mathscr{C}) = \text{rank}(\mathscr{B})$. By the Gilbert construction,

$$\text{rank}(\mathscr{B}) = \sum_{1}^{\ell} \text{rank}(\mathscr{B}_i) = \sum_{1}^{\ell} r_i = n$$

Therefore, the realization is controllable. The observability can be proved similarly. ∎

Remark 11.18 (Comparison of MIMO State-Space Model Construction Approaches)

So far in this chapter, we have learned a few MIMO state-space model construction approaches to obtain state-space models in direct realization, block controller form, block observer form, and Gilbert diagonal form. The Gilbert diagonal realization is controllable and observable and therefore is a minimal realization. The restriction of this approach is that the least common denominator of all the entries of the MIMO transfer function matrix, like $d(s)$ in Equation 11.27, is required to have no repeated zeros (i.e., $\lambda_i \neq \lambda_j$).

The other approaches do not have this restriction; however, they usually lead to nonminimal realizations. The block controller form is always controllable, but usually unobservable with order equal to ℓm, where m is the number of inputs and $\ell = \deg d(s)$. The block observer form is always observable but usually uncontrollable with order equal to ℓp, where p is the number of outputs and $\ell = \deg d(s)$. The direct realization is usually uncontrollable and unobservable with order equal to the sum of the orders of all SISO subsystems. For nonminimal realizations, the Kalman decomposition approach of Sections 10.3.2 and 11.1.2 can be employed to find a minimal realization of the system by removing the uncontrollable and unobservable modes.

There exist other approaches to construct minimal realizations directly without the need of using the Kalman decomposition. For example, a MIMO transfer function can be represented by a general right MFD as $G(s) = N(s) \cdot D^{-1}(s)$. A greatest common right divisor $R(s)$ can be found and extracted from $D(s) = D_1(s)R(s)$ and $N(s) = N_1(s)R(s)$ to reduce $G(s)$ to an irreducible MFD, $G(s) = N_1(s) \cdot D_1^{-1}(s)$, then a state-space model constructed based on the irreducible MFD will be a minimal realization. Details regarding the irreducible MFD and greatest common right divisors can be found in the book by [Kailath, 1980]. ∎

11.5 Full-Order Observer and Output Feedback Control

Recall that we witnessed the power of the state-space controller when the four magic numbers in the state-feedback gain matrix $F = \begin{bmatrix} 139.31 & 24.452 & 30.138 & 30.67 \end{bmatrix}$ of Equation 7.120 in Section 7.6.4 were employed to successfully stabilize a highly unstable cart-inverted pendulum system. Later, in Sections 8.6.3, and 8.7, we learned more about the **state-feedback control and utilized it to work together with the pole placement approach, the root locus design, and the regulation/tracking theory** to solve the lightly damped system control problem, and achieve aircraft altitude regulation and flight path precision tracking. In Chapter 10, the **linear quadratic performance optimization with control-input constraint** was incorporated in the state-feedback control system design process to achieve an optimal control.

However, it is rare that all state variables are available and not contaminated in the measurement process. The state feedback concept would be impractical if not for the invention of the ingenious full-order observer. The brilliant **observer theory was invented to utilize not only the measured output but also the actuation input, the noise model, and the system model to determine an optimal estimate of all state variables.**

As mentioned earlier, there is a **duality relationship between the observer theory and the state-feedback control theory.** The knowledge and tools for state-feedback control can immediately be applied to the design and implementation of observers. Furthermore, as two subsystems of the controller, **they work together perfectly:** the observer is responsible to provide timely accurate assessment of the system states for the state-feedback controller to make the right decision and achieve the desired performance. In addition, we will see that **the observer and the state-feedback controller** can be designed separately without interfering each other; this important property is referred as the *separation principle*.

11.5.1 Brief Review of State-Feedback Control

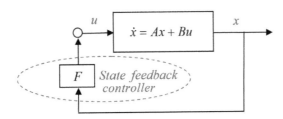

Fig. 11.9: A basic state-feedback control system.

In the following, we will briefly review the structure of the state-feedback control system. Then we will see **the extension of it to the output feedback control system is fairly straightforward: Simply add a full-order observer.**

The block diagram shown in Figure 11.9 representing the basic state-feedback control system is simple and can be easily implemented, yet it is effective if the state equation of the state-space model, $\dot{x} = Ax + Bu$, is given and all the state variables are available for feedback. The control law is, $u = Fx$, where F is a constant gain matrix to be determined so that the closed-loop system is stable and has a desired performance. By desired performance, it usually means that the specifications regarding the following are satisfied: robust stability, steady-state error, transient response, control-input constraints, and so on.

There are two main approaches available in designing the state-feedback gain matrix F. **One is the pole placement approach and the other is the linear quadratic optimization approach.** The pole placement approach can be effective if we know where the desired pole locations should be for the closed-loop system. Although the system behavior and performance are mainly determined by the pole locations of the system, it is by no means an easy task to find an optimal set of pole locations, especially for high-order systems. On the other hand, for the linear quadratic optimization approach, the issue is in the choice of the weighting matrices in the performance index integral. The guideline is to assign more weight on the state variable of interest, but it may not work if this state variable is implicitly affected by another state variable, which we wrongfully ignore. Therefore, **the pole placement or the weighting matrix need to be properly selected according to the system dynamics to achieve desired closed-loop system performance.**

Note that the basic state-feedback control system structure shown in Figure 11.9 works for any fixed operating condition control problem, like the cart-inverted pendulum control problem in Section 7.6 or the simple inverted pendulum control problem considered in Section 10.5.3.

On the other hand, **if the operating condition is required to follow a time-varying command or a tracking signal, then the basic state-feedback control system structure needs to be modified to include a tracking regulator like the one shown in Figure 10.8 of Section 10.2.4 for the pendulum positioning system.**

11.5.2 Observer-Based Controller

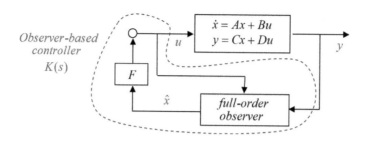

Fig. 11.10: A basic output feedback control system with full-order observer.

For the state-feedback control problem, all the state variables in x are assumed available for feedback. However, in some practical applications, not all state variables are available for feedback. Instead, the measured output is given together with the state equation as follows:

$$\dot{x} = Ax + Bu$$
$$y = Cx + Du \tag{11.31}$$

where $x \in R^n, u \in R^m, y \in R^p$.

Since only the measured output $y(t)$, instead of the state vector, is available for feedback, a full-order observer is constructed to generate $\hat{x}$, which is an estimate of x, to serve as a substitute of x for state-feedback control. That is,

$$u = F\hat{x} \tag{11.32}$$

Then, from Figure 11.10, it can be seen that the output feedback controller, also referred as the observer-based controller, includes the full-order observer and the state-feedback gain F matrix inside the dash-line enclosure.

Structure of the Full-Order Observer

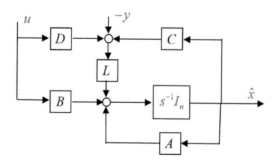

Fig. 11.11: Structure of the full-order observer.

The structure of the full-order observer is shown in Figure 11.11. The dynamics equation of the full-order observer, with u and y as the inputs and $\hat{x}$ as the state vector of the observer, is given by the *observer equation*:

$$\dot{\hat{x}} = A\hat{x} + Bu + L(C\hat{x} + Du - y)$$

which can be rewritten as

$$\dot{\hat{x}} = (A + LC)\hat{x} + \begin{bmatrix} B + LD & -L \end{bmatrix} \begin{bmatrix} u \\ y \end{bmatrix} \tag{11.33}$$

Note that the state-space model, (A, B, C, D), the input u, and the output y of the plant (i.e., the system to be controlled), are employed to construct the observer. **The only parameter matrix to be determined in the design process is L, which is referred as the observer gain matrix.** The observer itself is an n-th order dynamic system represented by a state equation with state vector $\hat{x}$ and input vector $\begin{bmatrix} u \\ y \end{bmatrix}$. The **stability of the observer is determined by $A + LC$.** The observer gain L can be chosen to make the observer stable (i.e., the eigenvalues of $A + LC$ are on the left-hand side of the complex plane) if and only if (C, A) is detectable. **The observer has to be stable since the steady-state reconstruction error $\varepsilon(t) = x(t) - \hat{x}(t)$ can only be zero if the observer is stable,** as shown in the following theorem.

Theorem 11.19 (Reconstruction Error of the Full-Order Observer)

Consider the plant of Equation 11.31 and its associated full-order observer described by Equation 11.33. Let the reconstruction error be $\varepsilon(t) = x(t) - \hat{x}(t)$. Show that

$$\varepsilon(t) \to 0 \quad \text{as} \quad t \to \infty \quad \text{for all initial error } \varepsilon(0)$$

if and only if the observer is stable, or the eigenvalues of $A + LC$ are on the left-hand side of the complex plane.

Proof: *Since*

$$\dot{\varepsilon}(t) = \dot{x}(t) - \dot{\hat{x}}(t) = Ax + Bu - A\hat{x} - LC\hat{x} - Bu - LDu + Ly$$
$$= Ax - A\hat{x} - LC\hat{x} - LDu + L(Cx + Du)$$

we have the differential equation,

$$\dot{\varepsilon}(t) = (A + LC)\varepsilon(t)$$

which yields the solution $\varepsilon(t) = e^{(A+LC)t}\varepsilon(0)$.   ∎

11.5.3 Design of Observer-Based Output Feedback Controller

Now, we can combine the three parts of the closed-loop system: the state-space model of the plant in Equation 11.31, the state-space model of the full-order observer in Equation 11.33, and the state-feedback controller in Equation 11.32 together and show them on the same graph in Figure 11.12. The plant model is in red, whose input u and output y are fed into the full-order observer, which is in black, to generate $\hat{x}$, which is an estimate of the state x. Then the state vector of the observer, $\hat{x}$ is fed back to the state-feedback gain matrix block F, which is in blue, to generate the control-input vector u to close the loop. **Notice that the observer-based output feedback controller is the combination of the full-order observer and the state-feedback controller;** hence, the state-space model of the observer-based output feedback controller can be derived from the block diagram of Figure 11.12.

Obviously, the output of the controller is u and the input to the controller is y. **The state vector of the observer also serves as the state vector of the output feedback controller.** From the block diagram of the closed-loop system in Figure 11.12, we have the state equation of the observer and the state-feedback equation in the following:

$$\dot{\hat{x}} = A\hat{x} + Bu + L(C\hat{x} + Du - y)$$
$$u = F\hat{x}$$

Replacing the control input u in the state equation by $F\hat{x}$ so that the state equation only has y as its input, then these two equations become

$$\dot{\hat{x}} = (A + BF + LC + LDF)\hat{x} - Ly := A_k\hat{x} + B_k y$$
$$u = F\hat{x} := C_k\hat{x} \tag{11.34}$$

This is the state-space model of the observer-based output feedback controller, (A_k, B_k, C_k), where

$$A_k = A + BF + LC + LDF, \quad B_k = -L, \quad C_k = F$$

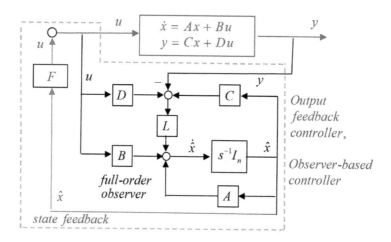

Fig. 11.12: State-space model of the observer-based output feedback controller.

Theorem 11.20 (Regulator Poles and Observer Poles)

For the closed-loop system with the observer-based controller shown in Figure 11.12, the closed-loop system poles are the regulator poles (the eigenvalues of $A + BF$) together with the observer poles (the eigenvalues of $A + LC$).

Proof:

From the state-space model of the plant in Equation 11.31 and the state-space model of the observer-based controller in Equation 11.34, we have the state equation of the closed-loop system as

$$\dot{x} = Ax + Bu = Ax + BF\hat{x}$$
$$\dot{\hat{x}} = (A + BF + LC + LDF)\hat{x} - Ly = (A + BF + LC + LDF)\hat{x} - L(Cx + DF\hat{x})$$

which is rewritten in matrix form as

$$\begin{bmatrix} \dot{x} \\ \dot{\hat{x}} \end{bmatrix} = \begin{bmatrix} A & BF \\ -LC & A + BF + LC \end{bmatrix} \begin{bmatrix} x \\ \hat{x} \end{bmatrix}$$

Hence, the closed-loop system poles are the roots of

$$\det \begin{bmatrix} sI - A & -BF \\ LC & sI - (A + BF + LC) \end{bmatrix} = 0$$

Since

$$\begin{bmatrix} I & 0 \\ -I & I \end{bmatrix} \begin{bmatrix} sI - A & -BF \\ LC & sI - (A + BF + LC) \end{bmatrix} \begin{bmatrix} I & 0 \\ I & I \end{bmatrix} = \begin{bmatrix} sI - (A + BF) & -BF \\ 0 & sI - (A + LC) \end{bmatrix}$$

we have

$$\det \begin{bmatrix} sI - A & -BF \\ LC & sI - (A + BF + LC) \end{bmatrix} = \det(sI - (A + BF)) \cdot \det(sI - (A + LC))$$

Therefore, the closed-loop system poles are the eigenvalues of $A + BF$ together with the eigenvalues of $A + LC$. ∎

Remark 11.21 (Design of the Output Feedback Controller)

Owing to Theorem 11.20 and the separation principle, the regulator poles and the observer poles can be independently chosen to meet the closed-loop performance requirement. Therefore, the key steps in designing a state-space output feedback controller are to find the regulator gain matrix F and the observer gain matrix L so that the regulator poles (the eigenvalues of $A + BF$) and the observer poles (the eigenvalues of $A + LC$) are at the desired locations on the left half complex plane. These two gain matrices can be obtained using the pole placement approach given in Sections 7.5 and 7.6.4 or the performance index optimization approach discussed in Sections 10.5.1 and 10.5.2. ∎

Example 11.22 (An Observer-Based Controller Design Using Pole Placement)

Consider the system

$$\dot{x}(t) = Ax(t) + Bu(t) = \begin{bmatrix} 0 & 0 \\ 1 & 0 \end{bmatrix} x(t) + \begin{bmatrix} 1 \\ 0 \end{bmatrix} u(t)$$

$$y(t) = Cx(t) = \begin{bmatrix} 1 & 1 \end{bmatrix} x(t) \tag{11.35}$$

To find the regulator gain matrix $F = \begin{bmatrix} f_1 & f_2 \end{bmatrix}$ so that the eigenvalues of $A + BF$ are at $-1 \pm j$, we should have

$$A + BF = \begin{bmatrix} 0 & 0 \\ 1 & 0 \end{bmatrix} + \begin{bmatrix} 1 \\ 0 \end{bmatrix} \begin{bmatrix} f_1 & f_2 \end{bmatrix} = \begin{bmatrix} f_1 & f_2 \\ 1 & 0 \end{bmatrix}$$

that gives

$$|\lambda I - (A + BF)| = \left| \begin{bmatrix} \lambda - f_1 & -f_2 \\ -1 & \lambda \end{bmatrix} \right| = \lambda^2 - f_1 \lambda - f_2 = \lambda^2 + 2\lambda + 2 = (\lambda + 1)^2 + 1$$

Hence,

$$f_1 = -2 \quad \text{and} \quad f_2 = -2$$

Next, we would like to find the observer gain matrix L so that the eigenvalues of $A + LC$ are at $-\sqrt{3} \pm j$. Let $L = \begin{bmatrix} \ell_1 & \ell_2 \end{bmatrix}^T$, then

$$A + LC = \begin{bmatrix} 0 & 0 \\ 1 & 0 \end{bmatrix} + \begin{bmatrix} \ell_1 \\ \ell_2 \end{bmatrix} \begin{bmatrix} 1 & 1 \end{bmatrix} = \begin{bmatrix} \ell_1 & \ell_1 \\ 1 + \ell_2 & \ell_2 \end{bmatrix}$$

Thus,

$$|\lambda I - (A + CL)| = \left| \begin{bmatrix} \lambda - \ell_1 & -\ell_1 \\ -1 - \ell_2 & \lambda - \ell_2 \end{bmatrix} \right| = \lambda^2 - (\ell_1 + \ell_2)\lambda + \ell_1(2\ell_2 - 1) = \lambda^2 + 2\sqrt{3}\lambda + 4$$

which gives

$$\ell_1 = -4 \quad \text{and} \quad \ell_2 = 0.5359$$

Now, according to Equation 11.34 the observer-based output feedback controller is

$$\dot{\hat{x}} = A_k \hat{x} + B_k y$$
$$u = C_k \hat{x}$$

(11.36)

where

$$A_k = A + BF + LC = \begin{bmatrix} -6 & -6 \\ 1.5359 & 0.5359 \end{bmatrix}, \quad B_k = -L = \begin{bmatrix} 4 \\ -0.5359 \end{bmatrix}, \quad C_k = F = \begin{bmatrix} -2 & -2 \end{bmatrix}$$

Now the plant model, Equation 11.35, and the observer-based controller, Equation 11.36, together construct a closed-loop system with the following state equation:

$$\begin{bmatrix} \dot{x} \\ \dot{\hat{x}} \end{bmatrix} = \begin{bmatrix} Ax + Bu \\ A_k \hat{x} + B_k y \end{bmatrix} = \begin{bmatrix} Ax + BC_k \hat{x} \\ A_k \hat{x} + B_k Cx \end{bmatrix} = \begin{bmatrix} A & BC_k \\ B_k C & A_k \end{bmatrix} \begin{bmatrix} x \\ \hat{x} \end{bmatrix}$$

$$= \begin{bmatrix} 0 & 0 & -2 & -2 \\ 1 & 0 & 0 & 0 \\ 4 & 4 & -6 & -6 \\ -0.5359 & -0.5359 & 1.5359 & 0.5359 \end{bmatrix} \begin{bmatrix} x \\ \hat{x} \end{bmatrix} := A_{CL} \begin{bmatrix} x \\ \hat{x} \end{bmatrix}$$

The eigenvalues of A_{CL}, the closed-loop system poles, can be found as $-1 \pm j$ and $-\sqrt{3} \pm j$, which are the eigenvalues of $A + BF$ together with the eigenvalues of $A + LC$, as shown in Theorem 11.20. ∎

The numerical results can be verified by running the following MATLAB code:

```
% CSD Ex11.22 Observer-based control Pole placement
 % Find F to place the regulator poles, eigenvalues of A+BF
A=[0 0;1 0]; B=[1;0]; C=[1 1]; P=[-1+i,-1-i];
F=place(A,B,P); F=-F,
eig_ABF=eig(A+B*F),
 % Find L to place the observer poles, eigenvalues of A+LC
At=A'; Bt=C'; Ct=B'; Pt=[-sqrt(3)+i,-sqrt(3)-i];
Ft=place(At,Bt,Pt); Ft=-Ft; L=Ft',
eig_ALC=eig(A+L*C),
 % Find the closed-loop system poles
Ak=A+B*F+L*C, Bk=-L, Ck=F, A_cl=[A  B*Ck;Bk*C Ak],
eig_cl=eig(A_cl)
```

11.6 LQG Control Problem and the H_2 Control Theory

The H_2 control problem formulation considers a more general set of the H_2 norm optimization problems than the LQG (linear quadratic Gaussian) control problem. We will start from a brief description of the LQG control problem, of which the solution requires an observer to provide an optimal estimate of all state variables and an optimal state-feedback control to minimize a performance index. Then we will describe the standard H_2 control problem formulation and solutions according to the celebrated Doyle, Glover, Khargonekar, and Francis paper [Doyle et al., 1989].

11.6.1 The LQG Control Problem

Consider the state-space model of the system P,

$$P: \begin{aligned} \dot{x}(t) &= Ax(t) + Bu(t) + W_d d(t) \\ y(t) &= Cx(t) + W_n n(t) \end{aligned} \tag{11.37}$$

where A, $W_d \in R^{n \times n}$, $B \in R^{n \times m}$, $C \in R^{p \times n}$, $W_n \in R^{p \times p}$, and the variables $x(t)$, $y(t)$, $u(t)$, $d(t)$, and $n(t)$ are the state vector, measured output, control input, disturbance input, and measurement noise, respectively. The pairs (A, B) and (C, A) are stabilizable and the detectable, respectively. The disturbance input $d(t)$ and the measurement noise $n(t)$ are assumed white noises with the covariances $E[d(t)d^T(t+\tau)] = I_n \delta(\tau)$ and $E[n(t)n^T(t+\tau)] = I_p \delta(\tau)$, respectively.

The objective of the LQG (Linear Quadratic Gaussian) control problem is to design an output feedback controller (A_k, B_k, C_k),

$$K: \begin{aligned} \dot{x}_K(t) &= A_K x_K(t) + B_K y(t) \\ u(t) &= C_K x_K(t) \end{aligned} \tag{11.38}$$

so that the closed-loop system is stable and the performance index

$$PI = E\left[\int_0^\infty \left(x^T(t) W_x^T W_x x(t) + u^T(t) W_u^T W_u u(t) \right) \, dt \right] \tag{11.39}$$

is minimized, where $E[\cdot]$ stands for the expected value.

Next, we will describe the standard H_2 control problem formulation and solutions. Then we will rephrase the LQG control problem in the standard H_2 control problem format so that the standard H_2 control solution formula can be applied to the LQG control problem.

11.6.2 The Standard H_2 Control Problem

The standard H_2 control problem formulation starts from a generalized plant G with state-space model given by the equation,

$$G: \begin{aligned} \dot{x}(t) &= Ax(t) + B_1 w(t) + B_2 u(t) \\ z(t) &= C_1 x(t) + + D_{12} u(t) \\ y(t) &= C_2 x(t) + D_{21} w(t) \end{aligned} \tag{11.40}$$

which can be rewritten in matrix form as follows:

$$G: \begin{bmatrix} \dot{x}(t) \\ z(t) \\ y(t) \end{bmatrix} = \begin{bmatrix} A & B_1 & B_2 \\ C_1 & 0 & D_{12} \\ C_2 & D_{21} & 0 \end{bmatrix} \begin{bmatrix} x(t) \\ w(t) \\ u(t) \end{bmatrix} \tag{11.41}$$

This state-space model has two output vectors: the measured output vector $y(t)$, which consists of all the measurable signals available for feedback, and the controlled output vector $z(t)$, which is composed of tracking error, disturbance response and control-input costs. The generalized plant also has two input vectors: the control-input vector $u(t)$ as usual and the exogenous input $w(t)$ that may include the disturbance input, measurement noise, and reference input/command.

The matrices $A \in R^{n \times n}$, $B_1 \in R^{n \times m_1}$, $B_2 \in R^{n \times m_2}$, $C_1 \in R^{p_1 \times n}$, $C_2 \in R^{p_2 \times n}$, $D_{12} \in R^{p_1 \times m_2}$, $D_{21} \in R^{p_2 \times m_1}$ are assumed to satisfy the following conditions:

$$
\text{(i)} \quad (A, B_2) \text{ is stabilizable and } (C_2, A) \text{ is detectable.}
$$

$$
\text{(ii)} \quad D_{12}^T \begin{bmatrix} C_1 \ D_{12} \end{bmatrix} = \begin{bmatrix} 0 \ I \end{bmatrix} \quad \text{and} \quad \begin{bmatrix} B_1 \\ D_{21} \end{bmatrix} D_{21}^T = \begin{bmatrix} 0 \\ I \end{bmatrix} \tag{11.42}
$$

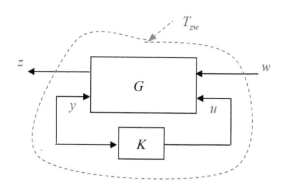

Fig. 11.13: Closed-loop system with generalized plant G and controller K.

The objective of the H_2 control problem is to find a controller

$$
K : \quad \begin{aligned} \dot{x}_K(t) &= A_K x_K(t) + B_K y(t) \\ u(t) &= C_K x_K(t) \end{aligned} \tag{11.43}
$$

so that the closed-loop system shown in Figure 11.13 is internally stable and the H_2 norm of the closed-loop system transfer function from w to z, $\|T_{zw}\|_2$, is minimized.

Now, before we get into the solution of the problem we need to digress a little bit to review some background materials, like how to find a state-space model for the closed-loop system transfer function T_{zw}, the physical meaning of the H_2 norm, and the relevant computation algorithms. We will organize these review materials in the form of exercises, definitions, theorems, and remarks.

Exercise 11.23 (The Closed-Loop Transfer Function T_{zw} in the System Shown in Figure 11.13)

Since the generalized plant G has two input vectors, w and u, and two output vectors, z and y, it can be broken down into four subsystems, G_{11}, G_{12}, G_{21}, and G_{22}. Thus,

$$
\begin{bmatrix} z \\ y \end{bmatrix} = G \begin{bmatrix} w \\ u \end{bmatrix} = \begin{bmatrix} G_{11} & G_{12} \\ G_{21} & G_{22} \end{bmatrix} \begin{bmatrix} w \\ u \end{bmatrix} \quad \rightleftharpoons \quad \begin{aligned} z &= G_{11}w + G_{12}u \\ y &= G_{21}w + G_{22}u \end{aligned}
$$

With the feedback control, $u = Ky$, the closed-loop transfer function from w to z can be found as follows:

$$z(s) = \left[G_{11}(s) + G_{12}(s)K(s)(I - G_{22}(s)K(s))^{-1}G_{21}(s) \right] w(s) := T_{zw}(s)w(s) \tag{11.44}$$

Proof: Left as an exercise.   ∎

Exercise 11.24 (The State-Space Model of T_{zw} in the System Shown in Figure 11.13)

For ease of computation, we will use a state-space model of T_{zw} instead of the s-domain transfer function obtained in Exercise 11.23. The state-space model of T_{zw} can be found by combining the generalized plant model in Equation 11.40 and the controller model in Equation 11.43 as follows:

$$\begin{bmatrix} \dot{x} \\ \dot{x}_K \end{bmatrix} = \begin{bmatrix} A & B_2 C_K \\ B_K C_2 & A_K \end{bmatrix} \begin{bmatrix} x \\ x_K \end{bmatrix} + \begin{bmatrix} B_1 \\ B_K D_{21} \end{bmatrix} w$$

$$z = \begin{bmatrix} C_1 & D_{12} C_K \end{bmatrix} \begin{bmatrix} x \\ x_K \end{bmatrix} \tag{11.45}$$

Proof: Left as an exercise.   ∎

Remark 11.25 (H_2 Norm of a SISO System $P(s)$)

Assume $Z(s) = P(s)V(s)$, where the output $z(t)$, input $v(t)$, and the impulse response $p(t)$ are the inverse Laplace transforms of $Z(s)$, $V(s)$, and $P(s)$, respectively. The definition of the square of the H_2 norm of $P(s)$ is defined as

$$\|P\|_2^2 := \frac{1}{2\pi} \int_{-\infty}^{\infty} |P(j\omega)|^2 d\omega \tag{11.46}$$

which by Parseval's theorem, we have

$$\|P\|_2^2 = \|p\|_2^2 := \int_0^{\infty} |p(t)|^2 dt \tag{11.47}$$

Assume the input is a unit impulse function $v(t) = \delta(t)$; then, $Z(s) = P(s)$, which implies $\|P\|_2^2 = \|p\|_2^2 = \|z\|_2^2$. Therefore, **the H_2 norm of the system is the square root of the total energy of the impulse response of the system, or is the square root of the output energy of the system driven by a unit impulse input. For MIMO systems, the square of the H_2 norm of the system is the sum of the total output energies at the outputs of the system driven by unit impulse function at all inputs.**   ∎

Definition 11.26 (Controllability and Observability Grammians)

For a stable system $G(s) = (A, B, C)$, the controllability and observability grammians are defined as

$$L_c = \int_0^{\infty} e^{At} BB^T e^{A^T t} dt \quad \text{and} \quad L_o = \int_0^{\infty} e^{A^T t} C^T C e^{At} dt$$

respectively.   ∎

Theorem 11.27 (Computation of Controllability and Observability Grammians)

The controllability grammian $L_c = \int\limits_0^\infty e^{At} BB^T e^{A^T t} dt$ satisfies the Lyapunov equation

$$AL_c + L_c A^T + BB^T = 0$$

The observability grammian $L_o = \int\limits_0^\infty e^{A^T t} C^T C e^{At} dt$ satisfies the Lyapunov equation

$$A^T L_o + L_o A + C^T C = 0$$

∎

Theorem 11.28 (Computation of H_2 Norm)

For a stable system $G(s) = (A, B, C)$, the H_2 norm of the system is

$$\|G\|_2 = \sqrt{trace\left(CL_c C^T\right)} = \sqrt{trace\left(B^T L_o B\right)}.$$

∎

11.6.3 Solutions to the Standard H_2 Control Problem

The key steps to obtain the solution for the standard H_2 control problem are to find the optimal state-feedback gain matrix F and the optimal observer gain matrix L.

The optimal state-feedback gain matrix F is

$$F = -B_2^T X \tag{11.48}$$

where X is the stabilizing solution of the algebraic Riccati equation [Zhou et al., 1995, Kailath, 1980],

$$A^T X + XA - XB_2 B_2^T X + C_1^T C_1 = 0 \tag{11.49}$$

with the corresponding Hamiltonian matrix [Zhou et al., 1995, Kailath, 1980],

$$H = \begin{bmatrix} A & -B_2 B_2^T \\ -C_1^T C_1 & -A^T \end{bmatrix} \tag{11.50}$$

The optimal observer gain matrix L is

$$L = -YC_2^T \tag{11.51}$$

where Y is the stabilizing solution of the algebraic Riccati equation

$$AY + YA^T - YC_2^T C_2 Y + B_1 B_1^T = 0 \tag{11.52}$$

with the corresponding Hamiltonian matrix

$$J = \begin{bmatrix} A^T & -C_2^T C_2 \\ -B_1 B_1^T & -A \end{bmatrix} \tag{11.53}$$

Then the optimal H_2 controller is

$$K_{opt}(s): \quad \begin{aligned} \dot{x}_K(t) &= (A + B_2 F + LC_2)x_K(t) - Ly(t) \\ u(t) &= Fx_K(t) \end{aligned} \tag{11.54}$$

and the minimum H_2 norm is

$$\min \|T_{zw}\|_2^2 = \|G_c B_1\|_2^2 + \|FG_f\|_2^2 = \|G_c L\|_2^2 + \|C_1 G_f\|_2^2 \tag{11.55}$$

where

$$\begin{aligned} G_c &= (A + B_2 F, \ I, \ C_1 + D_{12}F) \\ G_f &= (A + LC_2, \ B_1 + L_2 D_{21}, \ I) \end{aligned} \tag{11.56}$$

11.6.4 Application of the Standard H_2 Control Formula

In the following, the H_2 control solution formulas shown in the previous subsection, Section 11.6.3, will be employed to solve the LQG control problem described in Section 11.6.1.

Recall that the LQG control problem is to minimize the performance index of Equation 11.39 and one of the main objectives of the H_2 control problem is to minimize $\|T_{zw}\|_2$, the H_2 norm of the closed-loop system transfer function T_{zw}. To equalize these two measures, the controlled output of the generalized plant has to be defined as

$$z(t) = \begin{bmatrix} W_x x(t) \\ W_u u(t) \end{bmatrix} := \begin{bmatrix} e(t) \\ v(t) \end{bmatrix} \tag{11.57}$$

where $e(t) = W_x x(t)$ and $v(t) = W_u u(t)$ represent the weighted error and the weighted control input constraint. The weighting matrices here play the same roles as $Q = W_x^T W x$ and $R = W_u^T W_u$ in the LQR control problem we studied in Chapter 10. Meanwhile, the disturbance input $d(t)$ and the measurement noise $n(t)$ are grouped together as the exogenous input vector:

$$w(t) := \begin{bmatrix} d(t) \\ n(t) \end{bmatrix} \tag{11.58}$$

Now, with the definition of z and w, and together with the LQG plant model P given in Equation 11.37, we have the following generalized plant model for the LQG problem:

$$G_{LQG}: \quad \begin{bmatrix} \dot{x}(t) \\ \begin{bmatrix} e(t) \\ v(t) \end{bmatrix} \\ y(t) \end{bmatrix} = \begin{bmatrix} A & \begin{bmatrix} W_d & 0 \end{bmatrix} & B \\ \begin{bmatrix} W_x \\ 0 \end{bmatrix} & \begin{matrix} 0 & 0 \\ 0 & 0 \end{matrix} & \begin{bmatrix} 0 \\ W_u \end{bmatrix} \\ C & \begin{bmatrix} 0 & W_n \end{bmatrix} & 0 \end{bmatrix} \begin{bmatrix} x(t) \\ \begin{bmatrix} d(t) \\ n(t) \end{bmatrix} \\ u(t) \end{bmatrix} \tag{11.59}$$

To satisfy the generalized plant assumptions in Equation 11.42, we rescale the control input $u(t)$ and the noise input $n(t)$,

$$u(t) \ \rightarrow \ \hat{u}(t) = W_u u(t), \qquad n(t) \ \rightarrow \ \hat{n}(t) = W_n n(t) \tag{11.60}$$

so that the generalized plant becomes

$$\hat{G}_{LQG}: \quad \begin{bmatrix} \dot{x}(t) \\ \begin{bmatrix} e(t) \\ v(t) \end{bmatrix} \\ y(t) \end{bmatrix} = \begin{bmatrix} A & \begin{bmatrix} W_d & 0 \end{bmatrix} & BW_u^{-1} \\ \begin{bmatrix} W_x \\ 0 \end{bmatrix} & \begin{matrix} 0 & 0 \\ 0 & 0 \end{matrix} & \begin{bmatrix} 0 \\ I \end{bmatrix} \\ C & \begin{bmatrix} 0 & I \end{bmatrix} & 0 \end{bmatrix} \begin{bmatrix} x(t) \\ \begin{bmatrix} d(t) \\ \hat{n}(t) \end{bmatrix} \\ \hat{u}(t) \end{bmatrix} \tag{11.61}$$

According to the standard H_2 control notations, we have the following matrices for the generalized plant:

$$A = A, \quad B_1 = \begin{bmatrix} W_d & 0 \end{bmatrix}, \quad B_2 = BW_u^{-1}$$

$$C_1 = \begin{bmatrix} W_x \\ 0 \end{bmatrix}, \quad D_{12} = \begin{bmatrix} 0 \\ I \end{bmatrix} \tag{11.62}$$

$$C_2 = C, \quad D_{21} = \begin{bmatrix} 0 & I \end{bmatrix}$$

Now, we are ready to work on the following demonstration example.

Example 11.29 (LQG/H_2 Output Feedback Controller for the Simple Inverted Pendulum)

In Section 4.4.3, a state-feedback controller $u = Fx = \begin{bmatrix} -34 & -7.4 \end{bmatrix} x$ was designed based on the pole placement approach to place the closed-loop system poles at $-4 \pm j3$ so that the damping ratio and the natural frequency are $\varsigma = 0.8$ and $\omega_n = 5$ rad/s, respectively. The same simple inverted pendulum system was employed again in Section 10.5.3 to demonstrate how to formulate a state-feedback control problem as an LQR optimization problem, especially on the selection of the Q and R weighting matrices in the performance index.

In this LQG/H_2 control problem formulation, the selection of W_x (part of C_1 in the generalized plant) and W_u (part of D_{12} before changing $u(t)$ to $\hat{u}(t)$) is equivalent to that of Q and R since $Q = W_x^T W_x$ and $R = W_u^T W_u$. For ease of comparison, we will employ the same simple inverted pendulum dynamics model—linearized model for design and nonlinear model for simulation—to validate the output feedback LQG/H_2 control system design.

The linearized state-space model of the nonlinear simple inverted pendulum dynamics of Equation 10.43 at the unstable equilibrium $x^* = \begin{bmatrix} 0 & 0 \end{bmatrix}^T$ is

$$\dot{x}(t) = Ax(t) + Bu(t) + W_d d(t) = \begin{bmatrix} 0 & 1 \\ 9 & -0.6 \end{bmatrix} x(t) + \begin{bmatrix} 0 \\ 1 \end{bmatrix} u(t) + W_d d(t)$$

$$y(t) = Cx(t) + W_n n(t) = \begin{bmatrix} 1 & 0 \end{bmatrix} x(t) + W_n n(t) \tag{11.63}$$

Notice that the output $y(t)$ consists of only one state variable, $x_1(t) = \theta(t)$, the angular displacement of the pendulum stick, contaminated with the measurement noise $n(t)$.

Owing to the separation principle, the designs of the state feedback and the observer do not interfere with each other. Since in Example 10.25 we had already designed the state-feedback part using the LQR approach, which is actually half of the LQG/H_2 control design, we will select the equivalent weighting matrices in the performance index as

$$W_x = \begin{bmatrix} \sqrt{1000} & 0 \\ 0 & \sqrt{20} \end{bmatrix} \quad \text{and} \quad W_u = \sqrt{1.2}$$

Notice that the W_x and W_u are equivalent to the Q and R selected in Example 10.25.

For the weighting matrices W_d and W_n in the observer design, the trade-off between W_d and W_n is very similar to that between W_x and W_n. Recall that only the relative weights are important in determining the trade-off of the weighting matrices, so we will fix W_n at $W_n = 1$ and have three cases of design based on the selection of the weighting matrix W_d:

$$\textbf{Case A}: \ W_d = \begin{bmatrix} 100 \\ 0 \end{bmatrix}, \quad \textbf{Case B}: \ W_d = \begin{bmatrix} 10 \\ 0 \end{bmatrix}, \quad \textbf{Case C}: \ W_d = \begin{bmatrix} 1 \\ 0 \end{bmatrix} \tag{11.64}$$

Now, with these matrices in the generalized plant,

$$A = \begin{bmatrix} 0 & 1 \\ 9 & -0.6 \end{bmatrix}, \quad B_1 = \begin{bmatrix} W_d & 0 \end{bmatrix} = \begin{bmatrix} 100 & 0 \\ 0 & 0 \end{bmatrix}, \quad B_2 = BW_u^{-1} = \begin{bmatrix} 0 \\ 1/\sqrt{1.2} \end{bmatrix}$$

$$C_1 = \begin{bmatrix} W_x \\ 0 \end{bmatrix} = \begin{bmatrix} \sqrt{1000} & 0 \\ 0 & \sqrt{20} \\ 0 & 0 \end{bmatrix}, \quad D_{12} = \begin{bmatrix} 0 \\ 0 \\ 1 \end{bmatrix}, \quad C_2 = C = \begin{bmatrix} 1 & 0 \end{bmatrix}, \quad D_{21} = \begin{bmatrix} 0 & 1 \end{bmatrix}$$

(11.65)

we can solve the two algebraic Riccati equations, compute the state-feedback gain matrix F and the observer gain matrix L, and complete the LQG/H_2 controller design.

The stabilizing solution of the state-feedback Riccati equation

$$A^T X + XA - XB_2 B_2^T X + C_1^T C_1 = 0$$

is

$$X = \begin{bmatrix} 361.08 & 47.086 \\ 47.086 & 11.007 \end{bmatrix}$$

and the state-feedback gain is

$$F = -B_2^T X = \begin{bmatrix} -42.983 & -10.048 \end{bmatrix}$$

Note that this F matrix here is a factor W_u different from the F obtained in Example 10.25. Actually the design is exactly identical; the difference is the mathematical scaling defined by Equation 11.60. The regulator poles (i.e., the eigenvalues of $A + B_2 F$), are

$$-4.8863 \pm j2.5224$$

which are exactly the same as those obtained in Example 10.25.

For the observer design in Case A, the stabilizing solution of the observer Riccati equation

$$AY + YA^T - YC_2^T C_2 Y + B_1 B_1^T = 0$$

is

$$Y = \begin{bmatrix} 100.10 & 9.6136 \\ 9.6136 & 67.186 \end{bmatrix}$$

and the observer gain is

$$L = -YC_2^T = \begin{bmatrix} -100.10 \\ -9.6136 \end{bmatrix}$$

The observer poles (i.e., the eigenvalues of $A + LC_2$) are

$$-100.09 \quad \text{and} \quad -0.60617$$

The Simulink simulation diagram is shown in Figure 11.14, which is almost the same as that shown in Figure 10.19 except the controller now is an output feedback controller instead of the state feedback one.

Three LQG/H_2 controllers are designed according to different selections of the weighting matrices W_d and W_n. **The simulation results of Case A with $W_d = \begin{bmatrix} 100 & 0 \end{bmatrix}^T$, $W_n = 1$ are shown in blue on Figure 11.15. The blue initial state responses, $x_1(t)$, $x_2(t)$, and $u(t)$, are almost as good as their** counterparts shown in Figure 10.22, which used the same state-feedback gain matrix F. Thus, the Case A LQG/H_2 controller places the two regulator poles, eigenvalues of $A + B_2F$, at exactly the same locations: $-4.8863 \pm j2.5224$. The only difference is that the LQG/H_2 controller adds two observer poles, -100.09 and -0.60617, to the system as the result of selecting weighting matrix $W_d = [100 \ 0]^T$, $W_n = 1$ in *Case A* observer design. For Case A design, the addition of the observer poles has only slightly reduced the performance compared with the perfect state feedback case.

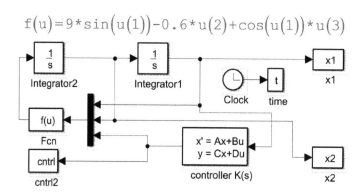

Fig. 11.14: The diagram of the Simulink program, `SIP_SSNLmodel.mdl`, used in the simulation.

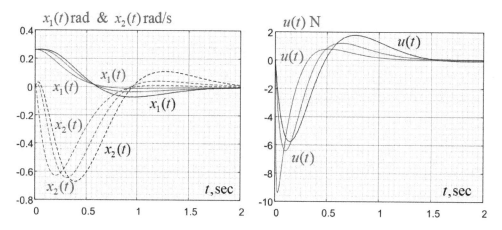

Fig. 11.15: Simulation results of the three cases LQG/H_2 controller performance.

For Case B design, the design of the state-feedback part remains the same, still placing the $A + B_2F$ eigenvalues at the same $-4.8863 \pm j2.5224$. But the observer weighting matrices are changed to $W_d = [1 \ 0]^T$, $W_n = 1$, which leads the observer poles (i.e., the eigenvalues of $A + LC_2$), to -10.833 and 0.99845. The initial state response associated with Case B's design is also shown in Figure 11.15, but in red. The response of Case B design is a little bit worse than that of Case A design.

In Case C design, the weighting matrix W_d is further reduced to $W_d = [1 \ 0]^T$, $W_n = 1$. **The regulator parts are still unchanged, but the two observer poles have moved to new locations:** -3.6322 **and** -2.4833. **The initial state response associated with Case C design is also shown in Figure 11.15, but in brown. It is obvious that the brown response is not as good as the other two.**

From the simulation results, we can see that when the disturbance weight W_d is chosen to be much larger than W_n, the control design will emphasize disturbance response recovery more than the noise effect reduction. On the other hand, if the noise reduction is more urgent, the designer would increase W_n or reduce W_d. ∎

The MATLAB codes used to conduct the computation and simulation are given in the following:

```
% CSD_ex11p29.m  May 10, 2020  SIP H2 Cntrl
% This program, CSD_ex11p29.m, will Call Simulink file: SIP_SSNLmodel.mdl
% automatically to conduct simulations and call SIP_plot3A.m, SIP_plot3B.m,
% and SIP_plot3C.m, to plot the simulation results.
d2r=pi/180; r2d=1/d2r; x10_deg=15, x10=x10_deg*d2r, x20=0,
x0=[x10;x20], A=[0 1; 9 -0.6], B=[0; 1], eig(A), C=[1 0],
Wx=[sqrt(1000) 0; 0 sqrt(20)], Wu=sqrt(1.2), Wn=1, B2=B*inv(Wu),
C1=[Wx;zeros(1,2)], C2=C, D12=[zeros(2,1);1], D21=[0 1],
X=are(A,B2*B2',C1'*C1), F=-B2'*X, eig_ABF=eig(A+B2*F),
%% Design A
Wd=[100; 0], B1=[Wd zeros(2,1)], Y=are(A',C2'*C2,B1*B1'), L=-Y*C2',
Ak=A+B2*F+L*C2, Bk=-L, Ck=F, eig_ALC=eig(A+L*C2), Acl=[A B2*Ck;Bk*C2 Ak],
Bcl=[B1;Bk*D21], Ccl=[C1 D12*Ck], Dcl=zeros(3,2),
sys_cl=ss(Acl,Bcl,Ccl,Dcl), damp(sys_cl), eig_Acl=eig(Acl),
% Simulation
sim_time=2,
sim_options=simset('SrcWorkspace', 'current', 'DstWorkspace', 'current');
open('SIP_SSNLmodel'), sim('SIP_SSNLmodel', [0, sim_time], sim_options);
run('SIP_plot3A')
%% Design B
Wd=[10; 0], B1=[Wd zeros(2,1)], Y=are(A',C2'*C2,B1*B1'), L=-Y*C2',
Ak=A+B2*F+L*C2, Bk=-L, Ck=F, eig_ALC=eig(A+L*C2), Acl=[A B2*Ck;Bk*C2 Ak],
Bcl=[B1;Bk*D21], Ccl=[C1 D12*Ck], Dcl=zeros(3,2),
sys_cl=ss(Acl,Bcl,Ccl,Dcl), damp(sys_cl), eig_Acl=eig(Acl),
% Simulation
sim_time=2,
sim_options=simset('SrcWorkspace', 'current', 'DstWorkspace', 'current');
open('SIP_SSNLmodel'), sim('SIP_SSNLmodel', [0, sim_time], sim_options);
run('SIP_plot3B')
%% Design C
Wd=[1; 0], B1=[Wd zeros(2,1)], Y=are(A',C2'*C2,B1*B1'), L=-Y*C2',
Ak=A+B2*F+L*C2, Bk=-L, Ck=F, eig_ALC=eig(A+L*C2), Acl=[A B2*Ck;Bk*C2 Ak],
Bcl=[B1;Bk*D21], Ccl=[C1 D12*Ck], Dcl=zeros(3,2),
sys_cl=ss(Acl,Bcl,Ccl,Dcl), damp(sys_cl), eig_Acl=eig(Acl),
% Simulation
sim_time=2,
sim_options=simset('SrcWorkspace', 'current', 'DstWorkspace', 'current');
open('SIP_SSNLmodel'), sim('SIP_SSNLmodel', [0, sim_time], sim_options);
run('SIP_plot3C')
```

where `SIP_plot3A.m` is given below, and its copies `SIP_plot3B.m`, `SIP_plot3C.m` will print in different colors.

```
%Filename: SIP_plot3A.
```

```
figure(10), subplot(1,2,1), plot(t,x1,'b-',t,x2,'b--'), grid on,
grid minor, title('x1 and x2'), hold on, subplot(1,2,2),
plot(t,cntrl,'b-'), grid on, grid minor, title('cntrl'), hold on
```

11.7 Exercise Problems

P11.1: Recall that the observable subspace is the range space of $\mathcal{O}^T$, the transpose of the observability matrix, while the unobservable subspace is the null space of $\mathcal{O}$, the observability matrix. The null space of $\mathcal{O}$ is the orthogonal complement of the range space of $\mathcal{O}^T$. In this exercise, we will identify the observable and the unobservable subspaces of a state-space model, and use the basis vectors of these subspaces to construct a similarity transformation to transform the model into an observability decomposition form. The state-space model of the system to be considered is given as,

$$\dot{x}(t) = Ax(t) + Bu(t) = \begin{bmatrix} -8 & -9 & -12 \\ 6 & 7 & 12 \\ -1 & -1 & -3 \end{bmatrix} x(t) + \begin{bmatrix} 1 \\ 0 \\ 0 \end{bmatrix} u(t)$$

$$y(t) = Cx(t) + Du(t) = \begin{bmatrix} 4 & 6 & 8 \end{bmatrix} x(t) + u(t)$$

P11.1a: Find the observability matrix $\mathcal{O}$, and determine if the system is observable.

P11.1b: Find the observable subspace of the system, which is the range space of $\mathcal{O}^T$, the transpose of the observability matrix.

P11.1c: Find the unobservable subspace of the system, which is the null space of $\mathcal{O}$, the observability matrix.

P11.1d: Use the procedure shown in Theorem 11.5 to transform the state-space model into the observability decomposition form.

P11.1e: Is the system detectable? Explain.

P11.1f: Delete the unobservable mode of the state-space model in observability decomposition form to obtain an observable second-order subsystem $(\hat{A}_{11}, \hat{B}_1, \hat{C}_1, D)$. Is the subsystem controllable?

P11.1g: Show that the observable second-order subsystem $(\hat{A}_{11}, \hat{B}_1, \hat{C}_1, D)$ is controllable.

P11.1h: Is the system $(\hat{A}_{11}, \hat{B}_1, \hat{C}_1, D)$ in P11.1g a minimal realization? Explain.

P11.1i: Find the poles of the system $(\hat{A}_{11}, \hat{B}_1, \hat{C}_1, D)$.

P11.1j: Compute the zeros of the system $(\hat{A}_{11}, \hat{B}_1, \hat{C}_1, D)$ using Theorem 10.17.

P11.1k: Find the transfer function $G_{\min}(s) = \hat{C}_1(sI - \hat{A}_{11})\hat{B}_1 + D$, and verify the zeros of the system obtained in P11.1j.

P11.2: Consider a MIMO system described by the following transfer function matrix:

$$G(s) = \begin{bmatrix} \dfrac{-s}{(s-1)(s+3)^2} & \dfrac{s}{(s-1)(s+3)^2} \\ \dfrac{s+2}{(s-1)(s+3)^2} & \dfrac{1}{(s-1)(s+3)^2} \end{bmatrix}$$

P11.2a: Find a state-space model in block observer form for the MIMO system.

P11.2b: Find the poles and zeros of the system using the state-space model obtained in P11.2a.

P11.2c: Is the state-space model controllable? If it is not controllable, find a similarity transformation to transform it into the controllability decomposition form, and then check if the system is stabilizable.

P11.2d: If the transformed state-space model is stabilizable, delete the uncontrollable modes to obtain the controllable subsystem.

P11.2e: Show that the controllable subsystem is observable, and, therefore, the controllable subsystem obtained in P11.2d is a minimal realization.

P11.2f: Find the poles and zeros of the minimal realization.

P11.2g: Comment on the difference between the results obtained in P11.2b and P11.2f.

P11.3: Consider a third-order SISO system described by the following state-space model,

$$\begin{bmatrix} \dot{x}_1 \\ \dot{x}_2 \end{bmatrix} = \begin{bmatrix} A_{11} & A_{12} \\ A_{21} & A_{22} \end{bmatrix} \begin{bmatrix} x_1 \\ x_2 \end{bmatrix} + \begin{bmatrix} B_1 \\ B_2 \end{bmatrix} u = \begin{bmatrix} 0 & -1 & 0 \\ -3 & -2 & 0 \\ 10 & 1 & -2 \end{bmatrix} \begin{bmatrix} x_1 \\ x_2 \end{bmatrix} + \begin{bmatrix} 1 \\ 1 \\ -2 \end{bmatrix} u$$

$$y = \begin{bmatrix} C_1 & C_2 \end{bmatrix} \begin{bmatrix} x_1 \\ x_2 \end{bmatrix} = \begin{bmatrix} 1 & 0 & 0 \end{bmatrix} \begin{bmatrix} x_1 \\ x_2 \end{bmatrix}$$

(11.66)

where x_1 is a 2×1 vector. Note that the state-space model is in observability decomposition form.

P11.3a: Show that the system is not observable, but it is detectable.

P11.3b: Show that the subsystem

$$\dot{x}_1 = A_{11}x_1 + B_1 u = \begin{bmatrix} 0 & -1 \\ -3 & -2 \end{bmatrix} x_1 + \begin{bmatrix} 1 \\ 1 \end{bmatrix} u$$

$$y = C_1 x_1 = \begin{bmatrix} 1 & 0 \end{bmatrix} x_1$$

(11.67)

is a minimal realization of the system.

P11.3c: Find a state-feedback gain matrix F_1 so that the eigenvalues of $A_{11} + B_1 F_1$ (i.e., the regulator poles) are $-1 \pm j$.

P11.3d: Find an observer gain matrix L_1 so that the eigenvalues of $A_{11} + L_1 C_1$ (i.e., the observer poles) are $-1.414 \pm j$.

P11.3e: Construct the observer-based output feedback controller, as shown in Figure 11.12.

P11.3f: Show that the observer-based output feedback controller can be represented by the following state-space model:

$$\dot{x}_K(t) = A_K x_K(t) + B_K y(t) = (A_{11} + B_1 F_1 + L_1 C_1) x_K(t) - L_1 y(y)$$
$$u(t) = C_K x_K(t) = F_1 x_K(t)$$

(11.68)

P11.3g: Combine Equation 11.66, the state-space model of the plant, together with Equation 11.68, the state-space model of the observer-based output feedback controller, to form the state-space model of the closed-loop system. Then compute the eigenvalues of the closed-loop system, which should include the regulator poles (i.e., the eigenvalues of $A_{11} + B_1 F_1$), the observer poles (i.e., the eigenvalues of $A_{11} + L_1 C_1$), and the unobservable pole of the plant (i.e., the eigenvalues of the matrix A_{22}).

P11.4: In this exercise problem, we will revisit the lightly damped pendulum positioning system considered in Section 10.2.2. The LQR approach was employed to design a state-feedback controller in P10.7, an exercise problem in Chapter 10, to minimize a performance index. Since not all the state variables can be measured without contamination in practice, the more versatile LQG/H_2 output feedback design approach is employed here to address the issue. The linearized state-space model of the lightly damped pendulum positioning system is described by

$$\dot{x}(t) = Ax(t) + Bu(t) + W_d d(t) = \begin{bmatrix} 0 & 1 \\ -21.32 & -0.135 \end{bmatrix} x(t) + \begin{bmatrix} 0 \\ 30 \end{bmatrix} u(t) + W_d d(t)$$
$$y(t) = Cx(t) + W_n n(t) = \begin{bmatrix} 1 & 0 \end{bmatrix} x(t) + W_n n(t)$$

(11.69)

Notice that the output $y(t)$ consists of only one state variable $x_1(t) = \theta(t)$, the angular displacement of the pendulum, contaminated with the measurement noise $n(t)$. As discussed in Section 11.6.4, the generalized plant can be set up as shown in Equations 11.59, 11.60, 11.61, and 11.62.

P11.4a: The selection of W_x and W_u are similar to Q and R—the weighting matrices in the performance index shown in P10.7—since $Q = W_x^T W_x$ and $R = W_u^T W_u$. Recall that only the relative weights are important in determining the trade-off of the weighting matrices, so we will fix W_u at $W_u = 1$ and tentatively select W_x as I_2, a 2×2 identity matrix. Similarly, we will fix W_n, the noise weighting, at $W_n = 1$, and tentatively choose the disturbance weighting matrix as $W_d = \begin{bmatrix} 1 & 0 \end{bmatrix}^T$. Based on the selection of these weighting matrices and the matrices A, B, and C in Equation 11.69, compute the optimal state-feedback gain matrix F and the optimal observer gain matrix L using the formulas in Equations 11.48, 11.49, 11.51, and 11.52.

P11.4b: Construct the optimal H_2 controller using Equation 11.54.

P11.4c: Find the closed-loop system poles, which are the eigenvalues of $A + BF$ and $A + LC$, and their corresponding damping ratios and natural frequencies.

P11.4d: Let the initial state be

$$x(0)^T = \begin{bmatrix} 20° & 0°/s \end{bmatrix} = \begin{bmatrix} 0.349 \, \text{rad} & 0 \, \text{rad}/s \end{bmatrix}$$

Plot the state response $x(t)$ and the control input $u(t)$.

P11.4e: Comment on the pole locations and the simulation results of the closed-loop system.

P11.4f: Change the weighting matrices W_x and W_d, repeat the above design and simulations, and comment on how the weighting matrices affect the performance.

A

Complex Numbers

A.1 Definition and Significance of Complex Numbers

A complex number $X = \sigma + i\omega$ consists of two parts: the real part σ and the imaginary part $i\omega$, where σ and ω are real numbers and i is the imaginary number $i = \sqrt{-1}$. Although the imaginary number $\sqrt{-1}$ has eventually become one of the most important inventions in human history, originally it was created by mathematicians merely for a simple mathematical completeness purpose so that an n-th order algebraic equation would always have n solutions. In addition to the $i = \sqrt{-1}$ notation, the alternative notation $j = \sqrt{-1}$ is also well adopted especially in the engineering community. The reason for choosing i seemed to be related to the terminology *imaginary number*, yet the rationale of the engineering community's choice for j probably was to avoid using the same notation as the electrical current i.

Rafael Bombelli (1526-1572), an Italian mathematician, is generally regarded as the inventor of the number $\sqrt{-1}$, as he was the first to make rules of computation for complex numbers and envision their usefulness. The further developments by Leonhard Euler (1707-1783), Pierre-Simon Laplace (1749-1827), Augustin-Louis Cauchy (1789-1857), William Rowan Hamilton (1805-1865), James Clerk Maxwell (1831-1879), Edward John Routh (1831-1907), Harry Nyquist (1889-1976), Hendrik Wade Bode (1905-1982), Walter Richard Evans (1920-1999), and many contemporary mathematicians, scientists, and engineers have made the imaginary number become one of the main reasons of today's modern civilization. **These developments, all based on the complex number/variable, include Euler' formula, the Laplace transform, Cauchy's complex contour mapping theory, Hamilton's quaternion, Maxwell's governor stability analysis, Routh-Hurwitz stability criterion, Nyquist stability criterion, Bode frequency response plots, and Evan's root locus design approach, etc. It is fair to say that there would have no control theory if the imaginary number $\sqrt{-1}$ had never been invented.**

Although the terminology imaginary number seems to imply that *imaginary* is not real, it is actually very real and practical. For example, a complex root of the characteristic equation of a dynamic system will dictate how the system will behave. The imaginary part of the root determines the oscillation or vibration frequency of the system, and the real part of the root reveals how fast the system will react to commands or disturbances. The name complex number may mislead to a wrong idea that it is complicated or difficult to learn. As a matter of fact, the concept, geometry, and computation of complex numbers are simple and straightforward—all we need to know about the complex number are on Figure A.1.

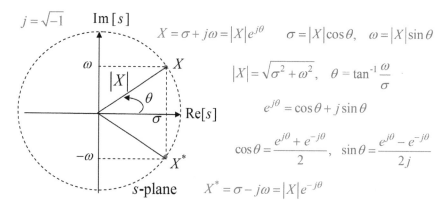

Fig. A.1: Geometry of complex numbers and the Euler formula.

A.2 Complex Number Representations

In Figure A.1, the complex number $X = \sigma + j\omega$ is represented by a point X on the complex plane (s-plane) in which the horizontal axis Re[s] is the real axis and the vertical axis Im[s] is the imaginary axis. Note that the complex number $X = \sigma + j\omega$ geometrically is a point or a vector (σ, ω) on the Cartesian coordinate plane. This complex number representation is called in *rectangular form*. It also can be represented in *polar form* as $X = |X|e^{j\theta}$. It is straightforward to convert from the rectangular form to the polar form, or vice versa as follows.

$$
\begin{aligned}
X = \sigma + j\omega &\rightarrow X = |X|e^{j\theta} : \quad |X| = \sqrt{\sigma^2 + \omega^2}, \ \theta = \tan^{-1}\frac{\omega}{\sigma} \\
X = |X|e^{j\theta} &\rightarrow X = \sigma + j\omega : \quad \sigma = |X|\cos\theta, \ \omega = |X|\sin\theta
\end{aligned}
\tag{A.1}
$$

The complex conjugate of

$$X = |X|e^{j\theta} = a + jb$$

is defined as

$$
\begin{aligned}
X^* = (a + jb)^* &= a - jb \\
&= \left(|X|e^{j\theta}\right)^* = |X|e^{-j\theta}
\end{aligned}
$$

Based on the definition, it is easy to show that

$$(X^*)^* = X \quad \text{and} \quad XX^* = |X|^2$$

The real part and the imaginary part of the complex number X are represented as

$$a = real(X), \quad b = imag(X)$$

and the magnitude (absolute value) and the angle (phase) of X are

$$|X| = abs(X), \quad \theta = angle(X)$$

A.3 Euler's Formula

From the following relationship between the rectangular form and the polar form,

$$X = |X|e^{j\theta} = \sigma + j\omega = |X|\cos\theta + j|X|\sin\theta \quad \rightarrow \quad e^{j\theta} = \cos\theta + j\sin\theta$$

we have obtained the famous *Euler's formula*, in which a complex function $e^{j\theta}$ can be written in terms of trigonometrical functions.

$$e^{j\theta} = \cos\theta + j\sin\theta \tag{A.2}$$

Replace θ by $-\theta$ in the above equation to obtain the complex conjugate of the Euler's formula,

$$e^{-j\theta} = \cos\theta - j\sin\theta \tag{A.3}$$

Then from Equations A.2 and A.3, we have the following cosine and sine functions written in terms of complex functions $e^{j\theta}$ and $e^{-j\theta}$.

$$\cos\theta = \frac{e^{j\theta} + e^{-j\theta}}{2}, \quad \sin\theta = \frac{e^{j\theta} - e^{-j\theta}}{2j} \tag{A.4}$$

A.4 Algebraic Operations

Assume the two complex numbers are given:

$$X_1 = a_1 + jb_1 = |X_1|e^{j\theta_1}, \quad X_2 = a_2 + jb_2 = |X_2|e^{j\theta_2}$$

Then the addition and substraction are carried out following the following rule:

$$X_1 \pm X_2 = (a_1 + jb_1) \pm (a_2 + jb_2) = (a_1 \pm a_2) + j(b_1 \pm b_2)$$

If the complex numbers are in polar form, they need to be converted into rectangular form before performing addition or substraction operations.

For multiplication or division, it is easier to carry out the operations in polar form:

$$X_1 X_2 = \left(|X_1|e^{j\theta_1}\right)\left(|X_2|e^{j\theta_2}\right) = \left(|X_1||X_2|\right)e^{j(\theta_1 + \theta_2)}$$

$$X_1/X_2 = \left(|X_1|e^{j\theta_1}\right) / \left(|X_2|e^{j\theta_2}\right) = \left(|X_1| / |X_2|\right)e^{j(\theta_1 - \theta_2)}$$

But it is still doable in rectangular form:

$$X_1 X_2 = (a_1 + jb_1)(a_2 + jb_2) = (a_1 a_2 - b_1 b_2) + j(a_1 b_2 + b_1 a_2)$$

$$\frac{X_1}{X_2} = \frac{a_1 + jb_1}{a_2 + jb_2} = \frac{(a_1 + jb_1)(a_2 - jb_2)}{(a_2 + jb_2)(a_2 - jb_2)} = \frac{(a_1 a_2 + b_1 b_2) + j(b_1 a_2 - a_1 b_2)}{a_2^2 + b_2^2}$$

A.5 MATLAB Commands for Complex Number Computations

The following MATLAB commands can be employed in complex number computations.

```
% CSD ExA.0 MATLAB complex number commands
 X=complex(a,b):   define X=a+jb
 X=a+ib or X=a+jb:   define X=a+jb
 real(X):   find the real part of the complex number X
 imag(X):   find the imaginary part of the complex number X
 abs(X):   find the magnitude of the complex number X
 angle(X):   find the angle (phase) of the complex number X
 conj(X):   find the conjugate of the complex number X
```

Example A.1 (**Compute** $c3 = c1 * c2$ **and** $c4 = c1/c2$, **where** $c1 = 1 + j\sqrt{3}$ **and** $c2 = 1 - j$)

```
% CSD ExA.1 Complex numbers computation c3=c1*c2 and c4=c1/c2
clear
c1=1+sqrt(3)*j              % Define complex number c1
mag_c1=abs(c1)             % Find the magnitude of c1
angle_c1=angle(c1)         % Find the angle (phase) of c1 in radian
deg_c1=angle_c1*180/pi     % Convert the angle from radian to degree
c2=1-j                     % Define another complex number c2
mag_c2=abs(c2)             % Find the magnitude of c2
angle_c2=angle(c2)         % Find the angle (phase) of c2 in radian
deg_c2=angle_c2*180/pi     % Convert the angle from radian to degree
c3=c1*c2                   % Find the product c3=c1*c2
mag_c3=abs(c3)             % Magnitude of c3
angle_c3=angle(c3)         % Angle of c3
deg_c3=angle_c3*180/pi     % Convert the angle from radian to degree
c4=c1/c2                   % Carry out the division
mag_c4=abs(c4)             % Magnitude of c4
angle_c4=angle(c4)         % Angle of c4
deg_c4=angle_c4*180/pi     % Convert to degree
```

∎

Example A.2 (**Compute** $x3 = x1 + x2$, **where** $x1 = 2e^{\pi/6}$ **and** $x2 = 2e^{j3\pi/4}$)

```
% CSD ExA.2 Complex numbers computation x3=x1+x2 and x4=x1/x2
clear
x1=2*exp(j*pi/6)       % Define complex number x1
x2=2*exp(j*3*pi/4)     % Define complex number x2
x3=x1+x2
x4=x1/x2
```

∎

Note that the unit of angle (phase) for computer computation should be always in radian instead of degree.

B

Laplace Transforms

It is well known that the Laplace transform transforms a differential equation problem into an algebraic equation problem, which is much easier to solve. **In fact, the Laplace transform performs two transformations in the same act: one is from differential to algebraic and the other is the transformation from the time domain to the frequency domain. The transformation to the frequency domain is a big step forward in the development of systems and control theory.**

B.1 Definition of Laplace Transform and Laplace Transform Pairs

The Laplace transform of $f(t)$ is defined as

$$F(s) = \mathscr{L}[f(t)] = \int_{0_-}^{\infty} e^{-st} f(t) dt \tag{B.1}$$

where $s = \sigma + j\omega$ is a complex variable, $0_- = \lim_{\varepsilon \to 0}(0 - \varepsilon)$ is the instant right before $t = 0$, and $f(t)$ is piecewise continuous when $t \geq 0$.

Based on the Laplace transform integral in Equation B.1, the Laplace transforms of the unit step function $u_s(t)$, the impulse function $\delta(t)$, the ramp function $t u_s(t)$, the polynomial function $t^n u_s(t)$, and the exponential function $e^{-at} u_s(t)$ can be obtained as follows:

$$\mathscr{L}[\delta(t)] = 1 \tag{B.2a}$$

$$\mathscr{L}[u_s(t)] = \frac{1}{s} \tag{B.2b}$$

$$\mathscr{L}[t] = \frac{1}{s^2} \tag{B.2c}$$

$$\mathscr{L}[t^n] = \frac{n!}{s^{n+1}} \tag{B.2d}$$

$$\mathscr{L}[e^{-at}] = \frac{1}{s+a} \tag{B.2e}$$

respectively. For notational simplicity, we will use the following Laplace transform pair notation to relate the t-domain function $f(t)$ with the s-domain function $F(s)$.

$$f(t) \quad \rightleftarrows \quad F(s)$$

Thus, the Laplace transform pair for the exponential function e^{-at} is

$$e^{-at} \quad \rightleftarrows \quad \frac{1}{s+a} \tag{B.3}$$

Note that the parameter a in Equation B.3 can be a complex number. Let $a = j\omega$, then the above Laplace transform pair can be rewritten as

$$\cos \omega t - j\sin \omega t = e^{-j\omega t} \quad \rightleftarrows \quad \frac{1}{s+j\omega} = \frac{s-j\omega}{(s+j\omega)(s-j\omega)} = \frac{s-j\omega}{s^2+\omega^2}$$

which leads to the following two Laplace transform pairs for $\cos \omega t$ and $\sin \omega t$ as follows

$$\cos \omega t \quad \rightleftarrows \quad \frac{s}{s^2+\omega^2}, \qquad \sin \omega t \quad \rightleftarrows \quad \frac{\omega}{s^2+\omega^2} \tag{B.4}$$

Similarly, if the parameter a in Equation B.3 is replaced by $\alpha + j\omega$ then the Laplace transform pair of Equation B.3 will become

$$e^{-\alpha t}(\cos \omega t - j\sin \omega t) = e^{-(\alpha+j\omega)t} \quad \rightleftarrows \quad \frac{1}{s+\alpha+j\omega} = \frac{s+\alpha-j\omega}{(s+\alpha)^2+\omega^2}$$

which leads to the following two Laplace transform pairs for $e^{-\alpha t}\cos \omega t$ and $e^{-\alpha t}\sin \omega t$ as follows

$$e^{-\alpha t}\cos \omega t \quad \rightleftarrows \quad \frac{s+\alpha}{(s+\alpha)^2+\omega^2}, \qquad e^{-\alpha t}\sin \omega t \quad \rightleftarrows \quad \frac{\omega}{(s+\alpha)^2+\omega^2} \tag{B.5}$$

B.2 Laplace Transform Properties and More Laplace Transform Pairs

Theorem B.1 (Linearity)

$$\mathscr{L}[a_1 f_1(t) + a_2 f_2(t)] = a_1 \mathscr{L}[f_1(t)] + a_2 \mathscr{L}[f_2(t)] \tag{B.6}$$

Theorem B.2 (Frequency Shift)

$$\text{If} \quad f(t) \rightleftarrows F(s), \quad \text{then} \quad e^{-at}f(t) \quad \rightleftarrows \quad F(s+a) \tag{B.7}$$

Theorem B.3 (Time Delay)

$$\text{If} \quad f(t) \rightleftarrows F(s), \quad \text{then} \quad f(t-T)\, u_s(t-T) \quad \rightleftarrows \quad e^{-sT}F(s)) \tag{B.8}$$

Theorem B.4 (Scaling)

$$\text{If} \quad f(t) \rightleftarrows F(s), \quad \text{then} \quad f(t/a) \quad \rightleftarrows \quad aF(as) \tag{B.9}$$

Theorem B.5 (Convolution)

$$\text{If} \quad f_1(t) \rightleftarrows F_1(s) \text{ and } f_2(t) \rightleftarrows F_2(s)$$

$$\text{then} \quad f_1(t) * f_2(t) = \int_{0_-}^{t} f_1(\tau)f_2(t-\tau)d\tau \quad \rightleftarrows \quad F_1(s)F_2(s) \tag{B.10}$$

Theorem B.6 (Differentiation)

$$df(t)/dt \rightleftarrows sF(s) - f(0_-)$$
$$d^2f(t)/dt^2 \rightleftarrows s^2F(s) - sf(0_-) - \dot{f}(0_-)$$

If $f(t) \rightleftarrows F(s)$, then $\qquad d^3f(t)/dt^3 \rightleftarrows s^3F(s) - s^2f(0_-) - s\dot{f}(0_-) - \ddot{f}(0_-)$ $\qquad$ (B.11)

$$\vdots$$

Theorem B.7 (Integration)

If $f(t) \rightleftarrows F(s)$, then $\quad \displaystyle\int_{0_-}^{t} f(\tau)d\tau \quad \rightleftarrows \quad \frac{F(s)}{s}$ $\qquad$ (B.12)

Theorem B.8 (Final Value) *If* $f(t) \rightleftarrows F(s)$ *and the real part of all poles of* $sF(s)$ *are strictly negative, then the final value of* $f(t)$ *can be computed in the frequency domain as follows.*

$$\lim_{t \to \infty} f(t) = \lim_{s \to 0} sF(s)$$ $\qquad$ (B.13)

Theorem B.9 (Initial Value) *If* $f(t) \rightleftarrows F(s)$ *and* $\lim_{s \to \infty} sF(s)$ *exists, then the initial value of* $f(t)$ *at* $t = 0$ *can be computed in frequency domain as follows.*

$$f(0_+) = \lim_{s \to \infty} sF(s)$$ $\qquad$ (B.14)

More Laplace Transform Pairs

In the previous section, Section B.1, we reviewed five fundamental Laplace transform pairs in Equation B.2, and then employed the exponential Laplace transform pair in Equation B.2e and the Euler's Formula to derive the Laplace transform pairs for $\cos \omega t$, $\sin \omega t$, $e^{-\alpha t} \cos \omega t$, and $e^{-\alpha t} \sin \omega t$ as shown in Equation B.4 and Equation B.5.

Some students may feel there are too many Laplace transform pairs to memorize. Actually you do not need to, since most of them can be easily derived from the following two Laplace transform pairs:

$$t^n \quad \rightleftarrows \quad \frac{n!}{s^{n+1}} \qquad \text{and} \qquad e^{-at} \quad \rightleftarrows \quad \frac{1}{s+a}$$

which are Equations B.2d and B.2e, respectively. It is easy to see that the rest of Laplace transform pairs in Section B.1 are either special cases or can be easily derived from these two pairs. For example, Equations B.2b and B.2c are special cases of Equation B.2d. Equation B.2b is also a special case of Equation B.2e. As shown in Equations B.4 and B.5, the four undamped and damped sinusoidal function Laplace transform pairs are easily derived from Equation B.2e.

With Theorem B.2, the Frequency Shift Theorem, and the given Laplace transform pair

$$f(t) = t^n \quad \rightleftarrows \quad F(s) = \frac{n!}{s^{n+1}}$$

we can derive another useful Laplace transform pair in the following.

$$e^{-at}f(t) = e^{-at}t^n \quad \rightleftarrows \quad F(s+a) = \frac{n!}{(s+a)^{n+1}}$$ $\qquad$ (B.15)

B.3 Inverse Laplace Transform in the DC Motor Position Control System

One of the important features of the Laplace transform is its transformation of a differential equation into an algebraic equation so that the solution can be easily found. After the frequency-domain algebraic solution is found, it needs to be transformed back to the time domain to obtain the time-domain response. This backward transform is called the inverse Laplace transform. The inverse Laplace transform usually is carried out using the partial fraction expansion and the Laplace transform pairs table.

In this section, we will employ the simple DC motor position control system analysis example, which was introduced in Section 3.6, to review the most common three cases of step responses via the inverse Laplace transforms involving (A) multiple real poles; (B) real and distinct poles; (C) complex poles.

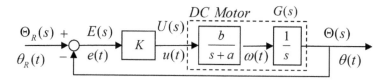

Fig. B.1: Design of a proportional controller K for the DC motor position control system.

For ease of reference, the block diagram of the simple DC motor position control system is shown again in Figure B.1. The transfer function of the closed-loop system is

$$\frac{\Theta(s)}{\Theta_R(s)} = \frac{bK}{s^2 + as + bK} = \frac{K}{s^2 + 2s + K} = \frac{\omega_n^2}{s^2 + 2\varsigma\omega_n s + \omega_n^2} \tag{B.16}$$

where $a = 2$, $b = 1$, and K is the proportional controller gain to be determined so that the closed-loop system has a desired step response. In the following, we will choose three different K values so that the closed-loop system is critically damped, overdamped, and underdamped, respectively.

Example B.10 (Case A Example with Multiple Real Poles When $K = 1$)

The closed-loop transfer function in Equation B.16 reveals that when $K = 1$, the characteristic equation will be

$$s^2 + 2s + K = 0$$

whose two roots are both at $s = -1$, and the damping ratio and natural frequency are $\varsigma = 1$ and $\omega_n = 1\text{rad}/s$, respectively. The system is critically damped.

With the unit step input $\Theta_R(s) = 1/s$, we have the output $\Theta(s)$ and its partial fraction expansion,

$$\Theta(s) = \frac{1}{s(s+1)^2} = \frac{A_1}{s} + \frac{A_2}{s+1} + \frac{A_3}{(s+1)^2} \tag{B.17}$$

where A_1, A_2, and A_3 are the real partial fraction expansion residue constants to be determined. These constants can be evaluated using at least three approaches. The first is

Residue Approach:

$$A_1 = \lim_{s \to 0} s\Theta(s) = \frac{1}{1^2} = 1, \quad A_3 = \lim_{s \to -1} (s+1)^2\Theta(s) = \frac{1}{-1} = -1$$

$$A_2 = \lim_{s \to -1} \frac{d}{ds}\left[(s+1)^2\Theta(s)\right] = \lim_{s \to -1} \frac{d}{ds}\left[\frac{1}{s}\right] = \lim_{s \to -1} \frac{-1}{s^2} = \frac{-1}{(-1)^2} = -1 \tag{B.18}$$

The second and the third approaches require Equation B.17 to be rewritten as a polynomial equation,

$$1 = A_1(s+1)^2 + A_2 s(s+1) + A_3 s \tag{B.19}$$

Note that Equation B.19 is valid for any value of the complex number s. The second approach is

Substitution Approach:

$$
\begin{aligned}
s = 0: & \quad 1 = A_1(0+1)^2 + 0 + 0 \quad \rightarrow \quad A_1 = 1 \\
s = -1: & \quad 1 = 0 + 0 + A_3(-1) \quad \rightarrow \quad A_3 = -1 \\
s = 1: & \quad 1 = A_1(1+1)^2 + A_2 \cdot 1(1+1) + A_3 \cdot 1 \quad \rightarrow \quad A_2 = -1
\end{aligned}
\tag{B.20}
$$

The choices of the poles $s = 0$ and $s = -1$ are obvious since they will make two terms zero to obtain $A_1 = 1$ and $A_3 = -1$ just by inspection. Substitution of $s = 1$ can create another independent equation to obtain $A_2 = -1$. Alternatively, A_2 can be more easily found by comparing the coefficients of s^2 term in Equation B.19: $(A_1 + A_2)s^2 = 0$; hence, $A_2 = -A_1 = -1$. The third approach is

Coefficient Comparison Approach:

$$
\begin{aligned}
s^2 \text{ term}: & \quad 0 = A_1 + A_2 \\
s \text{ term}: & \quad 0 = 2A_1 + A_2 + A_3 \quad \rightarrow \quad A_1 = 1, \quad A_2 = -1, \quad A_3 = -1 \\
\text{constant term}: & \quad 1 = A_1
\end{aligned}
\tag{B.21}
$$

The most efficient approach actually is a mix of the above three approaches. For example, A_1 and A_3 can be easily obtained by applying $s = 0$ and $s = -1$ in the Substitution Approach. Then the Coefficient Comparison Approach can be employed to find A_2 by comparing the coefficient of the s^2 term.

Now, plug the values of A_1, A_2, and A_3 into Equation B.17, and use the Laplace transform pairs $1/s \rightleftarrows 1$, $1/(s+a) \rightleftarrows e^{-at}$ and $1/(s+a)^2 \rightleftarrows te^{-at}$, we have the step response in the following,

$$\theta(t) = \mathcal{L}^{-1}[\Theta(s)] = 1 - e^{-t} - te^{-t}, \quad t \geq 0 \tag{B.22}$$

■

Example B.11 (Case B Example with Real Distinct Poles When $K = 0.5$)

The closed-loop transfer function in Equation B.16 reveals that when $K = 0.5$, the characteristic equation will be

$$s^2 + 2s + 0.5 = 0$$

whose two roots are at $s = -0.293$ and $s = -1.707$, and the damping ratio and natural frequency are $\varsigma = 1.414$ and $\omega_n = 0.707 \text{rad/s}$, respectively. The system is overdamped.

With the unit step input $\Theta_R(s) = 1/s$, we have the output $\Theta(s)$ and its partial fraction expansion,

$$\Theta(s) = \frac{0.5}{s(s+0.293)(s+1.707)} = \frac{A_1}{s} + \frac{A_2}{s+0.293} + \frac{A_3}{s+1.707} \tag{B.23}$$

where A_1, A_2, and A_3 are the real partial fraction expansion residue constants to be determined. These constants can be evaluated using any of the following three approaches.

Residue Approach:

$$A_1 = \lim_{s \to 0} s\Theta(s) = \frac{0.5}{0.293 \cdot 1.707} = 1$$

$$A_2 = \lim_{s \to -0.293} (s + 0.293)\Theta(s) = \frac{0.5}{-0.293 \cdot 1.414} = -1.207 \qquad \text{(B.24)}$$

$$A_3 = \lim_{s \to -1.707} (s + 1.707)\Theta(s) = \frac{0.5}{(-0.1.707) \cdot (-1.414)} = 0.207$$

The Substitution and the Coefficient Comparison approaches require Equation B.23 to be rewritten as a polynomial equation,

$$0.5 = A_1(s + 0.293)(s + 1.707) + A_2 s(s + 1.707) + A_3 s(s + 0.293) \qquad \text{(B.25)}$$

Substitution Approach:

$$s = 0: \quad 0.5 = A_1(0.293)(1.707) \quad \to \quad A_1 = 1$$

$$s = -0.293: \quad 0.5 = A_2(-0.293)(1.414) \quad \to \quad A_2 = -1.207 \qquad \text{(B.26)}$$

$$s = -1.707: \quad 0.5 = A_3(-1.707)(-1.707 + 0.293) \quad \to \quad A_3 = 0.207$$

Coefficient Comparison Approach:

s^2 term : $0 = A_1 + A_2 + A_3$

s term : $0 = 2A_1 + 1.707A_2 + 0.293A_3$ $\to$ $A_1 = 1, \quad A_2 = -1.207, \quad A_3 = 0.207$ (B.27)

constant term : $0.5 = 0.5A_1$

Now, plug the values of A_1, A_2, and A_3 into Equation B.23, and use the Laplace transform pairs $1/s \rightleftarrows 1$ and $1/(s+a) \rightleftarrows e^{-at}$, we have the step response in the following,

$$\theta(t) = \mathcal{L}^{-1}[\Theta(s)] = 1 - 1.207e^{-0.293t} + 0.207e^{-0.207t}, \quad t \geq 0 \qquad \text{(B.28)}$$

■

Example B.12 (Case C Example with Complex Conjugate Poles When $K = 2$)

The closed-loop transfer function in Equation B.16 reveals that when $K = 2$, the characteristic equation will be

$$s^2 + 2s + 2 = 0$$

whose two roots are at $s_1, s_2 = -1 \pm j$, and the damping ratio and natural frequency are $\varsigma = 0.707$ and $\omega_n = 1.414 \text{rad/s}$, respectively. The system is underdamped.

With the unit step input $\Theta_R(s) = 1/s$, we have the output $\Theta(s)$ and its partial fraction expansion,

$$\Theta(s) = \frac{2}{s(s+1-j)(s+1+j)} = \frac{A_1}{s} + \frac{c_1}{s+1-j} + \frac{c_1^*}{s+1+j} \qquad \text{(B.29)}$$

where c_1^* is the conjugate of c_1, and the real A_1 and the complex c_1 constants can be evaluated using any of the following three approaches.

Residue Approach:

$$c_1 = \lim_{s \to -1+j} (s+1-j)\Theta(s) = \frac{2}{(-1+j)(j2)} = \frac{-1}{1+j} = \frac{1}{\sqrt{2}}e^{j135°} = 0.707e^{j135°}$$

$$c_1^* = 0.707e^{-j135°}, \quad A_1 = \lim_{s \to 0} s\Theta(s) = 2/2 = 1 \qquad \text{(B.30)}$$

The Substitution and the Coefficient Comparison approaches require Equation B.29 to be rewritten as a polynomial equation,

$$2 = A_1(s+1-j)(s+1+j) + c_1 s(s+1+j) + c_1^* s(s+1-j) \tag{B.31}$$

Substitution Approach:

$$s = 0: \quad 2 = A_1(1-j)(1+j) \quad \rightarrow \quad A_1 = 1$$

$$s = -1+j: \quad 2 = c_1(-1+j)(j2) \quad \rightarrow \quad c_1 = \frac{-1}{1+j} = 0.707e^{j135°}, \; c_1^* = 0.707e^{-j135°} \tag{B.32}$$

Coefficient Comparison Approach:

s^2 term : $\quad 0 = A_1 + c_1 + c_1^*$

s term : $\quad 0 = 2A_1 + c_1 + c_1^* + j(c_1 - c_1^*) \quad \rightarrow \quad A_1 = 1, \quad c_1 = -0.5 + j0.5 = 0.707e^{j135°}$ (B.33)

constant term : $\quad 2 = 2A_1$

Now, plug the values of A_1, c_1, and c_1^* into Equation B.29 to obtain

$$\Theta(s) = \frac{1}{s} + \frac{0.707e^{j135°}}{s+1-j} + \frac{0.707e^{-j135°}}{s+1+j}$$

and then use the Laplace transform pairs $1/s \rightleftarrows 1$ and $1/(s+a) \rightleftarrows e^{-at}$, we have the step response in the following,

$$\theta(t) = 1 + 0.707\left(e^{j135°}e^{-(1-j)t} + e^{-j135°}e^{-(1+j)t}\right) = 1 + 0.707e^{-t}\left(e^{j(t+135°)} + e^{-j(t+135°)}\right)$$

$$= 1 + 1.414e^{-t}\cos(t+135°) = 1 - 1.414e^{-t}\sin(t+45°), \quad t \geq 0 \tag{B.34}$$

∎

Example B.13 (Solving the Example B.12 Problem Without Using Complex Numbers)

As mentioned earlier in Section B.1, the following undamped and damped sinusoidal Laplace transform pairs

$$\cos \omega t \quad \rightleftarrows \quad \frac{s}{s^2 + \omega^2}, \qquad \sin \omega t \quad \rightleftarrows \quad \frac{\omega}{s^2 + \omega^2}$$

and

$$e^{-\alpha t}\cos \omega t \quad \rightleftarrows \quad \frac{s+\alpha}{(s+\alpha)^2 + \omega^2}, \qquad e^{-\alpha t}\sin \omega t \quad \rightleftarrows \quad \frac{\omega}{(s+\alpha)^2 + \omega^2}$$

all can be easily derived using the following simple exponential Laplace transform pair

$$e^{-at} \quad \rightleftarrows \quad \frac{1}{s+a}$$

together with Euler's formula

$$e^{j\theta} = \cos \theta + j\sin \theta$$

In fact, as in Example B.12, almost all the computations involved the undamped or damped sinusoidal functions can be carried out just by using the simple exponential Laplace transform pair, $e^{-at} \rightleftarrows 1/(s+a)$ since the parameter a can be a complex number. However, it is still doable to solve the Example B.12 problem without using any complex number computation.

Alternatively, Equation B.29 can be expressed as

$$\Theta(s) = \frac{2}{s(s^2+2s+2)} = \frac{A_1}{s} + \frac{A_2 s + A_3}{s^2+2s+2} \tag{B.35}$$

where A_1, A_2, and A_3 are real constants to be determined. The Residue or the Substitution approach can be employed to find A_1, but they will not work for A_2 and A_3 without going through the computation of the complex numbers c_1 and c_1^* as done in Example B.12. We will use the Substitution approach to compute A_1, and then after that the Coefficient Comparison approach will be employed to find A_2 and A_3. To be able to apply the Substitution and the Coefficient Comparison approaches, Equation B.35 needs to be rewritten as the following polynomial equation.

$$2 = A_1(s^2+2s+2) + s(A_2 s + A_3) \tag{B.36}$$

Substitution Approach:

$$s = 0: \quad 2 = A_1(0+0+2) \quad \rightarrow \quad A_1 = 1 \tag{B.37}$$

Coefficient Comparison Approach:

$$s^2 \text{ term}: \quad 0 = A_1 + A_2$$
$$s \text{ term}: \quad 0 = 2A_1 + A_3 \quad \rightarrow \quad A_1 = 1, \quad A_2 = -1, \quad A_3 = -2 \tag{B.38}$$
$$\text{constant term}: \quad 2 = 2A_1$$

Now, plug the values of A_1, A_2, and A_3 into Equation B.35 to obtain

$$\Theta(s) = \frac{1}{s} + \frac{-s-2}{s^2+2s+2}$$

which can be rewritten into the form of damped sinusoidal Laplace transform pairs as shown in Equation B.5.

$$\Theta(s) = \frac{1}{s} + \frac{-s-1-1}{(s+1)^2+1} = \frac{1}{s} + \frac{-(s+1)}{(s+1)^2+1} + \frac{-1}{(s+1)^2+1} \tag{B.39}$$

Then use the Laplace transform pairs $1/s \rightleftarrows 1$, and the damped sinusoidal Laplace transform pairs in Equation B.5, we have the step response in the following.

$$\theta(t) = 1 - e^{-t}(\cos t + \sin t), \qquad t \geq 0 \tag{B.40}$$

Since the two sinusoidal functions $\cos t$ and $\sin t$ are of the same frequency, it is preferable to rewrite the sum of these two terms into one in the form of $A\sin(t+\phi)$ so that it can reveal the amplitude and phase of the sinusoidal function. Now, to get

$$\cos t + \sin t = A\sin(t+\phi) = A(\sin\phi\cos t + \cos\phi\sin t)$$

the following needs to hold.

$$A\sin\phi = 1 \quad \text{and} \quad A\cos\phi = 1$$

which implies that

$$A = \sqrt{2} = 1.414 \quad \text{and} \quad \phi = 45°$$

Therefore,

$$\theta(t) = 1 - 1.414e^{-t}\sin(t+45°), \qquad t \geq 0 \tag{B.41}$$

∎

B.4 MATLAB Commands for Laplace Transform Computations

The following MATLAB commands can be employed in Laplace transform computations.

`syms t s`	*Define symbolic variables t and s.*
`F=laplace(f)`	*Find F, the Laplace transform of f.*
`f=ilaplace(F)`	*Find f, the inverse Laplace transform of F.*
`digits(6)`	*Set variable precision digits to 6.*
`vpa(f)`	*Evaluate f up to 6 digits precision.*
`vpa(pi,10)`	*Evaluate pi up to 10 digits precision.*
`[R,P,K]=residue(N,D)`	*Find finds the residues, poles and direct term of a partial fraction expansion of the ratio of two polynomials N(s)/D(s).*
`roots(V)`	*Computes the roots of the polynomial whose coefficients are the elements of the vector V.*
`G=tf(num,den)`	*Define a system G whose transfer function is num/den.*
`P=pole(G)`	*Returns the poles of the system G.*
`Z=zero(G)`	*Returns the zeros of the system G.*
`[wn,ze,P]=damp(G)`	*Returns natural frequencies, damping ratios, and poles of the system G.*
`[y,t]=step(G,tf)`	*Generate step response array y and associate time t array in $0 < t < t_f$.*
`.* ./`	*Array (element-to-element) multiplication and division.*
`* /`	*Regular multiplication and division for scalars or matrices.*
`plot(y,t)`	*Plots vector y versus vector t.*

Example B.14 (Using MATLAB to Find the Laplace Transforms of t-Domain Functions and Compute the Inverse Laplace Transforms of the s-Domain Functions)

```
% Find the Laplace transform F from f
syms a w t s,
f2=t,
F2=laplace(f2),
f3=exp(-a*t),
F3=laplace(f3),
f4=sin(w*t),
F4=laplace(f4),
f5=cos(w*t),
F5=laplace(f5),
ilaplace(F5,s,t),
f6=exp(-a*t)*sin(w*t),
F6=laplace(f6),
ilaplace(F6,s,t),
f7=exp(-a*t)*cos(w*t),
F7=laplace(f7),
f0=sym('dirac(t)'),
```

```
F0=laplace(f0),
f1=sym('heaviside(t)'),
F1=laplace(f1),


% Find the inverse Laplace transform f from F
f00=ilaplace(F0,s,t),
f11=ilaplace(F1,s,t),
f22=ilaplace(F2,s,t)
f33=ilaplace(F3,s,t),
f44=ilaplace(F4,s,t),
f55=ilaplace(F5,s,t),
f66=ilaplace(F6,s,t),
f77=ilaplace(F7,s,t),


>> syms a w t s,
>> f6=exp(-a*t)*sin(w*t),
F6=laplace(f6),
ilaplace(F6,s,t),
f6=exp(-a*t)*sin(t*w)
F6 = w/((a + s)^2 + w^2)
ans = exp(-a*t)*sin(t*w)
>> f66=ilaplace(F6,s,t),
f66 = exp(-a*t)*sin(t*w)
```

■

Example B.15 (Using MATLAB to Compute the Residues of Partial Fraction Expansion)

```
% Find the residues of a partial fraction expansion
X1=tf([1],[1 2 1 0]),
[r1,p1,k1]=residue([1],[1 2 1 0]);
display('The residues r1 are: '), r1',
X2=tf([0.5],[1 2 0.5 0]),
[r2,p2,k2]=residue([0.5],[1 2 0.5 0]);
display('The residues r2 are:'), r2',
X3=tf([2],[1 2 2 0]),
[r3,p3,k3]=residue([2],[1 2 2 0]);
display('The residues r3 are: '), r3',
```

■

Example B.16 (Using MATLAB to Compute Inverse Laplace Transform)

```
% Find the inverse Laplace Transform
% Run the first 3 lines, then run the next 2 lines
syms t s
F1=1/(s*(s+0.5367)*(s+1.8633)),   % F1=1/(s*(s^2+2.4*s+1)),
f1=ilaplace(F1,s,t),
digits(4),
vpa(f1),
F2=1/(s*(s+1)^2)
f2=ilaplace(F2,s,t)
F3=1/(s*(s^2+1.4*s+1))
f3=ilaplace(F3,s,t)
digits(5)
vpa(f3)
```

■

Example B.17 (Using MATLAB `step` Command to Find Step Response and Compare It with Analytic Solutions)

```
% Filename: plot_StepResponse
% Compute poles, zeros, damping ratio, natural frequency, and
% step response.
G1=tf([2],[1 2 2]),
[wn1 zeta1]=damp(G1),
P1=pole(G1),
Z1=zero(G1),
% Find and plot step response using MATLAB step command,
sim_time=10,
[y1,t]=step(G1,sim_time);
figure(3),
subplot(1,2,1),
plot(t,y1,'b-')
grid on,
grid minor,
xlabel ('Time (sec)'),
ylabel ('step response y1'),
legend ('y1'),
% Find step response using inverse Laplace transform
syms t s
Ys=2/(s*(s^2+2*s+2)),
ys=ilaplace(Ys,s,t),
digits(5)
vpa(ys)
% Plot step response Using Equation(B.34) in Example B.12
ts=linspace(0,10,101);
y_K=1-1.414*exp(-ts).*sin(ts+pi/4);
% Plot step response Using Equation(B.40) in Example B.13
y_s=1-exp(-ts).*(cos(ts)+sin(ts));
subplot(1,2,2)
plot(ts,y_K,'ro',ts,y_s,'b--')
grid on,
grid minor,
xlabel ('Time (sec)'),
ylabel ('step response'),
legend ('y_K','y_s')
```

■

The step response of the system with transfer function

$$G_1(s) = \frac{2}{s^2 + 2s + 2}$$

based on the MATLAB `step` command,

```
[y1,t] = step(G1,sim_time)
```

is plotted on the left graph of Figure B.2. Meanwhile, the analytic step response solutions of the same system $G_1(s)$ were obtained from Equation B.34 in Example B.12, and from Equation B.40 in Example B.13 as

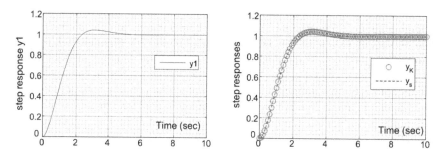

Fig. B.2: Comparison of the step response plots based on MATLAB step command and analytic solutions.

$$y_K(t) = 1 - 1.414e^{-t}\sin(t + 45°)$$

and

$$y_s(t) = 1 - e^{-t}(\cos(t) + \sin(t))$$

respectively. The plots of $y_K(t)$ and $y_s(t)$ are shown on the right graph of Figure B.2. It is clear that these three step responses are exactly identical.

Note that the two vector arrays y1 and t are generated by the step command so that their dimensions and corresponding values are matched perfectly. The step response plots of the two analytic solution functions $y_K(t)$ and $y_s(t)$ are also carried out using the array structure. The command ts=linspace(0,10,101) creates a vector array ts which consists of 101 equally spacing points within the 10 seconds interval, then the corresponding y_K and y_s vector arrays are constructed based on their respective analytic equations. **A special attention needs to be paid on the special array multiplication operator . *, which is an "element-to-element" multiplication instead of the regular matrix multiplication.**

C

Equilibriums and Linearized Models

Most of the systems to be controlled involve nonlinear dynamics, but most of the available control system design tools are linear approaches. Fortunately, linear control system design tools can still work very well with most of the nonlinear systems if the range of operation is reasonably linear. To design a linear controller for a nonlinear system, a general practice is to first identify an equilibrium point of interest with the nonlinear system so that a linearized state-space model can be obtained.

Consider the nonlinear state-space model equations,

$$\begin{aligned} \dot{x} &= f(x,u), \quad x \in R^n, u \in R^m \\ y &= h(x,u), \quad y \in R^p \end{aligned} \tag{C.1}$$

Often, we are interested in motions near a particular equilibrium point, x^*, u^*, y^*. In such circumstances, a linear approximation to the equations is a useful first step in analysis and design. To obtain a linear approximate model, the local perturbation variables $\bar{x}(t)$, $\bar{u}(t)$, $\bar{y}(t)$ are defined by the following relations,

$$x(t) = x^* + \bar{x}(t), \quad u(t) = u^* + \bar{u}(t), \quad y(t) = y^* + \bar{y}(t) \tag{C.2}$$

Since x^*, u^*, y^* are constant vectors, Eqs. (C.1) and (C.2) will lead to the following

$$\begin{aligned} \dot{x}(t) &= \dot{\bar{x}}(t) = f(x^* + \bar{x}(t), u^* + \bar{u}(t)) \\ y(t) &= y^* + \bar{y}(t) = h(x^* + \bar{x}(t), u^* + \bar{u}(t)) \end{aligned} \tag{C.3}$$

Now, according to Taylor series expansion for f, g, we have

$$\begin{aligned} f(x^* + \bar{x}, u^* + \bar{u}) &= f(x^*, u^*) + \left.\frac{\partial f}{\partial x}\right|_{x^*, u^*} \bar{x} + \left.\frac{\partial f}{\partial u}\right|_{x^*, u^*} \bar{u} + \text{h.o.t.} \\ h(x^* + \bar{x}, u^* + \bar{u}) &= h(x^*, u^*) + \left.\frac{\partial h}{\partial x}\right|_{x^*, u^*} \bar{x} + \left.\frac{\partial h}{\partial u}\right|_{x^*, u^*} \bar{u} + \text{h.o.t.} \end{aligned} \tag{C.4}$$

Recall that $f(x^*, u^*) = 0$ and $h(x^*, u^*) = y^*$, so that upon dropping the higher order terms we have the following linearized state-space model,

$$\begin{aligned} \dot{\bar{x}} &= \left.\frac{\partial f}{\partial x}\right|_{x^*, u^*} \bar{x} + \left.\frac{\partial f}{\partial u}\right|_{x^*, u^*} \bar{u} := A\bar{x} + B\bar{u} \\ \bar{y} &= \left.\frac{\partial h}{\partial x}\right|_{x^*, u^*} \bar{x} + \left.\frac{\partial h}{\partial u}\right|_{x^*, u^*} \bar{u} := C\bar{x} + D\bar{u} \end{aligned} \tag{C.5}$$

These differentials are called *Jacobian matrices*. Let us emphasize that the linear equations are only valid approximation in a sufficiently small neighborhood of the equilibrium point at which they are derived.

Example C.1 (Linearized Model of the Cart-Inverted Pendulum System)

Consider the nonlinear state-space model of the nonlinear cart-inverted system represented by Eqs. (7.87) and (7.88). For ease of reference, these equations are repeated in the following.

$$\dot{x}(t) := \begin{bmatrix} \dot{x}_1(t) \\ \dot{x}_2(t) \\ \dot{x}_3(t) \\ \dot{x}_4(t) \end{bmatrix} = \begin{bmatrix} f_1(x,u) \\ f_2(x,u) \\ f_3(x,u) \\ f_4(x,u) \end{bmatrix} := f(x,u) \tag{C.6}$$

where

$$f_1(x,u) = x_2$$
$$f_2(x,u) = (1/\Delta)(5885\sin x_1 - 378.8x_2 - 10\sin x_1 \cos x_1 x_2^2 + 79.25x_4 \cos x_1 - 317\cos x_1 u)$$
$$f_3(x,u) = x_4 \tag{C.7}$$
$$f_4(x,u) = (1/\Delta)(4.083\sin x_1 x_2^2 - 32.2x_4 - 98.5\sin x_1 \cos x_1 + 6.34x_2 \cos x_1 + 128.8u)$$
$$\Delta = 244 - 10\cos^2 x_1$$

The objective of the cart-inverted pendulum control system is to design a controller to stabilize the unstable equilibrium so that the pendulum can be stabilized at the upward position. Hence, we need to find a linearized state-space model of the system at the unstable equilibrium point $x^* = [0\ 0\ 0\ 0]^T$, and $u^* = 0$. The linearized state equation will be

$$\dot{\bar{x}}(t) = A\bar{x}(t) + B\bar{u}(t) \tag{C.8}$$

where

$$A = \begin{bmatrix} \frac{\partial f_1}{\partial x_1} & \frac{\partial f_1}{\partial x_2} & \frac{\partial f_1}{\partial x_3} & \frac{\partial f_1}{\partial x_4} \\ \frac{\partial f_2}{\partial x_1} & \frac{\partial f_2}{\partial x_2} & \frac{\partial f_2}{\partial x_3} & \frac{\partial f_2}{\partial x_4} \\ \frac{\partial f_3}{\partial x_1} & \frac{\partial f_3}{\partial x_2} & \frac{\partial f_3}{\partial x_3} & \frac{\partial f_3}{\partial x_4} \\ \frac{\partial f_4}{\partial x_1} & \frac{\partial f_4}{\partial x_2} & \frac{\partial f_4}{\partial x_3} & \frac{\partial f_4}{\partial x_4} \end{bmatrix}_{x^*=0,\ u^*=0} = \begin{bmatrix} 0 & 1 & 0 & 0 \\ 25.15 & -1.6188 & 0 & 0.33868 \\ 0 & 0 & 0 & 1 \\ -0.42094 & 0.027094 & 0 & -0.1376 \end{bmatrix}$$

$$B = \begin{bmatrix} \frac{\partial f_1}{\partial u} \\ \frac{\partial f_2}{\partial u} \\ \frac{\partial f_3}{\partial u} \\ \frac{\partial f_4}{\partial u} \end{bmatrix}_{x^*=0,\ u^*=0} = \begin{bmatrix} 0 \\ -1.3547 \\ 0 \\ 0.5504 \end{bmatrix} \tag{C.9}$$

Note that in this example the perturbed variables $\dot{\bar{x}}$, $\bar{x}$, and $\bar{u}$ in Equation C.8 are equal to the real physical variables $\dot{x}$, x, and u, respectively, since the state vector and the input at the equilibrium are zero, i.e., $x^* = 0$ and $u^* = 0$. In general, the perturbed variables are different from the real physical variables according to Equation C.2.   ∎

Example C.2 (Equilibrium and Linearized Model of a Pendulum Positioning System)

Consider the nonlinear, lightly damped pendulum positioning system represented by Equation 10.4. For ease of reference, the equation is repeated in the following,

$$\dot{x} = \begin{bmatrix} \dot{x}_1 \\ \dot{x}_2 \end{bmatrix} = \begin{bmatrix} x_2 \\ -a_0 \sin x_1 - a_1 x_2 + b_0 T \end{bmatrix} := f(x, T) = \begin{bmatrix} f_1(x_1, x_2, T) \\ f_2(x_1, x_2, T) \end{bmatrix} \tag{C.10}$$
$$y = x_1 := h(x_1, x_2, T)$$

where $a_1 = 0.135$, $a_0 = 22.073$, and $b_0 = 30$. The state variables are $x_1(t) = \theta(t)$ and $x_2(t) = \dot{\theta}(t)$, which are the angular displacement and the angular velocity of the pendulum, respectively.

Assume the system will operate in the vicinity of $y(t) = x_1(t) = \theta(t) = \theta^* = 15° = \pi/12$ rad. Then the equilibrium of the system can be found by solving the state equations with the derivative of the state variables set to zero. Now, we have

$$\begin{bmatrix} \dot{x}_1 \\ \dot{x}_2 \end{bmatrix} = 0 \;\rightarrow\; \begin{array}{c} x_2 = 0 \\ -a_0 \sin 15° - a_1 x_2 + b_0 T = 0 \end{array} \;\rightarrow\; \begin{bmatrix} x_1^* \\ x_2^* \end{bmatrix} = \begin{bmatrix} 15° \\ 0 \end{bmatrix}, \; T^* = 0.19043 \text{Nm}$$

At this equilibrium $(x_1^*, x_2^*, y^*, T^*) = (15°, 0°/\text{s}, 15°, 0.19043 \text{ Nm})$, the linearized state-space model can be found as

$$\dot{\bar{x}}(t) = A\bar{x}(t) + B\bar{T}(t)$$
$$\bar{y}(t) = C\bar{x}(t) \tag{C.11}$$

where the matrices A, B, and C are computed via Jacobian matrices J_x, J_T, and J_y, respectively, as follows:

$$A = J_x = \left[\frac{\partial f}{\partial x}\right]_{x^*,T^*} = \begin{bmatrix} \partial f_1/\partial x_1 & \partial f_1/\partial x_2 \\ \partial f_2/\partial x_1 & \partial f_2/\partial x_2 \end{bmatrix}_{x^* = \begin{bmatrix} \pi/12 \\ 0 \end{bmatrix}, T^*} = \begin{bmatrix} 0 & 1 \\ -a_0 \cos(\pi/12) & -a_1 \end{bmatrix}$$

$$B = J_T = \left[\frac{\partial f}{\partial T}\right]_{x^*,T^*} = \begin{bmatrix} \partial f_1/\partial T \\ \partial f_2/\partial T \end{bmatrix}_{x^*,T^*} = \begin{bmatrix} 0 \\ b_0 \end{bmatrix}$$

$$C = J_y = \left[\frac{\partial h}{\partial x}\right]_{x^*,T^*} = \begin{bmatrix} \frac{\partial h}{\partial x_1} & \frac{\partial h}{\partial x_2} \end{bmatrix}_{x^*,T^*} = \begin{bmatrix} 1 & 0 \end{bmatrix}$$

Note that in this example the perturbed variables $\dot{\bar{x}}$, $\bar{x}$, $\bar{y}$, and $\bar{T}$ in Equation C.11 are equal to the real physical variables minus the equilibrium values, which are $\dot{x}$, $x - x^*$, $y - y^*$, and $T - \bar{T}^*$, respectively. ∎

D

Mason's Gain Formula

One of the most efficient ways to compute the overall transfer function (or gains) of a large system is Mason's gain formula. Although Mason's gain formula can be applied to the block diagram, it is more intuitive for it to work together with the signal flow graph. The signal flow graph is virtually equivalent to the block diagram, but it looks neater and shows the signal flow path more clearly than its counterpart.

Theorem D.1 (Mason's Gain Formula)

Consider a system represented by a signal flow graph, in which the relationships among signals and systems are all algebraic. Then the transfer function from the input U to the output Y is

$$\frac{Y}{U} = \frac{1}{\Delta} \sum_{n=1}^{N} F_n \Delta_n \tag{D.1}$$

where

$N = total\ number\ of\ forward\ paths$

$F_n = the\ n\text{-}th\ forward\ path\ gain$

$M = total\ number\ of\ loops$

$\ell_i = the\ i\text{-}th\ loop\ gain$

$\Delta = 1 - \sum_{i}^{M} \ell_i + \sum_{i,j}^{NT} \ell_i \ell_j - \sum_{i,j,k}^{NT} \ell_i \ell_j \ell_k + \cdots$

The superscript NT means non-touching.

$\sum_{i,j}^{NT} \ell_i \ell_j$ *is the sum of the products of two non-touching loop gains.*

$\sum_{i,j,k}^{NT} \ell_i \ell_j \ell_k$ *is the sum of the products of three non-touching loop gains.*

Δ_n : *same as the Δ, but only the loops that do NOT touch the n-th forward path are considered.*

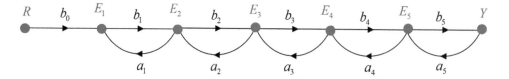

Fig. D.1: Find the transfer function of the five-loop system.

Example D.2 (Find the transfer function of a system with five loops)

Consider the five-loop system described by the signal flow graph shown in Figure D.1.

Conventional Elimination Approach

If the conventional approach is taken, we would write down the following six equations according to the signals entering into each of the six nodes: E_1, E_2, E_3, E_4, E_5, and Y.

$$Y = b_5 E_5, \quad E_5 = b_4 E_4 + a_5 Y, \qquad\qquad \text{Eliminate the}$$
$$E_4 = b_3 E_3 + a_4 E_5, \quad E_3 = b_2 E_2 + a_3 E_4, \quad \rightarrow \quad \text{intermediate variables} \quad \rightarrow \quad {}^{Y}\!/_{R} = \dots\dots$$
$$E_2 = b_1 E_1 + a_2 E_3, \quad E_1 = a_1 E_2 + b_0 R \qquad E_1, E_2, E_3, E_4, \text{ and } E_5$$

Then a tedious algebraic manipulation process has to be taken to eliminate the intermediate variables E_1, E_2, E_3, E_4, and E_5, in order to obtain the transfer function Y/R.

Mason's Gain Formula Approach

The first step in using Mason's gain formula is to find the forward path gain for each forward path. There is only one forward path from the input R to the output Y, and its forward path gain is

$$F_1 = b_0 b_1 b_2 b_3 b_4 b_5$$

Hence, the transfer function Y/R will be

$$\frac{Y}{R} = \frac{F_1 \Delta_1}{\Delta}$$

where Δ, and Δ_1 will be constructed using the loop gains of the system. There are five loops, and their loop gains are

$$\ell_1 = a_1 b_1, \; \ell_2 = a_2 b_2, \; \ell_3 = a_3 b_3, \; \ell_4 = a_4 b_4, \; \ell_5 = a_5 b_5$$

and the Δ will be

$$\Delta = 1 - \sum_{i}^{M} \ell_i + \sum_{i,j}^{NT} \ell_i \ell_j - \sum_{i,j,k}^{NT} \ell_i \ell_j \ell_k$$
$$= 1 - (\ell_1 + \ell_2 + \ell_3 + \ell_4 + \ell_5) + (\ell_1 \ell_3 + \ell_1 \ell_4 + \ell_1 \ell_5 + \ell_2 \ell_4 + \ell_2 \ell_5 + \ell_3 \ell_5) - (\ell_1 \ell_3 \ell_5)$$

Note that the second term $\sum_{i}^{M} \ell_i$ is the sum of all five individual loop gains, the third term $\sum_{i,j}^{NT} \ell_i \ell_j$ is the sum of the products of two non-touching loop gains. There are six pairs of non-touching loops. The fourth term $\sum_{i,j,k}^{NT} \ell_i \ell_j \ell_k$ is the sum of the products of three non-touching loop gains. It is easy to see that there is only one trio of non-touching loops, ℓ_1, ℓ_3, and ℓ_5.

Since all five loops are touching the forward path, there is no loop qualified to be considered in the construction of Δ_1; hence, we have $\Delta_1 = 1$. Therefore, the transfer function of the system is

$$\frac{Y}{R} = \frac{F_1 \Delta_1}{\Delta} = \frac{b_0 b_1 b_2 b_3 b_4 b_5}{1 - (\ell_1 + \ell_2 + \ell_3 + \ell_4 + \ell_5) + (\ell_1 \ell_3 + \ell_1 \ell_4 + \ell_1 \ell_5 + \ell_2 \ell_4 + \ell_2 \ell_5 + \ell_3 \ell_5) - (\ell_1 \ell_3 \ell_5)}$$

where

$$\ell_1 = a_1 b_1, \ \ell_2 = a_2 b_2, \ \ell_3 = a_3 b_3, \ \ell_4 = a_4 b_4, \ \text{and} \ \ell_5 = a_5 b_5$$

∎

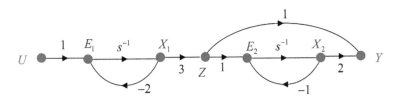

Fig. D.2: Find the transfer function using Mason's gain formula.

Example D.3 (Find the transfer function using Mason's gain formula)

Consider the system described by the signal flow graph shown in Figure D.2. There are two forward paths from the input U to the output Y, and the two forward path gains are

$$F_1 = 1 \cdot s^{-1} \cdot 3 \cdot 1 \cdot s^{-1} \cdot 2 = 6s^{-2}, \quad F_2 = 1 \cdot s^{-1} \cdot 3 \cdot 1 = 3s^{-1}$$

Meanwhile, there are two loops and their loop gains are

$$\ell_1 = -2s^{-1}, \quad \ell_2 = -s^{-1}$$

and these two loops are not touching each other. Thus,

$$\Delta = 1 - \sum_i^M \ell_i + \sum_{i,j}^{NT} \ell_i \ell_j = 1 - (\ell_1 + \ell_2) + \ell_1 \ell_2 = 1 + 3s^{-1} + 2s^{-2}$$

These two loops are touching the F_1 forward path, while the loop ℓ_2 is not touching the F_2 forward path. Hence, $\Delta_1 = 1$, and $\Delta_2 = 1 - \ell_2 = 1 + s^{-1}$. Therefore, the transfer function of the system is

$$\frac{Y}{U} = \frac{F_1 \Delta_1 + F_2 \Delta_2}{\Delta} = \frac{6s^{-2} + 3s^{-1}(1 + s^{-1})}{1 + 3s^{-1} + 2s^{-2}} = \frac{3s + 9}{s^2 + 3s + 2}$$

∎

E

Vectors and Matrices

What is a vector, and what is the difference between a vector and a scalar? According to most textbooks in fundamental physics, a vector is a quantity with direction and magnitude, while a scalar has only a magnitude. For example, distance and speed are scalars, but displacement and velocity are vectors. A point in a plane can be represented as a vector,

$$v = \begin{bmatrix} v_1 \\ v_2 \end{bmatrix} = \begin{bmatrix} v_1 & v_2 \end{bmatrix}^T \tag{E.1}$$

in a two-dimensional space referring to a coordinate system defined by the basis $\{e^1, e^2\}$. The vector $v = [4 \ 3]^T$ shown in Figure E.1(a) means that

$$v = \begin{bmatrix} e^1 & e^2 \end{bmatrix} \begin{bmatrix} 4 \\ 3 \end{bmatrix} = 4e^1 + 3e^2 \tag{E.2}$$

where the basis vectors can be considered as unit vectors with e^1 and e^2 pointing to the east and the north directions, respectively. If the vector v represents a displacement with respect to the origin of the coordinate, then the entries 4 and 3 are the components or the projections of the total distance $|v|$ onto the e^1 (east) axis and the e^2 (north) axis, respectively. As another example, if the vector v represents a velocity, then the entries 4 and 3 will be the components or the projections of the total speed $|v|$ onto the e^1 (east) axis and the e^2 (north) axis, respectively.

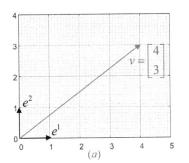 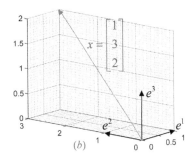

Fig. E.1: Graphical representation of vectors in two-dimensional and three-dimensional spaces.

Similarly, a point in the three-dimensional space as shown in Figure E.1(b) is represented by the vector $x = [1 \ 3 \ 2]^T$ with respect to the coordinated system defined by the basis $\{e^1, e^2, e^3\}$. This 3-tuple vector stands for

$$x = \begin{bmatrix} e^1 & e^2 & e^3 \end{bmatrix} \begin{bmatrix} 1 & 3 & 2 \end{bmatrix}^T = e^1 + 3e^2 + 2e^3 \tag{E.3}$$

where the basis vectors can be considered as unit vectors with e^1, e^2, and e^3 pointing to the east, the north, and the up directions, respectively. If the vector x represents a displacement with respect to the origin of the coordinate, then the entries 1, 3, and 2 are the components or the projections of the total distance $|x|$ onto the e^1 (east) axis, the e^2 (north) axis, and the e^3 (up) axis, respectively.

The basic concept of vector and vector space were originated from Euclidean geometry with which a vector representation $x = \begin{bmatrix} x_1 & x_2 \end{bmatrix}^T$ or $x = \begin{bmatrix} x_1 & x_2 & x_3 \end{bmatrix}^T$ is employed to describe a single vector quantity with direction and magnitude in the two-dimensional or three-dimensional space, and the vector entries are just the components of the same vector along the basis axes.

Since the end of the 19th century, the concept of vector and vector space has evolved into a much more general and complete vector space and matrix theory, which can be employed to solve more sophisticated problems in a more efficient way. The dimension of the vector space can be more than three, although it is impossible to graphically show an n-tuple vector, $x = \begin{bmatrix} x_1 & x_2 & \cdots & x_n \end{bmatrix}^T$, for $n > 3$, as we did in Figure E.1 for 2-tuple and 3-tuple vectors. Furthermore, the vector entries are not restricted to be the components of the same vector quantity; instead, they can be any variables of interest in the problem under consideration. For example, the vector $x = \begin{bmatrix} V & \alpha & q & \theta \end{bmatrix}^T$—representing the state variables: the speed, the angle of attack, the pitch rate, and the pitch angle, respectively, of the aircraft longitudinal subsystem—is considered as a point in the four-dimensional space.

The generalized vector space and matrix theory has greatly facilitated the advance of science, engineering, mathematics, and technology in almost every aspect including state-space control system theory, quantum mechanics, Fourier analysis, digital signal processing, and so on, in the past thirteen decades.

To explain what a matrix is, and its relationship with vectors, we will consider the following algebraic equation:

$$\begin{matrix} a_{11}x_1 + a_{12}x_2 = y_1 \\ a_{21}x_1 + a_{22}x_2 = y_2 \end{matrix} \quad \rightleftarrows \quad Ax = \begin{bmatrix} a_{11} & a_{12} \\ a_{21} & a_{22} \end{bmatrix} \begin{bmatrix} x_1 \\ x_2 \end{bmatrix} = \begin{bmatrix} y_1 \\ y_2 \end{bmatrix} = y \tag{E.4}$$

If the problem is to solve for the unknown vector x assuming the matrix A and the vector y are given, then it is a typical algebraic equation problem, which will be addressed later in Section E.3. The vectors x and y can be regarded as the input and the output, respectively, of a system or a linear operator represented by the matrix A. In the following example, the vectors are assumed as given, and we would like to find a matrix A that satisfies the equation $y = Ax$.

Example E.1 (Find a Matrix Representation of a Linear Operator That Rotates the Vector $x = \begin{bmatrix} 4 & 3 \end{bmatrix}^T$ CCW by 90° to $y = \begin{bmatrix} -3 & 4 \end{bmatrix}^T$)

Consider the vector x shown on Figure E.2. After rotating $x = \begin{bmatrix} 4 & 3 \end{bmatrix}^T$ CCW by 90°, the vector will move to the position represented by $y = \begin{bmatrix} -3 & 4 \end{bmatrix}^T$. This operation can be accomplished by multiplying the rotation matrix $\begin{bmatrix} 0 & -1 \\ 1 & 0 \end{bmatrix}$ to the vector x,

$$y = \begin{bmatrix} -3 \\ 4 \end{bmatrix} = \begin{bmatrix} 0 & -1 \\ 1 & 0 \end{bmatrix} \begin{bmatrix} 4 \\ 3 \end{bmatrix} = Ax \tag{E.5}$$

The same objective can also be achieved by multiplying the diagonal matrix $\begin{bmatrix} -3/4 & 0 \\ 0 & 4/3 \end{bmatrix}$ to the vector x,

$$y = \begin{bmatrix} -3 \\ 4 \end{bmatrix} = \begin{bmatrix} -3/4 & 0 \\ 0 & 4/3 \end{bmatrix} \begin{bmatrix} 4 \\ 3 \end{bmatrix} = Ax \qquad (E.6)$$

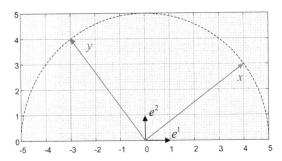

Fig. E.2: Matrix representation of a linear rotation operator.

Obviously, the solution is not unique. In fact, there are infinitely many solutions. How to find the whole set of the solutions will be addressed later in Section E.3. ∎

E.1 Vectors and Vector Space

Definition E.2 (Field)

Let $\mathscr{F}$ be a set of elements c_i, $i = 1, 2, \ldots$. $\mathscr{F}$ is a field if it satisfies the following conditions:

(1) $c_i + c_j$ and $c_i c_j$ are in $\mathscr{F}$.

(2) The elements 0 and 1 are in $\mathscr{F}$.

(3) If $c_i \in \mathscr{F}$, then $-c_i$ is also in $\mathscr{F}$.

(4) If $c_i \neq 0$ is in $\mathscr{F}$, then c_i^{-1} is also in $\mathscr{F}$.

(5) $c_i + c_j = c_j + c_i$, $c_i c_j = c_j c_i$.

(6) $(c_i + c_j) + c_k = c_i + (c_j + c_k)$, $(c_i c_j) c_k = c_i (c_j c_k)$.

(7) $c_i(c_j + c_k) = c_i c_j + c_i c_k$. ∎

Example E.3 (Examples of Field)

(a) The set of real numbers $\mathscr{R}$ is a field.

(b) The set of complex numbers $\mathscr{C}$ is a field.

(c) The set of integers is NOT a field.

(d) The set of rational functions with real coefficients is a field. ∎

Definition E.4 (Vector Space V over the Field $\mathscr{F}$)

A vector space $\mathbf{V}$ over the field $\mathscr{F}$ is a set of vectors $\mathbf{v^i}$, $i = 1, 2, \ldots$—with which the vector addition $\mathbf{v^i} + \mathbf{v^j}$ and the scalar multiplication $c\mathbf{v^i}$, where $c \in \mathscr{F}$, are defined—satisfies the following conditions:

(1) $\mathbf{v^i} + \mathbf{v^j}$ and $c\mathbf{v^i}$ are in $\mathbf{V}$.

(2) $\mathbf{v^i} + \mathbf{v^j} = \mathbf{v^j} + \mathbf{v^i}$.

(3) $(\mathbf{v^i} + \mathbf{v^j}) + \mathbf{v^k} = \mathbf{v^i} + (\mathbf{v^j} + \mathbf{v^k})$.

(4) The zero vector $\mathbf{0}$ *is in* $\mathbf{V}$.

(5) $c(\mathbf{v^i} + \mathbf{v^j}) = c\mathbf{v^i} + c\mathbf{v^j}$.

(6) $(c_i + c_j)\mathbf{v^i} = c_i\mathbf{v^i} + c_j\mathbf{v^i}$.

(7) $c_i(c_j\mathbf{v^i}) = (c_i c_j)\mathbf{v^i}$.

(8) $0 \cdot \mathbf{v^i} = \mathbf{0}$, $1 \cdot \mathbf{v^i} = \mathbf{v^i}$.

(9) For each $\mathbf{v^i}$ *in* $\mathbf{V}$, *there exists a* $-\mathbf{v^i}$ *in* $\mathbf{V}$.   ∎

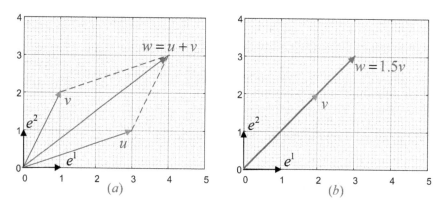

Fig. E.3: Vector addition and scalar multiplication.

Example E.5 (Vector Addition and Scalar Multiplication)

(a) Vector Addition (Figure E.3a)

$$u = \begin{bmatrix} e^1 & e^2 \end{bmatrix} \begin{bmatrix} 3 \\ 1 \end{bmatrix} = 3e^1 + e^2, \quad v = \begin{bmatrix} e^1 & e^2 \end{bmatrix} \begin{bmatrix} 1 \\ 2 \end{bmatrix} = e^1 + 2e^2$$
$$w = u + v = \begin{bmatrix} e^1 & e^2 \end{bmatrix} \left(\begin{bmatrix} 3 \\ 1 \end{bmatrix} + \begin{bmatrix} 1 \\ 2 \end{bmatrix} \right) = \begin{bmatrix} e^1 & e^2 \end{bmatrix} \begin{bmatrix} 4 \\ 3 \end{bmatrix}$$

(E.7)

(b) Scalar Multiplication (Figure E.3b)

$$w = 1.5v = 1.5 \begin{bmatrix} e^1 & e^2 \end{bmatrix} \begin{bmatrix} 2 \\ 2 \end{bmatrix} = \begin{bmatrix} e^1 & e^2 \end{bmatrix} \begin{bmatrix} 3 \\ 3 \end{bmatrix}$$

(E.8)

∎

Example E.6 (Examples of Vector Spaces)

(a) The set of real numbers $\mathscr{R}$ is a vector space over the field $\mathscr{R}$.

(b) The set of complex numbers $\mathscr{C}$ is a vector space over the field $\mathscr{C}$.

(c) The set of complex numbers $\mathscr{C}$ is a vector space over the field $\mathscr{R}$.

(d) The set of real numbers $\mathscr{R}$ is NOT a vector space over the field $\mathscr{C}$.

(e) $\mathscr{R}^n$ is a vector space over the field $\mathscr{R}$.

(f) $\mathscr{C}^n$ is a vector space over the field $\mathscr{C}$.

(g) Consider the interval $[t_1, t_2]$ on the real line. $\mathbf{C}[t_1, t_2]$, the set of all real-value continuous functions on $[t_1, t_2]$, is a vector space over the field $\mathscr{R}$. ∎

Definition E.7 (Subspace)

A nonempty subset $\mathbf{U}$ of a vector space $\mathbf{V}$ is a subspace of $\mathbf{V}$ if $\mathbf{U}$ is itself a vector space. ∎

Theorem E.8 (Subspace)

In the two-dimensional real vector space $\mathscr{R}^2$, every straight line passing through the origin is a subspace of $\mathscr{R}^2$. ∎

Linear Independence and Dimension of Vector Space

Definition E.9 (Linear Dependence)

A finite set of vectors $\mathbf{v}^1, \mathbf{v}^2, \cdots, \mathbf{v}^n$ in a vector space $\mathbf{V}$ over a field $\mathscr{F}$ is said to be linearly dependent if and only if there exist scalars $c_1, c_2, \cdots, c_n$ in $\mathscr{F}$, not all zero, such that

$$c_1\mathbf{v}^1 + c_2\mathbf{v}^2 + \cdots + c_n\mathbf{v}^n = \mathbf{0}. \tag{E.9}$$

If the finite set $\mathbf{v}^1, \mathbf{v}^2, ..., \mathbf{v}^n$ is not linearly dependent, it is called linearly independent. ∎

Example E.10 (Linear Dependence)

$$\mathbf{v}^1 := \begin{bmatrix} 1 \\ -j \end{bmatrix}, \quad \mathbf{v}^2 := \begin{bmatrix} j \\ 1 \end{bmatrix} \tag{E.10}$$

The set of vectors $\{\, \mathbf{v}^1, \mathbf{v}^2 \,\}$ is linearly independent in the field of real numbers. However, these two vectors are linearly dependent in the field of complex numbers since there exist $c_1 = 1$ and $c_2 = j$ so that $c_1\mathbf{v}^1 + c_2\mathbf{v}^2 = \mathbf{0}$. ∎

Definition E.11 (Dimension)

Let $\mathbf{V}$ be a vector space. Suppose there is some positive integer n such that $\mathbf{V}$ contains a set of n vectors that are linearly independent, while every set of $n + 1$ vectors in $\mathbf{V}$ is linearly dependent. Then $\mathbf{V}$ is called finite dimensional and n is the dimension of $\mathbf{V}$. ∎

Example E.12 (Dimension of Vector Space)

(a) $\mathscr{R}^n$ is n-dimensional.

(b) $\mathbf{C}[t_1, t_2]$ is infinite dimensional.

Recall that $\mathbf{C}[t_1,t_2]$, the set of all real-value continuous functions on $[t_1,t_2]$, is a vector space over the field $\mathscr{R}$. Let $x_0(t) = 1$ and $x_n(t) = t^n$, $n = 1,2,\cdots$ Note that $x_0(t)$, $x_1(t)$, $x_2(t)$, $\cdots$, $x_n(t)$ all belong to $\mathbf{C}[t_1,t_2]$, and this set of vectors is linearly independent, no matter how large n is because

$$c_0 + c_1 t + c_2 t^2 + \cdots + c_n t^n = 0 \quad \text{for every } t \text{ in } [t_1,t_2] \tag{E.11}$$

implies that

$$c_0 = c_1 = c_2 = \cdots = c_n = 0 \tag{E.12}$$

Hence, $\mathbf{C}[t_1,t_2]$ is infinite dimensional. ∎

Definition E.13 (Space Spanned by a Set of Vectors)

Let $\mathbf{V}$ be a vector space over $\mathscr{F}$. Suppose S is any nonempty subset of $\mathbf{V}$. Consider the set $\mathbf{M}$ of all finite linear combinations of elements of S (i.e., elements of the form)

$$c_1 \mathbf{v}^1 + c_2 \mathbf{v}^2 + \cdots + c_n \mathbf{v}^n$$

where n is any positive integer; $\mathbf{v}^1$, $\mathbf{v}^2$, $\cdots$, $\mathbf{v}^n$ are any elements of S; and c_1, $\cdots$, c_n are any scalars in $\mathscr{F}$. This set $\mathbf{M}$ is a vector space generated (or spanned) by S. ∎

Definition E.14 (Basis)

A finite set S in a vector space $\mathbf{V}$ is called a basis of $\mathbf{V}$ if S is linearly independent and if the vector space generated by S is all of $\mathbf{V}$. ∎

Theorem E.15 (Basis Vectors)

In an n-dimensional vector space, any set of n linearly independent vectors qualified as a basis. ∎

Definition E.16 (Vector and Vector Representation)

In an n-dimensional vector space $\mathbf{V}$, if a basis $\{e^1, e^2, \cdots, e^n\}$ is chosen, then every vector $\mathbf{v}$ in $\mathbf{V}$ can be uniquely written in the form

$$\mathbf{v} = a_1 e^1 + a_2 e^2 + \ldots + a_n e^n = [e^1 e^2 \cdots e^n]\, \mathbf{a} \tag{E.13}$$

where $\mathbf{a} = [a_1 \cdots a_n]^T$ is called the representation of $\mathbf{v}$ with respect to the basis $\{e^1, e^2, \cdots, e^n\}$. ∎

Example E.17 (Change of Basis)

For the vector $\mathbf{x}$ shown in Figure E.4, its vector representation is $x = [1\ 3]^T$ with respect to the basis $\{e^1, e^2\}$. If the basis is changed, the vector representation will change accordingly. Now, let the new basis be $\{\hat{e}^1, \hat{e}^2\}$, where

$$\hat{e}^1 = \begin{bmatrix} e^1 & e^2 \end{bmatrix} \begin{bmatrix} 2 \\ 2 \end{bmatrix} \quad \text{and} \quad \hat{e}^2 = \begin{bmatrix} e^1 & e^2 \end{bmatrix} \begin{bmatrix} -1 \\ 2 \end{bmatrix}$$

Combining the above two equations to obtain

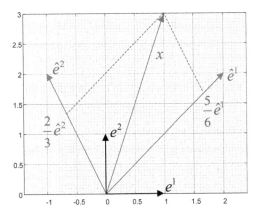

Fig. E.4: Change of basis.

$$\begin{bmatrix} \hat{e}^1 \ \hat{e}^2 \end{bmatrix} = \begin{bmatrix} e^1 \ e^2 \end{bmatrix} \begin{bmatrix} 2 & -1 \\ 2 & 2 \end{bmatrix} \quad \rightarrow \quad \begin{bmatrix} e^1 \ e^2 \end{bmatrix} = \begin{bmatrix} \hat{e}^1 \ \hat{e}^2 \end{bmatrix} \begin{bmatrix} 2 & -1 \\ 2 & 2 \end{bmatrix}^{-1}$$

Hence,

$$x = \begin{bmatrix} e^1 \ e^2 \end{bmatrix} \begin{bmatrix} 1 \\ 3 \end{bmatrix} = \begin{bmatrix} \hat{e}^1 \ \hat{e}^2 \end{bmatrix} \begin{bmatrix} 2 & -1 \\ 2 & 2 \end{bmatrix}^{-1} \begin{bmatrix} 1 \\ 3 \end{bmatrix} = \begin{bmatrix} \hat{e}^1 \ \hat{e}^2 \end{bmatrix} \begin{bmatrix} 5/6 \\ 2/3 \end{bmatrix} \tag{E.14}$$

Therefore, the vector representation of **x** with respect to the basis $\{\hat{e}^1, \hat{e}^2\}$ is $x = [5/6 \ 2/3]^T$, which is the sum of the two vectors: $(5/6)\hat{e}^1$ and $(2/3)\hat{e}^2$. ∎

E.2 Matrices and Linear Operators

As a vector is a representation of a point in the vector space, a matrix is a representation of a linear operator that defines a mapping from one vector space to another. Since a linear operator is a function, we will review the definition of a function.

Definition E.18 (Function)

Let **X** *and* **Y** *be arbitrary nonempty sets and let* **D** *be a nonempty subset of* **X** *as shown in Figure E.5. A function f is a mapping from* **D** *into* **Y** *that maps each x in* **D** *to a unique element f(x) in* **Y**. ∎

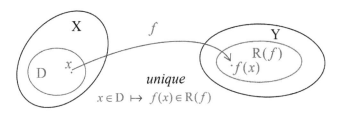

Fig. E.5: Mapping from **X** to **Y**.

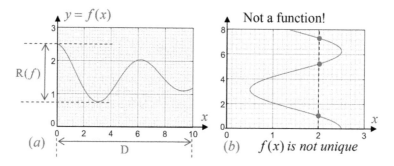

Fig. E.6: Examples of a function and a nonfunction.

Definition E.19 (Domain and Range)

The domain of f is the set **D** *on which the function f is defined, often written as* **D**(f). *The range of f is the set* **R**$(f) = \{f(x) : x$ *in* **D**$\}$. ∎

Definition E.20 (Linear Operator)

X, Y *are linear spaces over the field* $\mathscr{F}$. *A function T that maps vector* $\mathbf{x} \in \mathbf{X}$ *to vector* $T\mathbf{x} \in \mathbf{Y}$ *is said to be a linear operator if and only if*

$$T\left(c_1\mathbf{x}^1 + c_1\mathbf{x}^2\right) = c_1 T\mathbf{x}^1 + c_1 T\mathbf{x}^2 \tag{E.15}$$

for any vectors $\mathbf{x}^1$, $\mathbf{x}^2$ *in* **X** *and any scalars* c_1, c_2 *in* $\mathscr{F}$. ∎

Matrix Representation of a Linear Operator

Example E.21 (Find a Matrix Representation of a Linear Operator That Maps the Vector $x = [e^1\ e^2][1\ 1]^T$ **to** $z = [e^1\ e^2][0.707\ 2.121]^T$ **in** $\mathscr{R}^2$ **with the Same Basis)**

Note that in general a linear operator maps a vector $\mathbf{x} \in \mathbf{X}$ to vector $\mathbf{y} = T\mathbf{x} \in \mathbf{Y}$, where the vector spaces can be different and can have different dimensions. In this example, we assume the input and output vector spaces, **X** and **Y**, are $\mathscr{R}^2$ and have the same basis $\{e^1, e^2\}$.

Consider the input vector x and the output vector z shown on Figure E.7. The operation of moving x to z can be broken down into two steps: move to y first and then rotate y CCW by $45°$ to z. The matrix representations of these two linear operators are $\begin{bmatrix} 2 & 0 \\ 0 & 1 \end{bmatrix}$ and $\begin{bmatrix} 0.707 & -0.707 \\ 0.707 & 0.707 \end{bmatrix}$ as shown in the following:

$$x = \begin{bmatrix} e^1 & e^2 \end{bmatrix}\begin{bmatrix} 1 \\ 1 \end{bmatrix} \mapsto y = \begin{bmatrix} e^1 & e^2 \end{bmatrix}\begin{bmatrix} 2 & 0 \\ 0 & 1 \end{bmatrix}\begin{bmatrix} 1 \\ 1 \end{bmatrix} \mapsto z = \begin{bmatrix} e^1 & e^2 \end{bmatrix}\begin{bmatrix} 0.707 & -0.707 \\ 0.707 & 0.707 \end{bmatrix}\begin{bmatrix} 2 & 0 \\ 0 & 1 \end{bmatrix}\begin{bmatrix} 1 \\ 1 \end{bmatrix}$$

Hence, the matrix representation of the two combined operations is

$$\begin{bmatrix} 0.707 & -0.707 \\ 0.707 & 0.707 \end{bmatrix}\begin{bmatrix} 2 & 0 \\ 0 & 1 \end{bmatrix} = \begin{bmatrix} 1.414 & -0.707 \\ 1.414 & 0.707 \end{bmatrix}$$

and the input-output relationship is described by

$$z = \begin{bmatrix} 1.414 & -0.707 \\ 1.414 & 0.707 \end{bmatrix} x = \begin{bmatrix} 1.414 & -0.707 \\ 1.414 & 0.707 \end{bmatrix} \begin{bmatrix} 1 \\ 1 \end{bmatrix} = \begin{bmatrix} 0.707 \\ 2.121 \end{bmatrix} \qquad (\text{E.16})$$

if the bases of both the input and output vector spaces, $\mathbf{X}$ and $\mathbf{Y}$, are $\{e^1, e^2\}$.   ■

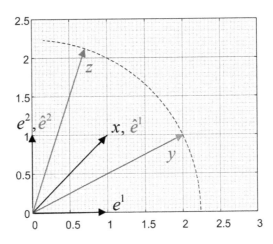

Fig. E.7: Matrix representation of a linear operator that maps vector $\mathbf{x} \in \mathbf{X}$ to vector $\mathbf{z} = T\mathbf{x} \in \mathbf{Y}$.

Example E.22 (Find a Matrix Representation of a Linear Operator That Maps the Vector $x = [e^1 \ e^2][1 \ 1]^T$ to $z = [\hat{e}^1 \ \hat{e}^2][0.707 \ 1.414]^T$ in $\mathcal{R}^2$ but with Different Bases)

In this example, we consider exactly the same linear operator as the one considered in Example E.21 but the basis for the output vector space $\mathbf{Y}$ is selected as $\{\hat{e}^1, \hat{e}^2\}$ while the basis for the input vector space $\mathbf{X}$ remains as $\{e^1, e^2\}$.

Since $\hat{e}^1 = x = \begin{bmatrix} e^1 & e^2 \end{bmatrix} \begin{bmatrix} 1 \\ 1 \end{bmatrix}$ and $\hat{e}^2 = e^2 = \begin{bmatrix} e^1 & e^2 \end{bmatrix} \begin{bmatrix} 0 \\ 1 \end{bmatrix}$, we have

$$\begin{bmatrix} \hat{e}^1 & \hat{e}^2 \end{bmatrix} = \begin{bmatrix} e^1 & e^2 \end{bmatrix} \begin{bmatrix} 1 & 0 \\ 1 & 1 \end{bmatrix} \quad \rightarrow \quad \begin{bmatrix} e^1 & e^2 \end{bmatrix} = \begin{bmatrix} \hat{e}^1 & \hat{e}^2 \end{bmatrix} \begin{bmatrix} 1 & 0 \\ 1 & 1 \end{bmatrix}^{-1}$$

and

$$z = \begin{bmatrix} e^1 & e^2 \end{bmatrix} \begin{bmatrix} 1.414 & -0.707 \\ 1.414 & 0.707 \end{bmatrix} \begin{bmatrix} 1 \\ 1 \end{bmatrix} = \begin{bmatrix} \hat{e}^1 & \hat{e}^2 \end{bmatrix} \begin{bmatrix} 1 & 0 \\ 1 & 1 \end{bmatrix}^{-1} \begin{bmatrix} 1.414 & -0.707 \\ 1.414 & 0.707 \end{bmatrix} \begin{bmatrix} 1 \\ 1 \end{bmatrix} = \begin{bmatrix} \hat{e}^1 & \hat{e}^2 \end{bmatrix} \begin{bmatrix} 0.707 \\ 1.414 \end{bmatrix}$$

Hence, the matrix representation of the linear operator is

$$\begin{bmatrix} 1 & 0 \\ 1 & 1 \end{bmatrix}^{-1} \begin{bmatrix} 1.414 & -0.707 \\ 1.414 & 0.707 \end{bmatrix} = \begin{bmatrix} 1.414 & -0.707 \\ 0 & 1.414 \end{bmatrix} \qquad (\text{E.17})$$

if the bases of the input and output vector spaces, $\mathbf{X}$ and $\mathbf{Y}$, are selected as $\{e^1, e^2\}$ and $\{\hat{e}^1, \hat{e}^2\}$, respectively.   ■

E.3 Linear Algebraic Equations

Consider the following equation:

$$Ax = y \quad \text{where} \quad A = \begin{bmatrix} a_{11} & a_{12} & \cdots & a_{1n} \\ a_{21} & a_{22} & \cdots & a_{2n} \\ \vdots & \vdots & \ddots & \vdots \\ a_{m1} & a_{m2} & \cdots & a_{mn} \end{bmatrix}, \quad x = \begin{bmatrix} x_1 \\ x_2 \\ \vdots \\ x_n \end{bmatrix}, \quad y = \begin{bmatrix} y_1 \\ y_2 \\ \vdots \\ y_m \end{bmatrix} \tag{E.18}$$

The entries a_{ij}'s, y_i's, and x_j's are all assumed to be in the field $\mathscr{F}$. The $m \times n$ matrix A and the $m \times 1$ vector y are assumed as given, and the problem is to solve for the $n \times 1$ variable vector x that satisfies the equation. The matrix A can be considered as a linear operator that maps $\mathscr{F}^n$ into $\mathscr{F}^m$ as shown in Figure E.8.

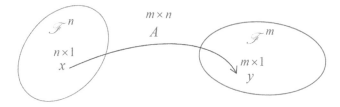

Fig. E.8: The matrix A in the linear algebraic equation is considered as a linear operator that maps $\mathscr{F}^n$ into $\mathscr{F}^m$.

Theorem E.23 (Range Space of the Linear Operator A)

The range space of the linear operator A is a subspace of $\mathscr{F}^m$, which is spanned by the column vectors of the A matrix. ∎

Let the j-th column of A be denoted by $\mathbf{a}^j$ (i.e., $A = [\mathbf{a}^1 \ \mathbf{a}^2 \ \cdots \ \mathbf{a}^n]$) then the matrix equation $y = Ax$ can be written as

$$y = Ax = \begin{bmatrix} \mathbf{a}^1 \ \mathbf{a}^2 \ \cdots \ \mathbf{a}^n \end{bmatrix} \begin{bmatrix} x_1 \\ x_2 \\ \vdots \\ x_n \end{bmatrix} = x_1 \mathbf{a}^1 + x_2 \mathbf{a}^2 + \cdots + x_n \mathbf{a}^n \tag{E.19}$$

It is easy to see that the range space $\mathbf{R}(A)$ is the set of all the linear combinations of the columns of A and the dimension of $\mathbf{R}(A)$ is the maximum number of linearly independent columns in A.

Definition E.24 (Rank)

The rank of a matrix A is the maximum number of linearly independent columns in A (i.e., the dimension of the range space of A). ∎

Example E.25 (Rank and Range Space of a Matrix)

Consider the matrix

$$A = \begin{bmatrix} 1 & 4 & 5 & 1 \\ 2 & 5 & 7 & 1 \\ 3 & 6 & 9 & 1 \end{bmatrix} := \begin{bmatrix} \mathbf{a}^1 \ \mathbf{a}^2 \ \mathbf{a}^3 \ \mathbf{a}^4 \end{bmatrix} \tag{E.20}$$

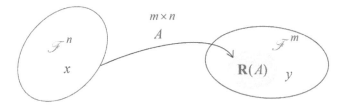

Fig. E.9: The range space of A is the subspace of $\mathscr{F}^m$ spanned by the column vectors of the A matrix.

By inspection, we can see that $\mathbf{a}^3 = \mathbf{a}^1 + \mathbf{a}^2$ and $\mathbf{a}^4 = (1/3)(\mathbf{a}^2 - \mathbf{a}^1)$ are linear combinations of the two linearly independent column vectors: $\mathbf{a}^1$ and $\mathbf{a}^2$. Hence the matrix has only two linearly independent column vectors—that is, the rank of A is 2 and the range space $\mathbf{R}(A)$ is a two-dimensional space spanned by $\mathbf{a}^1$ and $\mathbf{a}^2$. In fact, the range space can also be generated by any two of these four column vectors since any two out of these four column vectors are linearly independent. ∎

Theorem E.26 (Solution Existence Condition for $Ax = y$)

Consider the linear operator,

$$A: \quad F^n \to F^m, \quad x \mapsto Ax$$

Given A and a vector $y \in \mathscr{F}^m$, there exists a vector x such that $Ax = y$ if and only if the vector y is in the range space $\mathbf{R}(A)$. ∎

Definition E.27 (Null Space) *The null space of a linear operator A, $\mathbf{N}(A)$, is defined by*

$$\mathbf{N}(A) = \{x \in \mathscr{F}^n : Ax = 0\} \tag{E.21}$$

which means that $\mathbf{N}(A)$ contains all solutions of $Ax = 0$. ∎

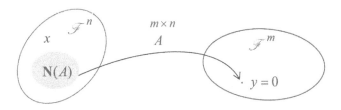

Fig. E.10: The null space of A is the subspace of $\mathscr{F}^n$ in which every vector x satisfies $Ax = 0$.

Example E.28 (Null Space of a Matrix)

Consider the matrix

$$A = \begin{bmatrix} 1 & 4 & 5 & 3 & 0 \\ 2 & 5 & 7 & 3 & 3 \\ 3 & 6 & 9 & 3 & 6 \end{bmatrix} := \begin{bmatrix} \mathbf{a}^1 & \mathbf{a}^2 & \mathbf{a}^3 & \mathbf{a}^4 & \mathbf{a}^5 \end{bmatrix} \tag{E.22}$$

which maps the five-dimensional real space $\mathscr{R}^5$ into the three-dimensional real space $\mathscr{R}^3$.

Let $x = \begin{bmatrix} x_1 & x_2 & x_3 & x_4 & x_5 \end{bmatrix}^T$, then we have

$$\begin{aligned} Ax &= x_1\mathbf{a}^1 + x_2\mathbf{a}^2 + x_3\mathbf{a}^3 + x_4\mathbf{a}^4 + x_5\mathbf{a}^5 \\ &= x_1\mathbf{a}^1 + x_2\mathbf{a}^2 + x_3(\mathbf{a}^1 + \mathbf{a}^2) + x_4(-\mathbf{a}^1 + \mathbf{a}^2) + x_5(4\mathbf{a}^1 - \mathbf{a}^2) \\ &= (x_1 + x_3 - x_4 + 4x_5)\mathbf{a}^1 + (x_2 + x_3 + x_4 - x_5)\mathbf{a}^2 \end{aligned} \tag{E.23}$$

The two vectors $\mathbf{a}^1$ and $\mathbf{a}^2$ are linearly independent, hence we have $Ax = 0$ if and only if the following two equations are satisfied:

$$\begin{aligned} x_1 + x_3 - x_4 + 4x_5 &= 0 \\ x_2 + x_3 + x_4 - x_5 &= 0 \end{aligned} \tag{E.24}$$

Since only two equations are given for five unknown variables, the set of solutions will be a three-dimensional subspace in $\mathscr{R}^5$. The three basis vectors for the subspace can be found as follows:

(i) Choose $x_1 = 3$, $x_2 = 0$, $x_3 = 0$, then $x_4 = -1$ and $x_5 = -1$, and we have the first basis vector $\alpha^1 = \begin{bmatrix} 3 & 0 & 0 & -1 & -1 \end{bmatrix}^T$ so that $A\alpha^1 = 0$.

(ii) Choose $x_1 = 0$, $x_2 = 3$, $x_3 = 0$, then $x_4 = -1$ and $x_5 = -1$, and we have the second basis vector $\alpha^2 = \begin{bmatrix} 0 & 3 & 0 & -1 & -1 \end{bmatrix}^T$ so that $A\alpha^2 = 0$.

(iii) Choose $x_1 = 0$, $x_2 = 0$, $x_3 = 3$, then $x_4 = -5$ and $x_5 = -2$, and we have the third basis vector $\alpha^3 = \begin{bmatrix} 0 & 0 & 3 & -5 & -2 \end{bmatrix}^T$ so that $A\alpha^3 = 0$.

The three vectors

$$\alpha^1 = \begin{bmatrix} 3 \\ 0 \\ 0 \\ -1 \\ -1 \end{bmatrix}, \quad \alpha^2 = \begin{bmatrix} 0 \\ 3 \\ 0 \\ -1 \\ -1 \end{bmatrix}, \quad \alpha^3 = \begin{bmatrix} 0 \\ 0 \\ 3 \\ -5 \\ -2 \end{bmatrix} \tag{E.25}$$

are linearly independent and satisfy Equation E.24; hence, they are qualified to serve as a basis for the null space of A. In other words, the null space can be described as follows:

$$\mathbf{N}(A) = \left\{ x : \begin{array}{l} x = c_1\alpha^1 + c_2\alpha^2 + c_3\alpha^3 \\ c_1, c_2, c_3 \in \mathscr{R} \end{array} \right\} \tag{E.26}$$

■

Theorem E.29 (Sum of the Dimensions of the Range Space and the Null Space)

Let A be an $m \times n$ matrix, then the sum of the dimensions of the range space and the null space equals n,

$$\dim \mathbf{R}(A) + \dim \mathbf{N}(A) = n \tag{E.27}$$

■

As in Example E.28, A is a 3×5 matrix, which has only two linearly independent columns. The range space is a two-dimensional subspace in $\mathscr{R}^3$ spanned by $\mathbf{a}^1$ and $\mathbf{a}^2$, and the null space is a three-dimensional subspace in $\mathscr{R}^5$ spanned by α^1, α^2, and α^3. Hence,

$$\dim R(A) + \dim N(A) = 2 + 3 = 5 = n$$

Solutions of the Linear Algebraic Equation

According to Theorem E.26, there exists a vector x such that $Ax = y$ if and only if the vector y is in the range space $\mathbf{R}(A)$. Therefore, there are three cases regarding the solution existence and solution uniqueness for the equation $Ax = y$:

Case 1: There is no solution if y is not in the range space $\mathbf{R}(A)$.

Case 2: If the matrix A is nonsingular, then there is a unique solution, $x = A^{-1}y$.

Case 3: If the matrix A is singular and y is in the range space $\mathbf{R}(A)$, then there exist infinitely many solutions.

Example E.30 (Solution Does Not Exist)

For the following linear algebraic equation

$$Ax = y, \quad \text{where} \quad A = \begin{bmatrix} 1 & 4 & 1 \\ 2 & 5 & 1 \\ 3 & 6 & 1 \end{bmatrix} \quad \text{and} \quad y = \begin{bmatrix} 0 \\ 1 \\ 1 \end{bmatrix} \tag{E.28}$$

there is no solution for x since the vector y is not in the range space $\mathbf{R}(A)$. The reason that y is not in $\mathbf{R}(A)$ can be seen from the fact that $rank(A) = 2$ and $rank([A \ y]) = 3$. ∎

Example E.31 (Unique Solution)

For the following linear algebraic equation

$$Ax = y, \quad \text{where} \quad A = \begin{bmatrix} 1 & 4 & 0 \\ 2 & 5 & 1 \\ 3 & 6 & 1 \end{bmatrix} \quad \text{and} \quad y = \begin{bmatrix} 7 \\ 8 \\ 9 \end{bmatrix} \tag{E.29}$$

there is a unique solution for x since the matrix A is nonsingular. The unique solution is

$$x = A^{-1}y = \begin{bmatrix} 1 & 4 & 0 \\ 2 & 5 & 1 \\ 3 & 6 & 1 \end{bmatrix}^{-1} \begin{bmatrix} 7 \\ 8 \\ 9 \end{bmatrix} = \begin{bmatrix} -1 \\ 2 \\ 0 \end{bmatrix}$$

∎

Example E.32 (Characterization of All Solutions)

For the following linear algebraic equation

$$Ax = y, \quad \text{where} \quad A = \begin{bmatrix} 1 & 4 & 1 \\ 2 & 5 & 1 \\ 3 & 6 & 1 \end{bmatrix} \quad \text{and} \quad y = \begin{bmatrix} 7 \\ 8 \\ 9 \end{bmatrix} \tag{E.30}$$

there exists at least one solution for x, $x = [-1 \ 2 \ 0]^T$, because the vector y is in the range space $\mathbf{R}(A)$. However, the A matrix is singular, which implies that the solution is not unique. To identify all the solutions for $Ax = y$, we will first find all the solutions of $Ax = 0$, which are the elements of the null space $\mathbf{N}(A)$.

Let

$$A = \begin{bmatrix} 1 & 4 & 1 \\ 2 & 5 & 1 \\ 3 & 6 & 1 \end{bmatrix} = \begin{bmatrix} \mathbf{a}^1 & \mathbf{a}^2 & \mathbf{a}^3 \end{bmatrix} \quad \text{and} \quad x = \begin{bmatrix} x_1 \\ x_2 \\ x_3 \end{bmatrix} \tag{E.31}$$

Note that A has only two linearly independent column vectors, and the second column $\mathbf{a}^2$ can be expressed as a linear combination of the other two columns as $\mathbf{a}^2 = \mathbf{a}^1 + 3\mathbf{a}^3$. Hence, we have

$$Ax = x_1\mathbf{a}^1 + x_2\mathbf{a}^2 + x_3\mathbf{a}^3 = x_1\mathbf{a}^1 + x_2(\mathbf{a}^1 + 3\mathbf{a}^3) + x_3\mathbf{a}^3 = (x_1 + x_2)\mathbf{a}^1 + (3x_2 + x_3)\mathbf{a}^3 = 0 \tag{E.32}$$

which leads to the following two equations:

$$x_1 + x_2 = 0 \quad \text{and} \quad 3x_2 + x_3 = 0$$

Let $x_1 = 1$, then we have $x_2 = -1$ and $x_3 = 3$ from solving the above two equations. Now we have a basis vector

$$\alpha^1 = \begin{bmatrix} 1 \\ -1 \\ 3 \end{bmatrix}$$

for the one-dimensional null space $\mathbf{N}(A)$, which contains all solutions of $Ax = 0$.

Therefore, the solutions of $Ax = y$ are

$$x = \begin{bmatrix} -1 \\ 2 \\ 0 \end{bmatrix} + c_1\alpha^1 = \begin{bmatrix} -1 \\ 2 \\ 0 \end{bmatrix} + c_1 \begin{bmatrix} 1 \\ -1 \\ 3 \end{bmatrix}$$

where c_1 can be any real number. ∎

Example E.33 (Revisit Example E.1)

In the following, we would like to revisit Example E.1 to find matrix representations of all linear operators that can move the vector $x = [4 \ 3]^T$ to $y = [-3 \ 4]^T$. To find all possible A matrices that satisfy the equation

$$y = \begin{bmatrix} -3 \\ 4 \end{bmatrix} = \begin{bmatrix} a_{11} & a_{12} \\ a_{21} & a_{22} \end{bmatrix} \begin{bmatrix} 4 \\ 3 \end{bmatrix} = Ax \tag{E.33}$$

we rearrange the equation as follows so that the entries of A become a vector of unknown variables to be determined,

$$Ma := \begin{bmatrix} \mathbf{m}^1 & \mathbf{m}^2 & \mathbf{m}^3 & \mathbf{m}^4 \end{bmatrix} a = \begin{bmatrix} 4 & 3 & 0 & 0 \\ 0 & 0 & 4 & 3 \end{bmatrix} \begin{bmatrix} a_{11} \\ a_{12} \\ a_{21} \\ a_{22} \end{bmatrix} = \begin{bmatrix} -3 \\ 4 \end{bmatrix} = y \tag{E.34}$$

Recall that in Example E.1, we have found two solutions:

$$A = \begin{bmatrix} 0 & -1 \\ 1 & 0 \end{bmatrix} \quad \text{or} \quad \begin{bmatrix} -3/4 & 0 \\ 0 & 4/3 \end{bmatrix}, \quad \text{which is equivalent to} \quad a = \begin{bmatrix} 0 \\ -1 \\ 1 \\ 0 \end{bmatrix} \quad \text{or} \quad \begin{bmatrix} -3/4 \\ 0 \\ 0 \\ 4/3 \end{bmatrix}$$

To find all the solutions of $Ma = y$, we will first find all the solutions of $Ma = 0$, which are the elements of the null space $\mathbf{N}(M)$.

Note that M has only two linearly independent column vectors, and m^2 and m^3 can be expressed in terms of m^1 and m^4, respectively, as $m^2 = (3/4)m^1$ and $m^3 = (4/3)m^4$. Hence, we have

$$Ma = a_{11}m^1 + a_{12}m^2 + a_{21}m^3 + a_{22}m^4 = \left(a_{11} + \frac{3}{4}a_{12} \right) m^1 + \left(\frac{4}{3}a_{21} + a_{22} \right) m^4 = 0$$

which leads to

$$a_{11} + (3/4)a_{12} = 0 \quad \text{and} \quad (4/3)a_{21} + a_{22} = 0$$

These two equations can be employed to find the two basis vectors of the null space $\mathbf{N}(M)$, which is a two-dimensional subspace in the four-dimensional real space $\mathscr{R}^4$.

(i) Choose $a_{11} = 1$ and $a_{22} = 0$, then $a_{12} = -4/3$ and $a_{21} = 0$, and we have the first basis vector $\alpha^1 = [1 \ -4/3 \ 0 \ 0]^T$ so that $M\alpha^1 = 0$.

(ii) Choose $a_{11} = 0$ and $a_{22} = 1$, then $a_{12} = 0$ and $a_{21} = -3/4$, and we have the second basis vector $\alpha^2 = [0 \ 0 \ -3/4 \ 1]^T$ so that $M\alpha^2 = 0$.

The two vectors

$$\alpha^1 = \begin{bmatrix} 1 \\ -4/3 \\ 0 \\ 0 \end{bmatrix}, \quad \alpha^2 = \begin{bmatrix} 0 \\ 0 \\ -3/4 \\ 1 \end{bmatrix} \tag{E.35}$$

are linearly independent and satisfy $Ma = 0$; hence, they are qualified to serve as a basis for the null space of M.

Therefore, the solutions of $Ma = y$ are

$$a := \begin{bmatrix} a_{11} \\ a_{12} \\ a_{21} \\ a_{22} \end{bmatrix} = \begin{bmatrix} 0 \\ -1 \\ 1 \\ 0 \end{bmatrix} + c_1 \alpha^1 + c_2 \alpha^2 = \begin{bmatrix} 0 \\ -1 \\ 1 \\ 0 \end{bmatrix} + c_1 \begin{bmatrix} 1 \\ -4/3 \\ 0 \\ 0 \end{bmatrix} + c_2 \begin{bmatrix} 0 \\ 0 \\ -3/4 \\ 1 \end{bmatrix}$$

where c_1 and c_2 can be arbitrary real numbers. ∎

E.4 Eigenvalues and Eigenvectors

Definition E.34 (Eigenvalues and Eigenvectors)

Let A be a linear operator that maps the n-dimensional complex space $\mathscr{C}^n$ into itself and x a nonzero vector in $\mathscr{C}^n$. Then x is an eigenvector of A corresponding to the eigenvalue λ if

$$Ax = \lambda x \tag{E.36}$$

∎

To find an eigenvalue of A, we rewrite $Ax = \lambda x$ as

$$(\lambda I - A)x = 0 \tag{E.37}$$

This equation has a nontrivial solution x if and only if $\det(\lambda I - A) = 0$, where $\det(\lambda I - A)$ is a polynomial of degree n in λ and is called the characteristic polynomial of A.

Example E.35 (Eigenvalues and Eigenvectors)

Consider the matrix

$$A = \begin{bmatrix} 0 & 1 \\ 2 & -1 \end{bmatrix}$$

Find the eigenvalues of the matrix A and their corresponding eigenvectors.

The eigenvalues of A are the roots of the following characteristic equation:

$$|\lambda I - A| = \begin{vmatrix} \lambda & -1 \\ -2 & \lambda + 1 \end{vmatrix} = \lambda^2 + \lambda - 2 = 0$$

They are $\lambda_1 = -2$ and $\lambda_2 = 1$. The eigenvector e^1 corresponding to eigenvalue $\lambda_1 = -2$ is computed in the following:

$$(\lambda_1 I - A)e^1 = \begin{bmatrix} \lambda_1 & -1 \\ -2 & \lambda_1 + 1 \end{bmatrix} \begin{bmatrix} e_{11} \\ e_{21} \end{bmatrix} = \begin{bmatrix} -2 & -1 \\ -2 & -1 \end{bmatrix} \begin{bmatrix} 1 \\ -2 \end{bmatrix} = \begin{bmatrix} 0 \\ 0 \end{bmatrix} \quad \rightarrow \quad e^1 = \begin{bmatrix} 1 \\ -2 \end{bmatrix}$$

Similarly, the eigenvector e^2 corresponding to eigenvalue $\lambda_2 = 1$ is computed as follows:

$$(\lambda_2 I - A)e^2 = \begin{bmatrix} \lambda_2 & -1 \\ -2 & \lambda_2 + 1 \end{bmatrix} \begin{bmatrix} e_{12} \\ e_{22} \end{bmatrix} = \begin{bmatrix} 1 & -1 \\ -2 & 2 \end{bmatrix} \begin{bmatrix} 1 \\ 1 \end{bmatrix} = \begin{bmatrix} 0 \\ 0 \end{bmatrix} \quad \rightarrow \quad e^2 = \begin{bmatrix} 1 \\ 1 \end{bmatrix}$$

∎

Diagonalization of the A Matrix via Similarity Transformation

Consider a state-space model of a dynamic system,

$$\begin{aligned} \dot{x}(t) &= Ax(t) + Bu(t) \\ y(t) &= Cx(t) \end{aligned} \tag{E.38}$$

Let $\hat{x}(t)$ be a new state vector defined as $\hat{x}(t) = T^{-1}x(t)$, where T is a nonsingular matrix with dimension compatible with the state vector. Then we have the new transformed state-space model in the following:

$$\begin{aligned} \dot{\hat{x}}(t) &= \hat{A}\hat{x}(t) + \hat{B}u(t) \\ y(t) &= \hat{C}\hat{x}(t) \end{aligned} \tag{E.39}$$

where

$$\hat{A} = T^{-1}AT, \quad \hat{B} = T^{-1}B, \quad \hat{C} = CT \tag{E.40}$$

Example E.36 (Diagonalization of the A Matrix)

Consider a state-space model,

$$\begin{aligned} \dot{x}(t) &= Ax(t) + Bu(t) \\ y(t) &= Cx(t) \end{aligned}$$

where the A, B, and C matrices are given by

$$A = \begin{bmatrix} 0 & 1 \\ 2 & -1 \end{bmatrix}, \quad B = \begin{bmatrix} 0 \\ 1 \end{bmatrix}, \quad C = \begin{bmatrix} 1 & 0 \end{bmatrix}$$

Find a similarity transformation, $\hat{x}(t) = T^{-1}x(t)$, so that the new state-space model has a diagonal $\hat{A} = T^{-1}AT$ matrix.

The A matrix of the state-space model is the same as that considered in Example E.35, and the eigenvalues and eigenvectors have been found as

$$\lambda_1 = -2, \quad e^1 = \begin{bmatrix} 1 \\ -2 \end{bmatrix}, \quad \text{and} \quad \lambda_2 = 1, \quad e^2 = \begin{bmatrix} 1 \\ 1 \end{bmatrix}$$

Let the similarity transformation matrix be

$$T = \begin{bmatrix} e^1 & e^2 \end{bmatrix} = \begin{bmatrix} 1 & 1 \\ -2 & 1 \end{bmatrix}$$

Then we have the new transformed state-space model with a diagonal $\hat{A}$ matrix,

$$\dot{\hat{x}}(t) = \hat{A}\hat{x}(t) + \hat{B}u(t) = T^{-1}AT\hat{x}(t) + T^{-1}Bu(t) = \begin{bmatrix} -2 & 0 \\ 0 & 1 \end{bmatrix}\hat{x}(t) + \begin{bmatrix} -1/3 \\ 1/3 \end{bmatrix}u(t)$$

$$y(t) = \hat{C}\hat{x}(t) = CT\hat{x}(t) = \begin{bmatrix} 1 & 1 \end{bmatrix}\hat{x}(t)$$

■

E.5 Singular Value Decomposition

Definition E.37 (Orthogonal and Unitary Matrices)

Let U be a square real matrix. Then U is orthogonal if $U^T U = I$, where U^T is the transpose of U. Similarly, let U be a square complex matrix. Then U is unitary if $U^*U = I$, where U^* is the conjugate transpose of U. ■

Theorem E.38 (Singular Value Decomposition)

Consider $A \in C^{m \times n}$, an $m \times n$ complex matrix. There exist unitary matrices $U \in C^{m \times m}$ and $V \in C^{n \times n}$ such that

$$A = U \begin{bmatrix} \Sigma & 0 \\ 0 & 0 \end{bmatrix} V^* \tag{E.41}$$

where $\Sigma = \text{diag}(\sigma_1, \sigma_2, \cdots, \sigma_r)$ and $\sigma_1 \geq \sigma_2 \geq \cdots \geq \sigma_r > 0$. Hence, $\text{rank}(A) = \text{rank}(\Sigma) = r$, and σ_1 is the maximum singular value of A. ■

Corollary E.39 (Eigenvalues of A^*A and the Null Space of A)

Partition the unitary matrix V in Equation E.41 into $V = \begin{bmatrix} V_1 & V_2 \end{bmatrix}$, where the columns of V_1 are the first r columns of V. Then the r column vectors of V_1 are the eigenvectors corresponding to the r nonzero eigenvalues of A^*A, which are $\sigma_1^2, \sigma_2^2, \cdots, \sigma_r^2$, and the $n - r$ columns of V_2 span the null space of A.

Proof: *Since*

$$A^*A = V \begin{bmatrix} \Sigma & 0 \\ 0 & 0 \end{bmatrix} UU^* \begin{bmatrix} \Sigma & 0 \\ 0 & 0 \end{bmatrix} V^* = V \begin{bmatrix} \Sigma^2 & 0 \\ 0 & 0 \end{bmatrix} V^*$$

we have

$$A \begin{bmatrix} V_1 & V_2 \end{bmatrix} = \begin{bmatrix} U_1 & U_2 \end{bmatrix} \begin{bmatrix} \Sigma & 0 \\ 0 & 0 \end{bmatrix}$$

and

$$A^* A \begin{bmatrix} V_1 & V_2 \end{bmatrix} = \begin{bmatrix} V_1 & V_2 \end{bmatrix} \begin{bmatrix} \Sigma^2 & 0 \\ 0 & 0 \end{bmatrix}$$

Hence,

$$AV_2 = 0 \quad \text{and} \quad A^* A V_1 = V_1 \Sigma^2$$

which means that the $n - r$ columns of V_2 span the null space of A, and the r columns of V_1 are the eigenvectors corresponding to the r nonzero eigenvalues of A^*A.   ■

Example E.40 (Singular Value Decomposition)

Consider a 2×2 complex matrix A in the following:

$$A = \begin{bmatrix} 1 & j \\ j & -1 \end{bmatrix}$$

There exist unitary matrices

$$U = \frac{1}{\sqrt{2}} \begin{bmatrix} -1 & -1 \\ -j & j \end{bmatrix}, \quad \text{and} \quad V = \frac{1}{\sqrt{2}} \begin{bmatrix} -1 & 1 \\ j & j \end{bmatrix} = \begin{bmatrix} V_1 & V_2 \end{bmatrix}$$

such that

$$A = U \begin{bmatrix} \Sigma & 0 \\ 0 & 0 \end{bmatrix} V^*$$

where $\Sigma = \sigma_1 = 2$, and σ_1 is called the maximum singular value of A. It can also be seen that

$$AV_2 = \begin{bmatrix} 1 & j \\ j & -1 \end{bmatrix} \begin{bmatrix} 1 \\ j \end{bmatrix} \frac{1}{\sqrt{2}} = \begin{bmatrix} 0 \\ 0 \end{bmatrix}$$

which implies that the column vector of V_2 spans the null space of the matrix A.

The relationship between the singular values of A and the eigenvalues of A^*A is verified as follows. There exist eigenvectors w_1 and w_2 associated with the eigenvalues λ_1 and λ_2, respectively, so that

$$A^* A \cdot W = W \cdot D$$

where

$$W = \begin{bmatrix} w_1 & w_2 \end{bmatrix} = \frac{1}{\sqrt{2}} \begin{bmatrix} j & j \\ 1 & -1 \end{bmatrix} \quad \text{and} \quad D = \begin{bmatrix} \lambda_1 & 0 \\ 0 & \lambda_2 \end{bmatrix} = \begin{bmatrix} 4 & 0 \\ 0 & 0 \end{bmatrix}$$

Note that $\sigma_1 = 2$, the maximum singular value of A, is the square root of $\lambda_1 = 4$, the maximum eigenvalue of A^*A.   ■

E.6 Positive Definite and Positive Semi-Definite Matrices

Definition E.41 (Positive Definite and Positive Semi-Definite Matrices)

(a) A symmetric $n \times n$ real matrix A is positive definite if $x^T A x > 0$ for every nonzero $n \times 1$ real vector x

(b) Similarly, the real matrix is positive semi-definite if $x^T Ax \geq 0$ for every nonzero real vector x.   ∎

Theorem E.42 (Eigenvalues Test of Matrix Definiteness)

(a) A symmetric real matrix A is positive definite if and only if all its eigenvalues are strictly positive.
(b) A symmetric real matrix A is positive semi-definite if and only if all its eigenvalues are nonnegative.

∎

Theorem E.43 (Factorization of a Positive Definite (Positive Semi-Definite) Matrix)

For any given $n \times n$ real matrix X, the matrix $A = X^T X$ is either positive definite or positive semi-definite, and $\text{rank}(A) = \text{rank}(X)$. $A = X^T X$ is positive definite if the rank is n.

On the other hand, a positive definite matrix A can be factorized as $A = R^T R$, where R is a unique upper triangular real matrix with all diagonal elements being nonzero. This factorization is called Cholesky decomposition. There exists no Cholesky decomposition for singular positive semi-definite matrices. However, there exists a Schur decomposition $A = USU$ if A is symmetric, where S is diagonal, and Q is an orthogonal matrix. ∎

Example E.44 (Factorization of Positive Definite Matrices)

Consider the following 2×2 real matrix X,

$$X = \begin{bmatrix} 1 & 2 \\ 3 & 4 \end{bmatrix}$$

which is nonsingular. Then the matrix

$$A = X^T X = \begin{bmatrix} 1 & 3 \\ 2 & 4 \end{bmatrix} \begin{bmatrix} 1 & 2 \\ 3 & 4 \end{bmatrix} = \begin{bmatrix} 10 & 14 \\ 14 & 20 \end{bmatrix}$$

is positive definite since X is of full rank. The positive definiteness of A can also be verified by the two positive eigenvalues of the A matrix: $\lambda_1 = 29.8661$ and $\lambda_2 = 0.1339$.

Conversely, any positive definite matrix A can be factored into the form $A = R^T R$ so that R is a unique upper triangular matrix. The Cholesky factorization is found as:

$$R = \begin{bmatrix} 3.1623 & 4.4272 \\ 0 & 0.6325 \end{bmatrix}$$

A general factorization $A = M^T M$, where M is not necessarily upper triangular, can be obtained using Schur decomposition, which is a special case of singular value decomposition. Consider the same positive definite matrix A. There exists an orthogonal matrix

$$U = \begin{bmatrix} -0.5760 & -0.8174 \\ -0.8174 & 0.5760 \end{bmatrix}$$

so that

$$A = U \Sigma U^T$$

where

$$\Sigma = \begin{bmatrix} \sigma_1 & 0 \\ 0 & \sigma_2 \end{bmatrix} = \begin{bmatrix} 29.8661 & 0 \\ 0 & 0.1339 \end{bmatrix}$$

Let

$$M = \Sigma^{1/2} U^T = \begin{bmatrix} -3.1481 & -4.4672 \\ -0.2991 & 0.2108 \end{bmatrix}$$

Then

$$M^T M = U \Sigma^{1/2} \Sigma^{1/2} U^T = \begin{bmatrix} 10 & 14 \\ 14 & 20 \end{bmatrix} = A$$

∎

Example E.45 (Factorization of Positive Semi-Definite Matrices)

Consider the following 3×3 real matrix X,

$$X = \begin{bmatrix} 1 & 2 & 3 \\ 4 & 5 & 6 \\ 5 & 7 & 9 \end{bmatrix}$$

which is singular with $\text{rank}(X) = 2 < 3$. Then the matrix

$$A = X^T X = \begin{bmatrix} 1 & 4 & 5 \\ 2 & 5 & 7 \\ 3 & 6 & 9 \end{bmatrix} \begin{bmatrix} 1 & 2 & 3 \\ 4 & 5 & 6 \\ 5 & 7 & 9 \end{bmatrix} = \begin{bmatrix} 42 & 57 & 72 \\ 57 & 78 & 99 \\ 72 & 99 & 126 \end{bmatrix}$$

is positive semi-definite since X is of rank 2, which is less than 3. The positive semi-definiteness of A can also be verified by the zero eigenvalue of the A matrix: $\lambda_1 = 245.3397$, $\lambda_2 = 0.6603$, and $\lambda_3 = 0$.

Conversely, any positive semi-definite matrix A can be factored into the form $A = M^T M$ so that M is of the same rank as A. The factorization is not unique. One way of achieving the factorization is using the singular value decomposition. Consider the same positive semi-definite A matrix as above. There exists an orthogonal matrix

$$U = \begin{bmatrix} -0.4116 & 0.8148 & -0.4082 \\ -0.5638 & 0.1243 & 0.8165 \\ -0.7160 & -0.5662 & -0.4082 \end{bmatrix}$$

so that

$$A = U \Sigma U^T$$

where

$$\Sigma = \begin{bmatrix} \sigma_1 & 0 & 0 \\ 0 & \sigma_2 & 0 \\ 0 & 0 & \sigma_3 \end{bmatrix} = \begin{bmatrix} 245.3397 & 0 & 0 \\ 0 & 0.6603 & 0 \\ 0 & 0 & 0 \end{bmatrix}$$

Let

$$M = \Sigma^{1/2} U^T = \begin{bmatrix} -6.4468 & -8.8312 & -11.2155 \\ 0.6621 & 0.1010 & -0.4601 \\ 0 & 0 & 0 \end{bmatrix}$$

Then

$$M^T M = U \Sigma^{1/2} \Sigma^{1/2} U^T = \begin{bmatrix} 42 & 57 & 72 \\ 57 & 78 & 99 \\ 72 & 99 & 126 \end{bmatrix} = A$$

∎

References

Alberto Bemporad and Manfred Morari. Control of systems integrating logic, dynamics, and constraints. *Automatica*, 35(3):407–427, 1999.

D. S. Bernstein. Feedback control: An invisisble thread in the history of technology. *IEEE Control Systems Magazine*, 22(2):53–68, April 2002.

C. C. Bissel. *A History of Automation*, book section 4, pages 1–18. Springer, 2009.

H. W. Bode. Relations between amplitude and phase in amplifier design. *Bell Systems Technical Journal*, 19:421–454, 1940.

M. S. Branicky, V. S. Borkar, and S. K. Mitter. A unified framework for hybrid control: Model and optimal control theory. *IEEE Transactions on Automatic Control*, 43(1):31–45, 1998.

R. W. Brockett. Feedback invariants for nonlinear systems. In *IFAC World Congress*, pages 1115–1120, Helsinki, 1978.

C. S. Buttrill, P. D. Arbuckle, and K. D. Hoffler. *Simulation model of a twin-tail, high performance airplane.* NASA Technical Memorandum 107601. NASA Langley Research Center, Hampton, Virginia, 1992.

Abhijit Chakraborty, Peter Seiler, and Gary J Balas. Susceptibility of f/a-18 flight controllers to the falling-leaf mode: Linear analysis. *Journal of guidance, control, and dynamics*, 34(1):57–72, 2011.

P. C. Chan, B. C. Chang, M. Bayram, H. G. Kwatny, and C. M. Belcastro. Robust tracking control of an aircraft with critical actuator jam failures. *Asian Journal of Control, https://doi.org/10.1002/asjc.2280*, pages 1–19, Dec. 2019.

B.C. Chang, H.G. Kwatny, E.R. Ballouz, and D.C. Hartman. Aircraft trim recovery from highly nonlinear upset conditions, aiaa2016-0880. In *Proceedings of the 2016 AIAA Guidance, Navigation, and Control Conference, SciTech Forum*, pages 1–19, San Diego, California, dx.doi.org/10.2514/6.2016-0880, Jan. 2016.

E. Clarke. Steady–state stability in transmission systems calculation by equivalent circuits or circle diagrams. *Transactions American Institute of Electrical Engineers*, XLV:22–41, 1926.

E. Clarke and R. G. Lorraine. Power limits of synchronous machines. *Electrical Engineering*, 52(11): 780–787, 1933.

E. J. Davison. Optimal control of linear time-invariant systems with polynomial-type measurable disturbances. *IEEE Proceedings*, 119:605–611, 1972.

E. J. Davison and S. H. Wang. Properties and calculation of transmission systems of linear multivariable systems. *Automatica*, 10:643–658, 1974.

C. A. Desoer and M. Vidyasagar. *Feedback Systems: Input–Output Properties*. Academic Press, 1975.

J. Doyle, K. Glover, P. Khargonekar, and B. Francis. State-space solutions to standard h_2 and h_{inf} optimal control problems. *IEEE Transactions on Automatic control*, 33:831–847, 1989.

W. R. Evans. Graphical analysis of control systems. *Transactions American Institute of Electrical Engineers*, 67:547–551, 1948.

Bruce A. Francis and W. Murray Wonham. The internal model principle of control theory. *Automatica*, 12:457–465, 1976.

H. L. Hazen. Theory of servo–mechanisms. *Journal of the Franklin Institute*, 218(3):279–331, 1934.

R. Hermann and A. J. Krener. Nonlinear controllability and observability. *IEEE Transactions on Automatic Control*, 22(5):728–740, 1977.

J. Huang. *Nonlinear Output Regulation: Theory and Applications*. SIAM, 2004.

A. Hurwitz. Uber die bedingungen, unter welchen eine gleichung nur wurzeln mit negativen reelen teilen bestizt. *Mathematische Annalen*, 46(2):273–284, 1895.

C. D. Johnson. Optimal control of the linear regulator with constant disturbances. *IEEE Transaction on Automatic Control*, AC–13(August):416–421, 1968.

C. D. Johnson. Further study of the linear regulator with disturbances – the case of vector disturbances satisfying a linear differential equation. *IEEE Transaction on Automatic Control*, AC–15(April):222–228, 1970.

Thomas Kailath. *Linear Systems*. Prentice-Hall, NJ, 1980.

R. E. Kalman. Contributions to the theory of optmal control. *Bol. Soc. Mat. Mexicana*, 5:102–119, 1960a.

R. E. Kalman. A new approach to linear filtering and prediction problems. *ASME Journal of Basic Engineering*, 82:34–45, 1960b.

R. E. Kalman. Mathematical description of linear dynamical systems. *SIAM J. Control*, 1(2):152–192, 1963.

R. E. Kalman and J. E. Bertram. Control system analysis and design via the 'second method' of lyapunov. i continuous-time systems. *ASME Journal of Basic Engineering*, 80(371–393), 1960.

R. E. Kalman and R. S. Bucy. New results in linear filtering and prediction theory. *ASME Journal of Basic Engineering*, (March):95–108, 1961.

R. E. Kalman, Y. C. Ho, and K. S. Narendra. Controllability of linear dynamical systems. *Contributions to Differential Equations*, 1:189–213, 1963.

K. C. Kalnitsky and H. G. Kwatny. An eigenvalue characterization of multivariable system zeros. *IEEE Transactions on Automatic Control*, AC–21(2):259–262, 1977.

C. G. Kang. Origin of stability analysis: 'On governors' by J. C. Maxwell. *IEEE Control Systems Magazine*, (October):77–88, 2016.

B. Kouvaritakis and A. G. J. MacFarlane. Geometric approach to analysis and synthesis of system zeros part 1. square systems. *International Journal of Control*, 23(2):149–166, 1976a.

B. Kouvaritakis and A. G. J. MacFarlane. Geometric approach to analysis and synthesis of system zeros part 2. non-square systems. *International Journal of Control*, 23(2):167–181, 1976b.

H. G. Kwatny. Optimal linear control theory and a class of pi controllers for process control. In *13th Joint Automatic Control Conference*, pages 274–281. AIAA, 1972.

C. Lanczos. *The Variational Principles of Mechanics*. Dover Publications, New York, 4th edition, 1970.

A. G. J. MacFarlane and N. Karcanias. Poles and zeros of linear multivariable systems: A survey of the algebraic, geometric and complex variable theory. *International Journal of Control*, 24(1):33–74, 1976.

J. C. Maxwell. On governors. *Proceedings Royal Society of London*, 16:270–283, 1868.

D. McRuer and D. Graham. A flight control century: Triumphs of the systems approach. *Journal of Guidance, Control and Dynamics*, 27(2):161–173, 2003.

N. Minorsky. Directional stability of automatically sterred bodies. *J. American Society of Naval Engineers*, 34:280–309, 1922.

H. Nyquist. Regeneration theory. *Bell Systems Technical Journal*, 11:126–147, 1932.

H. J. Pesch and M. Plail. The maximum principle of optimal control: A history of ingenious ideas and missed opportunities. *Control and Cybernetics*, 38(4A):973–995, 2009.

L. S. Pontryagin. *Ordinary Differential Equations*. Addison Wesley, 1962.

P. J. G. Ramadge and W. M. Wonham. The control of discrete event systems. *Proceedings of the IEEE*, 77(1):81–98, 1989.

H. H. Rosenbrock. Design of multivariable control systems using the inverse nyquist array. *Proceedings of the Institution of Electrical Engineers*, 116(11):1929–1936, 1969.

H. H. Rosenbrock. The zeros of a system. *International Journal of Control*, 18(2):297–299, 1973.

H. H. Rosenbrock. The structural properties of linear dynamical systems. *International Journal of Control*, 20(2):191–202, 1974.

E. J. Routh. *A treatise on the Stability of a Given State of Motion, Particularly Steady Motion*. MacMillan, New York, 1877.

C. W. Siemens. On uniform rotation. *Proceedings Royal Society of London*, 156:657–670, 1866.

Frank Smithies. *Cauchy and the Creation of Complex Function Theory*. Cambridge University Press, 1997.

H. J. Sussman and J. C. Willems. 300 years of optimal control: From the brachystochrone to the maximum principle. *IEEE Control Systems*, (June):32–44, 1997.

I. A. Vyshnegradskiy. On controllers of direct action (in russion). *Ilzvestiya St. Petersburg Technological Institute*, pages 21–62, 1877.

N. Wiener. *Extrapolation, Interpolation, and Smoothing of Stationary Time Series*. Wiley, New York, 1949.

W.M. Wonham and J.B. Pearson. Regulation and internal stabilization in linear multivariable systems. *SIAM J. Control*, 12:5–18, 1974.

G. Zames. Feedback and optimal sensitivity: Model reference transforms, multiplicative seminorms and approximate inverses. *IEEE Transactions on Automatic control*, 26:585–601, 1981.

K. Zhou, J. C. Doyle, and K. Glover. *Robust and Optimal Control*. Prentice Hall, 1995.

Index